UNITED STATES DEPARTMENT OF COMMERCE • Luther H. Hodges, *Secretary*

NATIONAL BUREAU OF STANDARDS • A. V. Astin, *Director*

Experimental Statistics

Mary Gibbons Natrella
National Bureau of Standards

Reprint of the Experimental Statistics Portion
of the AMC Handbook

By permission of the
Army Materiel Command

National Bureau of Standards Handbook 91

Issued August 1, 1963

Reprinted October 1966 With Corrections

For sale by the Superintendent of Documents, U.S. Government Printing Office
Washington, D.C. 20402 - Price $8.45

ERRATA NOTICE

The original printing of this Handbook (August 1963) contained a few errors that have been corrected in the reprinted editions. These corrections are marked with an asterisk (*) for identification. The errors occurred on the following pages: 4-10, 6-3, 6-14, 6-18, 6-27, 6-29, 6-30, 6-36, 12-6, T-14 and T-15 (Table A-7), and T-80 and T-81 (Table A-35).

Library of Congress Catalog Card Number: 63–60072

Preface

This Handbook brings together in a single volume material on experimental statistics that was previously printed for limited distribution as U.S. Army Ordnance Pamphlets ORDP 20–110, 20–111, 20–112, 20–113, and 20–114. These pamphlets are parts of the *AMC Engineering Design Handbook* series now under the jurisdiction of the Army Materiel Command. Future issues by the Army Materiel Command for its own use will be in the AMCP–706 series.

The material contained in the present publication was prepared in the Statistical Engineering Laboratory, National Bureau of Standards, under a contract with the former Office of Ordnance Research (now Army Research Office—Durham). Although originally developed with the needs of the Army in mind, it promises to be equally useful to other groups concerned with research and development, both within and outside the Government. To make this material more widely available to such groups, *Experimental Statistics* is now being published as a National Bureau of Standards Handbook for sale to the public through the Superintendent of Documents, U.S. Government Printing Office.

F. S. Besson, Jr.,
Lt. Gen. U.S. Army, *Commanding*,
Army Materiel Command.

A. V. Astin, *Director*,
National Bureau of
Standards.

FOREWORD

INTRODUCTION

This is one of a group of handbooks covering the engineering information and quantitative data needed in the design, development, construction, and test of ordnance equipment which (as a group) constitute the Ordnance Engineering Design Handbook.

PURPOSE OF HANDBOOK

The Handbook on Experimental Statistics has been prepared as an aid to scientists and engineers, engaged in Army Ordnance research and development programs, and especially as a guide and ready reference for military and civilian personnel who have responsibility for the planning and interpretation of experiments and tests relating to the performance of Army Ordnance equipment in the design and developmental stages of production.

SCOPE AND USE OF HANDBOOK

This Handbook is a collection of statistical procedures useful in ordnance applications. It is presented in five sections, viz:

ORDP 20-110, Section 1, Basic Concepts and Analysis of Measurement Data (Chapters 1-6)

ORDP 20-111, Section 2, Analysis of Enumerative and Classificatory Data (Chapters 7-10)

ORDP 20-112, Section 3, Planning and Analysis of Comparative Experiments (Chapters 11-14)

ORDP 20-113, Section 4, Special Topics (Chapters 15-23)

ORDP 20-114, Section 5, Tables

Section 1 provides an elementary introduction to basic statistical concepts and furnishes full details on standard statistical techniques for the analysis and interpretation of measurement data. Section 2 provides detailed procedures for the analysis and interpretation of enumerative and classificatory data. Section 3 has to do with the planning and analysis of comparative experiments. Section 4 is devoted to consideration and exemplification of a number of important but as yet non-standard statistical techniques, and to discussion of various other special topics. An index for the material in all five sections is placed at the end of Section 5. Section 5 contains all the mathematical tables needed for application of the procedures given in Sections 1 through 4.

An understanding of a few basic statistical concepts, as given in Chapter 1, is necessary; otherwise each of the first four sections is largely independent of the others. Each procedure, test, and technique described is illustrated by means of a worked example. A list of authoritative references is included, where appropriate, at the end of each chapter. Step-by-step instructions are given for attaining a stated goal, and the conditions under which a particular procedure is strictly valid are stated explicitly. An attempt is made to indicate the extent to which results obtained by a given procedure are valid to a good approximation when these conditions are not fully met. Alternative procedures are given for handling cases where the more standard procedures cannot be trusted to yield reliable results.

The Handbook is intended for the user with an engineering background who, although he has an occasional need for statistical techniques, does not have the time or inclination to become an expert on statistical theory and methodology.

The Handbook has been written with three types of users in mind. The first is the person who has had a course or two in statistics, and who may even have had some practical experience in applying statistical methods in the past, but who does not have statistical

v

ideas and techniques at his fingertips. For him, the Handbook will provide a ready reference source of once familiar ideas and techniques. The second is the person who feels, or has been advised, that some particular problem can be solved by means of fairly simple statistical techniques, and is in need of a book that will enable him to obtain the solution to his problem with a minimum of outside assistance. The Handbook should enable such a person to become familiar with the statistical ideas, and reasonably adept at the techniques, that are most fruitful in his particular line of research and development work. Finally, there is the individual who, as the head of, or as a member of a service group, has responsibility for analyzing and interpreting experimental and test data brought in by scientists and engineers engaged in ordnance research and development work. This individual needs a ready source of model work sheets and worked examples corresponding to the more common applications of statistics, to free him from the need of translating textbook discussions into step-by-step procedures that can be followed by individuals having little or no previous experience with statistical methods.

It is with this last need in mind that some of the procedures included in the Handbook have been explained and illustrated in detail twice: once for the case where the important question is whether the performance of a new material, product, or process exceeds an established standard; and again for the case where the important question is whether its performance is not up to the specified standards. Small but serious errors are often made in changing "greater than" procedures into "less than" procedures.

AUTHORSHIP AND ACKNOWLEDGMENTS

The Handbook on Experimental Statistics was prepared in the Statistical Engineering Laboratory, National Bureau of Standards, under a contract with the Office of Ordnance Research. The project was under the general guidance of Churchill Eisenhart, Chief, Statistical Engineering Laboratory.

Most of the present text is by Mary G. Natrella, who had overall responsibility for the completion of the final version of the Handbook. The original plans for coverage, a first draft of the text, and some original tables were prepared by Paul N. Somerville. Chapter 6 is by Joseph M. Cameron; most of Chapter 1 and all of Chapters 20 and 23 are by Churchill Eisenhart; and Chapter 10 is based on a nearly-final draft by Mary L. Epling.

Other members of the staff of the Statistical Engineering Laboratory have aided in various ways through the years, and the assistance of all who helped is gratefully acknowledged. Particular mention should be made of Norman C. Severo, for assistance with Section 2, and of Shirley Young Lehman for help in the collection and computation of examples.

Editorial assistance, art preparation, and the index were provided by John I. Thompson & Company, Washington, D. C.

Appreciation is expressed for the generous cooperation of publishers and authors in granting permission for the use of their source material. References for tables and other material, taken wholly or in part, from published works, are given on the respective first pages.

June 15, 1962

TABLE OF CONTENTS

Paragraph   *Page*

CHAPTER 1

SOME BASIC STATISTICAL CONCEPTS AND PRELIMINARY CONSIDERATIONS

1-1	INTRODUCTION	1-1
1-2	POPULATIONS, SAMPLES, AND DISTRIBUTIONS	1-1
1-3	STATISTICAL INFERENCES AND SAMPLING	1-3
1-3.1	Statistical Inferences	1-3
1-3.2	Random Sampling	1-4
1-4	SELECTION OF A RANDOM SAMPLE	1-6
1-5	SOME PROPERTIES OF DISTRIBUTIONS	1-6
1-6	ESTIMATION OF m AND σ	1-10
1-7	CONFIDENCE INTERVALS	1-11
1-8	STATISTICAL TOLERANCE LIMITS	1-14
1-9	USING STATISTICS TO MAKE DECISIONS	1-15
1-9.1	Approach to a Decision Problem	1-15
1-9.2	Choice of Null and Alternative Hypotheses	1-16
1-9.3	Two Kinds of Errors	1-17
1-9.4	Significance Level and Operating Characteristic (OC) Curve of a Statistical Test	1-17
1-9.5	Choice of the Significance Level	1-17
1-9.6	A Word of Caution	1-18

CHAPTER 2

CHARACTERIZING THE MEASURED PERFORMANCE OF A MATERIAL, PRODUCT, OR PROCESS

2-1	ESTIMATING AVERAGE PERFORMANCE FROM A SAMPLE	2-1
2-1.1	General	2-1
2-1.2	Best Single Estimate	2-1
2-1.3	Some Remarks on Confidence Interval Estimates	2-2
2-1.4	Confidence Intervals for the Population Mean When Knowledge of the Variability Cannot Be Assumed	2-2
2-1.4.1	Two-sided Confidence Interval	2-2
2-1.4.2	One-sided Confidence Interval	2-3
2-1.5	Confidence Interval Estimates When We Have Previous Knowledge of the Variability	2-4

Paragraph   *Page*

CHAPTER 2 (Cont)

2-2   ESTIMATING VARIABILITY OF PERFORMANCE FROM
          A SAMPLE.   2-6
2-2.1   General.   2-6
2-2.2   Single Estimates.   2-6
2-2.2.1 s^2 and s.   2-6
2-2.2.2   The Sample Range as an Estimate of the Standard Deviation   2-6
2-2.3   Confidence Interval Estimates.   2-7
2-2.3.1   Two-sided Confidence Interval Estimates.   2-7
2-2.3.2   One-sided Confidence Interval Estimates.   2-7
2-2.4   Estimating the Standard Deviation When No Sample Data
          are Available.   2-8
2-3   NUMBER OF MEASUREMENTS REQUIRED TO ESTAB-
          LISH THE MEAN WITH PRESCRIBED ACCURACY. . .   2-9
2-3.1   General.   2-9
2-3.2   Estimation of the Mean of a Population Using a Single
          Sample.   2-10
2-3.3   Estimation Using a Sample Which is Taken In Two Stages. .   2-10
2-4   NUMBER OF MEASUREMENTS REQUIRED TO ESTAB-
          LISH THE VARIABILITY WITH STATED PRECISION. .   2-12
2-5   STATISTICAL TOLERANCE LIMITS.   2-13
2-5.1   General.   2-13
2-5.2   Two-sided Tolerance Limits for a Normal Distribution.   2-13
2-5.3   One-sided Tolerance Limits for a Normal Distribution.   2-14
2-5.4   Tolerance Limits Which are Independent of the Form of the
          Distribution.   2-15
2-5.4.1   Two-sided Tolerance Limits (Distribution-Free).   2-15
2-5.4.2   One-sided Tolerance Limits (Distribution-Free).   2-15

CHAPTER 3

COMPARING MATERIALS OR PRODUCTS
WITH RESPECT TO AVERAGE PERFORMANCE

3-1   GENERAL REMARKS ON STATISTICAL TESTS.   3-1
3-2   COMPARING THE AVERAGE OF A NEW PRODUCT
          WITH THAT OF A STANDARD.   3-3
3-2.1   To Determine Whether the Average of a New Product Differs
          From the Standard.   3-4
3-2.1.1   Does the Average of the New Product Differ From the
          Standard (σ Unknown)?.   3-4
3-2.1.2   Does the Average of the New Product Differ From the
          Standard (σ Known)?.   3-8
3-2.2   To Determine Whether the Average of a New Product Exceeds
          the Standard.   3-13
3-2.2.1   Does the Average of the New Product Exceed the Standard
          (σ Unknown)?.   3-13

Paragraph   *Page*

CHAPTER 3 (Cont)

3-2.2.2   Does the Average of the New Product Exceed the Standard (σ Known)?.. 3-16

3-2.3   To Determine Whether the Average of a New Product is Less Than the Standard.. 3-20

3-2.3.1   Is the Average of the New Product Less Than the Standard (σ Unknown)?... 3-20

3-2.3.2   Is the Average of the New Product Less Than That of the Standard (σ Known)?.. 3-21

3-3   COMPARING THE AVERAGES OF TWO MATERIALS, PRODUCTS, OR PROCESSES.. 3-22

3-3.1   Do Products A and B Differ In Average Performance?...... 3-23

3-3.1.1   (Case 1) — Variability of A and B Is Unknown, But Can Be Assumed to be Equal.. 3-23

3-3.1.2   (Case 2) — Variability of A and B is Unknown, Cannot Be Assumed Equal.. 3-26

3-3.1.3   (Case 3) — Variability in Performance of Each of A and B is Known from Previous Experience, and the Standard Deviations are σ_A and σ_B, Respectively.................. 3-30

3-3.1.4   (Case 4) — The Observations are Paired.................... 3-31

3-3.2   Does the Average of Product A Exceed the Average of Product B?... 3-34

3-3.2.1   (Case 1) — Variability of A and B is Unknown, But Can Be Assumed to be Equal.. 3-34

3-3.2.2   (Case 2) — Variability of A and B is Unknown, Cannot Be Assumed Equal.. 3-36

3-3.2.3   (Case 3) — Variability in Performance of Each of A and B is Known from Previous Experience, and the Standard Deviations are σ_A and σ_B, Respectively.................. 3-37

3-3.2.4   (Case 4) — The Observations are Paired.................... 3-38

3-4   COMPARING THE AVERAGES OF SEVERAL PRODUCTS 3-40

CHAPTER 4

COMPARING MATERIALS OR PRODUCTS WITH RESPECT TO VARIABILITY OF PERFORMANCE

4-1   COMPARING A NEW MATERIAL OR PRODUCT WITH A STANDARD WITH RESPECT TO VARIABILITY OF PERFORMANCE.. 4-1

4-1.1   Does the Variability of the New Product Differ From That of the Standard?.. 4-1

4-1.2   Does the Variability of the New Product Exceed That of the Standard?... 4-3

4-1.3   Is the Variability of the New Product Less Than That of the Standard?... 4-5

Paragraph   *Page*

CHAPTER 4 (Cont)

4-2   COMPARING TWO MATERIALS OR PRODUCTS WITH RESPECT TO VARIABILITY OF PERFORMANCE...... 4-8

4-2.1   Does the Variability of Product A Differ From That of Product B?......................... 4-8

4-2.2   Does the Variability of Product A Exceed That of Product B?. 4-9

CHAPTER 5

CHARACTERIZING LINEAR RELATIONSHIPS BETWEEN TWO VARIABLES

5-1   INTRODUCTION.......................... 5-1

5-2   PLOTTING THE DATA.................... 5-1

5-3   TWO IMPORTANT SYSTEMS OF LINEAR RELATIONSHIPS......................... 5-3

5-3.1   Functional Relationships.................... 5-3

5-3.2   Statistical Relationships.................... 5-5

5-4   PROBLEMS AND PROCEDURES FOR FUNCTIONAL RELATIONSHIPS......................... 5-11

5-4.1   FI Relationships (General Case)............. 5-11

5-4.1.1   What Is the Best Line To Be Used for Estimating y From Given Values of x?.................... 5-12

5-4.1.2   What Are the Confidence Interval Estimates for: the Line as a Whole; a Point on the Line; a Future Value of Y Corresponding to a Given Value of x?.................... 5-15

5-4.1.3   What Is the Confidence Interval Estimate for β_1, the Slope of the *True* Line $y = \beta_0 + \beta_1 x$?........ 5-19

5-4.1.4   If We Observe n' New Values of Y (With Average $\bar{Y}'$), How Can We Use the Fitted Regression Line to Obtain an Interval Estimate of the Value of x that Produced These Values of Y?.................... 5-20

5-4.1.5   Using the Fitted Regression Line, How Can We Choose a Value (x') of x Which We May Expect with Confidence $(1 - \alpha)$ Will Produce a Value of Y Not Less Than Some Specified Value Q?.................... 5-21

5-4.1.6   Is the Assumption of Linear Regression Justified?........ 5-22

5-4.2   FI Relationships When the Intercept Is Known To Be Equal to Zero (Lines Through the Origin).................... 5-24

5-4.2.1   Line Through Origin, Variance of Y's Independent of x... 5-24

5-4.2.2   Line Through Origin, Variance Proportional to x $(\sigma^2_{Y \cdot x} = x\sigma^2)$ 5-25

5-4.2.3   Line Through Origin, Standard Deviation Proportional to x $(\sigma_{Y \cdot x} = x\sigma)$.................... 5-26

5-4.2.4   Line Through Origin, Errors of Y's Cumulative (Cumulative Data).................... 5-26

5-4.3   FII Relationships.................... 5-27

5-4.3.1   A Simple Method of Fitting the Line In the General Case. 5-27

5-4.3.2   An Important Exceptional Case.................... 5-29

Paragraph　　　　　　　　　　　　　　　　　　　　　　　　　　　　*Page*

CHAPTER 5 (Cont)

5-4.4　Some Linearizing Transformations.........................　5-30
5-5　PROBLEMS AND PROCEDURES FOR STATISTICAL RELATIONSHIPS.........................　5-31
5-5.1　SI Relationships.........................　5-31
5-5.1.1　What Is the Best Line To Be Used for Estimating $\bar{Y}_X$ for Given Values of X?.........................　5-33
5-5.1.2　What Are the Confidence Interval Estimates for: the Line as a Whole; a Point on the Line; a Single Y Corresponding to a New Value of X?.........................　5-36
5-5.1.3　Give a Confidence Interval Estimate for β_1, the Slope of the *True* Regression Line, $\bar{Y}_X = \beta_0 + \beta_1 X$?.........................　5-38
5-5.1.4　What Is the Best Line for Predicting $\bar{X}_Y$ From Given Values of Y?.........................　5-39
5-5.1.5　What Is the Degree of Relationship of the Two Variables X and Y as Measured by ρ, the Correlation Coefficient?.....　5-40
5-5.2　SII Relationships.........................　5-40
5-5.2.1　What Is the Best Line To Be Used for Estimating $\bar{Y}_X$ From Given Values of X?.........................　5-41
5-5.2.2　What Are the Confidence Interval Estimates for: the Line as a Whole; a Point on the Line; a Single Y Corresponding to a New Value of X?.........................　5-42
5-5.2.3　What Is the Confidence Interval Estimate for β_1, the Slope of the *True* Line $\bar{Y}_X = \beta_0 + \beta_1 X$?.........................　5-45

CHAPTER 6

POLYNOMIAL AND MULTIVARIABLE RELATIONSHIPS ANALYSIS BY THE METHOD OF LEAST SQUARES

6-1　INTRODUCTION.........................　6-1
6-2　LEAST SQUARES THEOREM.........................　6-3
6-3　MULTIVARIABLE FUNCTIONAL RELATIONSHIPS....　6-4
6-3.1　Use and Assumptions.........................　6-4
6-3.2　Discussion of Procedures and Examples.........................　6-5
6-3.3　Procedures and Examples.........................　6-6
6-4　MULTIPLE MEASUREMENTS AT ONE OR MORE POINTS.........................　6-17
6-5　POLYNOMIAL FITTING.........................　6-18
6-6　INEQUALITY OF VARIANCE.........................　6-19
6-6.1　Discussion of Procedures and Examples.........................　6-19
6-6.2　Procedures and Examples.........................　6-20
6-7　CORRELATED MEASUREMENT ERRORS.........................　6-22
6-7.1　Discussion of Procedures and Examples.........................　6-22
6-7.2　Procedures and Examples.........................　6-22
6-8　USE OF ORTHOGONAL POLYNOMIALS WITH EQUALLY SPACED x VALUES.........................　6-26
6-8.1　Discussion of Procedures and Examples.........................　6-26

Paragraph   *Page*

CHAPTER 6 (Cont)

6-8.2	Procedures and Examples	6-30
6-9	MATRIX METHODS	6-37
6-9.1	Formulas Using Triangular Factorization of Normal Equations	6-37
6-9.2	Triangularization of Matrices	6-38
6-9.3	Remarks	6-41

CHAPTER 7

CHARACTERIZING THE QUALITATIVE PERFORMANCE OF A MATERIAL, PRODUCT, OR PROCESS

7-1	GENERAL	7-1
7-2	BEST SINGLE ESTIMATE OF THE TRUE PROPORTION P	7-1
7-3	CONFIDENCE INTERVAL ESTIMATES OF THE TRUE PROPORTION P	7-2
7-3.1	Two-Sided Confidence Intervals	7-2
7-3.1.1	Exact Limits for $n \leq 30$	7-2
7-3.1.2	Exact Limits for $n > 30$	7-2
7-3.1.3	Approximate Limits for $n > 30$	7-2
7-3.2	One-Sided Confidence Intervals	7-3
7-3.2.1	Exact Limits for $n \leq 30$	7-3
7-3.2.2	Exact Limits for $n > 30$	7-3
7-3.2.3	Approximate Limits for $n > 30$	7-3
7-4	SAMPLE SIZE REQUIRED TO ESTIMATE THE TRUE PROPORTION	7-4
7-4.1	Determining the Sample Size Required to Estimate the True Proportion *With a Specified Limit Of Error In Both Directions* (i.e., When It Is Required To Estimate P Within $\pm\delta$)	7-4
7-4.1.1	Graphical Method	7-4
7-4.1.2	Numerical Method	7-5
7-4.2	Determining the Sample Size Required To Estimate the True Proportion *With a Specified Limit Of Error In Only One Direction* (i.e., When It Is Required To Estimate P Within $+\delta$; or, To Estimate P Within $-\delta$)	7-5

Paragraph *Page*

CHAPTER 8

COMPARING MATERIALS OR PRODUCTS WITH RESPECT TO A TWO-FOLD CLASSIFICATION OF PERFORMANCE (COMPARING TWO PERCENTAGES)

8-1 COMPARING AN OBSERVED PROPORTION WITH A STANDARD PROPORTION............................ 8-1

8-1.1 Does the New Product Differ From the Standard With Regard To the Proportion of Items Which Show the Characteristic of Interest? (Does P Differ From P_0?)..................... 8-1

8-1.1.1 Procedure for $n \leq 30$............................. 8-1

8-1.1.2 Procedure for $n > 30$............................. 8-2

8-1.2 Does the Characteristic Proportion for the New Product *Exceed* That For the Standard? (Is $P > P_0$?).............. 8-3

8-1.2.1 Procedure for $n \leq 30$............................. 8-3

8-1.2.2 Procedure for $n > 30$............................. 8-4

8-1.3 Is the Characteristic Proportion for the New Product Less Than That for the Standard? (Is $P < P_0$?)............. 8-5

8-1.3.1 Procedure for $n \leq 30$............................. 8-5

8-1.3.2 Procedure for $n > 30$............................. 8-5

8-1.4 Sample Size Required To Detect a Difference Of Prescribed Magnitude From a Standard Proportion When the Sign of the Difference IS NOT Important..................... 8-6

8-1.5 Sample Size Required To Detect a Difference Of Prescribed Magnitude From a Standard Proportion When the Sign of the Difference IS Important............................ 8-7

8-2 COMPARING TWO OBSERVED PROPORTIONS....... 8-9

8-2.1 Comparing Two Proportions When the Sample Sizes Are Equal... 8-9

8-2.1.1 Does the Characteristic Proportion for Product A Differ From That for Product B? (Does P_A Differ From P_B?)... 8-10

8-2.1.2 Does the Characteristic Proportion for Product A Exceed That for Product B? (Is P_A Larger Than P_B?).......... 8-11

8-2.2 Comparing Two Proportions When the Sample Sizes Are Unequal and Small ($n_A \neq n_B$; Both No Greater Than 20)..... 8-12

8-2.2.1 Does the Characteristic Proportion for Product A Differ From That for Product B?............................ 8-12

8-2.2.2 Does the Characteristic Proportion for Product A Exceed That for Product B? (Is P_A Larger than P_B?).......... 8-14

8-2.3 Comparing Two Proportions When the Sample Sizes Are Large... 8-16

8-2.3.1 Does the Characteristic Proportion for Product A Differ From That for Product B? (Does P_A Differ From P_B?)... 8-16

Paragraph   *Page*

CHAPTER 8 (Cont)

8-2.3.2	Is the Characteristic Proportion for Product A Larger Than That for Product B? (Is P_A Larger Than P_B?)	8-18
8-2.4	Sample Size Required to Detect a Difference Between Two Proportions	8-18
8-2.4.1	Sample Size Required to Detect a Difference of Prescribed Magnitude Between Two Proportions When the Sign of the Difference IS NOT Important	8-18
8-2.4.2	Sample Size Required to Detect a Difference of Prescribed Magnitude Between Two Proportions When the Sign of the Difference IS Important	8-20

CHAPTER 9

COMPARING MATERIALS OR PRODUCTS WITH RESPECT TO SEVERAL CATEGORIES OF PERFORMANCE (CHI-SQUARE TESTS)

9-1	COMPARING A MATERIAL OR PRODUCT WITH A STANDARD	9-2
9-1.1	When the Comparison Is With a Standard Material or Product	9-2
9-1.2	When the Comparison Is With a Theoretical "Standard"	9-4
9-2	COMPARING TWO OR MORE MATERIALS OR PRODUCTS	9-6
9-3	A TEST OF ASSOCIATION BETWEEN TWO METHODS OF CLASSIFICATION	9-8

CHAPTER 10

SENSITIVITY TESTING

10-1	EXPERIMENTAL SITUATION	10-1
10-2	KÄRBER METHOD OF ANALYSIS	10-3
10-2.1	General Solution For the Kärber Method	10-4
10-2.1.1	Procedure	10-4
10-2.1.2	Example	10-5

Paragraph   *Page*

CHAPTER 10 (Cont)

10-2.2   Simplified Solution (Kärber Method) For the Special Case When Test Levels Are Equally Spaced and Equal Numbers of Items Are Tested at Each Level................10-6
10-2.2.1   Procedure...10-6
10-2.2.2   Example...10-7
10-3   PROBIT METHOD OF ANALYSIS.....................10-8
10-3.1   Graphical Probit Solution..............................10-10
10-3.1.1   Procedure...10-10
10-3.1.2   Example...10-11
10-3.2   Exact Probit Solution....................................10-16
10-3.2.1   Procedure...10-16
10-3.2.2   Example...10-17
10-3.3   Testing Whether the Line Is An Adequate Representation of the Data...10-20
10-3.3.1   Procedure...10-20
10-3.3.2   Example...10-20
10-3.4   Using the Probit Regression Line For Prediction...........10-21
10-3.4.1   Level of Stimulus x' At Which a Specified Proportion P' of the Individuals Would Be Expected To Respond..........10-21
10-3.4.2   Level of Stimulus x' At Which 50% of the Individuals Would Be Expected To Respond....................10-21
10-3.4.3   Proportion of Individuals Which Would Be Expected To Respond At a Specified Level of Stimulus...............10-21
10-4   THE UP-AND-DOWN DESIGN.........................10-22
10-5   SENSITIVITY TESTS WHEN THE STIMULUS LEVELS CANNOT BE CONTROLLED.............................10-24

CHAPTER 11

GENERAL CONSIDERATIONS IN PLANNING EXPERIMENTS

11-1   THE NATURE OF EXPERIMENTATION...........11-1
11-2   EXPERIMENTAL PATTERN.......................11-3
11-3   PLANNED GROUPING.............................11-3
11-4   RANDOMIZATION................................11-4
11-5   REPLICATION...................................11-4
11-6   THE LANGUAGE OF EXPERIMENTAL DESIGN   11-5

Paragraph   *Page*

CHAPTER 12

FACTORIAL EXPERIMENTS

12-1	INTRODUCTION	12-1
12-1.1	Some General Remarks and Terminology	12-1
12-1.2	Estimates of Experimental Error for Factorial-Type Designs	12-3
12-1.2.1	Internal Estimates of Error	12-3
12-1.2.2	Estimates of Error from Past Experience	12-3
12-2	FACTORIAL EXPERIMENTS (EACH FACTOR AT TWO LEVELS)	12-3
12-2.1	Symbols	12-3
12-2.2	Analysis	12-5
12-2.2.1	Estimation of Main Effects and Interactions	12-5
12-2.2.2	Testing for Significance of Main Effects and Interactions	12-8
12-3	FACTORIAL EXPERIMENTS WHEN UNIFORM CONDITIONS CANNOT BE MAINTAINED THROUGHOUT THE EXPERIMENT (EACH FACTOR AT TWO LEVELS)	12-9
12-3.1	Some Experimental Arrangements	12-9
12-3.2	Analysis of Blocked Factorial Experiments When Each Factor Is at Two Levels	12-13
12-3.2.1	Estimation of Main Effects and Interactions	12-13
12-3.2.2	Testing for Significance of Main Effects and Interactions	12-13
12-4	FRACTIONAL FACTORIAL EXPERIMENTS (EACH FACTOR AT TWO LEVELS)	12-14
12-4.1	The Fractional Factorial Designs	12-14
12-4.2	Analysis	12-19
12-4.2.1	Estimates of Main Effects and Interactions	12-19
12-4.2.2	Testing for Significance of Main Effects and Interactions	12-21

CHAPTER 13

RANDOMIZED BLOCKS, LATIN SQUARES, AND OTHER SPECIAL-PURPOSE DESIGNS

13-1	INTRODUCTION	13-1
13-2	COMPLETELY-RANDOMIZED PLANS	13-1
13-2.1	Planning	13-1
13-2.2	Analysis	13-2

Paragraph   *Page*

CHAPTER 13 (Cont)

13-3   RANDOMIZED BLOCK PLANS.................... 13-2
13-3.1   Planning................................ 13-2
13-3.2   Analysis................................ 13-3
13-3.2.1   Estimation of the Treatment Effects.... 13-4
13-3.2.2   Testing and Estimating Differences in Treatment Effects 13-5
13-3.2.3   Estimation of Block Effects............ 13-5
13-3.2.4   Testing and Estimating Differences in Block Effects ... 13-6

13-4   INCOMPLETE BLOCK PLANS.................... 13-6
13-4.1   General................................ 13-6
13-4.2   Balanced Incomplete Block Plans........ 13-7
13-4.2.1   Planning............................ 13-7
13-4.2.2   Analysis............................ 13-14
13-4.2.2.1   Estimating Treatment Effects........... 13-15
13-4.2.2.2   Testing and Estimating Differences in Treatment
                     Effects........................... 13-16
13-4.2.2.3   Estimating Block Effects............. 13-17
13-4.2.2.4   Testing and Estimating Differences in Block Effects.. 13-18
13-4.3   Chain Block Plans..................... 13-19
13-4.3.1   Planning............................ 13-19
13-4.3.2   Analysis............................ 13-21
13-4.3.2.1   Estimating Treatment and Block Effects............ 13-24
13-4.3.2.2   Testing and Estimating Differences in Treatment
                     Effects........................... 13-28

13-5   LATIN SQUARE PLANS..................... 13-30
13-5.1   Planning.............................. 13-30
13-5.2   Analysis.............................. 13-32
13-5.2.1   Estimation of Treatment Effects....... 13-33
13-5.2.2   Testing and Estimating Differences in Treatment Effects 13-34
13-5.2.3   Estimation of Row (or Column) Effects............. 13-35
13-5.2.4   Testing and Estimating Differences in Row (or Column)
                  Effects............................. 13-35

13-6   YOUDEN SQUARE PLANS..................... 13-36
13-6.1   Planning.............................. 13-36
13-6.2   Analysis.............................. 13-40
13-6.2.1   Estimation of Treatment Effects....... 13-41
13-6.2.2   Testing and Estimating Differences in Treatment Effects 13-43
13-6.2.3   Estimation of Column Effects.......... 13-44
13-6.2.4   Testing and Estimating Differences in Column Effects.. 13-44
13-6.2.5   Estimation of Row Effects............. 13-45
13-6.2.6   Testing and Estimating Differences in Row Effects..... 13-46

Paragraph   *Page*

CHAPTER 14

EXPERIMENTS TO DETERMINE OPTIMUM CONDITIONS OR LEVELS

14-1	INTRODUCTION	14-1
14-2	THE RESPONSE FUNCTION	14-1
14-3	EXPERIMENTAL DESIGNS	14-3
14-4	FINDING THE OPTIMUM	14-3
14-5	RECOMMENDED SOURCES FOR FURTHER STUDY	14-4

CHAPTER 15

SOME SHORTCUT TESTS FOR SMALL SAMPLES FROM NORMAL POPULATIONS

15-1	GENERAL	15-1
15-2	COMPARING THE AVERAGE OF A NEW PRODUCT WITH THAT OF A STANDARD	15-1
15-2.1	Does the Average of the New Product Differ From the Standard?	15-1
15-2.2	Does the Average of the New Product Exceed the Standard?	15-2
15-2.3	Is the Average of the New Product Less Than the Standard?	15-3
15-3	COMPARING THE AVERAGES OF TWO PRODUCTS	15-4
15-3.1	Do the Products A and B Differ In Average Performance?	15-4
15-3.2	Does the Average of Product A Exceed the Average of Product B?	15-5
15-4	COMPARING THE AVERAGES OF SEVERAL PRODUCTS, DO THE AVERAGES OF t PRODUCTS DIFFER?	15-6
15-5	COMPARING TWO PRODUCTS WITH RESPECT TO VARIABILITY OF PERFORMANCE	15-7
15-5.1	Does the Variability of Product A Differ From that of Product B?	15-7
15-5.2	Does the Variability of Product A Exceed that of Product B?	15-8

Paragraph   *Page*

CHAPTER 16

SOME TESTS WHICH ARE INDEPENDENT OF THE FORM OF THE DISTRIBUTION

16-1   GENERAL...   16-1

16-2   DOES THE AVERAGE OF A NEW PRODUCT DIFFER FROM A STANDARD?.....................................   16-2
16-2.1   Does the Average of a New Product Differ From a Standard?   The Sign Test   16-2
16-2.2   Does the Average of a New Product Differ From a Standard?   The Wilcoxon Signed-Ranks Test   16-3

16-3   DOES THE AVERAGE OF A NEW PRODUCT EXCEED THAT OF A STANDARD?.....................   16-4
16-3.1   Does the Average of a New Product Exceed that of a Standard?   The Sign Test   16-4
16-3.2   Does the Average of a New Product Exceed that of a Standard?   The Wilcoxon Signed-Ranks Test   16-5

16-4   IS THE AVERAGE OF A NEW PRODUCT LESS THAN THAT OF A STANDARD?.....................   16-6
16-4.1   Is the Average of a New Product Less Than that of a Standard?   The Sign Test   16-6
16-4.2   Is the Average of a New Product Less Than that of a Standard?   The Wilcoxon Signed-Ranks Test   16-7

16-5   DO PRODUCTS A AND B DIFFER IN AVERAGE PERFORMANCE?.....................   16-8
16-5.1   Do Products A and B Differ in Average Performance?   The Sign Test For Paired Observations   16-8
16-5.2   Do Products A and B Differ in Average Performance?   The Wilcoxon-Mann-Whitney Test For Two Independent Samples   16-9

16-6   DOES THE AVERAGE OF PRODUCT A EXCEED THAT OF PRODUCT B?.....................   16-10
16-6.1   Does the Average of Product A Exceed that of Product B?   The Sign Test For Paired Observations   16-11
16-6.2   Does the Average of Product A Exceed that of Product B?   The Wilcoxon-Mann-Whitney Test For Two Independent Samples   16-11

16-7   COMPARING THE AVERAGES OF SEVERAL PRODUCTS, DO THE AVERAGES OF t PRODUCTS DIFFER?   16-13

Paragraph   *Page*

CHAPTER 17

THE TREATMENT OF OUTLIERS

17-1   THE PROBLEM OF REJECTING OBSERVATIONS...   17-1

17-2   REJECTION OF OBSERVATIONS IN ROUTINE
          EXPERIMENTAL WORK........................   17-2

17-3   REJECTION OF OBSERVATIONS IN A SINGLE
          EXPERIMENT...............................   17-2
17-3.1   When Extreme Observations In Either Direction are
              Considered Rejectable................   17-3
17-3.1.1   Population Mean and Standard Deviation Unknown —
              Sample in Hand is the Only Source of Information.....   17-3
17-3.1.2   Population Mean and Standard Deviation Unknown —
              Independent External Estimate of Standard Deviation is
              Available............................   17-3
17-3.1.3   Population Mean Unknown — Value for Standard Devia-
              tion Assumed.........................   17-3
17-3.1.4   Population Mean and Standard Deviation Known......   17-4
17-3.2   When Extreme Observations In Only One Direction are
              Considered Rejectable................   17-4
17-3.2.1   Population Mean and Standard Deviation Unknown —
              Sample in Hand is the Only Source of Information.....   17-4
17-3.2.2   Population Mean and Standard Deviation Unknown —
              Independent External Estimate of Standard Deviation is
              Available............................   17-5
17-3.2.3   Population Mean Unknown — Value for Standard Devia-
              tion Assumed.........................   17-5
17-3.2.4   Population Mean and Standard Deviation Known......   17-6

CHAPTER 18

THE PLACE OF CONTROL CHARTS
IN EXPERIMENTAL WORK

18-1   PRIMARY OBJECTIVE OF CONTROL CHARTS......   18-1

18-2   INFORMATION PROVIDED BY CONTROL CHARTS..   18-1

18-3   APPLICATIONS OF CONTROL CHARTS............   18-2

Paragraph   *Page*

CHAPTER 19

STATISTICAL TECHNIQUES FOR ANALYZING EXTREME-VALUE DATA

19-1   EXTREME-VALUE DISTRIBUTIONS................ 19-1

19-2   USE OF EXTREME-VALUE TECHNIQUES.......... 19-1
19-2.1   Largest Values................................ 19-1
19-2.2   Smallest Values.............................. 19-3
19-2.3   Missing Observations........................ 19-4

CHAPTER 20

THE USE OF TRANSFORMATIONS

20-1   GENERAL REMARKS ON THE NEED FOR TRANS-
         FORMATIONS.................................... 20-1

20-2   NORMALITY AND NORMALIZING TRANSFORMA-
         TIONS... 20-1
20-2.1   Importance of Normality...................... 20-1
20-2.2   Normalization By Averaging................... 20-2
20-2.3   Normalizing Transformations.................. 20-2

20-3   INEQUALITY OF VARIANCES, AND VARIANCE-
         STABILIZING TRANSFORMATIONS.................. 20-4
20-3.1   Importance of Equality of Variances.......... 20-4
20-3.2   Types of Variance Inhomogeneity.............. 20-5
20-3.3   Variance-Stabilizing Transformations......... 20-6

20-4   LINEARITY, ADDITIVITY, AND ASSOCIATED
         TRANSFORMATIONS.............................. 20-9
20-4.1   Definition and Importance of Linearity and Additivity.... 20-9
20-4.2   Transformation of Data To Achieve Linearity and
            Additivity................................. 20-11

20-5   CONCLUDING REMARKS........................... 20-11

Paragraph   *Page*

CHAPTER 21

THE RELATION BETWEEN CONFIDENCE INTERVALS AND TESTS OF SIGNIFICANCE

21-1   INTRODUCTION.................................... 21-1

21-2   A PROBLEM IN COMPARING AVERAGES.......... 21-2

21-3   TWO WAYS OF PRESENTING THE RESULTS...... 21-2

21-4   ADVANTAGES OF THE CONFIDENCE-INTERVAL APPROACH..................................... 21-4

21-5   DEDUCTIONS FROM THE OPERATING CHARACTERISTIC (OC) CURVE.......................... 21-6

21-6   RELATION TO THE PROBLEM OF DETERMINING SAMPLE SIZE.................................. 21-6

21-7   CONCLUSION..................................... 21-6

CHAPTER 22

NOTES ON STATISTICAL COMPUTATIONS

22-1   CODING IN STATISTICAL COMPUTATIONS........ 22-1

22-2   ROUNDING IN STATISTICAL COMPUTATIONS..... 22-2
22-2.1   Rounding of Numbers................................. 22-2
22-2.2   Rounding the Results of Single Arithmetic Operations.... 22-3
22-2.3   Rounding the Results of a Series of Arithmetic Operations.. 22-4

Paragraph   *Page*

CHAPTER 23

EXPRESSION OF THE UNCERTAINTIES
OF FINAL RESULTS

23-1   INTRODUCTION   23-1

23-2   SYSTEMATIC ERROR AND IMPRECISION BOTH
        NEGLIGIBLE (CASE 1)   23-2

23-3   SYSTEMATIC ERROR NOT NEGLIGIBLE, IMPRECI-
        SION NEGLIGIBLE (CASE 2)   23-3

23-4   NEITHER SYSTEMATIC ERROR NOR IMPRECISION
        NEGLIGIBLE (CASE 3)   23-4

23-5   SYSTEMATIC ERROR NEGLIGIBLE, IMPRECISION
        NOT NEGLIGIBLE (CASE 4)   23-5

LIST OF ILLUSTRATIONS

Fig. No.   *Title*   *Page*

1-1   Histogram representing the distribution of 5,000 Rockwell hardness
       readings   1-7

1-2   Normal curve fitted to the distribution of 5,000 Rockwell hardness
       readings   1-7

1-3   Frequency distributions of various shapes   1-8

1-4   Three different normal distributions   1-8

1-5   Percentage of the population in various intervals of a normal
       distribution   1-9

1-6   Sampling distribution of $\bar{X}$ for random samples of size n from a
       normal population with mean m   1-11

1-7   Sampling distribution of s^2 for samples of size n from a normal
       population with $\sigma = 1$ 1-11

1-8   Computed confidence intervals for 100 samples of size 4 drawn at
       random from a normal population with $m = 50,000$ psi, $\sigma = 5,000$
       psi.   Case A shows 50% confidence intervals; Case B shows 90%
       confidence intervals   1-12

1-9   Computed 50% confidence intervals for the population mean m
       from 100 samples of 4, 40 samples of 100, and 4 samples of 1000 . .   1-13

1-10   Computed statistical tolerance limits for 99.7% of the population
       from 100 samples of 4, 40 samples of 100, and 4 samples of 1000 . . .   1-14

2-1   The standard deviation of some simple distributions   2-9

2-2   Number of degrees of freedom required to estimate the standard
       deviation within $P\%$ of its true value with confidence coefficient γ . .   2-12

Fig. No.	Title	Page

3-1   OC curves for the two-sided t-test ($\alpha = .05$)   3-6

3-2   OC curves for the two-sided t-test ($\alpha = .01$) . . . . :   3-7

3-3   OC curves for the two-sided normal test ($\alpha = .05$)   3-11

3-4   OC curves for the two-sided normal test ($\alpha = .01$)   3-12

3-5   OC curves for the one-sided t-test ($\alpha = .05$)   3-14

3-6   OC curves for the one-sided t-test ($\alpha = .01$)   3-15

3-7   OC curves for the one-sided normal test ($\alpha = .05$)   3-18

3-8   OC curves for the one-sided normal test ($\alpha = .01$)   3-19

3-9   Probability of rejection of hypothesis $m_A = m_B$ when true, plotted against θ   3-25

4-1   Operating characteristics of the one-sided χ^2-test to determine whether the standard deviation σ_1 of a new product exceeds the standard deviation σ_0 of a standard. ($\alpha = .05$)   4-4

4-2   Operating characteristics of the one-sided χ^2-test to determine whether the standard deviation σ_1 of a new product is less than the standard deviation σ_0 of a standard. ($\alpha = .05$)   4-6

4-3   Operating characteristics of the one-sided F-test to determine whether the standard deviation σ_A of product A exceeds the standard deviation σ_B of product B. ($\alpha = .05$; $n_A = n_B$)   4-11

4-4   Operating characteristics of the one-sided F-test to determine whether the standard deviation σ_A of product A exceeds the standard deviation σ_B of product B. ($\alpha = .05$; $n_A = n_B$, $3n_A = 2n_B$, $2n_A = n_B$)   4-12

4-5   Operating characteristics of the one-sided F-test to determine whether the standard deviation σ_A of product A exceeds the standard deviation σ_B of product B. ($\alpha = .05$; $n_A = n_B$, $2n_A = 3n_B$, $n_A = 2n_B$)   4-13

5-1   Time required for a drop of dye to travel between distance markers .   5-2

5-2   Linear functional relationship of Type FI (only Y affected by measurement errors)   5-4

5-3   Linear functional relationship of Type FII (Both X and Y affected by measurement errors)   5-5

5-4   A normal bivariate frequency surface   5-6

5-5   Contour ellipses for normal bivariate distributions having different values of the five parameters, m_X, m_Y, σ_X, σ_Y, ρ_{XY}   5-7

5-6   Diagram showing effect of restrictions of X or Y on the regression of Y on X   5-8

5-7   Young's modulus of sapphire rods as a function of temperature — an FI relationship   5-12

5-8   Young's modulus of sapphire rods as a function of temperature, showing computed regression line and confidence interval for the line   5-14

5-9   Relationship between two methods of determining a chemical constituent — an FII relationship   5-28

5-10   Relationship between the weight method and the center groove method of estimating tread life — an SI relationship   5-32

Fig. No.   *Title*   *Page*

5-11   Relationship between weight method and center groove method —
       the line shown with its confidence band is for estimating tread life
       by center groove method from tread life by weight method 5-35
5-12   Relationship between weight method and center groove method —
       showing the two regression lines 5-39
5-13   Relationship between weight method and center groove method
       when the range of the weight method has been restricted — an
       SII relationship 5-42

10-1. Probit regression line (fitted by eye) 10-13

12-1   Examples of response curves showing presence or absence of
       interaction 12-2
12-2   A one-half replicate of a 2^7 factorial 12-15
12-3   A one-quarter replicate of a 2^7 factorial 12-15
12-4   A one-eighth replicate of a 2^7 factorial 12-15

14-1   A response surface 14-2
14-2   Yield contours for the surface of Figure 14-1 with 2^2 factorial
       design 14-2

19-1   Theoretical distribution of largest values 19-2
19-2   Annual maxima of atmospheric pressure, Bergen, Norway,
       1857-1926 19-3

20-1   Normalizing effect of some frequently used transformations . . 20-3
20-2   Variance-stabilizing effect of some frequently used trans-
       formations 20-7

21-1   Reprint of Figure 3-1. OC curves for the two-sided t-test
       ($\alpha = .05$) 21-3
21-2   Reprint of Figure 1-8. Computed confidence intervals for
       100 samples of size 4 drawn at random from a normal popula-
       tion with $m = 50,000$ psi, $\sigma = 5,000$ psi. Case A shows 50%
       confidence intervals; Case B shows 90% confidence intervals . . 21-5

LIST OF TABLES

Table No.	Title	Page
2-1	Table of factors for converting the range of a sample of n to an estimate of σ, the population standard deviation. Estimate of $\sigma = \text{range}/d_n$	2-6
3-1	Summary of techniques for comparing the average of a new product with that of a standard	3-4
3-2	Summary of techniques for comparing the average performance of two products	3-22
5-1	Summary of four cases of linear relationships	5-9
5-2	Computational arrangement for Procedure 5-4.1.2.1	5-17
5-3	Computational arrangement for test of linearity	5-22
5-4	Some linearizing transformations	5-31
5-5	Computational arrangement for Procedure 5-5.1.2.1	5-37
5-6	Computational arrangement for Procedure 5-5.2.2.1	5-44
6-1	Sample table of orthogonal polynomials	6-28
8-1	Observed frequencies from two samples in two mutually exclusive categories (a 2×2 table)	8-9
8-2	Rearrangement of Table 8-1 for convenient use in testing significance with Table A-29	8-12
9-1	Computational arrangement for Data Sample 9-1.1	9-3
9-2	Computational arrangement for Data Sample 9-1.2	9-5
9-3	Table of $\dfrac{f_{ij}^2}{n_i C_j}$ — computational arrangement for Data Sample 9-2	9-7
9-4	Table of $\dfrac{f_{ij}^2}{R_i C_j}$ — computational arrangement for Data Sample 9-3	9-10
10-1	Kärber method of analysis for fuze peak voltage test data	10-5
10-2	Simplified solution for the Kärber method of analysis when the test levels (x) are equally spaced and equal numbers of objects (n) are tested at each level	10-7
10-3	Graphical probit solution using Data Sample 10-1	10-11
10-4	Exact probit solution	10-17
10-5	Exact probit solution (second iteration)	10-19
10-6	Test of linearity — final probit equation	10-20

Table No.	Title	Page
11-1	Some requisites and tools for sound experimentation	11-2
12-1	Results of flame tests of fire-retardant treatments (factorial experiment of Data Sample 12-2)	12-4
12-2	Yates' method of analysis using Data Sample 12-2	12-8
12-3	Some blocked factorial plans (for use when factorial experiment must be sub-divided into homogeneous groups)	12-10
12-4	Some fractional factorial plans	12-16
12-5	Results of flame tests of fire-retardant treatments (fractional factorial experiment of Data Sample 12-4)	12-19
12-6	Yates' method of analysis using Data Sample 12-4	12-20
13-1	Schematic presentation of results for completely-randomized plans	13-2
13-2	Schematic presentation of results for randomized block plans	13-3
13-3	Balanced incomplete block plans $(4 \leq t \leq 10, r \leq 10)$	13-8
13-4	Schematic representation of results for a balanced incomplete block plan	13-13
13-5	Schematic representation of a chain block plan	13-19
13-6	Schematic representation of the chain block plan described in Data Sample 13-4.3.2	13-22
13-7	Spectographic determination of nickel (Data Sample 13-4.3.2)	13-23
13-8	Selected Latin squares	13-31
13-9	Youden square arrangements $(r \leq 10)$	13-37
16-1	Work table for Data Sample 16-7	16-13
18-1	Tests for locating and identifying specific types of assignable causes	18-2
18-2	Factors for computing 3-sigma control limits	18-3
20-1	Some frequently used transformations	20-5

Note: Tables A-1 through A-37 follow the last chapter of text.

Table No.	Title	Page
A-1	Cumulative normal distribution—values of P	T-2
A-2	Cumulative normal distribution—values of z_P	T-3
A-3	Percentiles of the χ^2 distribution	T-4
A-4	Percentiles of the t distribution	T-5
A-5	Percentiles of the F distribution	T-6
A-6	Factors for two-sided tolerance limits for normal distributions	T-10
A-7	Factors for one-sided tolerance limits for normal distributions	T-14
A-8	Sample sizes required to detect prescribed differences between averages when the sign of the difference is not important	T-16
A-9	Sample sizes required to detect prescribed differences between averages when the sign of the difference is important	T-17
A-10	Percentiles of the studentized range, q	T-18
A-11	Percentiles of $F' = \dfrac{w_A}{w_B}$	T-24
A-12	Percentiles for $\phi = \dfrac{\bar{X} - m_O}{w}$	T-26
A-13	Percentiles for $\phi' = \dfrac{\bar{X}_A - \bar{X}_B}{\frac{1}{2}(w_A + w_B)}$	T-26
A-14	Criteria for rejection of outlying observations	T-27
A-15	Critical values of L for Link-Wallace Test	T-28
A-16	Percentage points of the extreme studentized deviate from sample mean	T-30
A-17	Confidence belts for the correlation coefficient	T-31
A-18	Weighting coefficients for probit analysis	T-32
A-19	Maximum and minimum working probits and range	T-33
A-20	Factors for computing two-sided confidence limits for σ	T-34
A-21	Factors for computing one-sided confidence limits for σ	T-36
A-22	Confidence limits for a proportion (two-sided)	T-37
A-23	Confidence limits for a proportion (one-sided)	T-41
A-24	Confidence belts for proportions for $n > 30$	T-45
A-25	Sample size required for comparing a proportion with a standard proportion when the sign of the difference is not important	T-48

Table No.	Title	Page
A-26	Sample size required for comparing a proportion with a standard proportion when the sign of the difference is important	T-51
A-27	Table of arc sine transformation for proportions	T-54
A-28	Minimum contrasts required for significance in 2×2 tables with equal samples	T-55
A-29	Tables for testing significance in 2×2 tables with unequal samples	T-59
A-30	Tables for distribution-free tolerance limits (two-sided)	T-75
A-31	Tables for distribution-free tolerance limits (one-sided)	T-76
A-32	Confidence associated with a tolerance limit statement	T-77
A-33	Critical values of r for the sign test	T-78
A-34	Critical values of $T_\alpha(n)$ for the Wilcoxon signed-ranks test	T-79
A-35	Critical values of smaller rank sum for the Wilcoxon-Mann-Whitney Test	T-80
A-36	Short table of random numbers	T-82
A-37	Short table of random normal deviates	T-86

SECTION 1

BASIC STATISTICAL CONCEPTS

AND

STANDARD TECHNIQUES FOR
ANALYSIS AND INTERPRETATION OF MEASUREMENT DATA

DISCUSSION OF TECHNIQUES

IN CHAPTERS 2 THROUGH 6

The techniques described in Chapters 2 through 6 apply to the analysis of results of experiments expressed as measurements in some conventional units on a continuous scale. They do not apply to the analysis of data in the form of proportions, percentages, or counts.

It is assumed that the underlying population distributions are normal or nearly normal. Where this assumption is not very important, or where the actual population distribution would show only slight departure from normality, an indication is given of the effect upon the conclusions derived from the use of the techniques. Where the normality assumption is critical, or where the actual population distribution shows substantial departure from normality, or both, suitable warnings are given.

Table A-37 is a table of three-decimal-place random normal deviates that exemplify sampling from a normal distribution with zero mean ($m = 0$) and unit standard deviation ($\sigma = 1$). To construct numbers that will simulate measurements that are normally distributed about a true value of, say, 0.12, with a standard deviation of, say, 0.02, multiply the table entries by 0.02 and then add 0.12. The reader who wishes to get a feel for the statistical behavior of sample data, and to try out and judge the usefulness of particular statistical techniques, is urged to carry out a few "dry runs" with such simulated measurements of known characteristics.

All A-Tables referenced in these Chapters are contained in ORDP 20-114, Section 5.

CHAPTER 1

SOME BASIC STATISTICAL CONCEPTS AND PRELIMINARY CONSIDERATIONS

1-1   INTRODUCTION

Statistics deals with the collection, analysis, interpretation, and presentation of numerical data. Statistical methods may be divided into two classes—descriptive and inductive. Descriptive statistical methods are those which are used to summarize or describe data. They are the kind we see used everyday in the newspapers and magazines.

Inductive statistical methods are used when we wish to generalize from a small body of data to a larger system of similar data. The generalizations usually are in the form of estimates or predictions. In this handbook we are mainly concerned with inductive statistical methods.

1-2   POPULATIONS, SAMPLES, AND DISTRIBUTIONS

The concepts of a *population* and a *sample* are basic to inductive statistical methods. Equally important is the concept of a *distribution*.

Any finite or infinite collection of individual things—objects or events—constitutes a *population*. A population (also known as a universe) is thought of not as just a heap of things specified by enumerating them one after another, but rather as an aggregate determined by some property that distinguishes between things that do and things that do not belong. Thus, the term *population* carries with it the connotation of completeness. In contrast, a *sample*, defined as a portion of a population, has the connotation of incompleteness.

Examples of populations are:

(a) The corporals in the Marines on July 1, 1956.

(b) A production lot of fuzes.

(c) The rounds of ammunition produced by a particular production process.

(d) Fridays the 13th.

(e) Repeated weighings of the powder charge of a particular round of ammunition.

(f) Firings of rounds from a given production lot.

In examples (a), (b), and (c), the "individuals" comprising the population are material objects (corporals, fuzes, rounds); in (d) they are periods of time of a very restricted type; and in (e) and (f) they are physical operations. Populations (a) and (b) are clearly finite, and their constituents are determined by the official records of the Marine Corps and the appropriate production records, respectively. Populations (c), (d), and (e) are conceptually infinite. Offhand, the population example (f) would seem to be finite, because firing is a destructive operation; but in order to allow for variation in quality among "firings" performed in accordance with the same general procedure it is sometimes useful, by analogy with repetitive weighings, to regard an actual firing as a sample of size one from a conceptually infinite population of "possible" firings, any one of which might have been associated with the particular round conceived. In this connection, note that in examples (e) and (f) the populations involved are not completely defined until the weighing and firing procedures concerned have been fully specified.

Attention to some characteristic of the individuals of a population that is not the same for every individual leads immediately to recognition of the *distribution* of this characteristic in the population. Thus, the heights of the corporals in the Marines on July 1, 1956, the burning times of a production lot of fuzes, and the outcomes of successive weighings of a powder charge ("observed weights" of the charge) are examples of distributions. The presence or absence of an attribute is a characteristic of an individual in a population, such as "tatooed" or "not tatooed" for the privates in the Marines. This kind of characteristic has a particularly simple type of distribution in the population.

Attention to one, two, three, or more characteristics for each individual leads to a univariate, bivariate, trivariate, or multivariate distribution in the population. The examples of populations given previously were examples of univariate distributions. Simultaneous consideration of the muzzle velocities and weights of powder charges of rounds of ammunition from a given production process determines a bivariate distribution of these characteristics in the population. Simultaneous recognition of the frequencies of each of a variety of different types of accidents on Friday the 13th leads to a multivariate distribution. In connection with these examples, note that, as a general principle, the distribution of a characteristic or a group of characteristics in a population is not completely defined until the method or methods of measurement or enumeration involved are fully specified.

The distribution of some particular property of the individuals in a population is a collective property of the population; and so, also, are the average and other characteristics of the distribution. The methods of inductive statistics enable us to learn about such population characteristics from a study of samples.

An example will illustrate an important class of derived distributions. Suppose we select 10 rounds of ammunition from a given lot and measure their muzzle velocities when the rounds are fired in a given test weapon. Let $\bar{X}$ be the average muzzle velocity of the 10 rounds. If the lot is large, there will be many different sets of 10 rounds which could have been obtained from the lot. For each such sample of 10 rounds, there will correspond an average muzzle velocity $\bar{X}_i$. These averages, from all possible samples of 10, themselves form a distribution of sample averages. This kind of distribution is called the *sampling distribution of $\bar{X}$ for samples of size 10* from the population concerned. Similarly, we may determine the *range R* of muzzle velocities (i.e., the difference between the largest and the smallest) for each of all possible samples of 10 rounds each. These ranges R_i $(i = 1, 2, \ldots)$ collectively determine the *sampling distribution of the range* of muzzle velocities *in samples of size 10* from the population concerned. The methods of inductive statistics are based upon the mathematical properties of sampling distributions of sample *statistics* such as $\bar{X}$ and R.

Let us summarize: A population in Statistics corresponds to what in Logic is termed the "universe of discourse"—it's what we are talking about. By the methods of inductive statistics we can learn, from a study of samples, only about population characteristics—only about *collective* properties of the populations represented by the individuals in the samples—not about characteristics of specific individuals with unique idiosyn-crasies. The population studied may be large or small, but there must be a population; and it should be well defined. The characteristic of interest must be a collective property of the population.

1-3 STATISTICAL INFERENCES AND SAMPLING

1-3.1 STATISTICAL INFERENCES

If we were willing or able to examine an entire population, our task would be merely that of describing that population, using whatever numbers, figures, or charts we cared to use. Since it is ordinarily inconvenient or impossible to observe every item in the population, we take a sample—a portion of the population. Our task is now to generalize from our observations on this portion (which usually is small) to the population. Such generalizations about characteristics of a population from a study of one or more samples from the population are termed *statistical inferences*.

Statistical inferences take two forms: *estimates* of the magnitudes of population characteristics, and *tests of hypotheses* regarding population characteristics. Both are useful for determining which among two or more courses of action to follow in practice when the "correct" course is determined by some particular but unknown characteristic of the population.

Statistical inferences all involve reaching conclusions about population characteristics (or at least acting as if one had reached such conclusions) from a study of samples which are known or assumed to be portions of the population concerned. Statistical inferences are basically predictions of what would be found to be the case if the parent populations could be and were fully analyzed with respect to the relevant characteristic or characteristics.

A simple example will serve to bring out a number of essential features of statistical inferences and the methods of inductive statistics. Suppose that four cards have been drawn from a deck of cards and have been found to be the Ace of Hearts, the Five of Diamonds, the Three of Clubs, and the Jack of Clubs. The specific methods discussed in the following paragraphs will be illustrated from this example.

First of all, from the example, we can clearly conclude at once that the deck contained at least one Heart, at least one Diamond, and at least two Clubs. We also can conclude from the presence of the Five and the Three that the deck is definitely not a pinochle deck. These are perhaps trivial inferences, but their validity is above question and does not depend in any way on the *modus operandi* of drawing the four cards.

In order to be able to make inferences of a more substantial character, we must know the nature of the sampling operation that yielded the sample of four cards actually obtained. Suppose, for example, that the sampling procedure was as follows: The cards were drawn in the order listed, each card being selected *at random* from all the cards present in the deck when the card was drawn. This defines a hypothetical population of drawings. By using an appropriate technique of inductive statistics—essentially, a "catalog" of all possible samples of four, showing for each sample the conclusion to be adopted whenever that sample occurs—we can make statistical inferences about properties of this population of drawings. The statistical inferences made will be rigorous if, and only if, the inductive technique used is appropriate to the sampling procedure actually employed.

Thus, by taking the observed proportion of Clubs as an estimate of the proportion of Clubs in the abstract population of drawings, we may assert: the proportion of Clubs is 50%. Since random sampling of the type assumed assures that the proportion of Clubs in the population of drawings is the same as the proportion of Clubs in the deck, we may assert with equal validity: the proportion of Clubs in the deck is 50%. If the deck concerned actually was a standard bridge deck, then in the present instance our estimate is wrong in spite of being the best single estimate available.

We know from experience that with samples of four we cannot expect to "hit the nail on the head" every time. If instead of attempting to make a single-number estimate we had chosen to refer to a "catalog" of *interval estimates* (see, for example, Table A-22*), we would have concluded that the proportion of Clubs is between 14% and 86% inclusive, with an expectation of being correct 9 times out of 10. If the deck was in fact a standard bridge deck, then our conclusion is correct in this instance, but its validity depends on whether the sampling procedure employed in drawing the four cards corresponds to the sampling procedure assumed in the preparation of the "catalog" of answers.

It is important to notice, moreover, that strictly we have a right to make statistical inferences only with respect to the hypothetical population of drawings defined by the sampling operation concerned. In the present instance, as we shall see, the sampling operation was so chosen that the parameters (i.e., the proportions of Hearts, Clubs, and Diamonds) of the hypothetical population of drawings coincide with the corresponding parameters of the deck.

---

* The A-Tables referenced in this handbook are contained in Section 5, ORDP 20-114.

Hence, in the present case, inferences about the parameters of the population of drawings may be interpreted as inferences about the composition of the deck. This emphasizes the importance of selecting and employing a sampling procedure such that the relevant parameters of the population of drawings bear a known relation to the corresponding parameters of the real-life situation. Otherwise, statistical inferences with respect to the population of drawings carried over to the real-life population will be lacking in rigor, even though by luck they may sometimes be correct.

1-3.2 RANDOM SAMPLING

In order to make valid nontrivial generalizations from samples about characteristics of the populations from which they came, the samples must have been obtained by a sampling scheme which insures two conditions:

(a) Relevant characteristics of the populations sampled must bear a known relation to the corresponding characteristics of the population of all possible samples associated with the sampling scheme.

(b) Generalizations may be drawn from such samples in accordance with a given "book of rules" whose validity rests on the mathematical theory of probability.

If a sampling scheme is to meet these two requirements, it is necessary that the selection of the individuals to be included in a sample involve some type of *random selection*, that is, each possible sample must have a fixed and determinate probability of selection. (For a very readable expository discussion of the general principles of sampling, with examples of some of the more common procedures, see the article by Cochran, Mosteller, and Tukey[1]. For fuller details see, for example, Cochran's book[2].

The most widely useful type of random selection is *simple* (or *unrestricted*) *random sampling*. This type of sampling is defined by the requirement that each individual in the population has an equal chance of being the first member of the sample; after the first member is selected, each of the remaining individuals in the population has an equal chance of being the second member of the sample; and so forth. For a sampling scheme to qualify as simple random sampling, it is not sufficient that "each individual in the population have an equal chance of appearing in the sample," as is sometimes said, but it is sufficient that "each possible sample have an equal chance of being selected." Throughout this handbook, we shall assume that all samples are random samples in the sense of having been obtained by simple random sampling.

It cannot be overemphasized that the *randomness* of a sample is inherent in the sampling scheme employed to obtain the sample and not an intrinsic property of the sample itself. Experience teaches that it is not safe to assume that a sample selected haphazardly, without any conscious plan, can be regarded as if it had been obtained by simple random sampling. Nor does it seem to be possible to consciously draw a sample *at random*. As stated by Cochran, Mosteller, and Tukey[1],

We insist on some semblance of mechanical (dice, coins, random number tables, etc.) randomization before we treat a sample from an existent population as if it were random. We realize that if someone just "grabs a handful," the individuals in the handful almost always resemble one another (on the average) more than do the members of a simple random sample. Even if the "grabs" are randomly spread around so that every individual has an equal chance of entering the sample, there are difficulties. Since the individuals of grab samples resemble one another *more* than do individuals of random samples, it follows (by a simple mathematical argument) that the means of grab samples resemble one another *less* than the means of random samples of the same size. From a grab sample, therefore, we tend to *under*estimate the variability in the population, although we should have to *over*estimate it in order to obtain valid estimates of variability of grab sample means by substituting such an estimate into the formula for the variability of means of simple random samples. Thus, using simple random sample formulas for grab sample means introduces a double bias, both parts of which lead to an unwarranted appearance of higher stability.

Instructions for formally drawing a sample at random from a particular population are given in Paragraph 1-4.

Finally, it needs to be noticed that a particular sample often qualifies as "a sample" from any one of several populations. For example, a sample of n rounds from a single carton is a sample from that carton, from the production lot of which the rounds in that carton are a portion, and from the production process concerned. By drawing these rounds from the carton in accordance with a simple random sampling scheme, we can insure that they are a (simple) random sample from the carton, not from the production lot or the production process. Only if the production process is in a "state of statistical control" may our sample also be considered to be a simple random sample from the production lot and the production process. In a similar fashion, a sample of repeated weighings can validly be considered to be a random sample from the conceptually infinite population of repeated weighings by the same procedure only if the weighing procedure is in a state of statistical control (see Chapter 18, in Section 4, ORDP 20-113).

It is therefore important in practice to know from which of several possible "parent" populations a sample was obtained *by simple random sampling*. This population is termed the *sampled population*, and may be quite different from the population of interest, termed the *target population*, to which we would like our conclusions to be applicable. In practice, they are rarely identical, though the difference is often small. A sample from the target population of rounds of ammunition produced by a particular production process will actually be a sample from one or more production lots (sampled population), and the difference between sampled and target populations will be smaller if the sampled population comprises a larger number of production lots. The further the sampled population is removed from the target population, the more the burden of validity of conclusions is shifted from the shoulders of the statistician to those of the subject matter expert, who must place greater and greater (and perhaps unwarranted) reliance on "other considerations."

1-4   SELECTION OF A RANDOM SAMPLE

As has been brought out previously, the method of choosing a sample is an all-important factor in determining what use can be made of it. In order for the techniques described in this handbook to be valid as bases for making statements from samples about populations, we must have unrestricted random samples from these populations. In practice, it is not always easy to obtain a random sample from a given population. Unconscious selections and biases tend to enter. For this reason, it is advisable to use a table of random numbers as an aid in selecting the sample. Two tables of random numbers which are recommended are by L. H. C. Tippett[3] and The Rand Corporation[4]. These tables contain detailed instructions for their use. An excerpt from one of these tables[4] is given in Table A-36. This sample is included for illustration only; a larger table should be used in any actual problem. Repeated use of the same portion of a table of random numbers will not satisfy the requirements of randomness.

An illustration of the method of use of tables of random numbers follows. Suppose the population consists of 87 items, and we wish to select a random sample of 10. Assign to each individual a separate two-digit number between 00 and 86. In a table of random numbers, pick an arbitrary starting place and decide upon the direction of reading the numbers. Any direction may be used, provided the rule is fixed in advance and is independent of the numbers occurring. Read two-digit numbers from the table, and select for the sample those individuals whose numbers occur until 10 individuals have been selected. For example, in Table A-36, start with the second page of the Table (p. T-83), column 20, line 6, and read down. The 10 items picked for the sample would thus be numbers 38, 44, 13, 73, 39, 41, 35, 07, 14, and 47.

The method described is applicable for obtaining simple random samples from any sampled population consisting of a finite set of individuals. In the case of an infinite sampled population, these procedures do not apply. Thus, we might think of the sampled population for the target population of weighings as comprising all weighings which might conceptually have been made during the time while weighing was done. We cannot by mechanical randomization draw a random sample from this population, and so must recognize that we have a random sample only *by assumption*. This assumption will be warranted if previous data indicate that the weighing procedure is in a state of statistical control; unwarranted if the contrary is indicated; and a leap in the dark if no previous data are available.

1-5   SOME PROPERTIES OF DISTRIBUTIONS

Although it is unusual to examine populations in their entirety, the examination of a large sample or of many small samples from a population can give us much information about the general nature of the population's characteristics.

One device for revealing the general nature of a population distribution is a histo-gram. Suppose we have a large number of observed items and a numerical measurement for each item, such as, for example, a Rockwell hardness reading for each of 5,000 specimens. We first make a table showing the numerical measurement and the number of times (i.e., frequency) this measurement was recorded.

Rockwell Hardness Number	Frequency
55	1
56	17
57	135
58	503
59	1,110
60	1,470
61	1,120
62	490
63	125
64	26
65	3

Data taken, by permission, from *Sampling Inspection by Variables* by A. H. Bowker and H. P. Goode, Copyright, 1952, McGraw-Hill Book Company, Inc.

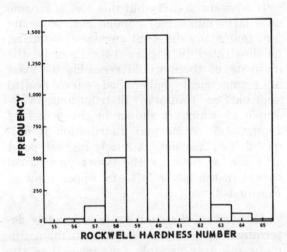

Figure 1-1. Histogram representing the distribution of 5,000 Rockwell hardness readings.

From this frequency table we can make the histogram as shown in Figure 1-1. The height of the rectangle for any hardness range is determined by the number of items in that hardness range. The rectangle is centered at the tabulated hardness value. If we take the sum of all the rectangular areas to be one square unit, then the area of an individual rectangle is equal to the *proportion* of items in the sample that have hardness values in the corresponding range. When the sample is large, as in the present instance, the histogram may be taken to exemplify the general nature of the corresponding distribution in the population.

If it were possible to measure hardness in finer intervals, we would be able to draw a larger number of rectangles, smaller in width than before. For a sufficiently large sample and a sufficiently fine "mesh," we would be justified in blending the tops of the rectangles into a continuous curve, such as that shown in Figure 1-2, which we could expect to more nearly represent the underlying population distribution.

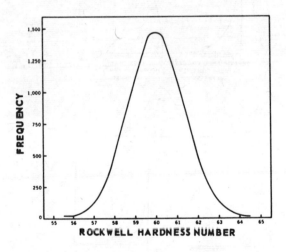

Figure 1-2. Normal curve fitted to the distribution of 5,000 Rockwell hardness readings.

If we were to carry out this sort of scheme on a large number of populations, we would find that many different curves would arise, as illustrated in Figure 1-3. Possibly, the majority of them would resemble the class of symmetrical bell-shaped curves called "normal" or "Gaussian" distributions, an example of which is shown in the center of Figure 1-3. A normal distribution is unimodal, i.e., has only a single highest point or *mode*, as also are the two asymmetrical curves in the lower left and upper right of Figure 1-3.

A "normal" distribution is completely determined by two parameters: m, the arithmetic mean (or simply "the mean") of the distribution, and σ, the standard deviation (often termed the "population mean" and "population standard deviation"). The *variance* of the distribution is σ^2. Since a normal curve is both unimodal and symmetrical,

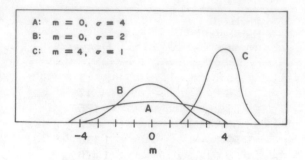

Figure 1-4.　*Three different normal distributions.*

m is also the *mode* and the value which divides the area under the curve in half, i.e., the *median*. It is useful to remember that σ is the distance from m to either of the two inflection points on the curve. (The inflection point is the point at which the curve changes from concave upward to concave downward.) This is a special property of the normal distribution. More generally, the mean of a distribution m is the "center of gravity" of the distribution; σ is the "radius of gyration" of the distribution about m, in the language of mechanics; and σ^2 is the second moment about m.

The parameter m is the *location parameter* of a normal distribution, while σ is a measure of its spread, scatter, or dispersion. Thus, a change in m merely slides the curve right or left without changing its profile, while a change in σ widens or narrows the curve without changing the location of its center. Three different normal curves are shown in Figure 1-4. (All normal curves in this section are drawn so that the area under the curve is equal to one, which is a standard convention.)

Figure 1-5 shows the percentage of elements of the population contained in various intervals of a normal distribution. z is the distance from the population mean in units of the standard deviation and is computed using the formula $z = (X-m)/\sigma$, where X represents any value in the population. Using z to enter Table A-1, we find P, the proportion

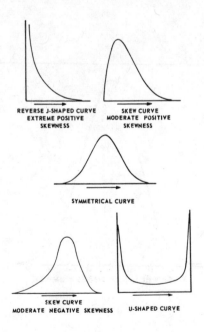

Figure 1-3.　*Frequency distributions of various shapes.*

Adapted with permission from *Elements of Statistical Reasoning* by A. E. Treloar, Copyright, 1939, John Wiley & Sons, Inc.

of elements in the population which have values of z smaller than any given z. Thus, as shown in Fig. 1-5, 34.13% of the population will have values of z between 0 and 1 (or between 0 and −1); 13.59% of the population, between 1 and 2 (or between −1 and −2); 2.14% between 2 and 3 (or between −2 and −3); and .14% beyond 3 (or beyond −3). Figure 1-5 shows these percentages of the population in various intervals of z.

For example, suppose we know that the chamber pressures of a lot of ammunition may be represented by a normal distribution, with the average chamber pressure $m = 50,000$ psi and standard deviation $\sigma = 5,000$ psi. Then $z = \dfrac{X-50,000}{5,000}$ and we know (Fig. 1-5) that if we fired the lot of ammunition in the prescribed manner we would expect 50% of the rounds to have a chamber pressure above 50,000 psi, 15.9% to have pressures above 55,000 psi, and 2.3% to have pressures above 60,000 psi, etc.

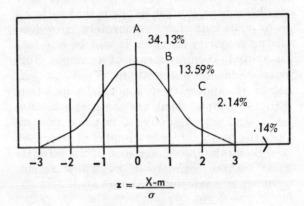

Figure 1-5. *Percentage of the population in various intervals of a normal distribution.*

1-6 ESTIMATION OF m and σ

In areas where a lot of experimental work has been done, it often happens that we know m or σ, or both, fairly accurately. However, in the majority of cases it will be our task to estimate them by means of a sample. Suppose we have n observations, $X_1, X_2, \ldots, X_n$ taken at random from a normal population. From a sample, what are the best estimates of m and σ? Actually, it is usual to compute the best unbiased estimates of m and σ^2, and then take the square root of the estimate of σ^2 as the estimate of σ. These recommended estimates of m and σ^2 are:*

$$\overline{X} = \frac{1}{n} \sum_{i=1}^{n} X_i$$

$$s^2 = \frac{\sum_{i=1}^{n} (X_i - \overline{X})^2}{n - 1}$$

$\overline{X}$ and s^2 are the *sample mean* and *sample estimate of variance*, respectively. (s is often called "the sample standard deviation," but this is not strictly correct and we shall avoid the expression and simply refer to s.) For computational purposes, the following formula for s^2 is more convenient:

$$s^2 = \frac{n \sum_{i=1}^{n} X_i^2 - \left(\sum_{i=1}^{n} X_i \right)^2}{n (n - 1)}$$

* The Greek symbol Σ is often used as shorthand for "the sum of." For example,

$$\sum_{i=1}^{4} X_i = X_1 + X_2 + X_3 + X_4$$

$$\sum_{i=1}^{3} (X_i + Y_i) = (X_1 + Y_1) + (X_2 + Y_2) + (X_3 + Y_3)$$

$$\sum_{i=1}^{3} X_i Y_i = X_1 Y_1 + X_2 Y_2 + X_3 Y_3$$

$$\sum_{i=1}^{3} c = c + c + c = 3c$$

Nearly every sample will contain different individuals, and thus the estimates $\overline{X}$ and s^2 of m and σ^2 will differ from sample to sample. However, these estimates are such that "on the average" they tend to be equal to m and σ^2, respectively, and in this sense are *unbiased*. If, for example, we have a large number of random samples of size n, the average of their respective estimates of σ^2 will tend to be near σ^2. Furthermore, the amount of fluctuation of the respective s^2's about σ^2 (or of the $\overline{X}$'s about m, if we are estimating m) will be smaller in a certain well-defined sense than the fluctuation would be for any estimates other than the recommended ones. For these reasons, $\overline{X}$ and s^2 are called the "best unbiased" estimates of m and σ^2, respectively.*

As might be expected, the larger the sample size n, the more faith we can put in the estimates $\overline{X}$ and s^2. This is illustrated in Figures 1-6 and 1-7. Figure 1-6 shows the distribution of $\overline{X}$ (sample mean) for samples of various sizes from the same normal distribution. The curve for $n = 1$ is the distribution for individuals in the population. All of the curves are centered at m, the popula-

* On the other hand, s is not an unbiased estimator of σ. Thus, in samples of size n from a normal distribution, the situation is:

Sample size, n	s is an unbiased estimator of:
2	0.797 σ
3	0.886
4	0.921
5	0.940
6	0.952
7	0.959
8	0.965
9	0.969
10	0.973
20	0.987
30	0.991
40	0.994
60	0.996
120	0.998
∞	1.000

tion mean, but the scatter becomes less as n gets larger. Figure 1-7 shows the distribution of s^2 (sample variance) for samples of various sizes from the same normal distribution.

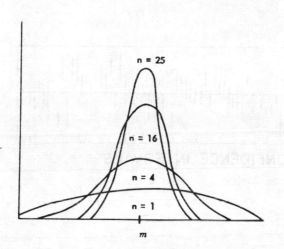

Figure 1-6. *Sampling distribution of $\bar{X}$ for random samples of size n from a normal population with mean m.*

Reproduced by permission from *The Methods of Statistics,* 4th ed., by L. H. C. Tippett, Copyright, 1952, John Wiley & Sons, Inc.

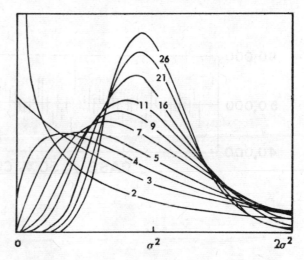

Figure 1-7. *Sampling distribution of s^2 for sample size n from a normal population with $\sigma = 1$.*

Adapted with permission from *Some Theory of Sampling,* by W. Edwards Deming, Copyright, 1950, John Wiley & Sons, Inc.

1-7 CONFIDENCE INTERVALS

Inasmuch as estimates of m and σ vary from sample to sample, interval estimates of m and σ may sometimes be preferred to "single-value" estimates. Provided we have a random sample from a normal population, we can make interval estimates of m or σ with a chosen degree of confidence. The level of confidence is not associated with a particular interval, but is associated with the method of calculating the interval. The interval obtained from a particular sample either brackets the true parameter value (m or σ, whichever we are estimating) or does not. The confidence coefficient γ is sim-

ply the proportion of samples of size n for which intervals computed by the prescribed method may be expected to bracket m (or σ). Such intervals are known as *confidence intervals,* and always are associated with a prescribed confidence coefficient. As we would expect, larger samples tend to give narrower confidence intervals for the same level of confidence.

Suppose we are given the lot of ammunition mentioned earlier (Par. 1-5) and wish to make a confidence interval estimate of the average chamber pressure of the rounds in the lot. The true average is 50,000 psi, although this value is unknown to us. Let us take a random sample of four rounds and from this sample, using the given procedure, calculate the upper and lower limits for our confidence interval. Consider all the possible samples of size 4 that could have been taken, and the resulting confidence intervals computed from each. If we compute 50% (90%) confidence intervals, then we expect 50% (90%) of the computed intervals to cover the true value, 50,000 psi. See Figure 1-8.

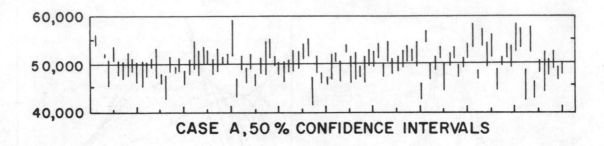

CASE A, 50 % CONFIDENCE INTERVALS

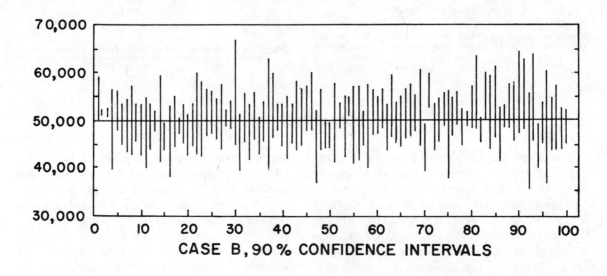

CASE B, 90 % CONFIDENCE INTERVALS

Figure 1-8.   Computed confidence intervals for 100 samples of size 4 drawn at random from a normal population with m = 50,000 psi, σ = 5,000 psi.   Case A shows 50% confidence intervals; Case B shows 90% confidence intervals.

In Case A of Figure 1-8, 51 of the 100 intervals actually include the true mean. For 50% confidence interval estimates, we would expect in the long run that 50% of the intervals would include the true mean. Fifty-one out of 100 is a reasonable deviation from the expected 50%. In Case B, 90 out of 100 of the intervals contain the true mean. This is precisely the expected number for 90% intervals.

Note also (Fig. 1-8) that the successive confidence intervals vary both in position and width. This is because they were computed (see Par. 2-1.4) from the sample statistics $\overline{X}$ and s, both of which vary from sample to sample. If, on the other hand, the standard deviation of the population distribution σ were known, and the confidence intervals were computed from the successive $\overline{X}$'s and σ (procedure given in Par. 2-1.5), then the resulting confidence intervals would all be the same width, and would vary in position only.

Finally, as the sample size increases, confidence intervals tend not only to vary less in both position and width, but also to "pinch in" ever closer to the true value of the population parameter concerned, as illustrated in Figure 1-9.

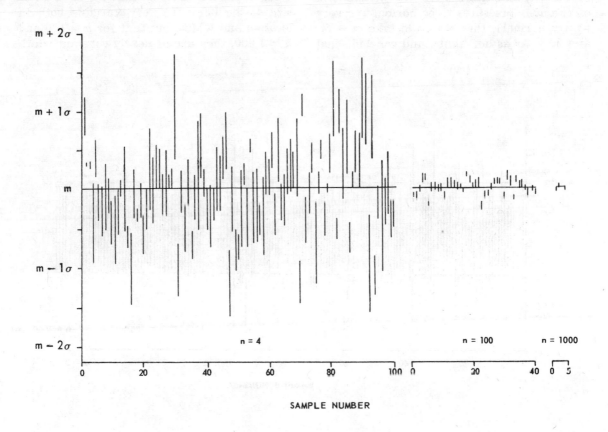

Figure 1-9.   Computed 50% confidence intervals for the population mean m from 100 samples of 4, 40 samples of 100, and 4 samples of 1000.

1-8　STATISTICAL TOLERANCE LIMITS

Sometimes what is wanted is not an estimate of the mean and variance of the population distribution but, instead, two outer values or limits which contain nearly all of the population values. For example, if extremely low chamber pressures or extremely high chamber pressures might cause serious problems, we may wish to know approximate limits to the range of chamber pressures in a lot of ammunition. More specifically, we may wish to know within what limits 99%, for example, of the chamber pressures lie. If we knew the mean m and standard deviation σ of chamber pressures in the lot, and if we knew the distribution of chamber pressures to be normal (or very nearly normal), then we could take $m - 3\sigma$ and $m + 3\sigma$ as our limits, and conclude that

approximately 99.7% of the chamber pressures lie within these limits (see Fig. 1-5). If we do not know m and σ, then we may endeavor to approximate the limits with *statistical tolerance limits* of the form $\overline{X} - Ks$ and $\overline{X} + Ks$, based on the sample statistics $\overline{X}$ and s, with K chosen so that we may expect these limits to include *at least P* percent of the chamber pressures in the lot, at some prescribed level of confidence α.

Three sets of such limits for $P = 99.7\%$, corresponding to sample sizes $n = 4, 100$, and 1,000, are shown by the bars in Figure 1-10. It should be noted that for samples of size 4, the bars are very variable both in location and width, but that for $n = 100$ and $n = 1,000$, they are of nearly constant width

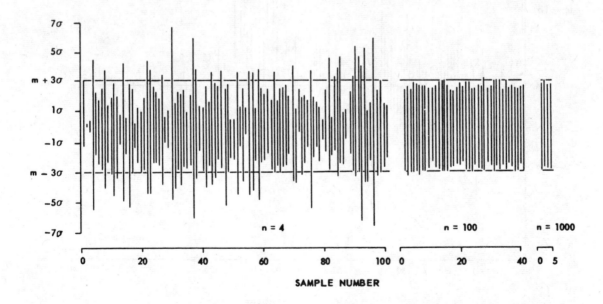

Figure 1-10.　Computed statistical tolerance limits for 99.7% of the population from 100 samples of size 4, 40 samples of size 100, and 4 samples of size 1000.

and position—and their end points approximate very closely to $m - 3\sigma$ and $m + 3\sigma$. In other words, statistical tolerance intervals tend to a fixed size (which depends upon P) as the sample size increases, whereas confidence intervals shrink down towards zero width with increasing sample size, as illustrated in Figure 1-9.

The difference in the meanings of the terms *confidence intervals, statistical tolerance limits,* and *engineering tolerance limits* should be noted. A *confidence interval* is an interval within which we estimate a given population parameter to lie (e.g., the population mean m with respect to some characteristic). *Statistical tolerance limits* for a given population are limits within which we expect a stated proportion of the population to lie with respect to some measurable characteristic. *Engineering tolerance limits* are specified outer limits of acceptability with respect to some characteristic usually prescribed by a design engineer.

1-9   USING STATISTICS TO MAKE DECISIONS

1-9.1   APPROACH TO A DECISION PROBLEM

Consider the following more-or-less typical practical situation: Ten rounds of a new type of shell are fired into a target, and the depth of penetration is measured for each round. The depths of penetration are 10.0, 11.1, 10.5, 10.5, 11.2, 10.8, 9.8, 12.2, 11.0, and 9.9 cm. The average penetration depth of the comparable standard shell is 10.0 cm. We wish to know whether the new type shells penetrate farther on the average than the standard type shells.

If we compute the arithmetic mean of the ten shells, we find it is 10.70 cm. Our first impulse might be to state that on the average the new shell will penetrate 0.7 cm. farther than the standard shell. This, indeed, is our best single guess, but how sure can we be that this actually is close to the truth? One thing that might catch our notice is the variability in the individual penetration depths of the new shells. They range from 9.8 cm. to 12.2 cm. The standard deviation as measured by s calculated from the sample is 0.73 cm. Might not our sample of ten shells have contained some atypical ones of the new type which have unusually high penetrating power? Could it be that the new shell is, on the average, no better than the standard one? If we were obliged to decide,

on the basis of the results obtained from these ten shells alone, whether to keep on making the standard shells or to convert our equipment to making the new shell, how can we make a valid choice?

A very worthwhile step toward a solution in such situations is to compute, from the data in hand, a confidence interval for the unknown value of the population parameter of interest. The procedure (given in Par. 2-1.4) applied to the foregoing depth-of-penetration data for the new type of shell yields the interval from 10.18 to 11.22 cm. as a 95% confidence interval for the population mean depth of penetration of shells of the new type. Inasmuch as this interval lies entirely to the right of the mean for the standard shell, 10.00 cm., we are justified in concluding that the new shell *is*, on the average, better than the standard, with only a 5% risk of being in error. Nevertheless, taking other considerations into account (e.g., cost of the new type, cost of changing over, etc.), we may conclude finally that the improvement—which may be as little as 0.18 cm., and probably not more than 1.22 cm.—is not sufficient to warrant conversion to the new type. On the other hand, the evidence that the new type is almost certainly better plus the prospect that the improvement may be as great as 1.22 cm. may serve to recommend further developmental activity in the direction "pioneered" by the new type.

A somewhat different approach, which provides a direct answer to our question "Could it be that the new shell is on the average no better than the standard?" but not to the question of whether to convert to the new type, is to carry out a so-called *test of significance* (or test of a statistical hypothesis). In the case of the foregoing example, the formal procedure for the corresponding test of significance (Par. 3-2.2.1) turns out to be equivalent (as explained in ORDP 20-113, Chapter 21) to noting whether or not the confidence interval computed does or does not include the population mean for the standard shell (10.0 cm.). If, as in the present instance, the population mean for the standard shell is *not* included, this is taken to be a *negative* answer to our question. In other words, this is taken to be conclusive evidence (at the *5% level of significance*) *against* the *null hypothesis* that "the new shell is on the average *no better* than the standard." Rejection of the null hypothesis in this case is equivalent to accepting the indefinite *alternative hypothesis* that "the new shell *is better* on the average than the standard." If, on the other hand, the population mean for the standard shell *is* included in the confidence interval, this is taken as an *affirmative* answer to our question—not in the positive sense of definitely confirming the null hypothesis ("is no better"), but in the more-or-less neutral sense of the absence of conclusive evidence to the contrary.

As the foregoing example illustrates, an advantage of the confidence-interval approach to a decision problem is that the confidence interval gives an indication of how large the difference, if any, is likely to be, and thus provides some of the additional information usually needed to reach a final decision on the action to be taken next. For many purposes, this is a real advantage of confidence intervals over tests of significance.

However, all statistical decision problems are not amenable to solution via confidence intervals. For instance, the question at issue may be whether or not two particular characteristics of shell performance are mutually independent. In such a situation, any one of a variety of tests of significance can be used to test the null hypothesis of "no dependence." Some of these may have a reasonably good chance of rejecting the null hypothesis, and thus "discovering" the existence of a dependence when a dependence really exists—even though the exact nature of the dependence, if any, is not understood and a definitive measure of the extent of the dependence in the population is lacking.

A precise test of significance will be possible if: (a) the sampling distribution of some sample statistic is known (at least to a good approximation) for the case of "no dependence"; and (b) the effect of dependence on this statistic is known (e.g., tends to make it larger). For a confidence-interval approach to be possible, two conditions are necessary: (a) there must be agreement on what constitutes the proper measure (parameter) of dependence of the two characteristics in the population; and, (b) there must be a sample estimate of this dependence parameter whose sampling distribution is known, to a good approximation at least, for all values of the parameter. Confidence intervals tend to provide a more complete answer to statistical decision problems when they are available, but tests of significance are of wider applicability.

1-9.2 CHOICE OF NULL AND ALTERNATIVE HYPOTHESES

A statistical test always involves a *null hypothesis*, which is considered to be the hypothesis under test, as against a class of *alternative hypotheses*. The null hypothesis acts as a kind of "origin" or "base" (in the sense of "base line"), from which the alternative hypotheses deviate in one way or another to greater and lesser degrees. Thus, in the case of the classical problem of the tossing of a coin, the null or base hypothesis specifies that the probability of "heads" on any single trial equals 1/2. If, in a particular situation, the occurrence of "heads" were an *advantage,* then we might be particularly interested in the *one-sided* class of alternative hypotheses that the probability of "heads" on any single trial equals *P,* where *P* is some (unknown) fraction exceeding 1/2. If neither "heads" nor 'tails" were intrinsically advantageous, but a bias in favor of either could be employed to advantage, then we could probably be interested in the more general *two-sided* class of alternative hypotheses specifying that the probability of "heads" on any single toss equals *P,* where *P* is some fraction (less than, or greater than, but) *not* equal to 1/2.

The important point is that the null hypothesis serves as an origin or base. In the coin-tossing instance, it also happens to be a favored, or traditional, hypothesis. This is merely a characteristic of the example selected. Indeed, the null hypothesis is often the very antithesis of what we would really like to be the case.

1-9.3 TWO KINDS OF ERRORS

In basing decisions on the outcomes of statistical tests, we always run the risks of making either one or the other of two types of error. If we reject the null hypothesis when it is true, e.g., announce a difference which really does not exist, then we make an *Error of the First Kind.* If we fail to reject a null hypothesis when it is false, e.g., fail to find an improvement in the new shell over the old when an improvement exists, then we make what is called an *Error of the Second Kind.* Although we do not know in a given instance whether we have made an error of either kind, we can know the *probability* of making either type of error.

1-9.4 SIGNIFICANCE LEVEL AND OPERATING CHARACTERISTIC (OC) CURVE OF A STATISTICAL TEST

The risk of making an error of the first kind, α, equals what is by tradition called the *level of significance* of the test. The risk of making an error of the second kind, β, varies, as one would expect, with the magnitude of the real difference, and is summarized by the *Operating Characteristic (OC) Curve* of the test. See, for example, Figure 3-5. Also, the risk β of making an error of the second kind increases as the risk α of making an error of the first kind decreases. Compare Figure 3-5 with Figure 3-6. Only with "large" samples can we "have our cake and eat it too"—and then there is the cost of the test to worry about.

1-9.5 CHOICE OF THE SIGNIFICANCE LEVEL

The significance level of a statistical test is essentially an expression of our reluctance to give up or "reject" the null hypothesis. If we adopt a "stiff" significance level, 0.01 or even 0.001, say, this implies that we are very unwilling to reject the null hypothesis unjustly. A consequence of our ultraconservatism in this respect will usually be that the probability of not rejecting the null hypothesis when it is really false will be large unless the actual deviation from the null hypothesis is large. This is clearly an entirely satisfactory state of affairs if we are quite satisfied with the status quo and are only interested in making a change if the change represents a very substantial improvement. For example, we may be quite satisfied with the performance of the standard type of shell in all respects, and not be willing to consider changing to the new type unless the mean depth of penetration of the new type were at least, say, 20% better (12.0 cm.).

On the other hand, the standard shell may be unsatisfactory in a number of respects and the question at issue may be whether the new type shows promise of being able to replace it, either "as is" or with further development. Here "rejection" of the null hypothesis would not imply necessary abandonment of the standard type and shifting over to the new type, but merely that the new type shows "promise" and warrants further investigation. In such a situation, one could afford a somewhat higher risk of rejecting the null hypothesis falsely, and would take $\alpha = 0.05$ or 0.10 (or even 0.20, perhaps), in the interest of increasing the chances of detecting a small but promising improvement with a small-scale experiment. In such exploratory work, it is often more important to have a good chance of detecting a small but promising improvement than to protect oneself against crying "wolf, wolf" occasionally—because the "wolf, wolf" will be found out in due course, but a promising approach to improvement could be lost forever.

In summary, the significance level α of a statistical test should be chosen in the light of the attending circumstances, including costs. We are sometimes limited in the choice of significance level by the availability of necessary tables for some statistical tests. Two values of α, $\alpha = .05$ and $\alpha = .01$, have been most frequently used in research and development work; and are given in tabulations of test statistics. We have adopted these "standard" levels of significance for the purposes of this handbook.

1-9.6 A WORD OF CAUTION

Many persons who regularly employ statistical tests in the interpretation of research and development data do not seem to realize that all probabilities associated with such tests are calculated on the supposition that some definite set of conditions prevails. Thus, α, the level of significance (or probability of an error of the first kind), is computed on the assumption that the null hypothesis is strictly true in all respects; and β, the risk of an error of the second kind, is computed on the assumption that a particular specific alternative to the null hypothesis is true *and* that the statistical test concerned is carried out at the α-level of significance. Consequently, whatever may be the actual outcome of a statistical test, it is mathematically impossible to infer from the

outcome anything whatsoever about the odds for or against some particular set of conditions being the truth.

Indeed, it is astonishing how often erroneous statements of the type "since r exceeds the 1% level of significance, the odds are 99 to 1 that there *is* a correlation between the variables" occur in research literature. How ridiculous this type of reasoning can be is brought out by the following simple example [5]: The *American Experience Mortality Table* gives .01008 as the probability of an individual aged 41 dying within the year. If we accept this table as being applicable to living persons today (which is analogous to accepting the published tables of the significance levels of tests which we apply to our data), and *if* a man's age really is 41, then the odds *are* 99 to 1 that he will live out the year. On the other hand, if we accept the table and happen to hear that some prominent individual has just died, then we *cannot* (and *would not*) conclude that the odds are 99 to 1 that his age was different from 41.

Suppose, on the other hand, that in some official capacity it is our practice to check the accuracy of age statements of all persons who say they are 41 and *then* die within the year. This practice (assuming the applicability of the American Experience Mortality Table) will lead us in the long run to suspect unjustly the word of one person in 100 whose age *was* 41, who told us so, and who then was unfortunate enough to die within the year. The *level of significance* of the test is in fact 0.01008 (1 in 100). On the other hand, this practice will also lead us to discover mis-statements of age of *all* persons professing to be 41 who are really some other age *and* who happen to die within the year. The probabilities of our discovering such mis-statements will depend on the actual ages of the persons making them. We shall, however, let slip by as correct all statements "age 41" corresponding to individuals who *are not* 41 but who do not happen to die within the year.

The moral of this is that all statistical tests can and should be viewed in terms of the consequences which may be expected to ensue from their repeated use in suitable circumstances. When viewed in this light, the great risks involved in drawing conclusions from exceedingly small samples becomes manifest to anyone who takes the time to study the OC curves for the statistical tests in common use.

REFERENCES

1. W. G. Cochran, F. Mosteller, and J. W. Tukey, "Principles of Sampling," *Journal of the American Statistical Association*, Vol. 49, pp. 13-35, 1954. (Copies of this article can be obtained from the American Statistical Association, 1757 K St., N.W., Washington 6, D. C. Price: 50 cents.)

2. W. G. Cochran, *Sampling Techniques*, John Wiley & Sons, Inc., New York, N. Y., 1953.

3. L. H. C. Tippett, *Random Sampling Numbers*, Tracts for Computers, No. 15, Cambridge University Press, 1927.

4. The Rand Corporation, *A Million Random Digits*, The Free Press, Glencoe, Ill., 1955.

5. C. Eisenhart, "The Interpretation of Tests of Significance," *Bulletin of the American Statistical Association*, Vol. 2, No. 3, pp. 79-80, April, 1941.

SOME RECOMMENDED ELEMENTARY TEXTBOOKS

A. H. Bowker and G. J. Lieberman, *Engineering Statistics*, Prentice-Hall, Inc., Englewood Cliffs, N. J., 1959.

W. J. Dixon and F. J. Massey, Jr., *Introduction to Statistical Analysis* (2d edition), McGraw-Hill Book Co., Inc., New York, N. Y., 1957.

M. J. Moroney, *Facts from Figures*, Penguin Books, Inc., Baltimore, Md., 1951.

L. H. C. Tippett, *The Methods of Statistics*, 4th edition), John Wiley & Sons, Inc., New York, N. Y., 1952.

W. A. Wallis and H. V. Roberts, *Statistics, A New Approach*, The Free Press, Glencoe, Ill., 1956.

CHAPTER 2

CHARACTERIZING THE MEASURED PERFORMANCE OF
A MATERIAL, PRODUCT, OR PROCESS

2-1 ESTIMATING AVERAGE PERFORMANCE FROM A SAMPLE

2-1.1 GENERAL

In this Chapter we present two important kinds of estimates of the average performance of a material, product, or process from a sample. These include the best single estimate, and *confidence interval* estimates.*

Specific procedures are given for obtaining confidence interval estimates when:

(a) we have a sample from a normal population whose variability is unknown; and,

(b) we have a sample from a normal population whose variability is known.

When the departures from normality are not great, or when the sample sizes are moderately large, interval estimates made as described in Paragraphs 2-1.4 and 2-1.5 will have confidence levels very little different from the chosen or nominal level.

The following data will serve to illustrate the application of the procedures.

Data Sample 2-1—Thickness of Mica Washers

Form: Measurements $X_1, X_2, \ldots, X_n$ of n items selected independently at random from a much larger group.

_____

* The reader who is not familiar with the meaning and interpretation of confidence intervals should refer to Chapter 1, and to Paragraph 2-1.3 of this Chapter.

Example: Ten mica washers are taken at random from a large group, and their thicknesses measured in inches:

.123	.132
.124	.123
.126	.126
.129	.129
.120	.128

In general, what can we say about the larger group on the basis of our sample? We show how to answer two questions:

(a) What is our *best* guess as to the average thickness in the whole lot?

(b) Can we give an interval which we expect, with certain confidence, to bracket the true average—i.e., a *confidence interval?*

These two questions are answered in the paragraphs which follow, using the data shown above. Another question, which is sometimes confused with (b) above, is treated in Paragraph 2-5. This is the question of setting *statistical tolerance limits,* or estimating an interval which will include, with prescribed confidence, a specified proportion of the individual items in the population.

2-1.2 BEST SINGLE ESTIMATE

The most common and ordinarily the *best* single estimate of the population mean m is simply the arithmetic mean of the measurements.

Procedure

Compute the arithmetic mean $\bar{X}$ of the n measurements $X_1, X_2, \ldots, X_n$.

$$\bar{X} = \frac{1}{n}\left(\sum_{i=1}^{n} X_i\right)$$

Example

Compute the arithmetic mean $\bar{X}$ of 10 measurements (Data Sample 2-1):

$$\bar{X} = \frac{.123 + .124 + .126 + \ldots + .128}{10}$$

$$= \frac{1.260}{10}$$

$$= .1260 \text{ inch}$$

2-1.3 SOME REMARKS ON CONFIDENCE INTERVAL ESTIMATES

When we take a sample from a lot or a population, the sample average will seldom be exactly the same as the lot or population average. We do hope that it is fairly close, and we would like to state an interval which we are confident will bracket the lot mean. If we made such interval estimates in a particular fashion a large number of times, and found that these intervals actually did contain the true mean in 99% of the cases, we might say that we were operating at a 99% confidence level. Our particular kind of interval estimates might likewise be called "99% confidence intervals." Similarly, if our intervals included the true average "95% of the time"—strictly, in 95% of the times or instances involved—we would be operating at a 95% confidence level, and our intervals would be called 95% confidence intervals. In general, if in the long run we expect $100(1 - \alpha)\%$ of our intervals to contain the true value, we are operating at the $100(1 - \alpha)\%$ confidence level.

We may choose whatever confidence level we wish. Confidence levels γ commonly used are 99% and 95%, which correspond to $\alpha = .01$ and $\alpha = .05$. If we wish to estimate the mean of some characteristic of a large group (population) using the results of a random sample from that group, the procedures of Paragraphs 2-1.4 and 2-1.5 will allow us to make interval estimates at any chosen confidence level. It is assumed that the characteristic of interest has a normal distribution in the population. We may elect to make a two-sided interval estimate, expected to bracket the mean from both above and below; or we may make a one-sided interval estimate, limited on either the upper or the lower side, which is expected to contain the mean and to furnish either an upper or a lower bound to its magnitude.

2-1.4 CONFIDENCE INTERVALS FOR THE POPULATION MEAN WHEN KNOWLEDGE OF THE VARIABILITY CANNOT BE ASSUMED

2-1.4.1 Two-Sided Confidence Interval

This procedure gives an interval which is expected to bracket m, the true mean, $100(1-\alpha)\%$ of the time.

Procedure

Problem: What is a two-sided $100(1 - \alpha)\%$ confidence interval for the true mean m?

(1) Choose the desired confidence level, $1 - \alpha$

(2) Compute:
$\bar{X}$, the arithmetic mean (see Paragraph 2-1.2), and

$$s = \sqrt{\frac{n\Sigma X^2 - (\Sigma X)^2}{n(n - 1)}}$$

Example

Problem: What is a two-sided 95% confidence interval for the mean thickness in the lot? (Data Sample 2-1)

(1) Let $1 - \alpha = .95$
$\alpha = .05$

(2)

$\bar{X} = .1260$ inch

$s = 0.00359$ inch

Procedure

(3) Look up $t = t_{1-\alpha/2}$ for $n-1$ degrees of freedom* in Table A-4.

(4) Compute:

$$X_U = \bar{X} + t\frac{s}{\sqrt{n}}$$

$$X_L = \bar{X} - t\frac{s}{\sqrt{n}}$$

Conclude: The interval from X_L to X_U is a $100(1-\alpha)\%$ confidence interval for the population mean; i.e., we may assert with $100(1-\alpha)\%$ confidence that $X_L < m < X_U$.

Example

(3) $t = t_{.975}$ for 9 degrees of freedom = 2.262

(4)

$$X_U = .1260 + \frac{2.262\,(.00359)}{\sqrt{10}}$$
$$= .1286 \text{ inch}$$

$$X_L = .1260 - \frac{2.262\,(.00359)}{\sqrt{10}}$$
$$= .1234 \text{ inch}$$

Conclude: The interval from .1234 to .1286 inch is a 95% confidence interval for the lot mean; i.e., we may assert with 95% confidence that .1234 inch < lot mean < .1286 inch.

2-1.4.2 One-Sided Confidence Interval

The preceding computations can be used to make another kind of confidence interval statement. We can say that $100(\alpha/2)\%$ of the time the entire interval in Paragraph 2-1.4.1 will lie above the true mean (i.e., X_L, the lower limit of the interval will be larger than the true mean). The rest of the time—namely $100(1-\alpha/2)\%$ of the time—X_L will be less than the true mean. Hence the interval from X_L to $+\infty$ is a $100(1-\alpha/2)\%$ one-sided confidence interval for the true mean. In the example, Paragraph 2-1.4.1, $100(1-\alpha/2)\%$ equals 97.5%. Thus, either of two open-ended intervals, "larger than .1234 inch," or "less than .1286 inch" can be called a 97.5% one-sided confidence interval for the population mean.

We now give the step-by-step procedure for determining a one-sided confidence interval for the population mean corresponding to a different choice of confidence level.

---

* In *A Dictionary of Statistical Terms*,[1] we find the following, under the phrase "degrees of freedom":

"This term is used in statistics in slightly different senses. It was introduced by Fisher on the analogy of the idea of degrees of freedom of a dynamical system, that is to say the number of independent coordinate values which are necessary to determine it. In this sense the degrees of freedom of a set of observations (which *ex hypothesi* are subject to sampling variation) is the number of values which could be assigned arbitrarily within the specification of the system; for example, in a sample of constant size n grouped into k intervals there are $k-1$ degrees of freedom because, if $k-1$ frequencies are specified, the other is determined by the total size n;
. . .

A sample of n variate values is said to have n degrees of freedom, whether the variates are dependent or not, and a statistic calculated from it is, by a natural extension, also said to have n degrees of freedom. But, if k functions of the sample values are held constant, the number of degrees of freedom is reduced by k. For example, the statistic $\sum_{i=1}^{n}(x_i - \bar{x})^2$ where $\bar{x}$ is the sample mean, is said to have $n-1$ degrees of freedom. . . ."

In this example, $s^2 = \sum_{i=1}^{n}(X_i - \bar{X})^2/(n-1)$ and has "$n-1$" degrees of freedom

Procedure	**Example**

Problem: What is a one-sided $100(1 - \alpha)\%$ confidence interval for the true mean?

Problem: What is a value which we expect, with 99% confidence, to be exceeded by the lot mean? (Alternatively, what is a value which we expect, with 99% confidence, to exceed the lot mean?) (Data Sample 2-1)

(1) Choose the desired confidence level, $1 - \alpha$.

(1) Let $1 - \alpha = .99$
$\alpha = 0.01.$

(2) Compute:
$\bar{X}$
s

(2)
$\bar{X} = .1260$ inch
$s = 0.00359$ inch

(3) Look up $t = t_{1-\alpha}$ for $n - 1$ degrees of freedom in Table A-4.

(3) $t = t_{.99}$ for 9 degrees of freedom
$= 2.821$

(4) Compute:

$$X'_L = \bar{X} - t \frac{s}{\sqrt{n}}$$

(or compute

$$X'_U = \bar{X} + t \frac{s}{\sqrt{n}})$$

(4)

$$X'_L = .1260 - \frac{(2.821)\,(.00359)}{\sqrt{10}}$$

$$= .1228$$

(or $X'_U = .1292$)

Conclude: We are $100(1 - \alpha)\%$ confident that the lot mean m is greater than X'_L (or, we are $100(1 - \alpha)\%$ confident that the lot mean m is less than X'_U), i.e., we may assert with $100(1 - \alpha)\%$ confidence that $m > X_L$ (or, that $m < X_U$).

Conclude: We are 99% confident that the lot mean is greater than .1228 inch (or, we are 99% confident that the lot mean is less than .1292 inch), i.e., we may assert with 99% confidence that mean thickness in lot > .1228 inch (or, that mean thickness in lot < .1292 inch).

2-1.5 CONFIDENCE INTERVAL ESTIMATES WHEN WE HAVE PREVIOUS KNOWLEDGE OF THE VARIABILITY

We have assumed in the previous paragraph (2-1.4) that we had no previous information about the variability of performance of items and were limited to using an estimate of variability obtained from the sample at hand. Suppose that in the case of the mica washers we had taken samples many times previously from the same process and found that, although each lot had a different average, there was always essentially the same amount of variation within a lot. We would then be able to take σ, the standard deviation of the lot, as known and equal to the value indicated by this previous experience. This assumption should not be made casually, but only when warranted after real investigation of the stability of the variation among samples, using control chart techniques.

The procedure for computing these confidence intervals is simple. In the procedures of Paragraph 2-1.4, merely replace s by σ and t by z and the formulas remain the same. Values of z are given in Table A-2. Note that t_P for an infinite number of degrees of freedom (Table A-4) is exactly equal to z_P. The following procedure is for the two-sided confidence interval.

Procedure

Problem: Find a two-sided $100(1 - \alpha)\%$ confidence interval for the lot mean, using known σ.

(1) Choose the desired confidence level, $1 - \alpha$.

(2) Compute:
$\bar{X}$

(3) Look up $z = z_{1-\alpha/2}$ in Table A-2.

(4) Compute:

$$X_U = \bar{X} + z \frac{\sigma}{\sqrt{n}}$$

$$X_L = \bar{X} - z \frac{\sigma}{\sqrt{n}}$$

Conclude: The interval from X_L to X_U is a $100(1 - \alpha)\%$ confidence interval for the lot mean.

Example

Problem: What is a two-sided 95% confidence interval for the lot mean? (Data Sample 2-1; and σ is known to equal .0040 inch.)

(1) Let $1 - \alpha = .95$
$\alpha = .05$

(2)
$\bar{X} = .1260$ inch

(3)
$z = z_{.975}$
$= 1.960$

(4)
$$X_U = .1260 + 1.960 \frac{(.004)}{\sqrt{10}}$$

$$= .1285$$
$$X_L = .1235$$

Conclude: The interval from .1235 to .1285 inch is a 95% confidence interval for the lot mean.

Discussion: When the value of σ, the standard deviation in the population, is known, Procedure 2-1.5 should always be used in preference to Procedure 2-1.4, which is independent of our knowledge of σ. When available, Procedure 2-1.5 (σ known) will usually lead to a confidence interval for the population mean that is narrower than the confidence interval that would have been obtained by Procedure 2-1.4 (σ unknown). This is the case for our illustrative examples based on Data Sample 2-1, but the difference is very slight because σ and s were both very small—only 0.03% of the mean.

Whatever level of confidence is chosen, the t value required for the application of Procedure 2-1.4 (σ unknown) will always be larger than the corresponding z value required for Procedure 2-1.5 (σ known). This is evident from Table A-4. For very small samples, the difference can be considerable. Nevertheless, it can happen, as a result of unusual sampling fluctuations, that the value of s obtained in a particular sample is so small in comparison to σ that, if Procedure 2-1.4 (σ unknown) were used, the resulting confidence interval would be narrower than the confidence interval given by Procedure 2-1.5 (σ known). This would have been the case, for instance, if Data Sample 2-1 had yielded an s less than $1.960(0.0040)/2.262 = 0.00347$. With samples of size 10 (i.e., 9 degrees of freedom for s), the probability of such an occurrence is about one in three. In such a case, however, one must NOT adopt the confidence interval corresponding to Procedure 2-1.4 (σ unknown) because it is narrower. To choose between Procedure 2-1.4 (σ unknown) and Procedure 2-1.5 (σ known), when the value of σ IS known, by selecting the one which yields the narrower confidence interval in each instance, would result in a level of confidence somewhat lower than claimed.

2-2　ESTIMATING VARIABILITY OF PERFORMANCE FROM A SAMPLE

2-2.1　GENERAL

We take the standard deviation of performance in the population as our measure of the characteristic variability of performance. Presented here are various ways of estimating the population standard deviation, including:

(a) single-value estimates;

(b) confidence-interval estimates based on random samples from the population; and,

(c) techniques for estimating the population standard deviation when no appropriate random samples are available.

The first two procedures are illustrated by application to the following data.

Data Sample 2-2—Burning Time of Rocket Powder

Form: n independent measurements X_1, X_2, . . ., X_n selected at random from a much larger group.

Example: Ten unit amounts of rocket powder selected at random from a large lot were tested in a chamber and their burning times recorded as follows (seconds):

50.7	69.8
54.9	53.4
54.3	66.1
44.8	48.1
42.2	35.5

2-2.2　SINGLE ESTIMATES

2-2.2.1　s^2 and s

The best estimate of σ^2, the variance of a normal population, is:

$$s^2 = \frac{\sum_{i=1}^{n} (X_i - \bar{X})^2}{n - 1} = \frac{\sum_{i=1}^{n} X_i^2 - \frac{\left(\sum_{i=1}^{n} X_i \right)^2}{n}}{n - 1}$$

For computational purposes, we usually find it more convenient to use the following formula:

$$s^2 = \frac{n \sum_{i=1}^{n} X_i^2 - \left(\sum_{i=1}^{n} X_i \right)^2}{n (n - 1)}$$

The formulas are algebraically identical. With any formula, it is important to carry a sufficient number of decimal places. If too few places are carried, the subtractions involved may result in a loss of significant figures in s^2. Excessive rounding may even lead to a negative value for s^2. The formula recommended for computational purposes is to be preferred on this account because only one subtraction is involved; and with a desk calculator one usually can retain all places in the computation of $\sum X_i^2$ and $(\sum X_i)^2$.

We take

$$s = \sqrt{s^2} = \sqrt{\frac{n \sum_{i=1}^{n} X_i^2 - \left(\sum_{i=1}^{n} X_i \right)^2}{n (n - 1)}}$$

as our estimate of σ, the population standard deviation.

Example: Using Data Sample 2-2, $\sum X_i^2 = 27987.54$, $\sum X_i = 519.8$, and thus $s^2 = 107.593$; and $s = 10.37$ seconds.*

2-2.2.2　The Sample Range as an Estimate of the Standard Deviation

The *range* of n observations is defined as the difference between the highest and the

TABLE 2-1. TABLE OF FACTORS FOR CONVERTING THE RANGE OF A SAMPLE OF n TO AN ESTIMATE OF σ, THE POPULATION STANDARD DEVIATION. ESTIMATE OF σ = RANGE/d_n

Size of Sample n	d_n	$\dfrac{1}{d_n}$	$\sqrt{n}$ [See Note]
2	1.128	.8865	1.414
3	1.693	.5907	1.732
4	2.059	.4857	2.000
5	2.326	.4299	2.236
6	2.534	.3946	2.449
7	2.704	.3698	2.646
8	2.847	.3512	2.828
9	2.970	.3367	3.000
10	3.078	.3249	3.162
12	3.258	.3069	3.464
16	3.532	.2831	4.000

Note: d_n is approximately equal to $\sqrt{n}$ for $3 \leq n \leq 10$. Thus, for small n a quick estimate of σ can be obtained by dividing the range by $\sqrt{n}$.

* In a final report, values of s should be rounded to two significant figures, but as a basis for further calculations it is advisable to retain one or two additional figures. For fuller explanation, see Chapters 22 and 23, Section 4, ORDP 20-113.

lowest of the n values. For small samples, the sample range is a reasonably efficient substitute for s as an estimator of the standard deviation of a normal population—not as efficient as s, but easier to calculate. Using the range is particularly valuable for a "quick look" at data from small samples.

As the sample size gets larger, the range is not only troublesome to calculate, but is a very inefficient estimator of σ. Table 2-1 gives the factors which convert from observed range in a sample of n observations to an estimate of population standard deviation σ.

2-2.3 CONFIDENCE INTERVAL ESTIMATES*

2-2.3.1 Two-Sided Confidence Interval Estimates

We are interested in determining an interval which we may confidently expect to bracket the true value of the standard deviation of a normal population.

Procedure	Example
Problem: What is a two-sided $100(1 - \alpha)\%$ confidence interval for σ?	*Problem:* What is a 95% confidence interval for σ, the standard deviation of burning time in the lot of powder? (Data Sample 2-2)
(1) Choose the desired confidence level, $1 - \alpha$.	(1) Let $1 - \alpha = .95$ $\alpha = .05$
(2) Compute: $$s = \sqrt{\frac{n\Sigma X_i^2 - (\Sigma X_i)^2}{n(n-1)}}$$	(2) $s = 10.37$ seconds
(3) Look up B_U and B_L for $n - 1$ degrees of freedom in Table A-20.	(3) For 9 degrees of freedom, $B_L = .6657$ $B_U = 1.746$
(4) Compute: $s_L = B_L s$ $s_U = B_U s$	(4) $s_L = (10.37)(.6657)$ $= 6.90$ seconds $s_U = (10.37)(1.746)$ $= 18.11$ seconds

Conclude: The interval from s_L to s_U is a two-sided $100(1 - \alpha)\%$ confidence interval estimate for σ; i.e., we may assert with $100(1 - \alpha)\%$ confidence that $s_L < \sigma < s_U$.

Conclude: The interval from 6.90 to 18.11 is a two-sided 95% confidence interval for σ; i.e., we may assert with 95% confidence that 6.90 seconds $< \sigma < 18.11$ seconds.

2-2.3.2 One-Sided Confidence Interval Estimates

In some applications we are not particularly interested in placing both an upper and a lower bound on σ, but only in knowing whether the variability is excessively *large* (or, exceptionally *small*). We would like to make a statement such as the following: We can state

---

* The reader who is not familiar with the meaning and interpretation of confidence intervals should refer to Chapter 1, and to Paragraph 2-1.3 of this chapter. The remarks of Paragraph 2-1.3 concerning confidence intervals for the average carry over to confidence intervals for a measure of variability.

with $100(1-\alpha)\%$ confidence that the variability as measured by σ is less than some value s'_U computed from the sample. Similarly, but not simultaneously, we may wish to state with $100(1-\alpha)\%$ confidence that σ is greater than some value s'_L. Either statement is a one-sided confidence interval estimate.

Procedure	Example
Problem: What is a value s'_U such that we may have $100(1-\alpha)\%$ confidence that σ is less than s'_U?	*Problem:* What is a value s'_U such that we have 95% confidence that σ is less than s'_U? (Data Sample 2-2)
(1) Choose the desired confidence level, $1-\alpha$.	(1) Let $1-\alpha = .95$ $\alpha = .05$
(2) Compute: s	(2) $s = 10.37$ seconds
(3) Look up $A_{1-\alpha}$ for $n-1$ degrees of freedom in Table A-21.	(3) For 9 degrees of freedom, $A_{.95} = 1.645$
(4) Compute: $s'_U = A_{1-\alpha}\, s$	(4) $s'_U = (1.645)(10.37)$ $= 17.06$ seconds
(5) With $100(1-\alpha)\%$ confidence we can assert that σ is less than s'_U.	(5) We are 95% confident that the variability as measured by σ is *less than* $s'_U = 17.06$ seconds.

Should a lower bound to σ be desired, follow Procedure 2-2.3.2 with s'_U and $A_{1-\alpha}$ replaced by s'_L and A_α, respectively. Then it can be asserted with $100(1-\alpha)\%$ confidence that $\sigma > s'_L$.

2-2.4 ESTIMATING THE STANDARD DEVIATION WHEN NO SAMPLE DATA ARE AVAILABLE

It is often necessary to have some idea of the magnitude of the variation of some characteristic as measured by σ, its standard deviation in the population. In planning experiments, for example, the sample size required to meet certain requirements is a function of σ. In almost any situation, one can get at least a very rough estimate of σ. The minimum necessary information involves the form of the distribution and the spread of values. For example, if the values of the individual items can be assumed to follow a normal distribution, then either of the following rules can be used to get an estimate of σ:

(a) Estimate two values a_1 and b_1 between which you expect 99.7% (almost all) of the individuals to be. Then, estimate

$$\sigma \text{ as } \frac{|a_1 - b_1|}{6}$$

(b) Estimate two values a_2 and b_2 between which you expect 95% of the individuals to be. Then, estimate σ as $\dfrac{|a_2 - b_2|}{4}$

If the distribution concerned cannot be assumed to be normal but can be assumed to follow one of the top four forms in Figure 2-1, then the standard deviation may be estimated as indicated in the figure. This figure also illustrates the distribution and rules for (a) and (b) above.

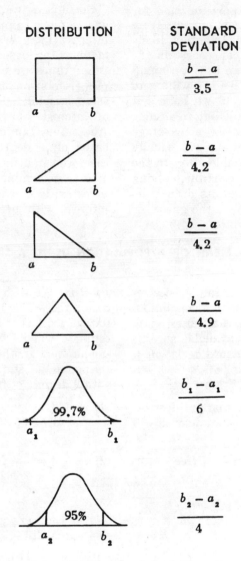

DISTRIBUTION   STANDARD DEVIATION

$$\frac{b - a}{3.5}$$

$$\frac{b - a}{4.2}$$

$$\frac{b - a}{4.2}$$

$$\frac{b - a}{4.9}$$

$$\frac{b_1 - a_1}{6}$$

$$\frac{b_2 - a_2}{4}$$

Figure 2-1. The standard deviation of some simple distributions.

Adapted with permission from *Some Theory of Sampling*, by W. Edwards Deming, Copyright, 1950, John Wiley & Sons, Inc.

2-3 NUMBER OF MEASUREMENTS REQUIRED TO ESTABLISH THE MEAN WITH PRESCRIBED ACCURACY

2-3.1 GENERAL

In planning experiments, we may need to know how many measurements or how large a sample to take in order to determine the mean of some distribution with prescribed accuracy. Suppose we are willing to allow a margin of error d, and a risk α that our estimate of m will be off by an amount d or greater. Since the sampling distribution of

$\bar{X}$ is "normal" to a good approximation for samples of four or more measurements from almost every population distribution likely to be met in practice, we can ascertain the required sample size n if we have an available estimate s of σ, or if we are willing to assume that we know σ. If we have not made an estimate or are unwilling to assume a value for σ, then we must use a two-stage sample. The two-stage method will usually result in a smaller total sample size. In the two-stage method, we must start by guessing a value of σ, but the end results do not depend upon how good or bad is the guess.

Sometimes we may have available to us one or more samples from the population of interest, from which we can derive an estimate s of σ based on ν degrees of freedom. Other times we may have one or more samples from some other population that has the same standard deviation as the population of interest, but possibly a different mean. Again, we can derive an estimate s of σ based on ν degrees of freedom. In either case, we can utilize this preliminary estimate of σ to determine the sample size n required to estimate the mean of the population of interest with prescribed accuracy.

2-3.2　ESTIMATION OF THE MEAN OF A POPULATION USING A SINGLE SAMPLE

Procedure

Problem: We wish to know the sample size required to ascertain the mean m of a population. We are willing to take a risk α that our estimate is off by d or more. There is available an estimate s of the population standard deviation σ, based on ν degrees of freedom.

(1)　Choose d, the allowable margin of error, and α, the risk that our estimate of m will be off by d or more.

(2)　Look up $t_{1-\alpha/2}$ for ν degrees of freedom in Table A-4.

(3)　Compute:

$$n = \frac{t^2 s^2}{d^2}$$

Example

Problem: We wish to know the average thickness of the washers in a given lot. We are willing to take a risk that 5 times in 100 the error in our estimate will be 0.002 inch or more. From a sample from another lot we have an estimate of the population standard deviation of $s = .00359$ with 9 degrees of freedom.

(1)　Let $d = 0.002$ inch

　　　$\alpha = .05$

(2)　　　$t = t_{.975}$ for 9 degrees of freedom

　　　　　$= 2.262.$

(3)

$$n = \frac{(2.262)^2 (.00359)^2}{(.002)^2} = 16.5$$

$= 17$ (conventionally rounded up to the next integer.)

Conclude: If we now compute the mean $\bar{X}$ of a random sample of size n from the population we may have $100 (1 - \alpha) \%$ confidence that the interval $\bar{X} - d$ to $\bar{X} + d$ will include the population mean m.

Conclude: We may conclude that if we now compute the mean $\bar{X}$ of a random sample of size $n = 17$ from the lot of washers, we may have 95% confidence that the interval $\bar{X} - .002$ to $\bar{X} + .002$ will include the lot mean.

If we know σ, or assume some value for σ, replace s by σ and $t_{1-\alpha/2}$ by $z_{1-\alpha/2}$ in the above procedure. Values of $z_{1-\alpha/2}$ are given in Table A-2.

2-3.3　ESTIMATION USING A SAMPLE WHICH IS TAKEN IN TWO STAGES

It is possible that we do not have a good estimate of σ, the standard deviation of the population. When the cost of sampling is high, rather than take a larger sample than is really necessary, we might prefer to take the sample in two stages. The method (sometimes called

Stein's method) goes roughly as follows: Make a guess for the value of σ. From this determine n_1 the size of the first sample. The first sample will provide an estimate s of the population standard deviation. Use this value of s to determine how large the second sample should be.

Procedure	**Example**

Problem: We wish to know the sample size required to ascertain the mean m of a population. We are willing to take a risk α that our estimate is off by d or more units.

Problem: We have a large lot of devices, and wish to determine the average of some property. We are willing to take a risk of .05 of the estimate being in error by 30 units.

(1) Choose d, the allowable margin of error, and α, the risk that our estimate of m will be off by d or more.

(1) Let $d = 30$
$\alpha = .05$

(2) Let σ' be the best possible guess for the value of σ, the standard deviation of the population (see Paragraph 2-2.4).

(2) From our knowledge of similar devices our best estimate of σ is 200 units.

(3) Look up $z_{1-\alpha/2}$ in Table A-2.

(3) $z_{.975} = 1.960$

(4) Compute:

$$n' = \left(\frac{z_{1-\alpha/2}\ \sigma}{d}\right)^2$$

n' is the first estimate of the total sample size required.

(4)

$$n' = \frac{(1.960)^2\ (200)^2}{(30)^2}$$

$$= 170.7$$

(5) Choose n_1 the size of the first sample. n_1 should be considerably less than n'. (If the guessed value of σ is too large, this will protect us against a first sample which is already larger than we need.) A rough rule might be to make $n_1 \geq 30$ unless $n' < 60$, in which case let n_1 be somewhere between $.5n'$ and $.7n'$.

(5) Let $n_1 = 50$

(6) Make the necessary observations on the sample of n_1. Compute s_1, the standard deviation.

(6) From tests on 50 devices chosen at random, $s_1 = 160$ units.

(7) Look up $t_{1-\alpha/2}$ for $n_1 - 1$ degrees of freedom in Table A-4.

(7) $t = t_{.975}$ for 49 degrees of freedom
$= 2.01$.

(8) Compute

$$n = \frac{t^2\ s_1^2}{d^2}$$

n is the total required sample size for the first and second samples combined. We then require a second sample size of $n_2 = n - n_1$.

(8)

$$n = \frac{(2.01)^2\ (160)^2}{(30)^2}$$

$$= 114.9$$

$$= 115$$

$n_2 = 115 - 50$
$= 65$

We will require an additional 65 devices to be tested.

If now we obtain the second sample of size n_2 and compute the mean $\bar{X}$ of the total sample of size $n = n_1 + n_2$, we may have $100\ (1 - \alpha)\ \%$ confidence that the interval $\bar{X} - d$ to $\bar{X} + d$ will include the population mean m.

2-4 NUMBER OF MEASUREMENTS REQUIRED TO ESTABLISH THE VARIABILITY WITH STATED PRECISION

We may wish to know the size of sample required to estimate the standard deviation with certain precision. If we can express this precision as a percentage of the true (unknown) standard deviation, we can use the curves in Figure 2-2.

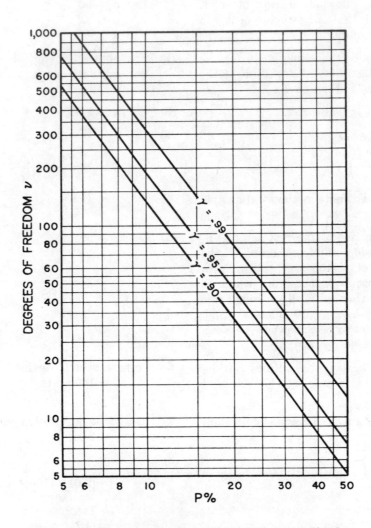

Figure 2-2. *Number of degrees of freedom required to estimate the standard deviation within P% of its true value with confidence coefficient* γ.

Adapted with permission from *Journal of the American Statistical Association*, Vol. 45 (1950), p. 258, from article entitled "Sample Size Required for Estimating the Standard Deviation as a Percent of its True Value" by J. A. Greenwood and M. M. Sandomire. The manner of graphing is adapted with permission from *Statistics Manual* by E. L. Crow, F. A. Davis, and M. W. Maxfield, NAVORD Report 3369, NOTS 948, U. S. Naval Ordnance Test Station, China Lake, Calif., 1955. (Reprinted by Dover Publications, Inc., New York, N.Y., 1960.)

Procedure	Example

Procedure

Problem: If we are to make a simple series of measurements, how many measurements are required to estimate the standard deviation within P percent of its true value, with prescribed confidence?

(1) Specify P, the allowable percentage deviation of the estimated standard deviation from its true value.

(2) Choose γ, the confidence coefficient.

(3) In Figure 2-2, find P on the horizontal scale, and use the curve for the appropriate γ. Read on the vertical scale the required degrees of freedom.

(4) For a simple series of measurements, the required number is equal to one plus the degrees of freedom.

Example

Problem: How large a sample would be required to estimate the standard deviation within 20% of its true value, with confidence coefficient equal to 0.95?

(1) Let $P = 20\%$

(2) Let $\gamma = .95$

(3) For $\gamma = .95$, $P = 20\%$, the required degrees of freedom equals 46.

(4) $n = 46 + 1$
       $= 47$

2-5   STATISTICAL TOLERANCE LIMITS

2-5.1   GENERAL

Sometimes we are more interested in the approximate *range* of values in a lot or population than we are in its average value. Statistical tolerance limits furnish limits between, above, or below which we confidently expect to find a prescribed proportion of individual items of the population. Thus, we might like to be able to give two values A and B between which we can be fairly certain that at least a proportion P of the population will lie, (two-sided limits), or a value A above which at least a proportion P will lie, (one-sided limit).

Thus for the data on thickness of mica washers (Data Sample 2-1), we could give two thickness values, stating with chosen confidence that a proportion P (at least) of the washers in the lot have thicknesses between these two limits. We call the confidence coefficient γ, and it refers to the proportion of the time that our method will result in correct statements. If a normal distribution can be assumed, use the procedures of Paragraphs 2-5.2 and 2-5.3; otherwise use the procedures of Paragraph 2-5.4.

2-5.2   TWO-SIDED TOLERANCE LIMITS FOR A NORMAL DISTRIBUTION

When the mean m and standard deviation σ of a normally distributed quantity are known, symmetrical limits that include a prescribed proportion P of the distribution are readily obtained by adding and subtracting $z_\alpha \sigma$ from the known mean m, where z_α is read from Table A-2 with $\alpha = \frac{1}{2}(P+1)$. When m and σ are not known, we can use an interval of the form $\overline{X} \pm Ks$. Since both $\overline{X}$ and s will vary from sample to sample it is impossible to determine K so that the limits $\overline{X} \pm Ks$ will always include a specified proportion P of the underlying normal distribution. It is, however, possible to determine K so that in a long series of samples from the same or different normal distributions a definite proportion γ of the intervals $\overline{X} \pm Ks$ will include P or more of the underlying distribution(s).

Procedure	**Example**

Problem: We would like to state two limits between which we are 100 γ percent confident that 100 P percent of the values lie.

Problem: We would like to state thickness limits between which we are 95% confident that 90% of the values lie (Data Sample 2-1).

(1) Choose P, the proportion, and γ, the confidence coefficient.

(1) Let $P = .90$
$\gamma = .95$

(2) Compute from the sample:
$\bar{X}$
s

(2)
$\bar{X} = .1260$ inch
$s = 0.00359$ inch

(3) Look up K for chosen P and γ in Table A-6.

(3) $K = 2.839$

(4) Compute:
$$X_U = \bar{X} + Ks$$
$$X_L = \bar{X} - Ks$$

(4)
$$X_U = .1260 + 2.839\,(.00359)$$
$$= 0.136 \text{ inch}$$
$$X_L = .1260 - 2.839\,(.00359)$$
$$= 0.116 \text{ inch}$$

Conclude: With 100 γ % confidence we may predict that a proportion P of the individuals of the population have values between X_L and X_U.

Conclude: With 95% confidence, we may say that 90% of the washers have thicknesses between 0.116 and 0.136 inch.

2-5.3 ONE-SIDED TOLERANCE LIMITS FOR A NORMAL DISTRIBUTION

Sometimes we are interested only in estimating a value above which, or below which, a proportion P (at least) will lie. In this case the one-sided upper tolerance limit will be $X_U = \bar{X} + Ks$; and $X_L = \bar{X} - Ks$ will be the one-sided lower limit. The appropriate values for K are given in Table A-7 and are not the same as those of Paragraph 2-5.2.

Procedure	**Example**

Problem: To find a single value above which we may predict with confidence γ that a proportion P of the population will lie.

Problem: To find a single value above which we may predict with 90% confidence that 99% of the population will lie. (Data Sample 2-1).

(1) Choose P the proportion and γ, the confidence coefficient.

(1) Let $P = .99$
$\gamma = .90$

(2) Compute:
$\bar{X}$
s

(2)
$\bar{X} = .1260$ inch
$s = 0.00359$ inch

(3) Look up K in Table A-7 for the appropriate n, γ, and P.

(3) $K\,(10, .90, .99) = 3.532$

(4) $X_L = \bar{X} - Ks$

(4) $X_L = .1260 - 3.532\,(.00359)$
$= .1133$ inch
Thus we are 90% confident that 99% of the mica washers will have thicknesses above .113 inch.

Note: Factors for some values of n, γ, and P not covered in Table A-7 may be found in Sandia Corporation Monograph SCR-13[2]. Alternatively, one may compute K using the following formulas:

$$a = 1 - \frac{z_\gamma^2}{2(n-1)} \qquad \text{(where } z \text{ can be found in Table A-2)}$$

$$b = z_P^2 - \frac{z_\gamma^2}{n}$$

$$K = \frac{z_P + \sqrt{z_P^2 - ab}}{a}$$

2-5.4 TOLERANCE LIMITS WHICH ARE INDE-PENDENT OF THE FORM OF THE DISTRIBUTION

The methods given in Paragraphs 2-5.2 and 2-5.3 are based on the assumption that the observations come from a normal distribution. If the distribution is not in fact normal, then the effect will be that the true proportion P of the population between the tolerance limits will vary from the intended P by an amount depending on the amount of departure from normality. If the departure from normality is more than slight we can use a procedure which assumes only that the distribution has no discontinuities. The tolerance limits so obtained will be substantially wider than those assuming normality.

2-5.4.1 Two-Sided Tolerance Limits (Distribution-Free)

Table A-30 gives values (r, s) such that we may assert with confidence at least γ that $100P\%$ of a population lies between the rth smallest and the sth largest of a random sample of n from that population. For example, from Table A-30 with $\gamma = .95$, $P = .75$, and $n = 60$, we may say that if we have a sample of $n = 60$, then we may have a confidence of at least $\gamma = .95$ that $100P\% = 75\%$ of the population will lie between the fifth largest ($s = 5$) and the fifth smallest ($r = 5$) of the sample values. That is, if we were to take many random samples of 60, and take the fifth largest and fifth smallest of each, we should expect to find that at least 95% of the resulting intervals would contain 75% of the population.

Table A-32 may be useful for sample sizes of $n \leqq 100$. This table gives the confidence γ with which we may assert that $100P\%$ of the population lies between the largest and smallest values of the sample.

2-5.4.2 One-Sided Tolerance Litmits (Distribution-Free)

Table A-31 gives the largest value of m such that we may assert with confidence at least γ that $100P\%$ of a population lies below the mth largest (or above the mth smallest) of a random sample of n from that population. For example, from Table A-31 with $\gamma = .95$, $P = .90$, and $n = 90$, we may say that we are 95% confident that 90% of a population will lie below the fifth largest value of a sample of size $n = 90$.

REFERENCES

1. M. G. Kendall and W. R. Buckland, *A Dictionary of Statistical Terms*, p. 79, Oliver and Boyd, London, 1957.
2. D. B. Owen, *Table of Factors for One-Sided Tolerance Limits for a Normal Distribution*, Sandia Corporation Monograph SCR-13, April 1958.

CHAPTER 3

COMPARING MATERIALS OR PRODUCTS WITH RESPECT TO AVERAGE PERFORMANCE

3-1 GENERAL REMARKS ON STATISTICAL TESTS

One of the most frequent uses of statistics is in testing for differences. If we wish to know whether a treatment applied to a standard round affects its muzzle velocity, we may conduct an experiment and apply a statistical test to the experimental results to see whether we would be justified in concluding that there is a difference between the performance of treated and untreated rounds. In another case, two manufacturing processes may be available—process A is cheaper and therefore preferable unless process B is demonstrated to be superior in some respect. Again, we apply a statistical test to the experimental results to see whether process B has demonstrated superiority.

Ordinarily, the statistical test applied to the results observed on a sample will point the way to decision between a pair of alternatives. For some tests, the two alternative decisions will be formally stated as follows:

(a) There *is* a difference between the (population) averages of two materials, products, processes, etc.

(b) No difference has been demonstrated.

In other cases, the formal statement of the two alternative decisions will be:

(a) The (population) average of product A *is* greater than that of product B.

(b) We have no reason to believe that the (population) average of product A is greater than that of product B.

In this Chapter and others, we shall consider a number of statistical tests of differences. The application of each statistical test will result in making one of two decisions, as in the pairs given. *In each case the pair of alternative decisions is chosen before the data are observed—this is important!*

Since we ordinarily obtain information on one or both of the products by means of a sample, we may sometimes make an erroneous decision. However, the chance of making the wrong decision can be reduced by increasing the number of observations. There are two ways in which we can make a wrong decision:

(a) When we conclude that there is a difference where in fact there is none, we say that we make an *Error of the First Kind;*

(b) When we fail to find a difference that really exists, then we say that we make an *Error of the Second Kind.*

In any particular case, we never can be absolutely sure that the correct decision has been made, but we can know the probability of making either type of error.

The probability of making an Error of the First Kind is usually denoted by α; and the probability of making an Error of the Second Kind is denoted by β. The ability of a given statistical test to detect a difference (e.g., between averages) will in general depend on the size of the difference δ; thus, β has no meaning unless associated with a particular difference δ. The value of β, $\beta(\delta)$, associated with a particular difference δ will decrease as δ increases. For a particular statistical test, the ability to detect a difference will be determined by three quantities:

α, $\beta(\delta)$, and n the sample size. The complementary quantity $1-\beta(\delta)$ is termed the *power* of the test to detect a difference δ with a sample of size n, when the test is carried out at the α-level of significance.

The decision procedure is a very logical one. Suppose we wish to test whether two types of vacuum tubes have the same resistance in ohms, on the average. We take samples of each type and measure their resistances. If the sample mean of one type of tube differs sufficiently from the sample mean of the other, we shall say that the two kinds of tubes differ in their average resistance. Otherwise, we shall say we failed to find a difference. How large must the difference be in order that we may conclude that the two types differ, or that the observed difference is "significant"?* This will depend on several factors: the amount of variability in the tubes of each type; the number of tubes of each type; and the risk we are willing to take of stating that a difference exists when there really is none, i.e., the risk of making an Error of the First Kind. We might proceed as follows: we would be willing to state that the true averages differ, if a difference larger than the observed difference could arise by chance less than five times in a hundred when the true averages are in fact equal. The probability of an Error of the First Kind is then $\alpha = .05$, or, as we commonly say, we have adopted a .05 *significance level*. The use of a *significance level* of .05 or .01 is common, and these levels are tabulated extensively for many tests. There is nothing unique about these levels, however, and a test user may choose any value for α that he feels is appropriate.

As we have mentioned, the ability to detect a difference will in general depend on the size of the difference δ. Let us denote by $\beta(\delta)$ the probability of failing to detect a specified difference δ. If we plot $\beta(\delta)$ versus the difference δ, we have what we call an Operating Characteristic (OC) curve. Actually, we usually plot $\beta(\delta)$ versus some

convenient function of δ. Figures 3-1 through 3-8 show OC curves for a number of statistical tests when conducted at the $\alpha = .05$ or $\alpha = .01$ significance levels.

An OC curve depicts the discriminatory power of a particular statistical test. For specified values of n and α, there is a unique OC curve. The curve is useful in two ways. If we have specified n and α, we can use the OC curve to read $\beta(\delta)$ for various values of δ. If we are still at liberty to set the sample size for our experiment, and have a particular value of δ in mind, we can see what value of n is required by looking at the OC curves for specified α. If, for the α chosen, the sample size required to achieve a reasonably small $\beta(\delta)$ is too large, and if it really is important to detect a difference of δ when it exists, then a less conservative (i.e., larger) value of α must be used. Various uses of the OC curves shown in Figures 3-1 through 3-8 are described in detail in the appropriate paragraphs of this Chapter.

It is evident that for any $\beta(\delta)$, n will increase as δ decreases. It requires larger samples to recognize smaller differences. In some cases, the experiment as originally thought of will be seen to require prohibitively large sample sizes. We then must compromise between the sharp discriminatory power we think we need, the cost of the amount of testing required to achieve that power, and the risk of claiming a difference when none exists. If the experiment has already been run, and the sample size was fixed from other considerations, the OC curve will show what chance the experiment had of detecting a particular difference δ.

To use the OC curves in this Chapter, we must know the population standard deviation σ, or at least be willing to choose some range for σ. It is quite often possible to assign some upper bound to the variability, even without the use of past data (see Paragraph 2-2.4). After the experiment has been run, a possibly better estimate of σ will be available, and a hindsight look at the OC curve using this value will help to evaluate the experiment.

---

* Or more accurately, *statistically significant*. A difference may be *statistically significant* and yet be *practically unimportant*.

We outline a number of different tests in this Chapter. For each test, we give the procedure to be followed for a specified significance level α and sample size n. For most of the tests, we also give the OC curve which enables us to obtain the (approximate) value of β for any given difference. Tables are provided for determining n, the sample size required when α, δ, and $\beta(\delta)$ have been specified. The tests given are exact when:

(a) the observations for each item are taken randomly from a single population of possible observations; and,

(b) the quality characteristic measured is normally distributed within this population. Ordinarily, the assumption of normality is not crucial, particularly if the sample size is not very small.

Alternate procedures for most of the tests in this Chapter are given in ORDP 20-113, Chapters 15 and 16. Chapter 16 gives tests which require neither normality assumptions nor knowledge of the variability of the populations; but this greater generality is achieved at the price of somewhat reduced discriminating power when normality can be assumed and the knowledge about the variability of the populations, needed for the tests of this Chapter, is in hand. Chapter 15 gives shortcut tests for small samples from normal populations which involve less computation than the tests of this Chapter with negligible loss of efficiency.

3-2 COMPARING THE AVERAGE OF A NEW PRODUCT WITH THAT OF A STANDARD

The average performance of a standard product is known to be m_0. We shall consider three different problems:

(a) To determine whether the average of a new product *differs* from the standard, Paragraph 3-2.1.

(b) To determine whether the average of a new product *exceeds* the standard, Paragraph 3-2.2.

(c) To determine whether the average of a new product is *less* than the standard, Paragraph 3-2.3.

For summary of the procedures appropriate for each of these three problems, see Table 3-1.

It is necessary to decide which of the three problems is appropriate before taking the observations. If this is not done and the choice of the problem is influenced by the observations, (for example, Paragraph 3-2.1 vs. 3-2.2), the significance level of the test, i.e., the probability of an *Error of the First Kind*, and the operating characteristics of the test may differ considerably from their nominal values.

Ordinarily the variability of a new product is not known. At other times previous experience may enable us to state a value of σ. We shall outline the solutions of the three problems (Paragraphs 3-2.1, 3-2.2, and 3-2.3) for both cases, i.e., where the variability is estimated from the sample, and where σ is known from previous experience.

Symbols to be used:

m = average of new material, product or process (unknown).

m_0 = average of standard material, product or process (known).

$\bar{X}$ = average of sample of n measurements on new product.

s = standard deviation estimate computed from n measurements on the new product (used where σ is unknown).

σ = the known standard deviation of the new product.

Data Sample 3-2—Weight of Powder

For a certain type of shell, specifications state that the amount of powder should average 0.735 pound. In order to determine whether the average for a new stock meets the specification, 20 shells are taken at random, and the amount of powder contained in each is weighed.

The sample average $\bar{X}$ = .710 pound.

The sample standard deviation estimate s = .0504 pound. In illustrating the known-σ case, we assume σ known to be equal to 0.06 pound.

TABLE 3-1. SUMMARY OF TECHNIQUES FOR COMPARING THE AVERAGE OF A NEW PRODUCT WITH THAT OF A STANDARD
(FOR DETAILS AND WORKED EXAMPLES SEE PARAGRAPHS 3-2.1, 3-2.2, AND 3-2.3)

We Wish to Test Whether	Paragraph Reference	Knowledge of Variation of New Item	Test to be Made	Operating Characteristics of the Test (for $\alpha = .05$ and $\alpha = .01$)	Sample Size Required n	Notes
m differs from m_0	3-2.1.1	σ unknown; s = estimate of σ from sample.	$\lvert \bar{X} - m_0 \rvert > u$	See Figs. 3-1 and 3-2*	Use Table A-8. For $\alpha = .05$, add 2 to tabular value. For $\alpha = .01$, add 4 to tabular value.	$u = t_{1-\alpha/2}\left(\dfrac{s}{\sqrt{n}}\right)$ (t for $n-1$ degrees of freedom)
	3-2.1.2	σ known	$\lvert \bar{X} - m_0 \rvert > u$	See Figs. 3-3 and 3-4	Use Table A-8.	$u = z_{1-\alpha/2}\left(\dfrac{\sigma}{\sqrt{n}}\right)$
m is larger than m_0	3-2.2.1	σ unknown; s = estimate of σ from sample.	$(\bar{X} - m_0) > u$	See Figs. 3-5 and 3-6*	Use Table A-9. For $\alpha = .05$, add 2 to tabular value. For $\alpha = .01$, add 3 to tabular value.	$u = t_{1-\alpha}\left(\dfrac{s}{\sqrt{n}}\right)$ (t for $n-1$ degrees of freedom)
	3-2.2.2	σ known	$(\bar{X} - m_0) > u$	See Figs. 3-7 and 3-8	Use Table A-9.	$u = z_{1-\alpha}\left(\dfrac{\sigma}{\sqrt{n}}\right)$
m is smaller than m_0	3-2.3.1	σ unknown; s = estimate of σ from sample.	$(m_0 - \bar{X}) > u$	See Figs. 3-5 and 3-6*	Use Table A-9. For $\alpha = .05$, add 2 to the tabular values. For $\alpha = .01$, add 3 to the tabular values.	$u = t_{1-\alpha}\left(\dfrac{s}{\sqrt{n}}\right)$ (t for $n-1$ degrees of freedom)
	3-2.3.2	σ known	$(m_0 - \bar{X}) > u$	See Figs. 3-7 and 3-8	Use Table A-9.	$u = z_{1-\alpha}\left(\dfrac{\sigma}{\sqrt{n}}\right)$

* It is necessary to have some value for σ (or two bounding values) in order to use the Operating Characteristic curve. Although σ is unknown, in many situations it is possible to have some notion, however loose, about the magnitude of σ and thereby to get helpful information from the OC curve. Paragraph 2-2.4 gives assistance in estimating σ from general knowledge of the process.

3-2.1 TO DETERMINE WHETHER THE AVERAGE OF A NEW PRODUCT DIFFERS FROM THE STANDARD

3-2.1.1 Does the Average of the New Product Differ from the Standard (σ Unknown)?

[Two-sided t-test]

Procedure

(1) Choose α, the significance level of the test.

(2) Look up $t_{1-\alpha/2}$ for $n - 1$ degrees of freedom in Table A-4.

(3) Compute
$\bar{X}$ and s from the n measurements.

(4) Compute
$$u = t_{1-\alpha/2}\frac{s}{\sqrt{n}}$$

(5) If $\lvert \bar{X} - m_0 \rvert > u$, decide that the average of the new type differs from that of the standard; otherwise, that there is no reason to believe that they differ.

(6) *Note:* The interval $\bar{X} \pm u$ is a $100(1 - \alpha)\%$ confidence interval estimate of the true average of the new type.

Example

(1) Let $\alpha = .05$

(2) $t_{.975}$ for 19 degrees of freedom $= 2.093$

(3)
$$\bar{X} = .710 \text{ pound}$$
$$s = .0504 \text{ pound}$$
(Data Sample 3-2)

(4)
$$u = \frac{(2.093)(.0504)}{\sqrt{20}}$$
$$= .0236$$

(5) $\lvert \bar{X} - m_0 \rvert = \lvert .710 - .735 \rvert = .025$. We conclude that the average amount of powder in the new stock differs from 0.735, the specified standard amount.

(6) *Note:* $.710 \pm .0236$ is a 95% confidence interval estimate of the true average of the new stock.

Operating Characteristics of the Test. Figures 3-1 and 3-2 give the operating characteristic (OC) curves of the preceding test for $\alpha = .05$ and $\alpha = .01$, respectively, and various values of n.

Choose:

$\delta = |m - m_0|$,
the true absolute difference between the averages (unknown, of course)
Some value of σ.

(One may use an estimate from previous data; lacking such an estimate, see Paragraph 2-2.4. If the OC curve is consulted after the experiment, we may use the estimate from the experiment.)

Compute

$$d = \frac{\delta}{\sigma} .$$

We then can read from the OC curve for a given significance level α and sample size n, a value of $\beta(\delta)$. The $\beta(\delta)$ read from the curve is $\beta(\delta \,|\, \sigma, \alpha, n)$, i.e., $\beta(\delta, \text{ given } \sigma, \alpha, n)$—the probability of failing to detect this difference when the given test is carried out with a sample of size n, at the α-level of significance, and the population standard deviation actually is σ.

If we use too large a value for σ, the effect is to underestimate d, and consequently to overestimate $\beta(\delta)$, the probability of not detecting a difference of δ when it exists. Conversely, if we choose too small a value of σ, then we shall overestimate d and underestimate $\beta(\delta)$. The true value of $\beta(\delta)$ is determined, of course, by the sample size n and the significance level α employed, *and* the true value of σ.

Selection of Sample Size n. If we choose

$\delta = |m - m_0|$, the absolute value of the average difference that we desire to detect
α, the significance level of the test
β, the probability of failing to detect a difference δ

and compute

$$d = \frac{|m - m_0|}{\sigma}$$

then we may use Table A-8 to obtain a good approximation to the required sample size. If we take $\alpha = .01$, then we must add 4 to the value obtained from the table. If we take $\alpha = .05$, then we must add 2 to the table value. (In order to compute d, we must choose a value for σ. See Paragraph 2-2.4 if no other information is available.)

As an example, suppose that we plan to take $\alpha = .05$, and want to have $\beta = .50$ for a difference of .024 pound; that is, we wish to conduct a test at a significance level of .05 that will have a 50-50 chance of detecting a difference of 0.024 pound. What sample size should we require? Suppose previous experience suggests that σ lies between .04 and .06 pound.

Taking $\sigma = .04$, with $\delta = |m - m_0| = .024$, gives $d = 0.6$. Using Table A-8, with $\alpha = .05$, $1 - \beta = .50$, we find the required sample size as $n = 11 + 2 = 13$. Taking $\sigma = .06$, yields $d = .4$. From the same table, we find that the required sample size is $25 + 2 = 27$. To be safe, we would use $n = 27$. For $\sigma \leq .06$, with a significance level of .05, this would give the two-sided t test at least a 50% chance of detecting a difference of 0.024 pound.

If, when planning an investigation leading to a two-sided t-test, we overestimate σ, the consequences are two-fold: first, we overestimate the sample size required, and thus unnecessarily increase the cost of the test; but, by employing a sample size that is larger than necessary, the actual value of $\beta(\delta)$ will be somewhat less than we intended, which will be all to the good. On the other hand, if

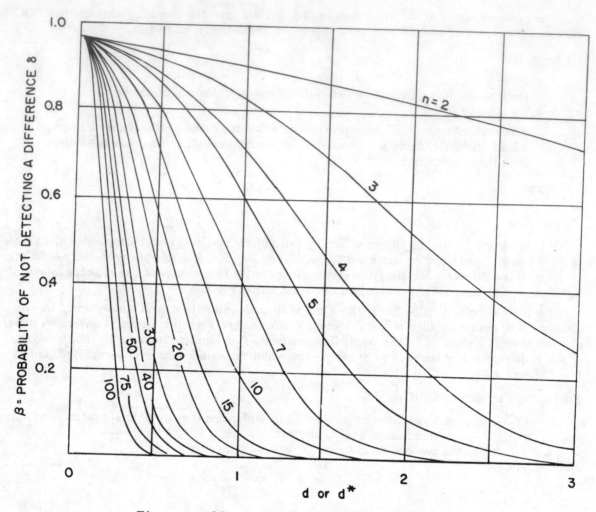

Figure 3-1. OC curves for the two-sided t-test ($\alpha = .05$).

Adapted with permission from *Annals of Mathematical Statistics*, Vol. 17, No. 2, June 1946, pp. 178-197, from article entitled "Operating Characteristics for the Common Statistical Tests of Significance" by C. D. Ferris, F. E. Grubbs, and C. L. Weaver.

Note: These curves apply to the following tests:

(a) Does the average m of a new product differ from a standard m_0?

$$\delta = |m - m_0|$$

$$d = \frac{|m - m_0|}{\sigma} \qquad \text{See Paragraph 3-2.1.1.}$$

(b) Do the averages of two products differ?

$$\delta = |m_A - m_B|$$

$$d^* = \frac{|m_A - m_B|}{\sigma} \frac{1}{\sqrt{n_A + n_B - 1}} \sqrt{\frac{n_A\, n_B}{n_A + n_B}},$$

where $\sigma_A = \sigma_B = \sigma$ by assumption, and n_A and n_B are the respective sample sizes from products A and B. See Paragraph 3-3.1.1.

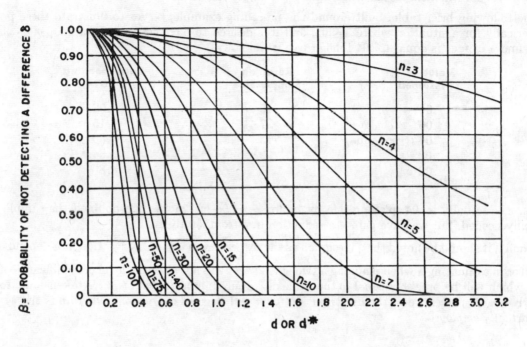

Figure 3-2. OC curves for the two-sided t-test ($\alpha = .01$).

Adapted with permission from *Engineering Statistics* by A. H. Bowker and G. J. Lieberman, Copyright, 1959, Prentice-Hall, Inc.

Note: These curves apply to the following tests:

(a) Does the average m of a new product differ from a standard m_0?

$$\delta = |m - m_0|$$

$$d = \frac{|m - m_0|}{\sigma} \qquad \text{See Paragraph 3-2.1.1.}$$

(b) Do the averages of two products differ?

$$\delta = |m_A - m_B|$$

$$d^* = \frac{|m_A - m_B|}{\sigma} \frac{1}{\sqrt{n_A + n_B - 1}} \sqrt{\frac{n_A n_B}{n_A + n_B}},$$

where $\sigma_A = \sigma_B = \sigma$ by assumption, and n_A and n_B are the respective sample sizes from products A and B. See Paragraph 3-3.1.1.

we underestimate σ, we shall underestimate the sample size actually required, and by using too small a sample size, $\beta(\delta)$ will be somewhat larger than we intended, and our chances of detecting real differences when they exist will be correspondingly lessened.

The following brief table, built around the preceding example, serves to illustrate these points numerically for a situation where $\alpha = .05$, and it is desired to have $\beta(\delta) = .50$ for $\delta = |m - m_0| = .024$, and σ in fact is equal to .04 though this is unknown.

Value of σ Assumed	Resulting Sample Size	Corresponding β (.024)
.08	45	.02
.06	27	.15
.04 (true value)	13	.50
.03	9	.64
.02	5	.80

Thus, if σ actually is .04, playing safe by taking $\sigma = .06$ has more than doubled the sample size actually needed, but we have gained a reduction in β from .50 to .15.

Finally, it should be noted that, inasmuch as the test criterion $u = t_{1-\alpha/2} \dfrac{s}{\sqrt{n}}$ does not depend on σ, an error in estimating σ when planning a two-sided t-test will not alter the level of significance of the test, which will be precisely equal to the value of α desired, *provided* that $t_{1-\alpha/2}$ is taken equal to the $100(1 - \alpha/2)$ percentile of the t distribution for $n - 1$ degrees of freedom, where n is the *sample size actually employed*.

3-2.1.2　Does the Average of the New Product Differ from the Standard (σ Known)?

[Two-sided Normal Test]

Procedure	**Example**
(1)　Choose α, the significance level of the test.	(1)　Let $\alpha = .05$
(2)　Look up $z_{1-\alpha/2}$ in Table A-2.	(2)　$z_{.975} = 1.960$
(3)　Compute $\bar{X}$, the mean of the n measurements.	(3)　$\bar{X} = .710$ pound (Data Sample 3-2)
(4)　Compute $$u = z_{1-\alpha/2} \frac{\sigma}{\sqrt{n}}$$	(4)　σ is known to be equal to .06 pound. $$u = \frac{1.96\,(.06)}{\sqrt{20}}$$ $$= .0263$$
(5)　If $|\bar{X} - m_0| > u$ decide that the average of the new type differs from that of the standard; otherwise, that there is no reason to believe that they differ.	(5)　$|\bar{X} - m_0| = |.710 - .735| = .025$. We conclude that there is no reason to believe that the average amount of powder in the new stock differs from 0.735 (the specified standard amount).
(6)　Note that the interval $\bar{X} \pm u$ is a $100(1 - \alpha)\%$ confidence interval estimate of the true average m of the new type.	(6)　Note that $(.710 \pm .0263)$ is a 95% confidence interval estimate for the true average m of the new stock.

Operating Characteristics of the Test. Figures 3-3 and 3-4 give the operating characteristics of the preceding test for $\alpha = .05$ and $\alpha = .01$, respectively. For any given n and $d = \dfrac{|m - m_0|}{\sigma}$, the value of $\beta(\delta) = \beta(\delta \,|\, \sigma, \alpha, n)$, the probability of failing to detect a difference of absolute size $\delta = |m - m_0|$, can be read off directly.

Selection of Sample Size n. If we specify α, the significance level, and β, the probability or risk we are willing to take of not detecting a difference of absolute size $\delta = |m - m_0|$, then we can use Table A-8 to obtain n, the required sample size. As an example, if σ is known to be 0.04 pound, and we wish to have a 50-50 chance of detecting a difference of 0.024 pound, then $d = 0.6$. From Table A-8, we find that the required sample size is 11.

When we know the correct value of σ, we can achieve a desired value of $\beta(\delta)$ with fewer observations by using the normal test at the desired level of significance α than by using the corresponding t-test. The saving is 2 or 4 observations according as $\alpha = .05$ or $.01$, respectively.

Overestimating or underestimating σ when planning a two-sided normal test has somewhat different consequences than when planning a two-sided t-test. If we *overestimate* σ and choose $\sigma' > \sigma$, we also *overestimate* the sample size required as in the case of the t-test. In addition, we *overestimate* the correct test criterion $u = z_{1-\alpha/2} \dfrac{\sigma}{\sqrt{n}}$ for the sample size n actually adopted, with the result that the effective significance level of the normal test is *reduced* to α', which is related to α by the equation

$$z_{1-\alpha'/2} = \left(\frac{\sigma'}{\sigma}\right) z_{1-\alpha/2}.$$

The actual probability of not detecting a difference of δ, $\beta'(\delta)$, is related to the intended risk $\beta(\delta)$ by the equation

$$z_{1-\beta'} = \left(\frac{\sigma'}{\sigma}\right) z_{1-\beta}.$$

$\beta'(\delta)$ will be less than $\beta(\delta)$ when $\sigma' > \sigma$ for all (large) δ for which $\beta(\delta) < 0.50$; $\beta'(\delta)$ will be larger than $\beta(\delta)$ for all (small) δ for which $\beta'(\delta) > 0.50$. For the particular δ for which $\beta(\delta) = 0.50$, $\beta'(\delta)$ also will equal 0.50. Conversely, if we *underestimate* σ, then we not only *underestimate* the sample size required but also the test criterion for the sample size actually used, so that the actual risk of an Error of the First Kind α' will be *larger* than α, and the risk of an Error of the Second Kind $\beta'(\delta)$ will be *increased* for large δ, and *decreased* for small δ.

The following calculations serve to illustrate these points numerically for situations bordering on the conditions assumed in the preceding sample-size calculation:

Intended significance level $\alpha = 0.05$.
Intended risk of *Error of the Second Kind* $\beta(\delta) = 0.50$ for $\delta = 0.024$.

TWO-SIDED NORMAL TEST

Value of σ Assumed	Sample Size Indicated	Actual Significance Level, α'	Actual Risk of Error of Second Kind, β' (0.024)
.08	43 (45)*	.00009 (.05)*	0.50 (.02)*
.06	25 (27)	.003 (.05)	0.50 (.15)
.04 (true value)	11 (13)	.05 (.05)	0.50 (.50)
.03	7 (9)	.14 (.05)	0.50 (.64)
.02	3 (5)	.33 (.05)	0.50 (.80)

* Values in parentheses are for corresponding two-sided t-test.

To obtain a numerical illustration of the more general case where $\beta(\delta) \neq 0.50$, let us modify the foregoing example by taking $\beta(\delta) = 0.20$, say, as the intended risk of an Error of the Second Kind for $\delta = 0.024$:

Intended significance level $\alpha = 0.05$.
Intended risk of Error of the Second Kind $\beta(\delta) = 0.20$ for $\delta = 0.024$.

TWO-SIDED NORMAL TEST

Value of σ Assumed	Sample Size Indicated	Actual Significance Level, α'	Actual Risk of Error of Second Kind, β' (0.024)
.08	88 (90)*	.00009 (.05)*	.046 (.0004)*
.06	50 (52)	.003 (.05)	.103 (.01)
.04 (true value)	22 (24)	.05 (.05)	.20 (.20)
.03	13 (15)	.14 (.05)	.26 (.43)
.02	6 (8)	.33 (.05)	.34 (.70)

* Values in parentheses are for corresponding two-sided t-test.

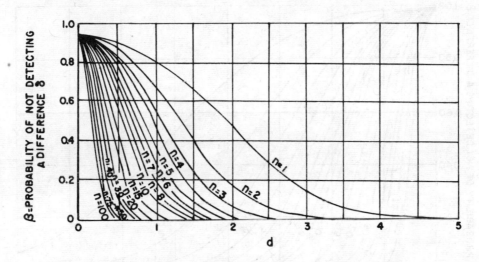

Figure 3-3. OC curves for the two-sided normal test ($\alpha = .05$).

Adapted with permission from *Annals of Mathematical Statistics*, Vol. 17, No. 2, June 1946, pp. 178-197, from article entitled "Operating Characteristics for the Common Statistical Tests of Significance" by C. D. Ferris, F. E. Grubbs, and C. L. Weaver.

Note: These curves apply to the following tests:

(a) Does the average m of a new product differ from a standard m_0?

$$\delta = |m - m_0|$$

$$d = \frac{|m - m_0|}{\sigma} \qquad \text{See Paragraph 3-2.1.2.}$$

(b) Do the averages of two products differ?

$$\delta = |m_A - m_R|$$

$$d = \frac{|m_A - m_B|}{\sqrt{\sigma_A^2 + \sigma_B^2}}; \ \sigma_A \text{ and } \sigma_B \text{ are known. See Paragraph 3-3.1.3.}$$

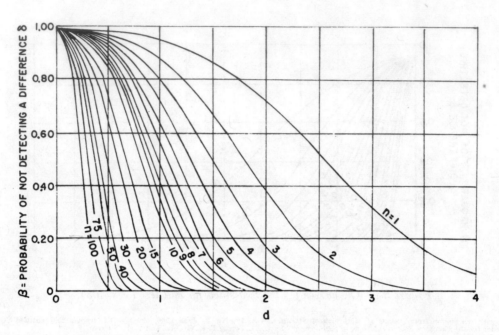

Figure 3-4. OC curves for the two-sided normal test $(\alpha = .01)$.

Note: These curves apply to the following tests:

(a)   Does the average m of a new product differ from a standard m_0?

$$\delta = |m - m_0|$$

$$d = \frac{|m - m_0|}{\sigma} \qquad \text{See Paragraph 3-2.1.2.}$$

(b)   Do the averages of two products differ?

$$\delta = |m_A - m_B|$$

$$d = \frac{|m_A - m_B|}{\sqrt{\sigma_A^2 + \sigma_B^2}}; \ \sigma_A \text{ and } \sigma_B \text{ are known. See Paragraph 3-3.1.3.}$$

3-2.2 TO DETERMINE WHETHER THE AVERAGE OF A NEW PRODUCT EXCEEDS THE STANDARD

3-2.2.1 Does the Average of the New Product Exceed the Standard (σ Unknown)?

[One-sided t-test]

Procedure	**Example**
(1) Choose α, the significance level of the test.	(1) Let $\alpha = .05$
(2) Look up $t_{1-\alpha}$ for $n-1$ degrees of freedom in Table A-4.	(2) $t_{.95}$ for 19 degrees of freedom = 1.729
(3) Compute $\bar{X}$ and s	(3) $\bar{X} = .710$ pound $s = .0504$ pound (Data Sample 3.2)
(4) Compute $$u = t_{1-\alpha}\frac{s}{\sqrt{n}}$$	(4) $$u = \frac{1.729\,(.0504)}{\sqrt{20}}$$ $$= 0.019$$
(5) If $(\bar{X} - m_0) > + u$, decide that the average of the new type exceeds that of the standard; otherwise, that there is no reason to believe that the average of the new type exceeds that of the standard.	(5) $(\bar{X} - m_0) = (.710 - .735) = -.025$. We conclude that there is no reason to believe that the average of the new product exceeds the specified standard.
(6) Note that the open interval from $(\bar{X} - u)$ to $+ \infty$ is a one-sided $100\,(1 - \alpha)\,\%$ confidence interval for the true mean of the new product.	(6) Note that the open interval from .691 to $+ \infty$ is a one-sided 95% confidence interval for true average of the new product.

Operating Characteristics of the Test. Figures 3-5 and 3-6 give the operating characteristic (OC) curves of the above test for $\alpha = .05$, and $\alpha = .01$, respectively, and various values of n.

Choose:

$\delta = (m - m_0)$, the true difference between averages, (unknown, of course)

Some value of σ. (We may use an estimate from previous data; lacking such an estimate, see Paragraph 2-2.4. If OC curve is consulted after the experiment, we may use the estimate from the experiment.)

Compute

$$d = \frac{\delta}{\sigma} .$$

We then can read from the OC curve for a given significance level α and sample size n, a value of $\beta(\delta)$. The $\beta(\delta)$ read from the curve is $\beta(\delta \,|\, \sigma, \alpha, n)$, i.e., $\beta(\delta \ given \ \sigma, \alpha, n)$—the probability of failing to detect this difference when the given test is carried out with a sample of size n, at the α-level of significance, and the population standard deviation actually is σ.

If we use too large a value for σ, the effect is to underestimate d and consequently to overestimate $\beta(\delta)$, the probability of not detecting a difference of δ when it exists. Conversely, if we choose too small a value of σ, then we shall overestimate d and underestimate $\beta(\delta)$. The true value of $\beta(\delta)$ is determined, of course, by the sample size n and significance level α employed, *and* the true value of σ.

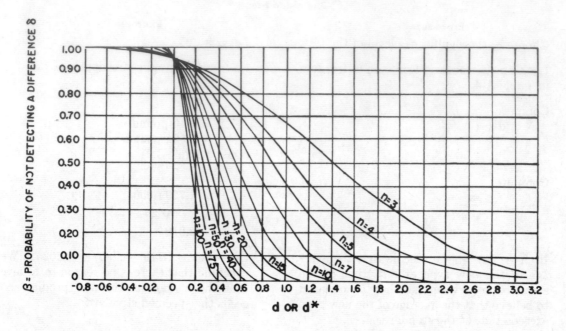

Figure 3-5. OC curves for the one-sided t-test ($\alpha = .05$).

Adapted with permission from *Engineering Statistics* by A. H. Bowker and G. J. Lieberman, Copyright, 1959, Prentice-Hall, Inc.

Note: These curves apply to the following tests:

(a) Does the average m of a new product exceed a standard m_0?

$$\delta = m - m_0$$

$$d = \frac{m - m_0}{\sigma} \qquad \text{See Paragraph 3-2.2.1.}$$

(b) Is the average m of a new product less than a standard m_0?

$$\delta = m_0 - m$$

$$d = \frac{m_0 - m}{\sigma} \qquad \text{See Paragraph 3-2.3.1.}$$

(c) Does the average of product A exceed that of product B?

$$\delta = m_A - m_B$$

$$d^* = \frac{m_A - m_B}{\sigma} \frac{1}{\sqrt{n_A + n_B - 1}} \sqrt{\frac{n_A n_B}{n_A + n_B}},$$

where $\sigma_A = \sigma_B = \sigma$ by assumption, and n_A and n_B are the respective sample sizes from products A and B. See Paragraph 3-3.2.1.

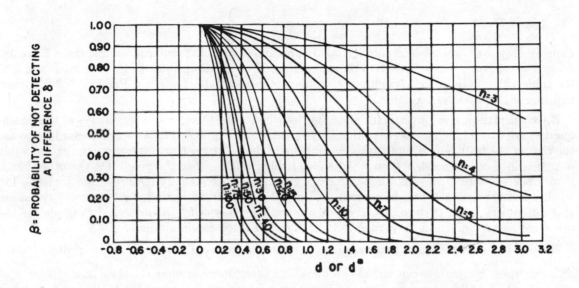

Figure 3-6. OC curves for the one-sided t-test ($\alpha = .01$).

Adapted with permission from *Engineering Statistics* by A. H. Bowker and G. J. Lieberman, Copyright, 1959, Prentice-Hall, Inc.

Note: These curves apply to the following tests:

(a) Does the average m of a new product exceed a standard m_0?

$$\delta = m - m_0$$

$$d = \frac{m - m_0}{\sigma} \qquad \text{See Paragraph 3-2.2.1.}$$

(b) Is the average m of a new product less than a standard m_0?

$$\delta = m_0 - m$$

$$d = \frac{m_0 - m}{\sigma} \qquad \text{See Paragraph 3-2.3.1.}$$

(c) Does the average of product A exceed that of product B?

$$\delta = m_A - m_B$$

$$d^* = \frac{m_A - m_B}{\sigma} \; \frac{1}{\sqrt{n_A + n_B - 1}} \sqrt{\frac{n_A \, n_B}{n_A + n_B}},$$

where $\sigma_A = \sigma_B = \sigma$ by assumption, and n_A and n_B are the respective sample sizes from products A and B. See Paragraph 3-3.2.1.

Selection of Sample Size n. If we choose

$$\delta = (m - m_0),$$

α, the significance level of the test

β, the probability of failing to detect a positive difference of size $(m - m_0)$

and compute

$$d = \frac{m - m_0}{\sigma}$$

then we may use Table A-9 to obtain a good approximation to the required sample size. If we are using $\alpha = .01$, then we must add 3 to the table value. If we are using $\alpha = .05$, then we must add 2 to the table value. (In order to compute d, we must choose a value for σ; see Paragraph 2-2.4 when no other information is available.)

If, when planning an investigation leading to a one-sided t-test, we overestimate σ, the consequences are two-fold: first, we overestimate the sample size required, and thus unnecessarily increase the cost of the test; but, by employing a sample size that is larger than necessary, the actual value of $\beta(\delta)$ will be somewhat less than we intended, which will be all to the good. On the other hand, if we underestimate σ, we shall underestimate the sample size actually required, and by using too small a sample size, $\beta(\delta)$ will be somewhat larger than we intended, and our chances of detecting real differences when they exist will be correspondingly lessened. (A numerical example for the *two*-sided t-test is given in Paragraph 3-2.1.1. The one-sided case is similar).

Finally, it should be noted, that inasmuch as the test criterion $u = t_{1-\alpha} \dfrac{s}{\sqrt{n}}$ does not depend on σ, an error in estimating σ when planning a one-sided t-test does not alter the level of significance of the test, which will be precisely equal to the value of α desired, *provided* that $t_{1-\alpha}$ is taken equal to the $100 (1 - \alpha)$ percentile of the t distribution for $n - 1$ degrees of freedom, where n is the *sample size actually employed.*

3-2.2.2   Does the Average of the New Product Exceed the Standard (σ Known)?

[One-sided Normal Test]

Procedure

(1) Choose α, the significance level of the test.

(2) Look up $z_{1-\alpha}$ in Table A-2.

(3) Compute
$\bar{X}$, the sample mean

(4) Compute

$$u = z_{1-\alpha} \frac{\sigma}{\sqrt{n}}$$

(5) If $(\bar{X} - m_0) > u$, decide that the average performance of the new type exceeds that of the standard; otherwise, that there is no reason to believe that the average of the new type exceeds that of the standard.

(6) Note that the open interval from $(\bar{X} - u)$ to $+ \infty$ is a one-sided $100 (1 - \alpha) \%$ confidence interval for the true mean of the new product.

Example

(1) Let $\alpha = .05$

(2) $z_{.95} = 1.645$

(3)

$\bar{X} = 0.710$ pound
(Data Sample 3-2)

(4) σ is known to be equal to .06 pound.

$$u = \frac{1.645 \,(.06)}{\sqrt{20}}$$

$$= .022$$

(5) $(\bar{X} - m_0) = .710 - .735 = -.025$, which is not larger than u. We conclude that there is no reason to believe that the average of the new product exceeds that of the standard.

(6) Note that the open interval from .688 to $+ \infty$ is a 95% one-sided confidence interval for the true mean of the new product.

Operating Characteristics of the Test. Figures 3-7 and 3-8 give the operating characteristics of the above test for $\alpha = .05$ and $\alpha = .01$, respectively. For any given n and $d = \dfrac{m - m_0}{\sigma}$, the value of $\beta(\delta) = \beta(\delta \mid \sigma, \alpha, n)$, the probability of failing to detect a positive difference $\delta = (m - m_0)$, can be read off directly.

Selection of Sample Size n. If we specify

> $\delta = (m - m_0)$, the magnitude of a positive difference of interest to us
> α, the significance level of the test
> β, the probability of failing to detect a positive difference of size δ

and compute

$$d = \frac{m - m_0}{\sigma}$$

then we may use Table A-9 to obtain the required sample size.

When we know the correct value of σ, we can achieve a desired value of $\beta(\delta)$ with fewer observations by using the normal test at the desired level of significance α than by using the corresponding t-test. The saving is 2 or 3 observations according as $\alpha = .05$ or $.01$, respectively.

Overestimating or underestimating σ when planning a one-sided normal test has somewhat different consequences than when planning a one-sided t-test. If we *overestimate* σ and choose $\sigma' > \sigma$, we also *overestimate* the sample size required as in the case of the t-test. In addition, we *overestimate* the correct test criterion $u = z_{1-\alpha} \dfrac{\sigma}{\sqrt{n}}$ for the sample size n actually adopted, with the result that the effective significance level of the normal test is *reduced* to α', which is related to α by the equation

$$z_{1-\alpha'} = \left(\frac{\sigma'}{\sigma}\right) z_{1-\alpha}.$$

The actual probability of not detecting a difference of δ, $\beta'(\delta)$, is related to the intended risk $\beta(\delta)$ by the equation

$$z_{1-\beta'} = \left(\frac{\sigma'}{\upsilon}\right) z_{1-\beta}.$$

$\beta'(\delta)$ will be less than $\beta(\delta)$ when $\sigma' > \sigma$ for all (large) δ for which $\beta(\delta) < 0.50$; $\beta'(\delta)$ will be larger than $\beta(\delta)$ for all (small) δ for which $\beta'(\delta) > 0.50$. For the particular δ for which $\beta(\delta) = 0.50$, $\beta'(\delta)$ also will equal 0.50. Conversely, if we *underestimate* σ, then we not only *underestimate* the sample size required but also the test criterion for the sample size actually used, so that the actual risk of an Error of the First Kind α' will be *larger* than α, and the risk of an Error of the Second Kind $\beta'(\delta)$ will be *increased* for large δ, and *decreased* for small δ. (Numerical examples for the two-sided normal test are given in Paragraph 3-2.1.2. The one-sided case is similar.)

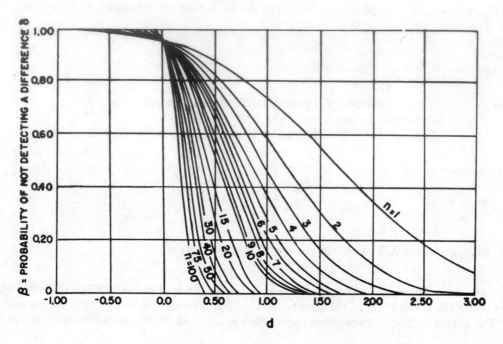

Figure 3-7. OC curves for the one-sided normal test ($\alpha = .05$).

Adapted with permission from *Engineering Statistics* by A. H. Bowker and G. J. Lieberman, Copyright, 1959, Prentice-Hall, Inc.

Note: These curves apply to the following tests:

(a) Does the average m of a new product exceed a standard m_0?

$$\delta = m - m_0$$

$$d = \frac{m - m_0}{\sigma} \qquad \text{See Paragraph 3-2.2.2.}$$

(b) Is the average m of a new product less than a standard m_0?

$$\delta = m_0 - m$$

$$d = \frac{m_0 - m}{\sigma} \qquad \text{See Paragraph 3-2.3.2.}$$

(c) Does the average of product A exceed that of product B?

$$\delta = m_A - m_B$$

$$d = \frac{m_A - m_B}{\sqrt{\sigma_A^2 + \sigma_B^2}}, \quad \sigma_A \text{ and } \sigma_B \text{ are known. See Paragraph 3-3.2.3.}$$

3-18

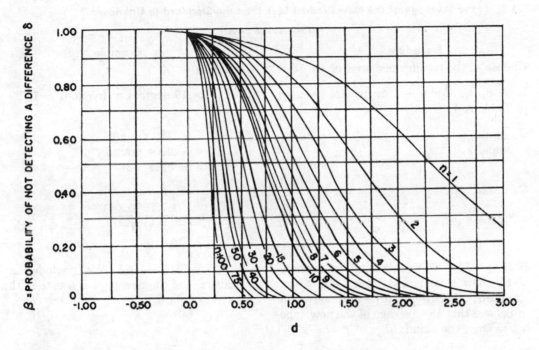

Figure 3-8. OC curves for the one-sided normal test ($\alpha = .01$).

Adapted with permission from *Engineering Statistics* by A. H. Bowker and G. J. Lieberman, Copyright, 1959, Prentice-Hall, Inc.

Note: These curves apply to the following tests:

(a) Does the average m of a new product exceed a standard m_0?

   $\delta = m - m_0$

   $d = \dfrac{m - m_0}{\sigma}$ See Paragraph 3-2.2.2.

(b) Is the average m of a new product less than a standard m_0?

   $\delta = m_0 - m$

   $d = \dfrac{m_0 - m}{\sigma}$ See Paragraph 3-2.3.2.

(c) Does the average of product A exceed that of product B?

   $\delta = m_A - m_B$

   $d = \dfrac{m_A - m_B}{\sqrt{\sigma_A^2 + \sigma_B^2}}$, σ_A and σ_B are known. See Paragraph 3-3.2.3.

3-2.3 TO DETERMINE WHETHER THE AVERAGE OF A NEW PRODUCT IS LESS THAN THE STANDARD

3-2.3.1 Is the Average of the New Product Less than the Standard (σ Unknown)?

[One-sided t-test]

Procedure	Example
(1) Choose α, the significance level of the test.	(1) Let $\alpha = .05$
(2) Look up $t_{1-\alpha}$ for $n - 1$ degrees of freedom in Table A-4.	(2) $t_{.95}$ for 19 degrees of freedom $= 1.729$
(3) Compute $\bar{X}$ and s	(3) $\bar{X} = .710$ pound $s = .0504$ pound (Data Sample 3-2)
(4) Compute $$u = t_{1-\alpha}\frac{s}{\sqrt{n}}$$	(4) $$u = \frac{1.729\,(.0504)}{\sqrt{20}}$$ $$= 0.019$$
(5) If $(m_0 - \bar{X}) > u$, decide that the average of the new type is less than that of the standard; otherwise, that there is no reason to believe that the average of the new type is less than the standard.	(5) $.735 - .710 = .025$. We conclude that the average of the new type is less than that of the standard.
(6) Note that the open interval from $-\infty$ to $(\bar{X} + u)$ is a one-sided $100\,(1 - \alpha)\,\%$ confidence interval for the true mean of the new type.	(6) Note that the open interval from $-\infty$ to $.729$ is a one-sided 95% confidence interval for the true mean of the new type.

Operating Characteristics of the Test.   Figures 3-5 and 3-6 give the operating characteristic (OC) curves of the above test for $\alpha = .05$, and $\alpha = .01$, respectively, for various values of n.

Choose:

$\delta = (m_0 - m)$,   the true difference between averages (unknown, of course)

Some value of σ. (We may use an estimate from previous data; lacking such an estimate, see Paragraph 2-2.4. If OC curve is consulted after the experiment, we may use the estimate from the experiment.)

Compute

$$d = \frac{\delta}{\sigma} \; .$$

We then can read from the OC curve for a given significance level α and sample size n, a value of $\beta(\delta)$. The $\beta(\delta)$ read from the curve is $\beta(\delta \,|\, \sigma, \alpha, n)$, i.e., $\beta(\delta \; given \; \sigma, \alpha, n)$—the probability of failing to detect this difference when the given test is carried out with a sample of size n, at the α-level of significance, and the population standard deviation actually is σ.

If we use too large a value for σ, the effect is to underestimate d and consequently to overestimate $\beta(\delta)$, the probability of not detecting a difference of δ when it exists. Conversely, if we choose too small a value of σ, then we shall overestimate d and underestimate $\beta(\delta)$. The true value of $\beta(\delta)$ is determined, of course, by the sample size n and significance level α employed, *and* the true value of σ.

Selection of Sample Size n. If we choose

$\delta = (m_0 - m)$,

α, the significance level of the test

β, the probability of failing to find a negative difference of size $(m_0 - m)$;

and compute

$$d = \frac{m_0 - m}{\sigma}$$

then we may use Table A-9 to obtain a good approximation to the required sample size. If we are using $\alpha = .01$, then we must add 3 to the table value. If we are using $\alpha = .05$, then we must add 2 to the table value. (In order to use the table, we must have a value for σ. See Paragraph 2-2.4 if no other information is available.)

The effect of overestimating or underestimating σ is the same as when a one-sided *t*-test is to be used to detect a *positive* difference of magnitude $\delta = m - m_0$. See Paragraph 3-2.2.1.

3-2.3.2 Is the Average of the New Product Less Than That of the Standard (σ Known)?

[One-sided Normal Test]

Procedure	**Example**
(1) Choose α, the significance level of the test.	(1) Let $\alpha = .05$
(2) Look up $z_{1-\alpha}$ in Table A-2.	(2) $z_{.95} = 1.645$
(3) Compute $\bar{X}$, the sample mean	(3) $\bar{X} = 0.710$ pound (Data Sample 3-2)
(4) Compute $u = z_{1-\alpha} \dfrac{\sigma}{\sqrt{n}}$	(4) σ is known to be equal to .06 pound. $u = \dfrac{1.645 \,(.06)}{\sqrt{20}}$ $= 0.022$
(5) If $(m_0 - \bar{X}) > u$, decide that the average of the new type is less than that of the standard; otherwise, that there is no reason to believe that the average of the new type is less than that of the standard.	(5) $(m_0 - \bar{X}) = (.735 - .710) = .025$, which is larger than u. We conclude that the average of the new type is less than the standard.
(6) Note that the open interval from $-\infty$ to $(\bar{X} + u)$ is a one-sided $100\,(1 - \alpha)\,\%$ confidence interval for the true mean of the new type.	(6) Note that the open interval from $-\infty$ to .732 is a one-sided 95% confidence interval for the true mean of the new type.

Operating Characteristics of the Test. Figures 3-7 and 3-8 give the operating characteristics of the test for $\alpha = .05$ and $\alpha = .01$, respectively. For any given n and $d = \dfrac{m_0 - m}{\sigma}$ the value of $\beta(\delta) = \beta(\delta \mid \sigma, \alpha, n)$, the probability of failing to detect a negative difference of size $(m_0 - m)$, can be read off directly.

Selection of Sample Size n. If we specify

$\delta = (m_0 - m)$, the magnitude of a negative difference of interest to us

α, the significance level of the test

β, the probability of failing to detect a negative difference of size δ,

and compute

$$d = \frac{m_0 - m}{\sigma}$$

then we may use Table A-9 to obtain the required sample size.

The effect of overestimating or underestimating σ is the same as when the one-sided normal test is to be used to detect a *positive* difference of magnitude $\delta = m - m_0$. See Paragraph 3-2.2.2.

3-3　COMPARING THE AVERAGES OF TWO MATERIALS, PRODUCTS, OR PROCESSES

We consider two problems:

(a)　We wish to test whether the averages of two materials, products, or processes differ, and we are not particularly concerned which is larger, Paragraph 3-3.1.

(b)　We wish to test whether the average of material, product, or process A exceeds that of material, product, or process B, Paragraph 3-3.2.

TABLE 3-2.　SUMMARY OF TECHNIQUES FOR COMPARING THE AVERAGE PERFORMANCE OF TWO PRODUCTS
(FOR DETAILS AND WORKED EXAMPLES, SEE PARAGRAPHS 3-3.1 AND 3-3.2)

We Wish to Test Whether	Paragraph Reference	Knowledge of Variation	Test to be Made	Operating Characteristics of Test	Determination of Sample Size n	Notes
m_A differs from m_B	3-3.1.1	$\sigma_A \simeq \sigma_B$; both unknown	$\|\bar{X}_A - \bar{X}_B\| > u$, where $u = t_{1-\alpha/2}\, s_P \sqrt{\dfrac{n_A + n_B}{n_A\, n_B}}$	For $\alpha = .05$ and $\alpha = .01$ see Figs. 3-1 and 3-2* and Par. 3-3.1.1.	Use Table A-8. For $\alpha = .05$, add 1 to the tabular value. For $\alpha = .01$, add 2 to the tabular value.	$s_P = \sqrt{\dfrac{(n_A - 1)\, s_A^2 + (n_B - 1)\, s_B^2}{n_A + n_B - 2}}$
	3-3.1.2	$\sigma_A \neq \sigma_B$; both unknown	$\|\bar{X}_A - \bar{X}_B\| > u$, where $u = t' \sqrt{\dfrac{s_A^2}{n_A} + \dfrac{s_B^2}{n_B}}$ See Notes.			t' is the value of $t_{1-\alpha/2}$ for the effective number of degrees of freedom $f = \dfrac{(s_A^2/n_A + s_B^2/n_B)^2}{\dfrac{(s_A^2/n_A)^2}{n_A + 1} + \dfrac{(s_B^2/n_B)^2}{n_B + 1}} - 2$
	3-3.1.3	σ_A, σ_B; both known	$\|\bar{X}_A - \bar{X}_B\| > u$, where $u = z_{1-\alpha/2} \sqrt{\dfrac{\sigma_A^2}{n_A} + \dfrac{\sigma_B^2}{n_B}}$	For $\alpha = .05$ and $\alpha = .01$, see Figs. 3-3 and 3-4.	Use Table A-8.	
m_A is greater than m_B	3-3.2.1	$\sigma_A \simeq \sigma_B$; both unknown	$(\bar{X}_A - \bar{X}_B) > u$, where $u = t_{1-\alpha}\, s_P \sqrt{\dfrac{n_A + n_B}{n_A\, n_B}}$	For $\alpha = .05$ and $\alpha = .01$ see Figs. 3-5 and 3-6* and Par. 3-3.2.1.	Use Table A-9. For $\alpha = .05$, add 1 to the tabular value. For $\alpha = .01$, add 2 to the tabular value.	$s_P = \sqrt{\dfrac{(n_A - 1)\, s_A^2 + (n_B - 1)\, s_B^2}{n_A + n_B - 2}}$
	3-3.2.2	$\sigma_A \neq \sigma_B$; both unknown	$(\bar{X}_A - \bar{X}_B) > u$, where $u = t' \sqrt{\dfrac{s_A^2}{n_A} + \dfrac{s_B^2}{n_B}}$			t' is the value of $t_{1-\alpha}$ for the effective number of degrees of freedom $f = \dfrac{(s_A^2/n_A + s_B^2/n_B)^2}{\dfrac{(s_A^2/n_A)^2}{n_A + 1} + \dfrac{(s_B^2/n_B)^2}{n_B + 1}} - 2$
	3-3.2.3	σ_A, σ_B; both known	$(\bar{X}_A - \bar{X}_B) > u$, where $u = z_{1-\alpha} \sqrt{\dfrac{\sigma_A^2}{n_A} + \dfrac{\sigma_B^2}{n_B}}$	For $\alpha = .05$ and $\alpha = .01$ see Figs. 3-7 and 3-8.	Use Table A-9.	

* Although the common σ is unknown, useful information may be obtained from the OC curve if a value (or 2 bounding values) of σ can be assumed.

It again is important to decide which problem is appropriate before making the observations. If this is not done and the choice of the problem is influenced by the observations, the significance level of the test, i.e., the probability of an Error of the First Kind, and the operating characteristics of the test may differ considerably from their nominal values. It is assumed that the appropriate problem has been selected and that n_A and n_B observations are taken from products A and B, respectively.

Ordinarily, we will not know σ_A or σ_B. In some cases, it may be safe to assume that σ_A is approximately equal to σ_B.* We give the solutions for the two problems (Paragraphs 3-3.1 and 3-3.2) for three situations with regard to knowledge of the variability, and for the special case where the observations are paired.

Case 1—The variability in performance of each of A and B is unknown but can be assumed to be about the same.

Case 2—The variability in performance of each of A and B is unknown, and it is not reasonable to assume that they both have the same variability.

Case 3—The variability in performance of each of A and B is known from previous experience. The standard deviations are σ_A and σ_B, respectively.

Case 4—The observations are paired.

3-3.1 DO THE PRODUCTS A AND B DIFFER IN AVERAGE PERFORMANCE?

3-3.1.1 (Case 1)—Variability of A and B is Unknown, But Can Be Assumed to be Equal.

Data Sample 3-3.1.1—Latent Heat of Fusion of Ice

Two methods were used in a study of the latent heat of fusion of ice. Both Method A (an electrical method) and Method B (a method of mixtures) were conducted with the specimens cooled to −0.72°C. The data represent the change in total heat from −0.72°C to water at 0°C, in calories per gram of mass.

Method A	Method B
79.98	80.02
80.04	79.94
80.02	79.98
80.04	79.97
80.03	79.97
80.03	80.03
80.04	79.95
79.97	79.97
80.05	
80.03	
80.02	
80.00	
80.02	

---

* For a procedure to test whether σ_A and σ_B differ, see Chapter 4.

[Two-sided t-test]

Procedure	Example

(1) Choose α, the significance level of the test.

(1) Let $\alpha = .05$

(2) Look up $t_{1-\alpha/2}$ for $\nu = (n_A + n_B - 2)$ degrees of freedom in Table A-4.

(2) $\quad n_A = 13$
$\quad\quad n_B = 8$
$\quad\quad\quad \nu = 19$ degrees of freedom
$t_{.975}$ for 19 d.f. $= 2.093$

(3) Compute: $\bar{X}_A$ and s_A^2, $\bar{X}_B$ and s_B^2, for the n_A and n_B measurements from A and B.

(3) $\quad \bar{X}_A = 80.02$
$\quad\quad s_A^2 = .000574$
$\quad\quad \bar{X}_B = 79.98$
$\quad\quad s_B^2 = .000984$

(4) Compute

$$s_P = \sqrt{\frac{(n_A - 1)\, s_A^2 + (n_B - 1)\, s_B^2}{n_A + n_B - 2}}$$

(4)

$$s_P = \sqrt{\frac{12\,(.000574) + 7\,(.000984)}{19}}$$
$$= \sqrt{.000725}$$
$$= .0269$$

(5) Compute

$$u = t_{1-\alpha/2}\, s_P \sqrt{\frac{n_A + n_B}{n_A\, n_B}}$$

(5)

$$u = 2.093\,(.0269)\sqrt{\frac{21}{104}}$$
$$= (.05630)\,(.4493)$$
$$= .025$$

(6) If $|\bar{X}_A - \bar{X}_B| > u$, decide that A and B differ with regard to their average performance; otherwise, that there is no reason to believe A and B differ with regard to their average performance.

(6) $|\bar{X}_A - \bar{X}_B| = .04$, which is larger than u. Conclude that A and B differ with regard to average performance.

(7) Let m_A, m_B be the true average performances of A and B (unknown of course). It is worth noting that the interval $(\bar{X}_A - \bar{X}_B) \pm u$ is a $100\,(1 - \alpha)\,\%$ confidence interval estimate of $(m_A - m_B)$.

(7) The interval $.04 \pm .025$, i.e., the interval from .015 to .065, is a 95% confidence interval for the true difference between the averages of the methods.

Operating Characteristics of the Test. Figures 3-1 and 3-2 give the operating characteristic (OC) curves of the above test for $\alpha = .05$ and $\alpha = .01$, respectively, for various values of $n = n_A + n_B - 1$.

Choose:

    $\delta = |m_A - m_B|$, the true absolute difference between the averages
    Some value of σ $(= \sigma_A = \sigma_B)$, the common standard deviation.
      (We may use an estimate from previous data; lacking such an estimate, see Paragraph 2-2.4. If OC curve is consulted after the experiment, we may use the estimate from the experiment.)

Compute

$$d^* = \frac{|m_A - m_B|}{\sigma}\, \frac{1}{\sqrt{n_A + n_B - 1}}\sqrt{\frac{n_A\, n_B}{n_A + n_B}}\ .$$

We then can read a value of $\beta(\delta)$ from the OC curve for a given significance level and effective sample size $n = n_A + n_B - 1$. The $\beta(\delta)$ read from the curve is $\beta(\delta \mid \sigma, \alpha, n_A, n_B)$ i.e., $\beta(\delta,$ given σ, α, n_A and $n_B)$ the probability of failing to detect a real difference between the two population means of magnitude $\delta = \pm(m_A - m_B)$ when the test is carried out with samples of sizes n_A and n_B, respectively, at the α-level of significance, *and* the two population standard deviations actually *are* both equal to σ.

If we use too large a value for σ, the effect is to make us underestimate d^* and consequently to overestimate $\beta(\delta)$. Conversely, if we choose too small a value of σ, then we shall overestimate d^* and underestimate $\beta(\delta)$. The true value of $\beta(\delta)$ is determined, of course, by the sample sizes n_A and n_B and significance level α actually employed, and the true value of σ ($= \sigma_A = \sigma_B$).

Since the test criterion u does not depend on the value of σ ($= \sigma_A = \sigma_B$), an error in estimating σ will not alter the significance level of the test, which will be precisely equal to the value of α desired, *provided that* the value of $t_{1-\alpha/2}$ is taken equal to the $100(1 - \alpha/2)$ percentile of the t-distribution for $n_A + n_B - 2$ degrees of freedom, where n_A and n_B are the sample sizes actually employed, *and* it actually *is* true that $\sigma_A = \sigma_B$.

If $\sigma_A \neq \sigma_B$, then, whatever may be the ratio σ_A/σ_B, the effective significance level α' will not differ seriously from the intended value α, provided that $n_A = n_B$, except possibly when both are as small as two. If, on the other hand, unequal sample sizes are used, and $\sigma_A \neq \sigma_B$, then the effective level of significance α' can differ considerably from the intended value α, as shown in Figure 3-9 where $\alpha = .05$.

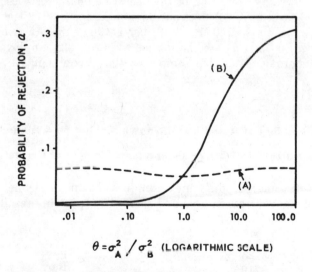

Figure 3-9. Probability of rejection of hypothesis $m_A = m_B$ when true, plotted against θ.

(A) $n_A = n_B = 10, P(|u|) > 2.101;$
(B) $n_A = 5, n_B = 15, P(|u|) > 2.101.$

Selection of Sample Size n. If we choose

$\delta = |m_A - m_B|$, the absolute value of the average difference that we desire to detect

α, the significance level of the test

β, the probability of failing to detect a difference of absolute size δ,

and compute

$$d = \frac{|m_A - m_B|}{\sqrt{2\sigma^2}}, \text{ where } \sigma = \sigma_A = \sigma_B ,$$

then we may use Table A-8 to obtain a good approximation to the required sample size $n \, (= n_A = n_B)$. If we take $\alpha = .01$, then we must add 2 to the value obtained from the table. If we take $\alpha = .05$, then we must add 1 to the table value.

In order to compute d, we must choose a value for $\sigma \, (= \sigma_A = \sigma_B)$. (See Paragraph 2-2.4 if no other information is available.) If we overestimate σ, the consequences are two-fold: first, we overestimate the sample size $n \, (= n_A = n_B)$ required, and thus unnecessarily increase the cost of the test; but, by employing a sample size that is larger than necessary, the actual value of $\beta(\delta)$ will be somewhat less than we intended, which will be all to the good. On the other hand, if we underestimate σ, we shall underestimate the sample size actually required, and by using too small a sample size, $\beta(\delta)$ will be somewhat larger than we intended, and our chances of detecting real differences when they exist will be correspondingly lessened. These effects of overestimating or underestimating $\sigma \, (= \sigma_A = \sigma_B)$ will be similar in magnitude to those considered and illustrated in Paragraph 3-2.1.1 for the case of comparing the mean m of a new material, product, or process, with a standard value m_0.

As explained in the preceding discussion of the operating characteristics of the test, an error in estimating $\sigma \, (= \sigma_A = \sigma_B)$ will have no effect on the significance level of the test, provided that the value of $t_{1-\alpha/2}$ is taken equal to the $100 \, (1 - \alpha/2)$ percentile of the t-distribution for $n_A + n_B - 2$ degrees of freedom, where n_A and n_B are the sample sizes actually employed; and if $\sigma_A \neq \sigma_B$, the effect will not be serious provided that the sample sizes are taken equal.

3-3.1.2   (Case 2)—Variability of A and B is Unknown, Cannot Be Assumed Equal.

Data Sample 3-3.1.2—Compressive Strength of Concrete

Two investigators using somewhat different techniques obtained specimen cores to determine the compressive strength of the concrete in a poured slab. The following results in psi were reported:

A	B
3128	1939
3219	1697
3244	3030
3073	2424
	2020
	2909
	1815
	2020
	2310

Procedure*

(1) Choose α, the significance level of the test. (Actually, the procedure outlined will give a significance level of only approximately α).

(2) Compute: $\bar{X}_A$ and s_A^2, $\bar{X}_B$ and s_B^2, for the n_A and n_B measurements from A and B.

(3) Compute:

$$V_A = \frac{s_A^2}{n_A}$$

and

$$V_B = \frac{s_B^2}{n_B},$$

the estimated variances of $\bar{X}_A$ and $\bar{X}_B$, respectively.

(4) Compute the "effective number of degrees of freedom"

$$f = \frac{(V_A + V_B)^2}{\dfrac{V_A^2}{n_A + 1} + \dfrac{V_B^2}{n_B + 1}} - 2$$

(5) Look up $t_{1-\alpha/2}$ for f' degrees of freedom in Table A-4, where f' is the integer nearest to f; denote this value by $t'_{1-\alpha/2}$.

(6) Compute

$$u = t'_{1-\alpha/2} \sqrt{V_A + V_B}$$

(7) If $|\bar{X}_A - \bar{X}_B| > u$, decide that A and B differ with regard to their average performance; otherwise, decide that there is no reason to believe A and B differ in average performance.

Example

(1) Let $\alpha = .05$

(2)
$$\bar{X}_A = 3166.0$$
$$s_A^2 = 6328.67$$
$$n_A = 4$$
$$\bar{X}_B = 2240.4$$
$$s_B^2 = 221{,}661.3$$
$$n_B = 9$$

(3)
$$V_A = \frac{6328.67}{4}$$
$$= 1582.17$$

$$V_B = \frac{221{,}661.3}{9}$$
$$= 24629.03$$

(4)
$$f = \frac{(26211.20)^2}{500652.4 + 60658911.9} - 2$$
$$= \frac{687027005}{61159564} - 2$$
$$= 11.233 - 2$$
$$= 9.233$$

(5)
$$f' = 9$$
$$t'_{.975} = 2.262$$

(6)
$$u = 2.262 \sqrt{26211.20}$$
$$= 2.262 (161.9)$$
$$= 366.2$$

(7) $|\bar{X}_A - \bar{X}_B| = 925.6$, which is larger than u. Conclude that A and B differ with regard to average performance.

---

* See footnote on page 3-28.

Procedure*

(8) If m_A, m_B are the true average performances of A and B (unknown of course), then it is worth noting that the interval $(\bar{X}_A - \bar{X}_B) \pm u$ is approximately a $100(1-\alpha)\%$ confidence interval estimate of $m_A - m_B$.

Example

(8) The interval 925.6 ± 366.2, i.e., the interval from 559.4 psi to 1291.8 psi is a 95% confidence interval for the true difference between the averages of the two methods.

Discussion.

To gain some understanding of the nature, properties, and limitations of this approximate procedure, note first that V_A and V_B are unbiased estimates of the true variances σ_A^2/n_A and σ_B^2/n_B of the means $\bar{X}_A$ and $\bar{X}_B$, respectively. Consequently, $V_A + V_B$ is an unbiased estimate of the true variance of the difference $\bar{X}_A - \bar{X}_B$, provided only that $\bar{X}_A$ and $\bar{X}_B$ are the means of *independent* random samples of n_A and n_B observations from populations A and B, respectively. Note next that the effective number of degrees of freedom f, defined by the expression in step (4), also can be expressed in the form

$$\frac{1}{f+2} = \frac{c^2}{f_A+2} + \frac{(1-c)^2}{f_B+2}$$

where

$$f_A = n_A - 1 \quad \text{and} \quad f_B = n_B - 1$$

are the degrees of freedom associated with the variance estimates V_A and V_B, respectively, and,

$$c = \frac{V_A}{V_A + V_B} \quad \text{and} \quad 1 - c = \frac{V_B}{V_A + V_B}$$

are the fractions of the estimated variance of the difference $\bar{X}_A - \bar{X}_B$ that are associated with $\bar{X}_A$ and $\bar{X}_B$, respectively. From this expression for f, it is evident that f can never be less than the smaller of f_A $(= n_A - 1)$ and f_B $(= n_B - 1)$, and f cannot be larger than

$$(f_A + 2) + (f_B + 2) - 2 = n_A + n_B.$$

When V_A is so large in comparison to V_B that V_B is negligible, then $c \simeq 1$ and $f \simeq f_A$, which is intuitively reasonable—the f_B degrees of freedom upon which V_B is based are not making a useful contribution to the estimate of the variance of the difference $\bar{X}_A - \bar{X}_B$. Similarly, when V_B dominates the situation, then $c \simeq 0$ and $f \simeq f_B$. In intermediate situations where neither V_A nor V_B can be neglected, both the f_A and the f_B degrees of freedom make useful contributions, and the effective number of degrees of freedom f expresses the *sum* of their joint contributions. Thus, in our illustrative example, $f_A = 3$ and $f_B = 8$, but $f = 9^+$. Both samples make their maximum contributions, that is, f achieves its maximum of $n_A + n_B$, only when $V_A/V_B = (n_A + 1)/(n_B + 1)$, i.e., when $s_A^2/s_B^2 = n_A(n_A + 1)/n_B(n_B + 1)$.

---

* The test procedure given here is an approximation, i.e., the stated significance level is only approximately achieved. The approximation is good provided n_A and n_B are not too small. A more accurate procedure is given in *Biometrika Tables for Statisticians*,[1] which (in the notation of the present procedure) provides 10% and 2% significance levels of $|v| = |(\bar{X}_A - \bar{X}_B) - (m_A - m_B)|/\sqrt{V_A + V_B}$ for $n_A \geq 6$, $n_B \geq 6$, and $0 \leq V_A/(V_A + V_B) \leq 1$. 5% and 1% significance levels of $|v|$ for $n_A \geq 8$ and $n_B \geq 8$ and the same range of $V_A/(V_A + V_B)$ are given by Trickett, Welch, and James.[2] (When using either of the tables (1) or (2), it should be noticed that our "α" corresponds to their "2α".)

The appropriate modification when the value of the ratio of the variances $\theta = \sigma_A^2/\sigma_B^2$ is known, but not their respective values, is indicated at the end of the Discussion that follows this procedure.

When samples of equal size ($n_A = n_B = n$) are involved, the present approximate procedure for Case 2 (σ_A and σ_B both unknown and presumably *unequal*) in Paragraph 3-3.1.2, and the exact procedure for Case 1 (σ_A and σ_B presumably *equal*, but their common value unknown) given in Paragraph 3-3.1.1 are the same in all respects *except* for the value of $t_{1-\alpha/2}$ to be used. In the exact procedure for Case 1, the value of $t_{1-\alpha/2}$ to be used when $n_A = n_B = n$ is the $100(1 - \alpha/2)$ percentile of the t-distribution for $\nu = 2(n - 1)$ degrees of freedom, and is completely determined by the choice of significance level α and the common sample size n. In contrast, the value of $t_{1-\alpha/2}$ to be used in the approximate procedure for Case 2 when $n_A = n_B = n$ is the $100(1 - \alpha/2)$ percentile for the integral number of degrees of freedom f' nearest to the effective degrees of freedom

$$f = (n + 1) \frac{(s_A^2 + s_B^2)^2}{s_A^4 + s_B^4} - 2,$$

and thus depends not only on the choice of significance level α and common sample size n, but also on the ratio s_A^2/s_B^2 of the sample estimates of σ_A^2 and σ_B^2. Furthermore, since f can vary from $(n - 1)$ to $2n$, and equals $2n$ only when $s_A^2 = s_B^2$, it is clear that the two procedures may lead to different results when $\sigma_A \simeq \sigma_B$. Consequently, *when samples of equal size ($n_A = n_B = n$) are involved, the procedure for Case 1 of Paragraph 3-3.1.1 should be used even when it cannot be assumed that $\sigma_A \simeq \sigma_B$.* If in fact $\sigma_A = \sigma_B$, then the effective significance level α' will be identically equal to the intended significance level α, and the test will have maximum sensitivity with respect to any real difference between the population means m_A and m_B. If, on the other hand, $\sigma_A \neq \sigma_B$, then the effective significance level α' will differ from the significance level α intended, but only slightly, as shown by curve (A) in Figure 3-9; and the test will tend to have greater sensitivity with respect to any real difference between m_A and m_B than would be the case if the procedure of the present section were used.

In contrast, *when the samples are of unequal size ($n_A \neq n_B$), the procedure of the present section should always be used unless it is known for certain that $\sigma_A = \sigma_B$.* Otherwise, the effective significance level α' may differ considerably from the significance level α intended, even when $\sigma_A \simeq \sigma_B$ as shown by curve (B) in Figure 3-9.

When the smaller sample comes from the more variable population, the effective number of degrees of freedom f to be used with the procedure of the present section is likely to be much smaller than $n_A + n_B - 2$, the degrees of freedom to be used with the procedure of Paragraph 3-3.1.1. Nevertheless, the small advantage of greater sensitivity to real differences between m_A and m_B that the procedure of Paragraph 3-3.1.1 provides when $\sigma_A = \sigma_B$ is rapidly offset, as the inequality of σ_A and σ_B increases, by the much firmer control of the effective significance level by the procedure of the present section, except when f is very small (say < 6).

Finally, it should be remarked that the effective number of degrees of freedom appropriate to the procedure of the present section is given more accurately by

$$f^* = \frac{(v_A + v_B)^2}{\dfrac{v_A^2}{n_A - 1} + \dfrac{v_B^2}{n_B - 1}} = \frac{(n_B\theta + n_A)^2}{\dfrac{n_B^2\theta^2}{n_A - 1} + \dfrac{n_A^2}{n_B^2}}$$

where

$$v_A = \frac{\sigma_A^2}{n_A} \quad \text{and} \quad v_B = \frac{\sigma_B^2}{n_B}$$

are the true variances of $\bar{X}_A$ and $\bar{X}_B$, respectively, and $\theta = \sigma_A^2/\sigma_B^2$.

3-29

It easily is shown that f^* never is less than the smaller of $n_A - 1$ and $n_B - 1$, and never exceeds $n_A + n_B - 2$. If we know the values of σ_A^2 and σ_B^2, then we could evaluate f^*; but under these circumstances we should use the procedure of Paragraph 3-3.1.3, not the present approximate procedure. If we do not know the values of σ_A^2 and σ_B^2, but do know their ratio θ, then the exact procedure (Case 3) of Paragraph 3-3.1.3 cannot be applied, but f^* can be evaluated. Under these circumstances, the approximate procedure of the present section should be followed, with f replaced by f^*. When we do not know the values of σ_A^2 and σ_B^2, nor even their ratio θ, then we must rely on the best available sample estimate of f^*; namely, f defined in Step (4) of the present procedure.

3-3.1.3 (Case 3)—Variability in Performance of Each of A and B is Known from Previous Experience, and the Standard Deviations are σ_A and σ_B, respectively.

Data Sample 3-3.1.3—Latent Heat of Fusion of Ice

The observational data are those of Data Sample 3-3.1.1 and, in addition, it now is assumed to be known that $\sigma_A = 0.024$ and $\sigma_B = 0.033$.

[Two-sided Normal Test]

Procedure	Example
(1) Choose α, the level of significance of the test.	(1) Let $\alpha = .05$
(2) Look up $z_{1-\alpha/2}$ in Table A-2.	(2) $z_{.975} = 1.960$
(3) Compute: $\bar{X}_A$ and $\bar{X}_B$, the means of the n_A and n_B measurements from A and B.	(3) $\bar{X}_A = 80.02$ $\sigma_A^2 = 0.000576$ $n_A = 13$ $\bar{X}_B = 79.98$ $\sigma_B^2 = 0.001089$ $n_B = 8$

(4) Compute

$$u = z_{1-\alpha/2} \sqrt{\frac{\sigma_A^2}{n_A} + \frac{\sigma_B^2}{n_B}}$$

(4)

$$u = 1.960 \sqrt{\frac{0.000576}{13} + \frac{0.001089}{8}}$$
$$= 1.960 \,(.0134)$$
$$= 0.026$$

(5) If $|\bar{X}_A - \bar{X}_B| > u$, decide that A and B differ with regard to their average performance; otherwise, decide that there is no reason to believe that A and B differ in average performance.

(5) $|\bar{X}_A - \bar{X}_B| = .04$, which is larger than u. Conclude that methods A and B differ with regard to their averages.

(6) Let m_A, m_B be the true average performances of A and B (unknown of course). It is worth noting that the interval $(\bar{X}_A - \bar{X}_B) \pm u$ is a $100\,(1 - \alpha)\,\%$ confidence interval estimate of $(m_A - m_B)$.

(6) The interval $.04 \pm .026$ i.e., the interval from .014 to .066 is a 95% confidence interval for the true difference between the averages of the methods.

Operating Characteristics of the Test. Figures 3-3 and 3-4 give the operating characteristic (OC) curves of the above test for $\alpha = .05$ and $\alpha = .01$, respectively, for various values of n.

If $n_A = n_B = n$, and $(m_A - m_B)$ is the true difference between the two averages, then putting

$$d = \frac{|m_A - m_B|}{\sqrt{\sigma_A^2 + \sigma_B^2}},$$

we can read β, the probability of failing to detect a difference of size $\pm (m_A - m_B)$.

If $n_A = cn_B$, we can put $d = \frac{|m_A - m_B|}{\sqrt{\sigma_A^2 + c\sigma_B^2}}$ and, using $n = n_A$, we can read β, the probability of

failing to detect a difference of size $\pm (m_A - m_B)$.

Selection of Sample Size. We choose

α, the significance level of the test
β, the probability of failing to detect a difference of size $(m_A - m_B)$.

If we wish $n_A = n_B = n$, we compute

$$d = \frac{|m_A - m_B|}{\sqrt{\sigma_A^2 + \sigma_B^2}}$$

and we may use Table A-8 directly to obtain the required sample size n.

If we wish to have n_A and n_B such that $n_A = cn_B$, then we may compute

$$d = \frac{|m_A - m_B|}{\sigma_A^2 + c\sigma_B^2}$$

and use Table A-8 to obtain $n = n_A$.

3-3.1.4   (Case 4)—The Observations are Paired.

Often, an experiment is, or can be, designed so that the observations are taken in pairs. The two units of a pair are chosen in advance so as to be as nearly alike as possible in all respects other than the characteristic to be measured, and then one member of each pair is assigned at random to treatment A, and the other to treatment B. For instance, the experimenter may wish to compare the effects of two different treatments on a particular type of device, material, or process. The word "treatments" here is to be understood in a broad sense: the two "treatments" may be different operators; different environmental conditions to which a material may be exposed, or merely two different methods of measuring one of its properties; two different laboratories in an interlaboratory test of a particular process of measurement or manufacture. Since the comparison of the two treatments is made *within* pairs, two advantages result from such pairing. First, the effect of extraneous variation is reduced and there is consequent increase in the precision of the comparison, and in its sensitivity to real differences between the treatments with respect to the measured characteristic. Second, the test may be carried out under a wide range of conditions representative of actual use without sacrifice of sensitivity and precision, thereby assuring wider applicability of any conclusions reached.

Data Sample 3-3.1.4—Capacity of Batteries

The data below are measurements of the capacity (in ampere hours) of paired batteries, one from each of two different manufacturers:

A	B	$X_d = X_A - X_B$
146	141	5
141	143	−2
135	139	−4
142	139	3
140	140	0
143	141	2
138	138	0
137	140	−3
142	142	0
136	138	−2

Procedure	Example
(1) Choose α, the significance level of the test.	(1) Let $\alpha = .05$
(2) Compute: $\bar{X}_d$ and s_d for the n differences, X_d. (Each X_d represents an observation on A minus the paired observation on B).	(2) $\bar{X}_d = -0.1$ $\quad s_d = 2.807$
(3) Look up $t_{1-\alpha/2}$ for $n-1$ degrees of freedom in Table A-4.	(3) $t_{.975}$ (9 d.f.) $= 2.262$
(4) Compute $$u = t_{1-\alpha/2}\frac{s_d}{\sqrt{n}}$$	(4) $$u = 2.262\left(\frac{2.807}{3.162}\right)$$ $$= 2.008$$
(5) If $|\bar{X}_d| > u$, decide that the averages differ; otherwise, that there is no reason to believe they differ.	(5) $|\bar{X}_d| = 0.1$, which is less than u. Conclude that batteries of the two manufacturers do not differ in average capacity.
(6) *Note:* The interval $\bar{X}_d \pm u$ is a $100(1-\alpha)\%$ confidence interval estimate of the average difference (A minus B).	(6) The interval -0.1 ± 2.0, i.e., the interval -2.1 to $+1.9$ is a 95% confidence interval estimate of the average difference in capacity between the batteries of the two manufacturers.

Operating Characteristics of the Test. Figures 3-1 and 3-2 give the operating characteristic (OC) curves of the above test for $\alpha = .05$ and $\alpha = .01$, respectively, for various values of n, the number of pairs involved.

Choose:

$\delta = |m_A - m_B|$, the true absolute difference between the averages (unknown, of course)

Some value of $\sigma \ (= \sigma_d)$, the true standard deviation of a signed difference X_d.
(We may use an estimate from previous data. If OC curve is consulted after the experiment, we may use the estimate from the experiment.)

Compute

$$d = \frac{\delta}{\sigma}.$$

We then can read from the OC curve for a given significance level α and sample size n, a value of of $\beta(\delta)$. The $\beta(\delta)$ read from the curve is $\beta(\delta \,|\, \sigma, \, \alpha, \, n)$, i.e., $\beta(\delta, \, given \, \sigma, \, \alpha, \, n)$—the probability of failing to detect a difference of $\pm (m_A - m_B)$ when it exists, if the given test is carried out with n pairs, at the α-level of significance, *and* the standard deviation of signed differences X_d actually *is* σ.

If we use too large a value for σ, the effect is to underestimate d, and consequently to overestimate $\beta(\delta)$, the probability of not detecting a difference of δ when it exists. Conversely, if we choose too small a value of σ, then we shall overestimate d and underestimate $\beta(\delta)$. The true value of $\beta(\delta)$ is determined, of course, by the sample size n and the significance level α employed, *and* the true value of $\sigma \ (= \sigma_d)$.

Selection of Number of Pairs n required. If we choose

$\delta = |m_A - m_B|$, the absolute value of the average difference that we desire to detect
α, the significance level of the test
β, the probability of failing to detect a difference of δ

and compute

$$d = \frac{|m_A - m_B|}{\sigma}$$

where σ is the standard deviation of the population of signed differences X_d for the type of pairs concerned, then we may use Table A-8 to obtain a good approximation to the required number of pairs n. If we take $\alpha = .01$, then we must add 4 to the value obtained from the table. If we take $\alpha = .05$, then we must add 2 to the table value. In order to compute d, we must choose a value for σ.

If, when planning the test, we overestimate σ, the consequences are two-fold: first, we overestimate the number of pairs required, and thus unnecessarily increase the cost of the test; but, by employing a sample size that is larger than necessary, the actual value of $\beta(\delta)$ will be somewhat less than we intended, which will be all to the good. On the other hand, if we underestimate σ, we shall underestimate the number of pairs actually required, and by using too small a sample size, $\beta(\delta)$ will be somewhat larger than we intended, and our chances of detecting real differences when they exist will be correspondingly lessened.

Finally, it should be noted, that inasmuch as the test criterion $u = t_{1-\alpha/2} \dfrac{s_d}{\sqrt{n}}$ does not depend on σ, an error in estimating σ when planning the test will not alter the level of significance, which will be precisely equal to the value of α desired, *provided that* $t_{1-\alpha/2}$ is taken equal to the $100 \, (1 - \alpha/2)$ percentile of the t-distribution for $n - 1$ degrees of freedom, where n is the *number of pairs actually employed.*

3-3.2　DOES THE AVERAGE OF PRODUCT A EXCEED THE AVERAGE OF PRODUCT B?

3-3.2.1　(Case 1)—Variability of A and B is Unknown, but can be Assumed to be Equal.

Data Sample 3-3.2.1—Surface Hardness of Steel Plates

A study was made of the effect of two grinding conditions on the surface hardness of steel plates used for intaglio printing. Condition A represents surfaces "as ground" and Condition B represents surfaces after light polishing with emery paper. The observations are hardness indentation numbers.

Condition A	Condition B
187	157
157	152
152	148
164	158
159	161
164	
172	

[One-sided t-test]

Procedure	Example

(1)　Choose α, the significance level of the test.

(1)　Let $\alpha = .05$

(2)　Look up $t_{1-\alpha}$ for $\nu = n_A + n_B - 2$ degrees of freedom in Table A-4.

(2)　$n_A = 7$
$n_B = 5$
$\nu = 10$
$t_{.95}$ for 10 d.f. = 1.812

(3)　Compute: $\bar{X}_A$ and s_A^2, $\bar{X}_B$ and s_B^2, from the n_A and n_B measurements from products A and B, respectively.

(3)　$\bar{X}_A = 165$
$s_A^2 = 134$
$\bar{X}_B = 155.2$
$s_B^2 = 26.7$

(4)　Compute
$$s_P = \sqrt{\frac{(n_A - 1)\, s_A^2 + (n_B - 1)\, s_B^2}{n_A + n_B - 2}}$$

(4)
$$s_P = \sqrt{\frac{6\,(134) + 4\,(26.7)}{10}}$$
$$= \sqrt{91.08}$$
$$= 9.544$$

(5)　Compute
$$u = t_{1-\alpha}\, s_P \sqrt{\frac{n_A + n_B}{n_A\, n_B}}$$

(5)
$$u = (1.812)\,(9.544)\sqrt{\frac{12}{35}}$$
$$= 17.294\,(.5855)$$
$$= 10.1$$

(6)　If $(\bar{X}_A - \bar{X}_B) > u$, decide that the average of A exceeds the average of B; otherwise, decide there is no reason to believe that the average of A exceeds the average of B.

(6)　$(\bar{X}_A - \bar{X}_B) = 9.8$, which is not larger than u. There is no reason to believe that the average hardness for Condition A exceeds the average hardness for Condition B.

(7)　Let m_A and m_B be the true averages of A and B. Note that the interval from $\{(\bar{X}_A - \bar{X}_B) - u\}$ to ∞ is a $1 - \alpha$ one-sided confidence interval estimate of the true difference $(m_A - m_B)$.

(7)　$(\bar{X}_A - \bar{X}_B) - u = 9.8 - 10.1 = -0.3$. The interval from -0.3 to ∞ is a 95% one-sided confidence interval estimate of the true difference between averages.

3-34

Operating Characteristics of the Test. Figures 3-5 and 3-6 give the operating characteristic (OC) curves of the above test for $\alpha = .05$ and $\alpha = .01$, respectively, for various values of $n = n_A + n_B - 1$.

Choose:

> $\delta = (m_A - m_B)$, the true difference between the averages
>
> Some value of σ ($= \sigma_A = \sigma_B$), the common standard deviation
> (We may use an estimate from previous data; lacking such an estimate, see Paragraph 2-2.4. If OC curve is consulted after the experiment, we may use the estimate from the experiment).

Compute

$$d^* = \frac{(m_A - m_B)}{\sigma} \frac{1}{\sqrt{n_A + n_B - 1}} \sqrt{\frac{n_A n_B}{n_A + n_B}} \ .$$

We then can read a value of $\beta(\delta)$ from the OC curve for a given significance level and effective sample size n. The $\beta(\delta)$ read from the curve is $\beta(\delta \,|\, \sigma, \alpha, n_A, n_B)$ i.e., $\beta(\delta$, given σ, α, n_A, and n_B) the probability of failing to detect a real difference between the two population means of magnitude $\delta = + (m_A - m_B)$ when the test is carried out with samples of sizes n_A and n_B, respectively, at the α-level of significance, *and* the two population standard deviations actually *are* both equal to σ.

If we use too large a value for σ, the effect is to make us underestimate d^*, and consequently to overestimate $\beta(\delta)$. Conversely, if we choose too small a value of σ, then we shall overestimate d^* and underestimate $\beta(\delta)$. The true value of $\beta(\delta)$ is determined, of course, by the sample sizes (n_A and n_B) and significance level α actually employed, *and* the true value of σ ($= \sigma_A = \sigma_B$).

Since the test criterion u does not depend on the value of σ ($= \sigma_A = \sigma_B$), an error in estimating σ will not alter the significance level of the test, which will be precisely equal to the value of α desired, *provided that* the value of $t_{1-\alpha}$ is taken equal to the $100(1 - \alpha)$ percentile of the t-distribution for $n_A + n_B - 2$ degrees of freedom, where n_A and n_B are the sample sizes actually employed, *and* it actually *is* true that $\sigma_A = \sigma_B$.

If $\sigma_A \neq \sigma_B$, then, whatever may be the ratio σ_A/σ_B, the effective significance level α' will not differ seriously from the intended value α, *provided that* $n_A = n_B$, except possibly when both are as small as two. If, on the other hand, unequal sample sizes are used, and $\sigma_A \neq \sigma_B$, then the effective level of significance α' can differ considerably from the intended value α, as shown in Figure 3-9.

Selection of Sample Size n. If we choose

> $\delta = (m_A - m_B)$, the value of the average difference that we desire to detect
>
> α, the significance level of the test
>
> β, the probability of failing to detect a difference of size δ

and compute

$$d = \frac{(m_A - m_B)}{\sqrt{2\sigma^2}}, \text{ where } \sigma = \sigma_A = \sigma_B \ ,$$

then we may use Table A-9 to obtain a good approximation to the required sample size $n \,(= n_A = n_B)$. If we take $\alpha = .01$, then we must add 2 to the table value. If we take $\alpha = .05$, then we must add 1 to the table value.

In order to compute d, we must choose a value for σ ($= \sigma_A = \sigma_B$). (See Paragraph 2-2.4 if no other information is available.) If we overestimate σ, the consequences are two-fold: first, we overestimate the sample size $n \,(= n_A = n_B)$ required, and thus unnecessarily increase the cost of the test; but, by employing a sample size that is larger than necessary, the actual value of $\beta(\delta)$ will be somewhat less than we intended, which will be all to the good. On the other hand, if we underestimate σ, we shall underestimate the sample size actually required, and by using too small a sample size, $\beta(\delta)$ will be somewhat larger than we intended, and our chances of detecting real differences when they exist will be correspondingly lessened. These effects of overestimating or underestimating σ ($= \sigma_A = \sigma_B$) will be similar in magnitude to those considered and illustrated in Paragraph 3-2.2.1 for the case of comparing the mean m of a new material, product, or process, with a standard value m_0.

As explained in the preceding discussion of the Operating Characteristics of the Test, an error in estimating σ ($= \sigma_A = \sigma_B$) will have no effect on the significance level of the test, provided that the value of $t_{1-\alpha}$ is taken equal to the $100 (1 - \alpha)$ percentile of the t-distribution for $n_A + n_B - 2$ degrees of freedom, where n_A and n_B are the sample sizes actually employed; and if $\sigma_A \neq \sigma_B$, the effect will not be serious provided that the sample sizes *are* taken equal.

3-3.2.2 (Case 2)—Variability of A and B is Unknown, Cannot Be Assumed Equal.

Consider the data of Data Sample 3-3.1.2. Suppose that (from a consideration of the methods, and *not* after looking at the results) the question to be asked was whether the average for Method A *exceeded* the average for Method B.

Procedure*	Example
(1) Choose α, the significance level of the test.	(1) Let $\alpha = .05$
(2) Compute: $\bar{X}_A$ and s_A^2, $\bar{X}_B$ and s_B^2, from the n_A and n_B measurements from A and B.	(2) $\bar{X}_A = 3166.0$ $s_A^2 = 6328.67$ $n_A = 4$ $\bar{X}_B = 2240.4$ $s_B^2 = 221{,}661.3$ $n_B = 9$

(3) Compute:

$$V_A = \frac{s_A^2}{n_A}$$

and

$$V_B = \frac{s_B^2}{n_B},$$

the estimated variances of $\bar{X}_A$ and $\bar{X}_B$, respectively.

(3)

$$V_A = \frac{6328.67}{4}$$
$$= 1582.17$$
$$V_B = \frac{221{,}661.3}{9}$$
$$= 24629.03$$

(4) Compute the "effective number of degrees of freedom"

$$f = \frac{(V_A + V_B)^2}{\dfrac{V_A^2}{n_A + 1} + \dfrac{V_B^2}{n_B + 1}} - 2$$

(4)

$$f = \frac{(26211.20)^2}{500652.4 + 60658911.9} - 2$$
$$= 11.233 - 2$$
$$= 9.233$$

(5) Look up $t_{1-\alpha}$ for f' degrees of freedom in Table A-4, where f' is the integer nearest to f; denote this value by $t'_{1-\alpha}$.

(5) $f' = 9$
$t'_{.95} = 1.833$

(6) Compute
$$u = t'_{1-\alpha} \sqrt{V_A + V_B}$$

(6)

$$u = 1.833 \sqrt{26211.20}$$
$$= 1.833 \ (161.90)$$
$$= 296.76$$

* See footnote on page 3-37.

Procedure*	Example
(7) If $(\bar{X}_A - \bar{X}_B) > u$, decide that the average of A exceeds the average of B; otherwise, decide that there is no reason to believe that the average of A exceeds the average of B.	(7) $\bar{X}_A - \bar{X}_B = 925.6$, which is larger than u. Conclude that the average for Method A exceeds the average for Method B.
(8) Let m_A and m_B be the true averages of A and B. Note that the interval from $\{(\bar{X}_A - \bar{X}_B) - u\}$ to ∞ is approximately a one-sided $100(1 - \alpha)\%$ confidence interval estimate of the true difference $(m_A - m_B)$.	(8) $(\bar{X}_A - \bar{X}_B) - u = 925.6 - 296.76 = 628.8$. The interval from 628.8 to ∞ is approximately a one-sided 95% confidence interval estimate of the true difference between the averages for the methods.

3-3.2.3   (Case 3)—Variability in Performance of Each of A and B is Known from Previous Experience and the Standard Deviations are σ_A and σ_B, Respectively.

Data Sample 3-3.2.3

The observational data are those of Data Sample 3-3.2.1 on surface hardness of steel plates. In addition, it now is assumed that the variability for the two conditions was known from previous experience to be $\sigma_A = 10.25$ and $\sigma_B = 5.00$.

[One-sided Normal Test]

Procedure	Example
(1) Choose α, the significance level of the test.	(1) Let $\alpha = .05$
(2) Look up $z_{1-\alpha}$ in Table A-2.	(2) $z_{1-\alpha} = 1.645$
(3) Compute: $\bar{X}_A$ and $\bar{X}_B$, the means of the n_A and n_B measurements from A and B.	(3) $\bar{X}_A = 165$ $\sigma_A^2 = 105$ $n_A = 7$ $\bar{X}_B = 155.2$ $\sigma_B^2 = 25$ $n_B = 5$
(4) Compute $$u = z_{1-\alpha}\sqrt{\frac{\sigma_A^2}{n_A} + \frac{\sigma_B^2}{n_B}}$$	(4) $u = 1.645\sqrt{15 + 5}$ $= 1.645\,(4.472)$ $= 7.4$
(5) If $(\bar{X}_A - \bar{X}_B) > u$, decide that the average of A exceeds the average of B; otherwise, decide that there is no reason to believe that the average of A exceeds the average of B.	(5) $(\bar{X}_A - \bar{X}_B) = 9.8$, which is larger than u. Conclude that the average hardness for Condition A exceeds the average hardness for Condition B.
(6) Let m_A and m_B be the true averages of A and B. Note that the interval from $\{(\bar{X}_A - \bar{X}_B) - u\}$ to ∞ is a $1 - \alpha$ one-sided confidence interval estimate of the true difference $(m_A - m_B)$.	(6) The interval from 2.4 to ∞ is a 95% one-sided confidence interval estimate of the true difference between averages.

---

* See footnotes, and also the discussion of the properties and limitations of this type of procedure, in Paragraph 3-3.1.2.

Operating Characteristics of the Test. Figures 3-7 and 3-8 give the operating characteristic (OC) curves of the above test for $\alpha = .05$ and $\alpha = .01$, respectively, for various values of n.

If $n_A = n_B = n$ and $(m_A - m_B)$ is the true positive difference between the averages, then putting

$$d = \frac{(m_A - m_B)}{\sqrt{\sigma_A^2 + \sigma_B^2}}$$

we can read β, the probability of failing to detect a difference of size $(m_A - m_B)$.

If $n_A = cn_B$, we can put

$$d = \frac{(m_A - m_B)}{\sqrt{\sigma_A^2 + c\sigma_B^2}}$$

and again read β, the probability of failing to detect a difference of size $(m_A - m_B)$.

Selection of Sample Size. We choose

    α, the significance level of the test
    β, the probability of failing to detect a difference of size $(m_A - m_B)$.

If we wish $n_A = n_B = n$, we compute

$$d = \frac{(m_A - m_B)}{\sqrt{\sigma_A^2 + \sigma_B^2}}$$

and we may use Table A-9 directly to obtain the required sample size n.

If we wish to have n_A and n_B such that $n_A = cn_B$, then we may compute

$$d = \frac{(m_A - m_B)}{\sqrt{\sigma_A^2 + c\sigma_B^2}}$$

and use Table A-9 to obtain $n = n_A$.

3-3.2.4   (Case 4)—The Observations are Paired.

Often, an experiment is, or can be, designed so that the observations are taken in pairs. The two units of a pair are chosen in advance so as to be as nearly alike as possible in all respects other than the characteristic to be measured, and then one member of each pair is assigned at random to Treatment A, and the other to Treatment B. For a discussion of the advantage of this approach, see Paragraph 3-3.1.4.

Data Sample 3-3.2.4—Molecular Weight of Dextrons

During World War II bacterial polysaccharides (dextrons) were considered and investigated for use as blood plasma extenders. Sixteen samples of hydrolyzed dextrons were supplied by various manufacturers in order to assess two chemical methods for determining the average molecular weight of dextrons.

Method A	Method B	$X_d = X_A - X_B$
62,700	56,400	6,300
29,100	27,500	1,600
44,400	42,200	2,200
47,800	46,800	1,000
36,300	33,300	3,000
40,000	37,100	2,900
43,400	37,300	6,100
35,800	36,200	− 400

Method A	Method B	$X_d = X_A - X_B$
33,900	35,200	−1,300
44,200	38,000	6,200
34,300	32,200	2,100
31,300	27,300	4,000
38,400	36,100	2,300
47,100	43,100	4,000
42,100	38,400	3,700
42,200	39,900	2,300

Procedure

(1) Choose α, the significance level of the test.

(2) Compute the $\bar{X}_d$ and s_d for the n differences, X_d. Each X_d represents an observation on A minus the paired observation on B.

(3) Look up $t_{1-\alpha}$ for $n - 1$ degrees of freedom in Table A-4.

(4) Compute

$$u = t_{1-\alpha} \frac{s_d}{\sqrt{n}}$$

(5) If $\bar{X}_d > u$, decide that the average of A exceeds that of B; otherwise, there is no reason to believe the average of A exceeds that of B.

(6) Note that the open interval from $\bar{X}_d - u$ to $+ \infty$ is a one-sided $100 (1 - \alpha) \%$ confidence interval for the true difference $(m_A - m_B)$.

Example

(1) Let $\alpha = .05$

(2) $\bar{X}_d = 2875$
$s_d = 2182.2$
$n = 16$

(3) $t_{.95}$ for 15 d.f. $= 1.753$

(4)

$$u = 1.753 \left(\frac{2182.2}{4} \right)$$
$$= 1.753 (545.6)$$
$$= 956.4$$

(5) $\bar{X}_d = 2875$, which is larger than u. Conclude that the average for Method A exceeds the average for Method B.

(6) $\bar{X}_d - u = (2875 - 956) = 1919$. The interval from 1919 to $+ \infty$ is a one-sided 95% confidence interval for the true difference between the averages of the two methods.

Operating Characteristics of the Test. Figures 3-5 and 3-6 give the operating characteristic (OC) curves of the test for $\alpha = .05$ and $\alpha = .01$, respectively, for various values of n, the number of pairs involved.

Choose:

$\delta = (m_A - m_B)$, the true difference between the averages (unknown, of course)

Some value of $\sigma (= \sigma_d)$, the true standard deviation of a signed difference X_d.
    (We may use an estimate from previous data. If OC curve is
    consulted after the experiment, we may use the estimate from
    the experiment.)

Compute

$$d = \frac{\delta}{\sigma} .$$

We can then read from the OC curve for a given significance level α and number of pairs n, a value of $\beta(\delta)$. The $\beta(\delta)$ read from the curve is $\beta(\delta \,|\, \sigma, \alpha, n)$, i.e., $\beta(\delta, \text{ given } \sigma, \alpha, n)$—the probability of failing to detect a difference $(m_A - m_B)$ of magnitude $+\delta$ when the given test is carried out with n pairs, at the α-level of significance, and the population standard deviation of the differences X_d actually *is* σ.

If we use too large a value for σ, the effect is to underestimate d, and consequently to overestimate $\beta(\delta)$, the probability of not detecting a difference $(m_A - m_B)$ of size $+\delta$ when it exists. Conversely, if we choose too small a value of σ, then we shall overestimate d and underestimate $\beta(\delta)$. The true value of $\beta(\delta)$ is determined, of course, by the actual number of pairs n, the significance level α employed, *and* the true value of $\sigma \,(= \sigma_d)$.

Selection of Number of Pairs (n). If we choose

$\delta = (m_A - m_B)$, the value of the (positive) average difference that we desire to detect
         α, the significance level of the test
         β, the probability of failing to detect a difference of $+\delta$

and compute

$$d = \frac{(m_A - m_B)}{\sigma}$$

where $\sigma \,(= \sigma_d)$ is the standard deviation of the population of signed differences X_d of the type concerned, then we may use Table A-9 to obtain a good approximation to the required number of pairs n. If we take $\alpha = .01$, then we must add 3 to the table value. If we take $\alpha = .05$, then we must add 2 to the table value. (In order to compute d, we must choose a value for σ.)

If, when planning the test, we overestimate σ, the consequences are two-fold: first, we overestimate the number of pairs required, and thus unnecessarily increase the cost of the test; but, by employing a sample size that is larger than necessary, the actual value of $\beta(\delta)$ will be somewhat less than we intended, which will be all to the good. On the other hand, if we underestimate σ, we shall underestimate the number of pairs actually required, and by using too small a sample size, $\beta(\delta)$ will be somewhat larger than we intended, and our chances of detecting real differences when they exist will be correspondingly lessened.

Finally, it should be noted, that inasmuch as the test criterion $u = t_{1-\alpha} \dfrac{s_d}{\sqrt{n}}$ does not depend on σ, an error in estimating σ when planning the test will not alter the level of significance, which will be precisely equal to the value of α desired, *provided* that $t_{1-\alpha}$ is taken equal to the $100\,(1 - \alpha)$ percentile of the t-distribution for $n - 1$ degrees of freedom, where n is the *number of pairs actually employed*.

3-4   COMPARING THE AVERAGES OF SEVERAL PRODUCTS

Do the averages of t products $1, 2, \ldots, t$ differ? We shall assume that $n_1 = n_2 = \ldots = n_t = n$. If the n's are in fact not all equal, but differ only slightly, then in the following procedure we may replace n by the harmonic mean of the n's,

$$n_H = t/(1/n_1 + 1/n_2 + \ldots + 1/n_t)$$

and obtain a satisfactory approximation.

Data Sample 3-4—Breaking-strength of Cement Briquettes

The following data relate to breaking-strength of cement briquettes (in pounds per square inch). The question to be answered is: Does the average breaking-strength differ for the different groups?

	Group				
	1	2	3	4	5
	518	508	554	555	536
	560	574	598	567	492
	538	528	579	550	528
	510	534	538	535	572
	544	538	544	540	506
ΣX_i	2670	2682	2813	2747	2634
n_i	5	5	5	5	5
$\bar{X}_i$	534.0	536.4	562.6	549.4	526.8
ΣX^2	1427404	1440924	1585141	1509839	1391364
$\dfrac{(\Sigma X)^2}{n}$	1425780	1438624.8	1582593.8	1509201.8	1387591.2
$\Sigma X^2 - \dfrac{(\Sigma X)^2}{n}$	1624	2299.2	2547.2	637.2	3772.8
s^2	406	574.8	636.8	159.3	943.2

Excerpted with permission from *Statistical Exercises, Part II, Analysis of Variance and Associated Techniques,* by N. L. Johnson, Copyright, 1957 Department of Statistics, University College, London.

Procedure	**Example**
(1) Choose α, the significance level (the risk of concluding that the averages differ, when in fact all averages are the same).	(1) Let $\alpha = .01$
(2) Compute: $s_1^2 , s_2^2 , \ldots , s_t^2 .$	(2) $\begin{aligned} s_1^2 &= 406.0 \\ s_2^2 &= 574.8 \\ s_3^2 &= 636.8 \\ s_4^2 &= 159.3 \\ s_5^2 &= 943.2 \end{aligned}$
(3) Compute $s_e^2 = \dfrac{1}{t}\,(s_1^2 + s_2^2 + \ldots + s_t^2)$	(3) $s_e^2 = \dfrac{2720.1}{5}$ $= 544.0$

If the n_i are not all equal, the following formula usually is to be preferred:

$$s_e^2 = \frac{(n_1 - 1)\, s_1^2 + (n_2 - 1)\, s_2^2 + \ldots + (n_t - 1)\, s_t^2}{(n_1 + n_2 + \ldots + n_t) - t}$$

$s_e = 23.32$

3-41

Procedure

(4) Look up $q_{1-\alpha}(t, \nu)$ in Table A-10 where
$\nu = (n_1 + n_2 + \ldots + n_t) - t$.

(5) Compute

$$w = \frac{q_{1-\alpha}\, s_e}{\sqrt{n}}$$

(6) If the absolute difference between any two sample means exceeds w, decide that the averages differ; otherwise, decide that there is no reason to believe the averages differ.

Example

(4)
$$\nu = 25 - 5$$
$$= 20$$
$$t = 5$$
$$q_{.99}(5, 20) = 5.29$$

(5)
$$w = \frac{5.29\,(23.32)}{\sqrt{5}}$$
$$= \frac{123.36}{2.236}$$
$$= 55.2$$

(6) The greatest difference between sample means is $562.6 - 526.8 = 35.8$, which is less than w. We, therefore, have no reason to believe that the group averages differ.

Note: It is worth noting that we simultaneously can make confidence interval estimates for each of the $\frac{t(t-1)}{2}$ pairs of differences between product averages, with a confidence of $1 - \alpha$ that *all* of the estimates are correct. The confidence intervals are $(\bar{X}_i - \bar{X}_j) \pm w$, where $\bar{X}_i$, $\bar{X}_j$, are sample means of the ith and jth products.

REFERENCES

1. E. S. Pearson and H. O. Hartley, *Biometrika Tables For Statisticians*, Vol. I, (2d edition), pp. 27, 136-7, Cambridge University Press, 1958.
2. W. H. Trickett, B. L. Welch, and G. S. James, "Further Critical Values for the Two-Means Problem," *Biometrika*, Vol. 43, pp. 203-205, 1956.

CHAPTER 4

COMPARING MATERIALS OR PRODUCTS WITH RESPECT TO VARIABILITY OF PERFORMANCE

4-1 COMPARING A NEW MATERIAL OR PRODUCT WITH A STANDARD WITH RESPECT TO VARIABILITY OF PERFORMANCE

The variability of a standard material, product, or process, as measured by its standard deviation, is known to be σ_0. We consider the following three problems:

(a) Does the variability of the new product *differ* from that of the standard? See Paragraph 4-1.1.

(b) Does the variability of the new product *exceed* that of the standard? See Paragraph 4-1.2.

(c) Is the variability of the new product *less* than that of the standard? See Paragraph 4-1.3.

It is important to decide which of the three problems is appropriate before taking the observations. If this is not done, and the choice of problem is influenced by the observations, both the significance level of the test (i.e., the probability of an Error of the First Kind) and the operating characteristics of the test may differ considerably from their nominal values.

The tests given are exact when:

(a) the observations for an item, product, or process are taken randomly from a single population of possible observations; and,

(b) within the population, the quality characteristic measured is normally distributed.

4-1.1 DOES THE VARIABILITY OF THE NEW PRODUCT DIFFER FROM THAT OF THE STANDARD?

The variability in the performance of a standard material, product, or process, as measured by its standard deviation, is known to be σ_0. We wish to determine whether a given item *differs* in variability of performance from the standard. We wish, from analysis of the data, to make one of the following decisions:

(a) The variability in performance of the new product *differs* from that of the standard.

(b) There is no reason to believe the variability of the new product is different from that of the standard.

Data Sample 4-1.1—Capacity of Batteries

The standard deviation σ_0 of capacity for batteries of a standard type is known to be 1.66 ampere hours. The following capacities (ampere hours) were recorded for 10 batteries of a new type: 146, 141, 135, 142, 140, 143, 138, 137, 142, 136.

We wish to compare the new type of battery with the standard type with regard to variability of capacity. The question to be answered is: Does the new type *differ* from the standard type with respect to variability of capacity (either a decrease or an increase is of interest)?

Procedure	**Example**
(1) Choose α, the level of significance of the test.	(1) Let $\quad \alpha = .05$

(2) Look up B_U and B_L both for $n - 1$ degrees of freedom in Table A-20.

(2) $n - 1 = 9$
B_U for 9 d.f. = 1.746
B_L for 9 d.f. = .6657

(3) Compute s, from the n observations

$$s = \sqrt{\frac{\Sigma X^2 - (\Sigma X)^2/n}{n - 1}}$$

(3)

$$s = \sqrt{\frac{196108 - 196000}{9}}$$

$$= \sqrt{\frac{108}{9}}$$

$$= \sqrt{12}$$

$$= 3.464$$

(4) Compute:

$$s_L = B_L s$$

$$s_U = B_U s$$

(4)

$$s_L = (.6657)(3.464)$$

$$= 2.31$$

$$s_U = (1.746)(3.464)$$

$$= 6.05$$

(5) If σ_0 does not lie between s_L and s_U, decide that the variability in performance of the new product *differs* from that of the standard; otherwise, that there is no reason to believe the new product differs from the standard with regard to variability.

(5) Since $\sigma_0 = 1.66$ does not lie between the limits 2.31 to 6.05, conclude that the variability for the new type *does* differ from the variability for the standard type.

(6) It is worth noting that the interval from s_L to s_U is a $100(1 - \alpha)\%$ confidence interval estimate of σ, the standard deviation of the new product. (See Par. 2-2.3.1).

(6) The interval from 2.31 to 6.05 ampere hours is a 95% confidence interval estimate for the standard deviation of the new type.

Operating Characteristics of the Test. Operating-characteristic (OC) curves for this Neyman-Pearson "unbiased Type A" test of the null hypothesis that $\sigma = \sigma_0$ relative to the alternative that $\sigma \neq \sigma_0$ are not currently available except for two special cases considered in the original Neyman-Pearson memoir.[1] These special cases and more general considerations indicate that the OC curves for this test will not differ greatly, except for the smallest sample sizes, from the OC curves for the corresponding traditional "equal-tail" test (see Figures 6.15 and 6.16 of Bowker and Lieberman[2]). The OC curve for the present test for a given significance level and sample size n will lie above the OC curve of the corresponding "equal-tail" test for $\sigma > \sigma_0$ and below the OC curve for the "equal-tail" test for $\sigma < \sigma_0$. In other words, the chances of failing to detect that σ exceeds σ_0 are somewhat greater with the present test than with the "equal-tail" test, and somewhat less of failing to detect that σ is less than σ_0. The reader is reminded, however, that if there is special interest in determining whether $\sigma > \sigma_0$, or special interest in determining whether $\sigma < \sigma_0$, the problem and procedure of this Paragraph is not at all appropriate, and Paragraph 4-1.2 or 4-1.3 should be consulted.

4-1.2 DOES THE VARIABILITY OF THE NEW PRODUCT EXCEED THAT OF THE STANDARD?

The variability in performance of a standard material, product, or process, as measured by its standard deviation, is known to be σ_0. We wish to determine whether the variability in performance of a new product *exceeds* that of the standard. We wish, from analysis of the data, to make one of the following decisions:

(a) The variability in performance of the new product *exceeds* that of the standard.

(b) There is no reason to believe the variability of the new product exceeds that of the standard.

In terms of Data Sample 4-1.1, let us suppose that—in advance of looking at the data!—the important question is: Does the variability of the new type *exceed* that of the standard?

Procedure	Example
(1) Choose α, the level of significance of the test.	(1) Let $\qquad \alpha = .05$
(2) Look up A_α for $n - 1$ degrees of freedom in Table A-21,	(2) $\qquad n - 1 = 9$ $A_{.05}$ for 9 d.f. $= .7293$
(3) Compute s, from the n observations.	(3) $\qquad s = 3.464$
(4) Compute $s_L = A_\alpha s$	(4) $\qquad s_L = .7293\ (3.464)$ $= 2.53$
(5) If s_L exceeds σ_0, decide that the variability of the new product exceeds that of the standard; otherwise, that there is no reason to believe that the new product exceeds the standard with regard to variability.	(5) Since 2.53 exceeds 1.66, conclude that the variability of the new type exceeds that of the standard type.
(6) It is worth noting that the interval above s_L is a $100\ (1 - \alpha)\ \%$ confidence interval estimate of σ, the standard deviation of the new product. (See Par. 2-2.3.2).	(6) The interval from 2.53 to $+\ \infty$ is a 95% confidence interval estimate of the standard deviation of the new type.

Operating Characteristics of the Test. Figure 4-1 provides operating-characteristic (OC) curves of the test for $\alpha = 0.05$ and various values of n. Let σ_1 denote the true standard deviation of the new product. Then the OC curves of Figure 4-1 show the probability $\beta = \beta\ (\lambda\,|\,.05, n)$ of failing to conclude that σ_1 exceeds σ_0 when $\sigma_1 = \lambda\sigma_0$ and the test is carried out at the $\alpha = 0.05$ level of significance using a value of s derived from a sample of size n. Similar OC curves for the case of $\alpha = 0.01$ are given in Figure 6.18 of Bowker and Lieberman.[2] OC curves are easily constructed for other values of n — and, if desired, other values of α — by utilizing the fact that if the test is conducted at the α level of significance using a value of s based on a sample of size n, then the probability of failing to conclude that σ_1 exceeds σ_0 when $\sigma_1 = \lambda\sigma_0$ is exactly β for

$$\lambda = \lambda\ (\alpha, \beta, n) = \sqrt{\chi^2_{1-\alpha}\ (n - 1)/\chi^2_\beta\ (n - 1)},$$

where $\chi^2_P\ (\nu)$ is the P-probability level of χ^2 for ν degrees of freedom, as given in Table A-3. Values of $\rho\ (\alpha, \beta, n_1) = \lambda^2\ (\alpha, \beta, n)$ corresponding to $\alpha = 0.05$ and $\alpha = 0.01$, for $\beta = 0.005, 0.01, 0.025, 0.05, 0.10, 0.25, 0.50, 0.75, 0.90, 0.95, 0.975, 0.99,$ and 0.995 are given in Tables 8.1 and 8.2 of Eisenhart.[3] for $n_1 = n - 1 = 1(1)30(10)100, 120, \infty$.

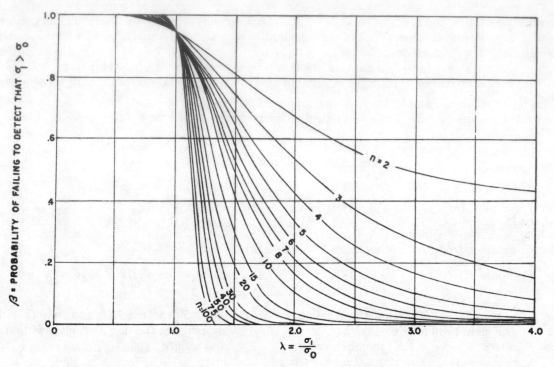

Figure 4-1.   Operating characteristics of the one-sided χ^2-test to determine whether the standard deviation σ_1 of a new product exceeds the standard deviation σ_0 of a standard ($\alpha = .05$).

Adapted with permission from *Annals of Mathematical Statistics*, Vol. 17, No. 2, June 1946, from article entitled "Operating Characteristics for the Common Statistical Tests of Significance" by C. D. Ferris, F. E. Grubbs, and C. L. Weaver.

Selection of Sample Size.   If we choose

$$\lambda = \frac{\sigma_1}{\sigma_0}$$

α, the significance level of the test

and, β, the probability of failing to detect that σ_1 exceeds σ_0 when $\sigma_1 = \lambda\sigma_0$

then for $\alpha = 0.05$ we may use the OC curves of Figure 4-1 to determine the necessary sample size n.

Example: Choose

$$\lambda = \frac{\sigma_1}{\sigma_0} = 1.5$$

$$\alpha = 0.05$$
$$\beta = 0.05$$

then from Figure 4-1 it is seen that $n = 30$ is not quite sufficient, and $n = 40$ is more than sufficient. Visual interpolation suggests $n = 35$.

Alternatively, one may compute the necessary sample size from the approximate formula

$$n = n\,(\alpha, \beta, \lambda) = 1 + \frac{1}{2}\left(\frac{z_{1-\alpha} + \lambda \cdot z_{1-\beta}}{\lambda - 1}\right)^2$$

where z_P is the P-probability point of the standard normal variable z, values of which are given in Table A-2 for various values of P. Thus, in the foregoing example we find

$$n = 1 + \frac{1}{2}\left(\frac{1.645 + (1.5)\,(1.645)}{1.5 - 1}\right)^2$$

$$= 1 + \frac{1}{2}\left(\frac{4.1125}{0.5}\right)^2 = 1 + \frac{1}{2}\,(8.225)^2 = 1 + \frac{1}{2}\,(67.65)$$

$$= 34.8$$

which rounds to $n = 35$. Chand[4] has found this formula generally quite satisfactory, and that "even for such a small value as $n = 5$" it "errs on the safe side in the sense that it gives (at least for $\alpha = \beta$) a sample size which will always be sufficient."

Check: For $n = 35$,

$$\lambda\,(.05, .05, 35) = \sqrt{\frac{\chi^2_{.95}\,(34)}{\chi^2_{.05}\,(34)}} = \sqrt{\frac{48.3}{21.4}} = \sqrt{2.26}$$

$$= 1.50$$

Hence $\beta = 0.05$ for $\lambda = 1.50$.

4-1.3 IS THE VARIABILITY OF THE NEW PRODUCT LESS THAN THAT OF THE STANDARD?

The variability in performance of a standard material, product, or process, as measured by its standard deviation, is known to be σ_0. We wish to determine whether the variability in performance of the new product is less than that of the standard. We wish, from analysis of the data, to make one of the following decisions:

(a) The variability in performance of the new product is *less than* that of the standard.

(b) There is no reason to believe the variability in performance of the new product is less than that of the standard.

Data Sample 4-1.3—Cutoff Bias of Tubes

A manufacturer has recorded the cutoff bias of a sample of ten tubes, as follows (volts):

12.1, 12.3, 11.8, 12.0, 12.4, 12.0, 12.1, 11.9, 12.2, 12.2.

The variability of cutoff bias for tubes of a standard type as measured by the standard deviation is $\sigma_0 = 0.208$ volt.

Let us assume with respect to Data Sample 4-1.3 that the important question is: Is the variability of the new type with respect to cutoff bias *less than* that of the standard type?

Procedure	Example
(1) Choose α, the level of significance of the test.	(1) Let $\alpha = .05$
(2) Look up $A_{1-\alpha}$ for $n - 1$ degrees of freedom in Table A-21.	(2) $n - 1 = 9$ $A_{.95}$ for 9 d.f. $= 1.645$
(3) Compute s, from the n observations $$s = \sqrt{\frac{\Sigma X^2 - (\Sigma X)^2/n}{n - 1}}$$	(3) $$s = \sqrt{\frac{.30}{9}}$$ $$= \sqrt{.0333}$$ $$= .1826$$

Procedure

(4) Compute $s_U = A_{1-\alpha} s$

Example

(4) $s_U = 1.645 \,(.1826)$
$= 0.300$

(5) If s_U is less than σ_0, decide that the variability in performance of the new product is less than that of the standard; otherwise, that there is no reason to believe the new product is less variable than the standard.

(5) Since .300 is *not* less than .208, conclude that there is no reason to believe that the new type is less variable than the standard.

(6) It is worth noting that the interval below s_U is a $100 \,(1 - \alpha) \,\%$ confidence interval estimate of σ, the standard deviation of the new product. (See Par. 2-2.3.2.)

(6) The interval below 0.300 is a 95% confidence interval estimate of the standard deviation of the new type.

Operating Characteristics of the Test. Figure 4-2 provides operating-characteristic (OC) curves of the test for $\alpha = 0.05$ and various values of n. Let σ_1 denote the true standard deviation of the new product. Then the OC curves of Figure 4-2 show the probability $\beta = \beta \,(\lambda \,|\, .05,\, n)$ of failing to conclude that σ_1 is less than σ_0 when $\sigma_1 = \lambda \sigma_0$ and the test is carried out at the $\alpha = 0.05$ level of significance using a value of s derived from a sample of size n. Similar OC curves for the case of $\alpha = 0.01$ are given in Figure 6.20 of Bowker and Lieberman.[2] OC curves are easily constructed

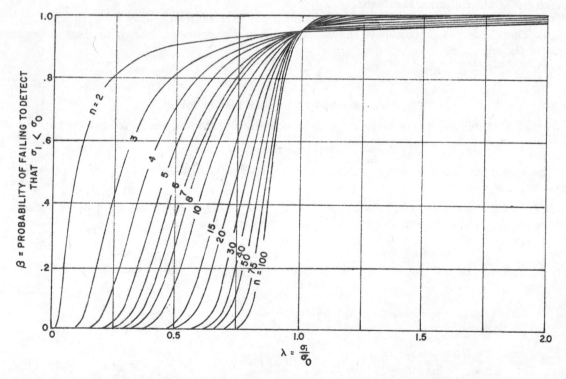

Figure 4-2. *Operating characteristics of the one-sided χ^2-test to determine whether the standard deviation σ_1 of a new product is less than the standard deviation σ_0 of a standard ($\alpha = .05$).*

Adapted with permission from *Annals of Mathematical Statistics*, Vol. 17, No. 2, June 1946, from article entitled "Operating Characteristics for the Common Statistical Tests of Significance" by C. D. Ferris, F. E. Grubbs, and C. L. Weaver.

for other values of n — and, if desired, other values of α — by utilizing the fact that if the test is conducted at the α level of significance using a value of s based on a sample of size n, then the probability of failing to conclude that σ_1 is less than σ_0 when $\sigma_1 = \lambda\sigma_0$ is exactly β for

$$\lambda = \lambda\,(\alpha, \beta, n) = \sqrt{\chi_\alpha^2\,(n-1)/\chi_{1-\beta}^2\,(n-1)},$$

where $\chi_P^2\,(\nu)$ is the P-probability level of χ^2 for ν degrees of freedom, as given in Table A-3.

Selection of Sample Size.   If we choose

$$\lambda = \tfrac{\sigma_1}{\sigma_0}$$

α, the significance level of the test
and, β, the probability of failing to detect that σ_1 is less than σ_0 when $\sigma_1 = \lambda\sigma_0$

then for $\alpha = 0.05$ we may use the OC curves of Figure 4-2 to determine the necessary sample size n.

Example: Choose

$$\lambda = \tfrac{\sigma_1}{\sigma_0} = 0.5$$
$$\alpha = 0.05$$
$$\beta = 0.05$$

then from Figure 4-2 it is seen that $n = 10$ is not quite sufficient, and $n = 15$ is more than sufficient. Visual interpolation suggests $n = 14$.

Alternatively, one may compute the necessary sample size from the approximate formula

$$n = n\,(\alpha, \beta, \lambda) = 1 + \frac{1}{2}\left(\frac{z_{1-\alpha} + \lambda \cdot z_{1-\beta}}{1-\lambda}\right)^2$$

where z_P is the P-probability point of the standard normal variable z, values of which are given in Table A-2 for various values of P.   Thus, in the foregoing example we find

$$n = 1 + \frac{1}{2}\left(\frac{1.645 + (0.5)\,(1.645)}{1 - 0.5}\right)^2$$

$$= 1 + \frac{1}{2}\left(\frac{2.4675}{0.5}\right)^2 = 1 + \frac{1}{2}\,(4.935)^2 = 1 + \frac{1}{2}\,(24.35)$$

$$= 13.18$$

which rounds to $n = 13$.

Check: For $n = 13$,

$$\lambda\,(.05, .05, 13) = \sqrt{\frac{\chi_{.05}^2\,(12)}{\chi_{.95}^2\,(12)}} = \sqrt{\frac{5.23}{21.03}} = \sqrt{0.2487}$$

$$= 0.499 < 0.50$$

Hence, $\beta = 0.05$ for $\lambda = 0.50$.

4-2 COMPARING TWO MATERIALS OR PRODUCTS WITH RESPECT TO VARIABILITY OF PERFORMANCE

We consider two problems:

(a) Does the variability of product A *differ* from that of product B? (We are not concerned which is larger).   See Paragraph 4-2.1.

(b) Does the variability of product A *exceed* that of product B?   See Paragraph 4-2.2.

It is important to decide which of these two problems is appropriate before taking the observations.   If this is not done, and the choice of problem is influenced by the observations, both the significance level of the test (i.e., the probability of an Error of the First Kind) and the operating characteristics of the test may differ considerably from their nominal values.   The tests given are exact when:

(a) the observations for an item, product, or process are taken randomly from a single population of possible observations; and,

(b) within the population, the quality characteristic measured is normally distributed.

In the following, it is assumed the appropriate problem is selected and then n_A, n_B observations are taken from items, processes, or products A and B, respectively.

4-2.1 DOES THE VARIABILITY OF PRODUCT A DIFFER FROM THAT OF PRODUCT B?

We wish to test whether the variability of performance of two materials, products, or processes differ, and we are not particularly concerned which is larger.   We wish, from analysis of the data, to make one of the following decisions:

(a) The two products differ with regard to their variability.
(b) There is no reason to believe the two products differ with regard to their variability.

Data Sample 4-2.1—Dive-bombing Methods

The performance of each of two different dive-bombing methods is measured a dozen times with the following results:

Method A	Method B
526	414
406	430
499	419
627	453
585	504
459	459
415	337
460	598
506	425
450	438
624	456
506	385

Let us suppose that, in the case of Data Sample 4-2.1, the question to be answered is: Do the two methods *differ* in variability (it being of interest if either is more variable than the other)?

Procedure	**Example**
(1) Choose α, the level of significance of the test.	(1) Let $\alpha = .05$
(2) Look up $F_{1-\alpha/2}$ for $(n_A - 1, n_B - 1)$ degrees of freedom, and $F_{1-\alpha/2}$ for $(n_B - 1, n_A - 1)$ degrees of freedom, in Table A-5.	(2) $n_A - 1 = 11$ $n_B - 1 = 11$ $F_{.975}(11, 11) = 3.48$
(3) Compute s_A^2 and s_B^2 from the observations from A and B, respectively.	(3) $s_A^2 = 5545$ $s_B^2 = 4073$
(4) Compute $F = s_A^2/s_B^2$	(4) $F = 5545/4073$ $= 1.36$
(5) If $F > F_{1-\alpha/2}(n_A - 1, n_B - 1)$ or $$F < \frac{1}{F_{1-\alpha/2}(n_B - 1, n_A - 1)}$$ decide that the two products differ with regard to their variability; otherwise, there is no reason to believe that they differ.	(5) $F_{.975}(11, 11) = 3.48$ $$\frac{1}{F_{.975}(11, 11)} = 0.29$$ Since F is not larger than 3.48, and is not smaller than 0.29, there is no reason to believe that the two bombing methods differ in variability.
(6) It is worth noting that the interval between $$\frac{1}{F_{1-\alpha/2}(n_A - 1, n_B - 1)}\left(\frac{s_A^2}{s_B^2}\right)$$ and $$F_{1-\alpha/2}(n_B - 1, n_A - 1)\left(\frac{s_A^2}{s_B^2}\right)$$ is a $100(1 - \alpha)\%$ confidence interval estimate of the ratio σ_A^2/σ_B^2.	(6) The interval between 0.39 (i.e., 0.29×1.36) and 4.73 (i.e., 3.48×1.36) is a 95% confidence interval estimate of the ratio of the true variances, σ_A^2/σ_B^2.

Operating Characteristics of the Test. Operating-characteristic (OC) curves for this traditional "equal-tail" test of the null hypothesis that $\sigma_A = \sigma_B$ relative to the alternative $\sigma_A \neq \sigma_B$ are given in Figures 7.1 and 7.2 of Bowker and Lieberman[2] for the case of equal sample sizes $n_A = n_B = n$, and significance levels $\alpha = 0.05$ and $\alpha = 0.01$, respectively. These curves may be used to determine the common sample size $n_A = n_B = n$ needed to achieve a preassigned risk β of failing to detect that $\sigma_A/\sigma_B = \lambda$ when the test is carried out at the $\alpha = 0.05$ or $\alpha = 0.01$ level of significance. The reader is reminded, however, that if there is special interest in determining whether $\sigma_A > \sigma_B$, the problem and procedure of this Paragraph is not at all appropriate, and Paragraph 4-2.2 should be consulted.

4-2.2 DOES THE VARIABILITY OF PRODUCT A EXCEED THAT OF PRODUCT B?

We wish to test whether the variability in performance of product A exceeds that of product B. We wish, as a result of analysis of the data, to make one of the following decisions:

(a) The variability of product A exceeds that of product B.

(b) There is no reason to believe that the variability of product A exceeds the variability of product B.

In terms of Data Sample 4-2.1, let us suppose that—in advance of looking at the data!—the important question is: Does the variability of Method A *exceed* that of Method B?

Procedure	**Example**
(1) Choose α, the level of significance of the test.	(1) Let $\alpha = .05$
(2) Look up $F_{1-\alpha}$ for $n_A - 1$, $n_B - 1$ degrees of freedom, in Table A-5.	(2) $n_A - 1 = 11$ $n_B - 1 = 11$ $F_{.95}(11, 11) = 2.82$
(3) Compute s_A^2, s_B^2, the sample variances of the observations from A and B, respectively.	(3) $s_A^2 = 5545$ $s_B^2 = 4073$
(4) Compute $F = s_A^2/s_B^2$.	(4) $F = 1.36$
(5) If $F > F_{1-\alpha}$, decide that the variability of product A exceeds that of B; otherwise, there is no reason to believe that the variability of A is greater than that of B.	(5) Since 1.36 is not larger than 2.82, there is no reason to believe that the variability of Method A is greater than the variability of Method B.
*(6) Note that the interval above $$\frac{1}{F_{1-\alpha}(n_A - 1, n_B - 1)}\left(\frac{s_A^2}{s_B^2}\right)$$ is a $100(1-\alpha)\%$ confidence interval estimate of σ_A^2/σ_B^2.	(6) $$\frac{1}{F_{.95}(11, 11)} = 0.35$$ The interval above 0.48 (i.e., 0.35×1.36) is a 95% confidence interval estimate of the ratio of the true variances, σ_A^2/σ_B^2.

Operating Characteristics of the Test. Figures 4-3, 4-4, and 4-5 provide operating-characteristic (OC) curves of the test for $\alpha = 0.05$ and various combinations of n_A and n_B. Let σ_A and σ_B denote the true standard deviations of the products A and B, respectively. These OC curves show the probability $\beta = \beta(\lambda|.05, n)$ of failing to conclude that σ_A exceeds σ_B when $\sigma_A = \lambda\sigma_B$ with $\lambda > 1$ and the test is carried out at the $\alpha = 0.05$ level of significance using the values of s_A and s_B derived from samples of size n_A and n_B, respectively. Similar OC curves for the case of $\alpha = 0.01$ and $n_A = n_B$ are given in Figure 7.4 of Bowker and Lieberman.[2] OC curves are easily constructed for other values of n_A and n_B — and, if desired, other values of α — by utilizing the fact that if the test is conducted at the α level of significance using values of s_A and s_B based on samples of size n_A and n_B, respectively, then the probability of failing to conclude that σ_A exceeds σ_B when $\sigma_A = \lambda\sigma_B$ is exactly β for

$$\lambda = \lambda(\alpha, \beta, n_A, n_B) = \sqrt{\frac{F_{1-\alpha}(n_A - 1, n_B - 1)}{F_\beta(n_A - 1, n_B - 1)}}$$

$$= \sqrt{F_{1-\alpha}(n_A - 1, n_B - 1) \cdot F_{1-\beta}(n_B - 1, n_A - 1)}$$

where $F_P(n_1, n_2)$ is the P-probability level of F for n_1 and n_2 degrees of freedom, as given in Table A-5. Values of $\phi(\alpha, \beta, n_1, n_2) = \lambda^2(\alpha, \beta, n_A, n_B)$ corresponding to $\alpha = 0.05$ and $\alpha = 0.01$, for $\beta = 0.005, 0.01, 0.025, 0.05, 0.10, 0.25, 0.50, 0.75, 0.90, 0.95, 0.975, 0.99$, and 0.995 are given in Tables 8.3 and 8.4 of Eisenhart[3] for all combinations of values of $n_1 = n_A - 1$ and $n_2 = n_B - 1$ derivable from the sequence 1(1)30(10)100, 120, ∞.

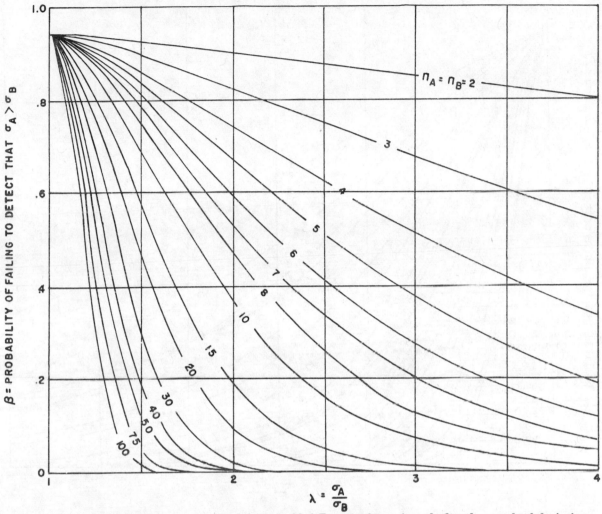

Figure 4-3.   Operating characteristics of the one-sided F-test to determine whether the standard deviation σ_A of product A exceeds the standard deviation σ_B of product B ($\alpha = .05; n_A = n_B$).

Adapted with permission from *Annals of Mathematical Statistics*, Vol. 17, No. 2, June 1946, from article entitled "Operating Characteristics for the Common Statistical Tests of Significance" by C. D. Ferris, F. E. Grubbs, and G. L. Weaver.

Selection of Sample Size.   If we choose

$$n_A = n_B = n$$

$$\lambda = \frac{\sigma_A}{\sigma_B}$$

α, the significance level of the test

β, the probability of failing to detect that σ_A exceeds σ_B when $\sigma_A = \lambda\sigma_B$

then for $\alpha = 0.05$, we may use the OC curve of Figure 4-3 to determine the necessary common sample size n.

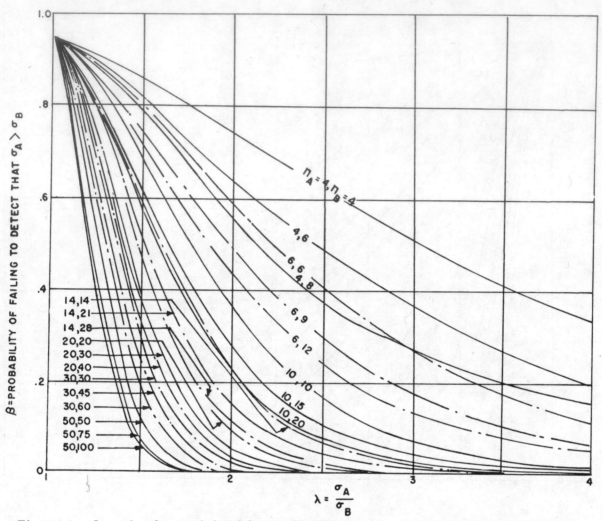

Figure 4-4.   *Operating characteristics of the one-sided F-test to determine whether the standard deviation*
σ_A of product A exceeds the standard deviation σ_B of product B
($\alpha = .05$; $n_A = n_B$, $3n_A = 2n_B$, $2n_A = n_B$).

Adapted with permission from *Annals of Mathematical Statistics*, Vol. 17, No. 2, June 1946, from article entitled "Operating Characteristics for the Common Statistical Tests of Significance" by C. D. Ferris, F. E. Grubbs, and C. L. Weaver.

Example: Choose

$$\lambda = \frac{\sigma_A}{\sigma_B} = 1.5$$
$$\alpha = 0.05$$
$$\beta = 0.05$$

then from Figure 4-3 it is seen that $n = 50$ is too small and $n = 75$ a bit too large. Visual inter-polation suggests $n = 70$.

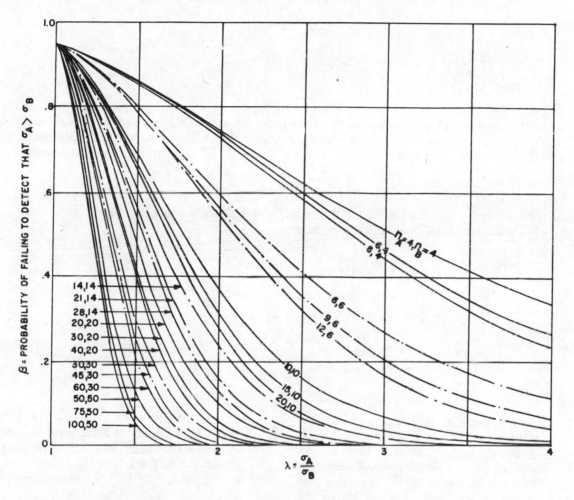

Figure 4-5. Operating characteristics of the one-sided F-test to determine whether the standard deviation
σ_A *of product A exceeds the standard deviation* σ_B *of product B*
$(\alpha = .05;\ n_A = n_B,\ 2n_A = 3n_B,\ n_A = 2n_B).$

Adapted with permission from *Annals of Mathematical Statistics*, Vol. 17, No. 2, June 1946, from article entitled "Operating Characteristics for the Common Statistical Tests of Significance" by C. D. Ferris, F. E. Grubbs, and C. L. Weaver.

Alternatively, for $n_A = n_B = n$ one may compute the necessary sample size from the approximate formula

$$n = n\,(\alpha,\,\beta,\,\lambda) = 2 + \left(\frac{z_{1-\alpha} + z_{1-\beta}}{\log_e \lambda}\right)^2$$

where z_P is the P-probability point of the standard normal variable z, values of which are given in

Table A-2 for various values of P. Thus in the foregoing example we find

$$n = 2 + \left(\frac{1.645 + 1.645}{.4055}\right)^2$$

$$= 2 + \left(\frac{3.290}{.4055}\right)^2 = 2 + (8.11)^2 = 2 + 65.8$$

$$= 68.$$

If instead of choosing $n_A = n_B$ we choose $3n_A = 2n_B$ or $2n_A = n_B$, then for $\alpha = 0.05$ we may use the OC curves of Figure 4-4 to determine the necessary combination of sample sizes n_A and n_B. Similarly, Figure 4-5 may be used if it is desired to have $2n_A = 3n_B$ or $n_A = 2n_B$. Alternatively, one may evaluate the harmonic mean h of $n_A - 2$ and $n_B - 2$ from the approximate formula

$$h = \left(\frac{z_{1-\alpha} + z_{1-\beta}}{\log_e \lambda}\right)^2$$

and then determine the integer values of n_A and n_B (satisfying any additional requirements, e.g., $n_A = 2n_B$) that most closely satisfy the equation

$$\frac{1}{h} = \frac{1}{2}\left\{\frac{1}{n_A - 2} + \frac{1}{n_B - 2}\right\}.$$

REFERENCES

1. J. Neyman and E. S. Pearson, "Contributions to the Theory of Testing Statistical Hypotheses, I. Unbiased Critical Regions of Type A and Type A₁," *Statistical Research Memoirs*, Vol. 1, Department of Statistics, University College, University of London, 1936.

2. A. H. Bowker and G. J. Lieberman, *Engineering Statistics*, Prentice-Hall, Inc., Englewood Cliffs, N. J., 1959.

3. Churchill Eisenhart, "Planning and Interpreting Experiments for Comparing Two Standard Deviations," Chapter 8 of *Selected Techniques of Statistical Analysis* (Edited by Churchill Eisenhart, Millard W. Hastay, and W. Allen Wallis), McGraw-Hill Book Co., Inc., New York, N. Y., 1947.

4. Uttam Chand, "On the Derivation and Accuracy of Certain Formulas for Sample Sizes and Operating Characteristics of Nonsequential Sampling Procedures," *Journal of Research of the National Bureau of Standards*, Vol. 47, No. 6, pp. 491-501, December 1951.

CHAPTER 5

CHARACTERIZING LINEAR RELATIONSHIPS
BETWEEN TWO VARIABLES

5-1 INTRODUCTION

In many situations it is desirable to know something about the relationships between two characteristics of a material, product, or process. In some cases, it may be known from theoretical considerations that two properties are functionally related, and the problem is to find out more about the structure of this relationship. In other cases, there is interest in investigating whether there exists a degree of association between two properties which could be used to advantage. For example, in specifying methods of test for a material, there may be two tests available, both of which reflect performance, but one of which is cheaper, simpler, or quicker to run. If a high degree of association exists between the two tests, we might wish to run regularly only the simpler test.

In this chapter, we deal only with linear relationships. Curvilinear relationships are discussed in Chapter 6 (see Paragraph 6-5). It is worth noting that many nonlinear relationships may be expressed in linear form by a suitable transformation (change of variable). For example, if the relationship is of the form $Y = aX^b$, then $\log Y = \log a + b \log X$. Putting $Y_T = \log Y$, $b_0 = \log a$, $b_1 = b$, $X_T = \log X$, we have the linear expression $Y_T = b_0 + b_1 X_T$ in terms of the new (transformed) variables X_T and Y_T.

A number of common linearizing transformations are summarized in Table 5-4 and are discussed in Paragraph 5-4.4.

5-2 PLOTTING THE DATA

Where only two characteristics are involved, the natural first step in handling the experimental results is to plot the points on graph paper. Conventionally, the *independent variable X* is plotted on the horizontal scale, and the *dependent variable Y* is plotted on the vertical scale.

There is no substitute for a plot of the data to give some idea of the general spread and shape of the results. A pictorial indication of the probable form and sharpness of the relationship, if any, is indispensable and sometimes may save needless computing. When investigating

a structural relationship, the plotted data will show whether a hypothetical linear relationship is borne out; if not, we must consider whether there is any theoretical basis for fitting a curve of higher degree. When looking for an empirical association of two characteristics, a glance at the plot will reveal whether such association is likely or whether there is only a patternless scatter of points.

In some cases, a plot will reveal unsuspected difficulties in the experimental setup which must be ironed out before fitting any kind of relationship. An example of this occurred in measuring the time required for a drop of dye to travel between marked distances along a water channel. The channel was marked with distance markers spaced at equal distances, and an observer recorded the time at which the dye passed each marker. The device used for recording time consisted of two clocks hooked up so that when one was stopped, the other started: Clock 1 recorded the times for Distance Markers 1, 3, 5, etc.; and Clock 2 recorded times for the even-numbered distance markers. When the elapsed times were plotted, they looked somewhat as shown in Figure 5-1. It is obvious that there was a systematic time difference between odd and even markers (presumably a lag in the circuit connecting the two clocks). One could easily have fitted a straight line to the odd-numbered distances and a different line to the even-numbered distances, with approximately constant difference between the two lines. The effect was so consistent, how-

ever, that the experimenter quite properly decided to find a better means of recording travel times before fitting any line at all.

If no obvious difficulties are revealed by the plot, and the relationship appears to be linear, then a line $Y = b_0 + b_1X$ ordinarily should be fitted to the data, according to the procedures given in this Chapter. Fitting by eye usually is inadequate for the following reasons:

(a) No two people would fit exactly the same line, and, therefore, the procedure is not objective;

(b) We always need some measure of how well the line does fit the data, and of the uncertainties inherent in the fitted line as a representation of the true underlying relationship—and these can be obtained only when a formal, well-defined mathematical procedure of fitting is employed.

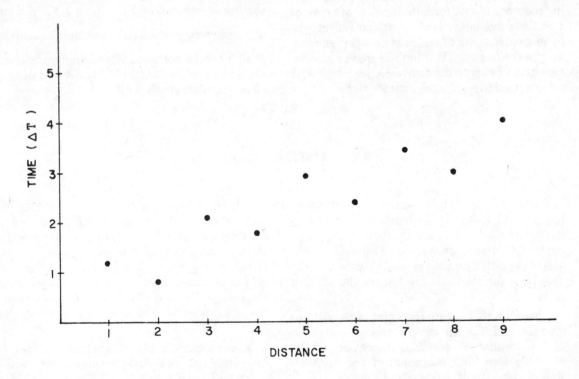

Figure 5-1. Time required for a drop of dye to travel between distance markers.

5-3 TWO IMPORTANT SYSTEMS OF LINEAR RELATIONSHIPS

Before giving the detailed procedure for fitting a straight line, we discuss different physical situations which can be described by a linear relationship between two variables. The methods of description and prediction may be different, depending upon the underlying system. In general, we recognize two different and important systems which we call *Statistical* and *Functional*. It is not possible to decide which is the appropriate system from looking at the data. The distinction must be made before fitting the line—indeed, before taking the measurements.

5-3.1 FUNCTIONAL RELATIONSHIPS

In the case of a Functional Relationship, there exists an exact mathematical formula (y as a function of x) relating the two variables, and the only reason that the observations do not fit this equation exactly is because of disturbances or errors of measurement in the observed values of one or both variables. We discuss two cases of this type:

FI—Errors of measurement affect only one variable (Y). (See Fig. 5-2).

FII—Both variables (X and Y) are subject to errors of measurement. (See Fig. 5-3).

Common situations that may be described by Functional Relationships include calibration lines, comparisons of analytical procedures, and relationships in which time is the X variable.

For instance, we may regard Figure 5-2 as portraying the calibration of a straight-faced spring balance in terms of a series of weights whose masses are accurately known. By Hooke's Law, the extension of the spring, and hence the position y of the scale pointer, should be determined exactly by the mass x upon the pan through a linear functional relationship* $y = \beta_0 + \beta_1 x$. In practice, however, if a weight of mass x_1 is placed upon the pan repeatedly and the position of the pointer is read in each instance, it usually is found that the readings Y_1 are not identical, due to variations in the performance of the spring and to reading errors. Thus, corresponding to the mass x_1 there is a distribution of pointer readings Y_1; corresponding to mass x_2, a distribution of pointer readings Y_2; and so forth—as indicated in Figure 5-2. It is customary to assume that these distributions are normal (or, at least symmetrical and all of the same form) and that the mean of the distribution of Y_i's coincides with the *true value* $y_i = \beta_0 + \beta_1 x_i$.

If, instead of calibrating the spring balance in terms of a series of accurately known weights, we were to calibrate it in terms of another spring balance by recording the corresponding pointer positions when a series of weights are placed first on the pan of one balance and then on the pan of the other, the resulting readings (X and Y) would be related by a linear structural relationship FII, as shown in Figure 5-3, inasmuch as both X and Y are affected by errors of measurement. In this case, corresponding to the repeated weighings of a single weight w_1 (whose true mass need not be known), there is a joint distribution of the pointer readings (X_1 and Y_1) on the two balances, represented by the little transparent *mountain* centered over the *true point* (x_1, y_1) in Figure 5-3; similarly at points (x_2, y_2) and (x_3, y_3), corresponding to repeated weighings of other weights w_2 and w_3, respectively. Finally, it should be noticed that this FII model is more general than the FI model in that it does *not* require linearity of response of each instrument to the independent variable w, but merely that the response curves

---

* *Note on Notation for Functional Relationships:*

We have used x and y to denote the true or accurately known values of the variables, and X and Y to denote their values measured with error. In the FI Relationship, the independent variable is always without error, and therefore in our *discussions* of the FI case and in the paragraph headings we always use x. In the Worksheet, and Procedures and Examples for the FI case, however, we use X and Y because of the computational similarity to other cases discussed in this Chapter (i.e., the computations for the Statistical Relationships).

In the FII case, both variables are subject to error, and clearly we use X and Y everywhere for the observed values.

of the two instruments be linearly related, that is, that $X = a + b \cdot f(w)$ and $Y = c + d \cdot f(w)$, where $f(w)$ may be linear, quadratic, exponential, logarithmic, or whatever.

Table 5-1 provides a concise characterization

of FI and FII relationships. Detailed problems and procedures with numerical examples for FI relationships are given in Paragraphs 5-4.1 and 5-4.2, and for FII relationships in Paragraph 5-4.3.

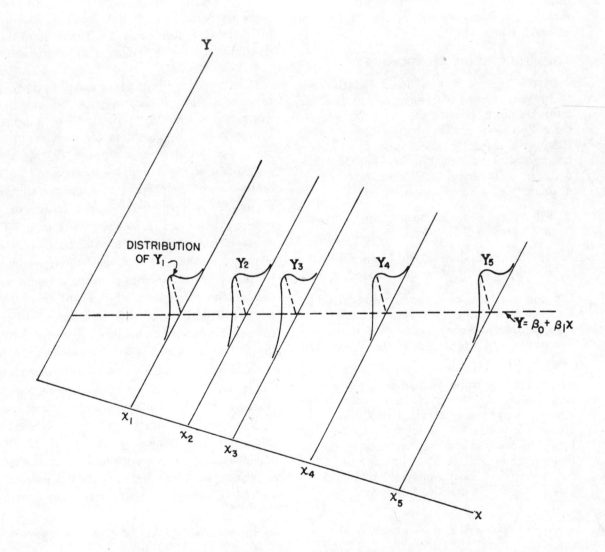

*Figure 5-2. Linear functional relationship of Type FI
(only Y affected by measurement errors).*

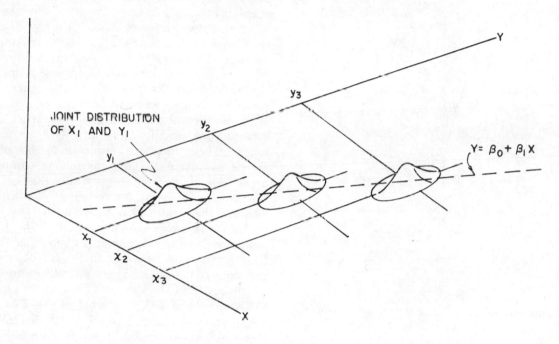

Figure 5-3.   Linear functional relationship of Type FII
(both X and Y affected by measurement errors).

5-3.2   STATISTICAL RELATIONSHIPS

In the case of a Statistical Relationship, there is no exact mathematical relationship between X and Y; there is only a statistical association between the two variables as characteristics of individual items from some particular population. If this statistical association is of bivariate normal type as shown in Figure 5-4, then the *average* value of the Y's associated with a particular value of X, say $\bar{Y}_X$, is found to depend linearly on X, i.e., $\bar{Y}_X = \beta_0 + \beta_1 X$; similarly, the *average* value of the X's associated with a particular value of Y, say $\bar{X}_Y$, depends linearly on Y (Fig. 5-4) i.e., $\bar{X}_Y = \beta_0' + \beta_1' Y$;

but—and this is important!—the two lines are *not* the same, i.e., $\beta_1' \neq \dfrac{1}{\beta_1}$ and $\beta_0' \neq -\dfrac{\beta_0}{\beta_1}$.*

---

* Strictly, we should write

$$m_{Y \cdot X} = \beta_0 + \beta_1 X ,$$

and

$$m_{X \cdot Y} = \beta_0' + \beta_1' Y$$

to conform to our notation of using m to signify a population mean. But this more exact notation tends to conceal the parallelism of the curve-fitting processes in the FI and SI situations. Consequently, to preserve appearances here and in the sequel, we use $\bar{Y}_X$ in place of $m_{Y \cdot X}$ and $\bar{X}_Y$ in place of $m_{X \cdot Y}$—and it should be remembered that these signify *population means*.

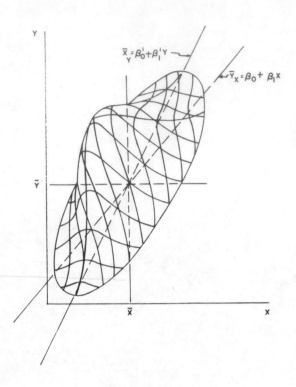

Figure 5-4. A normal bivariate frequency surface.

If a random sample of items is drawn from the population, and the two characteristics X and Y are measured on each item, then typically it is found that errors of measurement are negligible in comparison with the variation of each characteristic over the individual items. This general case is designated SI. A special case (involving preselection or restriction of the range of one of the variables) is denoted by SII.

SI Relationships. In this case, a random sample of items is drawn from some definite population (material, product, process, or people), and two characteristics are measured on each item.

A classic example of this type is the relationship between height and weight of men. Any observant person knows that weight tends to vary with height, but also that individuals of the same height may vary widely in weight. It is obvious that the errors made in measuring height or weight are very small compared to this inherent variation between individuals. We surely would not expect to predict the exact

weight of one individual from his height, but we might expect to be able to estimate the average weight of all individuals of a given height.

The height-weight example is given as one which is universally familiar. Such examples also exist in the physical and engineering sciences, particularly in cases involving the interrelation of two test methods. In many cases there may be two tests that, strictly speaking, measure two basically different properties of a material, product, or process, but these properties are statistically related to each other in some complicated way and both are related to some performance characteristic of particular interest, one usually more directly than the other. Their interrelationship may be obscured by inherent variations among sample units (due to varying density, for example). We would be very interested in knowing whether the relationship between the two is sufficient to enable us to predict with reasonable accuracy, from a value given by one test, the average value to be expected for the other—particularly if one test is considerably simpler or cheaper than the other.

The choice of which variable to call X and which variable to call Y is arbitrary—actually there are two regression lines. If a statistical association is found, ordinarily the variable which is easier to measure is called X. Note well that this is the only case of linear relationship in which it may be appropriate to fit two different lines, one for predicting Y from X and a different one for predicting X from Y, *and* the only case in which the sample correlation coefficient r is meaningful as an estimate of the degree of association of X and Y *in the population* as measured by the population coefficient of correlation $\rho = \sqrt{\beta_1\beta_1'}$. The six sets of contour ellipses shown in Figure 5-5 indicate the manner in which the location, shape, and orientation of the normal bivariate distribution varies with changes of the population means (m_X and m_Y) and standard deviations (σ_X and σ_Y) of X and Y and their coefficient of correlation in the population (ρ_{XY}).

If $\rho = \pm 1$, all the points lie on a line and $Y = \beta_0 + \beta_1 X$ and $X = \beta_0' + \beta_1' Y$ coincide. If $\rho = +1$, the slope is positive, and if $\rho = -1$, the slope is negative. If $\rho = 0$, then X and Y are said to be uncorrelated.

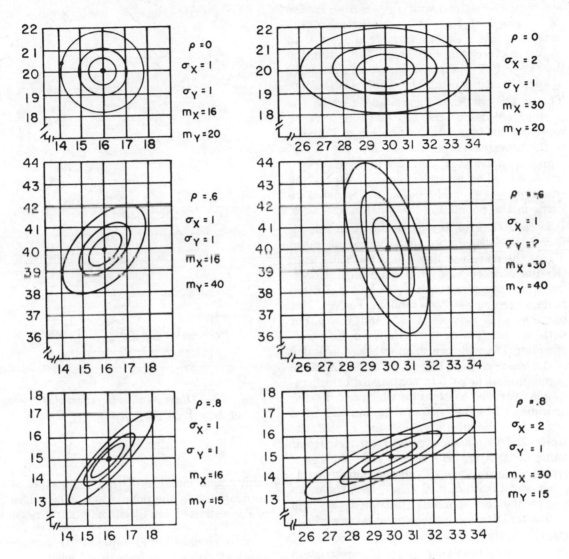

Figure 5-5.   Contour ellipses for normal bivariate distributions having different values of the five parameters m_X, m_Y, σ_X, σ_Y, ρ_{XY}.

SII Relationships.   The general case described above (SI) is the most familiar example of a statistical relationship, but we also need to consider a common case of Statistical Relationship (SII) that must be treated a bit differently.   In SII, one of the two variables, although a random variable in the population, is sampled only within a limited range (or at selected preassigned values).   In the height-weight example, suppose that the group of men included only those whose heights were between 5′4″ and 5′8″.   We now are able to fit a line predicting weight from height, but are unable to determine the correct line for predicting height from weight.   A correlation coefficient computed from such data is not a measure of the true correlation among height and weight in the (unrestricted) population.

The restriction of the range of X, when it is considered as the independent variable, does not spoil the estimates of $\bar{Y}_X$ when we fit the line $\bar{Y}_X = b_0 + b_1X$. The restriction of the range of the dependent variable (i.e., of Y in fitting the foregoing line, or of X in fitting the line $\bar{X}_Y = b_0' + b_1'Y$), however, gives a seriously distorted estimate of the true relationship. This is evident from Figure 5-6, in which the contour ellipses of the top diagram serve to represent the bivariate distribution of X and Y in the unrestricted population, and the "true" regression lines of $\bar{Y}_X$ on X and $\bar{X}_Y$ on Y are indicated. The central diagram portrays the situation when consideration is restricted to items in the population for which $a < X < b$. It is clear that for any particular X in this interval, the distribution and hence the mean $\bar{Y}_X$ of the corresponding Y's is the same as in the unrestricted case (top diagram). Consequently, a line of the form $\bar{Y}_X = b_0 + b_1X$ fitted to data involving either a random or selected set of values of X between $X = a$ and $X = b$, but with *no* selection or restrictions on the corresponding Y's, will furnish an unbiased estimate of the *true* regression line $\bar{Y}_X = \beta_0 + \beta_1X$ in the population at large. In contrast, if consideration is restricted to items for which $c < Y < d$, as indicated in the bottom diagram, then it is clear that the mean value, say $\bar{Y}_X'$, of the (restricted) Y's associated with any particular value of $X > m_X$ will be less than the corresponding mean value Y_X in the population as a whole. Likewise, if $X < m_X$, then the mean $\bar{Y}_X'$ of the corresponding (restricted) Y's will be greater than $\bar{Y}_X$ in the population as a whole. Consequently, a line of the form $\bar{Y}_X' = b_0 + b_1X$ fitted to data involving selection or restriction of Y's will *not* furnish an unbiased estimate of the true regression line $\bar{Y}_X = \beta_0 + \beta_1X$ in the population as a whole, and the distortion may be serious. In other words, introducing a restriction with regard to X does not bias inferences with regard to Y, when Y is considered as the dependent variable, but restricting Y will distort the dependence of $\bar{Y}_X$ on X so that the relationship observed will not be representative of the true underlying relationship in the population as a whole. Obviously, there is an equivalent statement in which the roles of X and Y are reversed. For further discussion and illustration of this point, and of the corresponding distortion of the sample correlation coeffi-

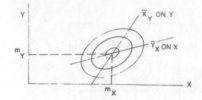

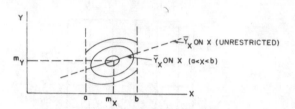

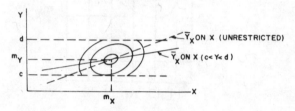

Figure 5-6. Diagram showing effect of restrictions of X or Y on the regression of Y on X.

cient r as a measure of the true coefficient of correlation ρ in the populations, when *either X or Y* is restricted, see Eisenhart[1] and Ezekiel.[2]

As an engineering example of SII, consider a study of watches to investigate whether there was a relationship between the cost of a stop watch and its temperature coefficient. It was suggested that a correlation coefficient be computed. This was not possible because the watches had not been selected at random from the total watch production, but a deliberate effort had been made to obtain a fixed number of low-priced, medium-priced, and high-priced stop watches.

In any given case, consider carefully whether one is measuring samples as they come (and thereby accepting the values of both properties that come with the sample) which is an SI Relationship, or whether one selects samples which

TABLE 5-1. SUMMARY OF FOUR CASES OF LINEAR RELATIONSHIPS

	Functional (F)		Statistical (S)	
	FI	**FII**	**SI**	**SII**
Distinctive Features and Example	x and y are linearly related by a mathematical formula, $y = \beta_0 + \beta_1 x$, or $x = \beta_0' + \beta_1' y$, which is not observed exactly because of disturbances or errors in one or both variables. Example: Determination of elastic constant of a spring which obeys Hooke's law. x = accurately-known weight applied, Y = measured value of corresponding elongation y.		X = Height; Y = Weight. Both measured on a random sample of individuals. X is *not* selected but "comes with" sample unit.	X = Height (preselected values); Y = Weight of individuals of preselected height. X is measured beforehand; only *selected* values of X are used at which to measure Y.
Errors of Measurement	Measurement error affects Y only.	X and Y both subject to error.	Ordinarily negligible compared to variation among individuals.	Same as SI.
Form of Line Fitted	$Y = b_0 + b_1 x$	See Paragraph 5-4.3.	$\bar{Y}_X = b_0 + b_1 X$ $\bar{X}_Y = b_0' + b_1' Y$	$\bar{Y}_X = b_0 + b_1 X$ only.
Procedure for Fitting	See Paragraphs 5-4.1, 5-4.2, and basic worksheet.	Procedure depends on what assumptions can be made. See Paragraph 5-4.3.	See Paragraph 5-5.1 and basic worksheet.	See Paragraph 5-5.2 and basic worksheet.
Correlation Coefficient	Not applicable	Not applicable	Sample estimate is $$r = \frac{S_{xy}}{\sqrt{S_{xx}}\,\sqrt{S_{yy}}}$$ See Paragraph 5-5.1.5.	Correlation may exist in the population, but r computed from *such* an experiment would provide a distorted estimate of the correlation.

are known to have a limited range of values of X (which is an SII Relationship).

Table 5-1 gives a brief summary characterization of SI and SII Relationships. Detailed problems and procedures with numerical examples are given for SI relationships in Paragraph 5-5.1 and for SII relationships in Paragraph 5-5.2.

BASIC WORKSHEET FOR ALL TYPES OF LINEAR RELATIONSHIPS

X denotes _____ Y denotes _____

$\Sigma X =$ _____ $\Sigma Y =$ _____

$\bar{X} =$ _____ $\bar{Y} =$ _____

Number of points: $n =$ _____

Step (1) ΣXY $=$ _____

(2) $(\Sigma X)(\Sigma Y)/n =$ _____

(3) S_{xy} $=$ Step (1) − Step (2)

(4) ΣX^2 $=$ _____   (7) ΣY^2 $=$ _____

(5) $(\Sigma X)^2/n$ $=$ _____   (8) $(\Sigma Y)^2/n$ $=$ _____

(6) S_{xx} $=$ Step (4) − Step (5)   (9) S_{yy} $=$ Step (7) − Step (8)

(10) $b_1 = \dfrac{S_{xy}}{S_{xx}}$ $=$ Step (3) ÷ Step (6)   (14) $\dfrac{(S_{xy})^2}{S_{xx}}$ $=$ _____

(11) $\bar{Y}$ $=$ _____   (15) $(n-2) s_Y^2$ $=$ Step (9) − Step (14)

(12) $b_1 \bar{X}$ $=$ _____   (16) s_Y^2 $=$ Step (15) ÷ $(n-2)$

(13) $b_0 = \bar{Y} - b_1 \bar{X} =$ Step (11) − Step (12) s_Y $=$ _____

Equation of the line:

$Y = b_0 + b_1 X$

_____

$s_{b_1} =$ _____

$s_{b_0} =$ _____

Estimated variance of the slope:

$s_{b_1}^2 = \dfrac{s_Y^2}{S_{xx}}$ $=$ Step (16) ÷ Step (6)

Estimated variance of intercept:

$s_{b_0}^2 = s_Y^2 \left\{ \dfrac{1}{n} + \dfrac{\bar{X}^2}{S_{xx}} \right\}$ $=$ _____

Note: The following are algebraically identical:

$S_{xx} = \Sigma(X - \bar{X})^2$; $S_{yy} = \Sigma(Y - \bar{Y})^2$; $S_{xy} = \Sigma(X - \bar{X})(Y - \bar{Y})$.

Ordinarily, in hand computation, it is preferable to compute as shown in the steps above. Carry all decimal places obtainable—i.e., if data are recorded to two decimal places, carry four places in Steps (1) through (9) in order to avoid losing significant figures in subtraction.

5-4   PROBLEMS AND PROCEDURES FOR FUNCTIONAL RELATIONSHIPS

5-4.1   FI RELATIONSHIPS (General Case)

There is an underlying mathematical (functional) relationship between the two variables, of the form $y = \beta_0 + \beta_1 x$. The variable x can be measured relatively accurately. Measurements Y of the value of y corresponding to a given x follow a normal distribution with mean $\beta_0 + \beta_1 x$ and variance $\sigma^2_{Y \cdot x}$ which is independent of the value of x. Furthermore, we shall assume that the deviations or *errors* of a series of observed Y's, corresponding to the same or different x's, all are mutually independent. See Paragraph 5-3.1 and Table 5-1.

The general case is discussed here, and the special case where it is known that $\beta_0 = 0$ (i.e., a line known to pass through the origin) is discussed in Paragraph 5-4.2. The procedure discussed here also will be valid if in fact $\beta_0 = 0$ even though this fact is not known beforehand. However, when it is known that $\beta_0 = 0$, the procedures of Paragraph 5-4.2 should be followed because they are simpler and somewhat more efficient.

It will be noted that SII, Paragraph 5-5.2, is handled computationally in exactly the same manner as FI, but both the underlying assumptions and the interpretation of the end results are different.

Data Sample 5-4.1—Young's Modulus vs. Temperature for Sapphire Rods

Observed values (Y) of Young's modulus (y) for sapphire rods measured at different temperatures (x) are given in the following table. There is assumed to be a linear functional relationship between the two variables x and y. (For the purpose of computation, the observed Y values were coded by subtracting 4000 from each. To express the line in terms of the original units, add 4000 to the computed intercept; the slope will not be affected.) The observed data are plotted in Figure 5-7.

x = Temperature °C	Y = Young's Modulus	Coded Y = Young's Modulus minus 4000
30	4642	642
100	4612	612
200	4565	565
300	4513	513
400	4476	476
500	4433	433
600	4389	389
700	4347	347
800	4303	303
900	4251	251
1000	4201	201
1100	4140	140
1200	4100	100
1300	4073	73
1400	4024	24
1500	3999	−1

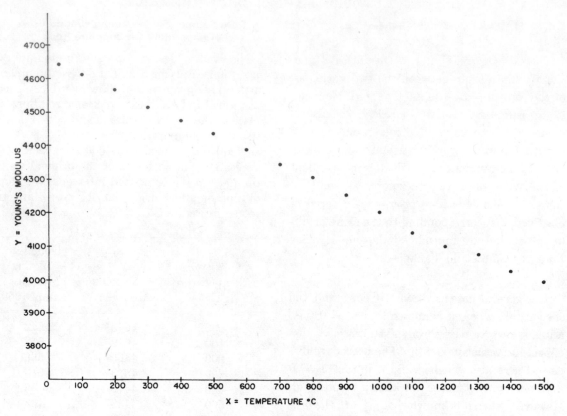

Figure 5-7.   Young's modulus of sapphire rods as a function of temperature—an FI relationship.

5-4.1.1 What is the Best Line to be Used for Estimating y From Given Values of x?

CAUTION: Extrapolation, i.e., use of the line for prediction outside the range of data from which the line was computed, may lead to highly erroneous conclusions.

Procedure

Using Worksheet (See Worksheet 5-4.1), compute the line $Y = b_0 + b_1x$. This is an estimate of the true equation $y = \beta_0 + \beta_1x$. The method of fitting a line given here is a particular application of the general method of least squares.   From Data Sample 5-4.1, the equation of the fitted line (in original units) is:

$$Y = 4654.9846 - 0.44985482\,x.$$

The equation in original units is obtained by adding 4000 to the computed intercept b_0. Since the Y's were coded by subtracting a constant, the computed slope b_1 was not affected. In Figure 5-8, the line is drawn and confidence limits for the line (computed as described in Paragraph 5-4.1.2.1) also are shown.

WORKSHEET 5-4.1
EXAMPLE OF FI RELATIONSHIP
YOUNG'S MODULUS AS FUNCTION OF TEMPERATURE

X denotes _____ Temperature, °C _____ Y denotes _____ Young's Modulus − 4000 _____

$\Sigma X =$ _____ 12030 _____ $\Sigma Y =$ _____ 5068 _____

$\bar{X} =$ _____ 751.875 _____ $\bar{Y} =$ _____ 316.75 _____

Number of points: $n =$ _____ 16 _____

(1) ΣXY $=$ 2,300,860

(2) $(\Sigma X)(\Sigma Y)/n =$ 3,810,502.5

(3) S_{xy} $=$ −1,509,642.5

(4) ΣX^2 $=$ 12,400,900   (7) ΣY^2 $=$ 2,285,614

(5) $(\Sigma X)^2/n$ $=$ 9,045,056.25   (8) $(\Sigma Y)^2/n$ $=$ 1,605,289.

(6) S_{xx} $=$ 3,355,843.75   (9) S_{yy} $=$ 680,325.

(10) $b_1 = \dfrac{S_{xy}}{S_{xx}}$ $=$ −.449,854,82   (14) $\dfrac{(S_{xy})^2}{S_{xx}}$ $=$ 679,119.9614

(11) $\bar{Y}$ $=$ 316.75   (15) $(n-2) s_Y^2$ $-$ 1,205.0386

(12) $b_1 \bar{X}$ $=$ −338.2346   (16) s_Y^2 $=$ 86.074 1857

(13) $b_0 = \bar{Y} - b_1\bar{X} =$ 654.9846 s_Y $=$ 9.277617

b_0 (in original units) $= 4654.9846$

Equation of the line: (in original units)	Estimated variance of the slope:

Equation of the line:
    (in original units)

$Y = b_0 + b_1 X$

    4654.9846 − .449,854,82 x

$s_{b_1} =$ _____ .005 064 _____

$s_{b_0} =$ _____ 4.458 638 _____

Estimated variance of the slope:

$s_{b_1}^2 = \dfrac{s_Y^2}{S_{xx}}$ $=$ 000 025 649 045

Estimated variance of intercept:

$s_{b_0}^2 = s_Y^2 \left\{ \dfrac{1}{n} + \dfrac{\bar{X}^2}{S_{xx}} \right\}$ $=$ 19.879 452

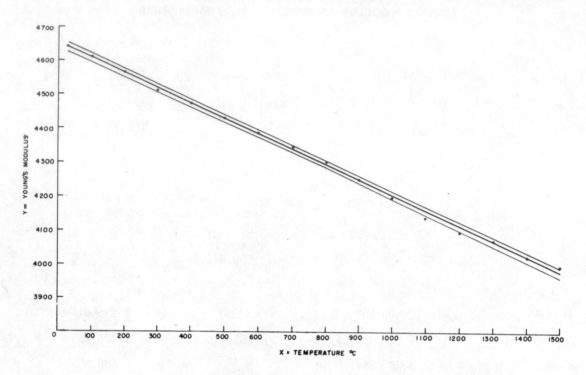

*Figure 5-8.　Young's modulus of sapphire rods as a function
of temperature—showing computed regression line
and confidence interval for the line.*

Using the Regression Equation for Prediction.
The fitted regression equation may be used for two kinds of predictions:

　(a)　To estimate the *true* value of y associated with a particular value of x, e.g., given $x = x'$ to estimate the value of $y' = \beta_0 + \beta_1 x'$; or,

　(b)　To predict a single new observed value Y corresponding to a particular value of x, e.g., given $x = x'$ to predict the value of a single measurement of y'.

Which prediction should be made?　In some cases, it is sufficient to say that the *true* value of y (for given x) lies in a certain interval, and in other cases we may need to know how large (or how small) an individual observed Y value is likely to be associated with a particular value of x.　The question of what to predict is similar to the question of what to specify (e.g., whether to specify average tensile strength or to specify minimum tensile strength) and can be answered

only with respect to a particular situation.　The difference is that here we are concerned with relationships between two variables and therefore must always talk about the value of y, or Y, for fixed x.

The predicted y' or Y' value is obtained by substituting the chosen value (x') of x in the fitted equation.　For a particular value of x, either type of prediction ((a) or (b)) gives the same numerical answer for y' or Y'.　The uncertainty associated with the prediction, however, does depend on whether we are estimating the *true* value of y', or predicting the value Y' of an individual measurement of y'.　If the experiment could be repeated many times, each time obtaining n pairs of (x, Y) values, consider the range of Y values which would be obtained for a given x.　Surely the individual Y values in all the sets will spread over a larger range than will the collection consisting of the average Y's (one from each set).

To estimate the *true* value of y associated with the value x', use the equation

$$y_c' = b_0 + b_1 x'.$$

The variance of y_c' as an estimate of the *true* value $y' = \beta_0 + \beta_1 x'$ is

$$\text{Var } y_c' = s_{Y \cdot x}^2 \left[\frac{1}{n} + \frac{(X' - \bar{X})^2}{S_{xx}} \right]$$

This variance is the variance of estimate of a point on the fitted line.

For example, using the equation relating Young's modulus to temperature, we predict a value for y at $x = 1200$:

$$y_c' = 4654.9846 - .44985482\,(1200)$$
$$y_c' = 4115.16$$
$$\text{Var } y_c' = 86.074 \left[.0625 + \frac{(1200 - 751.875)^2}{3,355,843.75} \right]$$
$$= 86.074\,(.0625 + .0598)$$
$$= 86.074\,(.1223)$$
$$\text{Var } y_c' = 10.53$$

To predict a single observed value of Y corresponding to a given value (x') of x, use the same equation

$$Y_c' = b_0 + b_1 x'.$$

The variance of Y_c' as an estimate of a single new (additional, future) measurement of y' is

$$\text{Var } Y_c' = s_{Y \cdot x}^2 \left[1 + \frac{1}{n} + \frac{(X' - \bar{X})^2}{S_{xx}} \right]$$

The equation for our example is

$$Y = 4654.9846 - .44985482\,x.$$

To predict the value of a single determination of Young's modulus at $x = 750$, substitute in this equation and obtain:

$$Y_i' = 4654.9846 \quad .44985482\,(750)$$
$$= 4317.59$$
$$\text{Var } Y_c' = s_Y^2 \left[1 + \frac{1}{n} + \frac{(X' - \bar{X})^2}{S_{xx}} \right]$$
$$= 86.074 \left[1 + .0625 + \frac{(750 - 751.875)^2}{3,355,843.75} \right]$$
$$= 86.074\,(1.0625)$$
$$= 91.45$$

5-4.1.2 What are the Confidence Interval Estimates for: the Line as a Whole; a Point on the Line; a Future Value of Y Corresponding to a Given Value of x?

Once we have fitted the line, we want to make predictions from it, and we want to know how good our predictions are. Often, these predictions will be given in the form of an interval together with a confidence coefficient associated with the interval—i.e., confidence interval estimates. Several kinds of confidence interval estimates may be made:

(a) A confidence band for the line as a whole.

(b) A confidence interval for a point on the line—i.e., a confidence interval for y' (the *true* value of y and the *mean* value of Y) corresponding to a single value of $x = x'$.

If the fitted line is, say, a calibration line which will be used over and over again, we will want to make the interval estimate described in (a). In other cases, the line as such may not be so important. The line may have been fitted only to investigate or check the structure of the relationship, and the interest of the experimenter may be centered at one or two values of the variables.

Another kind of interval estimate sometimes is required:

(c) A single observed value (Y') of Y corresponding to a new value of $x = x'$.

These three kinds of confidence interval statements have somewhat different interpretations. The confidence interval for (b) is interpreted as follows:

Suppose that we repeated our experiment a large number of times. *Each time*, we obtain n pairs of values (x_i, Y_i), fit the line, and compute a confidence interval estimate for $y' = \beta_0 + \beta_1 x'$, the value of y corresponding to the particular value $x = x'$. Such interval estimates of y' are expected to be correct (i.e., include the *true* value of y') a proportion $(1 - \alpha)$ of the time. If we were to make an interval estimate of y'' corresponding to another value of $x = x''$, these interval estimates also would be expected to include y'' the same proportion $(1 - \alpha)$ of the time. However, taken together, these intervals do not constitute a joint confidence statement about y' and y'' which would be expected to be correct exactly a proportion $(1 - \alpha)$ of the time; nor is the effective level of confidence $(1 - \alpha)^2$, because the two statements are not independent but are correlated in a manner intimately dependent on the values x' and x'' for which the predictions are to be made.

The confidence band for the whole line (a) implies the same sort of repetition of the experiment except that our confidence statements are not now limited to one x at a time, but we can talk about any number of x values simultaneously—about the whole line. Our confidence statement applies to the line as a whole, and therefore the confidence intervals for y corresponding to all the chosen x values will simultaneously be correct a proportion $(1 - \alpha)$ of the time. It will be noted that the intervals in (a) are larger than the intervals in (b) by the ratio

$\sqrt{2F}/t$. This wider interval is the "price" we pay for making joint statements about y for any number of or for all of the x values, rather than the y for a single x.

Another *caution* is in order. We cannot use the same computed line in (b) and (c) to make a large number of predictions, and claim that $100 (1 - \alpha) \%$ of the predictions will be correct. The *estimated* line may be very close to the *true line*, in which case nearly all of the interval predictions may be correct; or the line may be considerably different from the *true line*, in which case very few may be correct. In practice, provided our situation is *in control*, we should always revise our estimate of the line to include additional information in the way of new points.

5-4.1.2.1   What is the $(1 - \alpha)$ Confidence Band for the Line as a Whole?

Procedure	Example
(1) Choose the desired confidence level, $1 - \alpha$	(1) Let: $1 - \alpha = .95$ $\alpha = .05$
(2) Obtain s_Y from Worksheet.	(2) $s_Y = 9.277617$ from Worksheet 5-4.1
(3) Look up $F_{1-\alpha}$ for $(2, n - 2)$ degrees of freedom in Table A-5.	(3) $F_{.95} (2, 14) = 3.74$
(4) Choose a number of values of X (within the range of the data) at which to compute points for drawing the confidence band.	(4) Let: $X = 30$ $X = 400$ $X = 800$ $X = 1200$ $X = 1500,$ for example.
(5) At each selected value of X, compute: $\quad Y_c = \bar{Y} + b_1 (X - \bar{X})$ and $\quad W_1 = \sqrt{2F}\, s_Y \left[\dfrac{1}{n} + \dfrac{(X - \bar{X})^2}{S_{xx}} \right]^{\frac{1}{2}}$	(5) See Table 5-2 for a convenient computational arrangement and the example calculations.
(6) A $(1 - \alpha)$ confidence band for the whole line is determined by $\quad Y_c \pm W_1.$	(6) See Table 5-2.

Procedure

(7) To draw the line and its confidence band, plot Y_c at two of the extreme selected values of X. Connect the two points by a straight line. At each selected value of X, also plot $Y_c + W_1$ and $Y_c - W_1$. Connect the upper series of points, and the lower series of points, by smooth curves.

If more points are needed for drawing the curves for the band, note that, because of symmetry, the calculation of W_1 at n values of X actually gives W_1 at $2n$ values of X.

Example

(7) See Figure 5-8.

For example: W_1 (but not Y_c) has the same value at $X = 400$ (i.e., $\bar{X} - 351.875$) as at $X = 1103.75$ (i.e., $\bar{X} + 351.875$).

TABLE 5-2.   COMPUTATIONAL ARRANGEMENT FOR PROCEDURE 5-4.1.2.1

X	$(X - \bar{X})$	Y_c	$\dfrac{1}{n} + \dfrac{(X - \bar{X})^2}{S_{xx}}$	$s^2_{Y_c}$	s_{Y_c}	W_1	$Y_c + W_1$	$Y_c - W_1$
30	−721.875	4641.49	.21778	18.7452	4.3296	11.84	4653.33	4629.65
400	−351.875	4475.04	.09940	8.5558	2.9250	8.00	4483.04	4467.04
800	48.125	4295.10	.06319	5.4390	2.3322	6.38	4301.48	4288.72
1200	448.125	4115.16	.12234	10.5303	3.2450	8.88	4124.04	4106.28
1500	748.125	3980.20	.22928	19.7351	4.4424	12.15	3992.35	3968.05

$\bar{X} = 751.875$

coded $\bar{Y} = 316.75$

$\bar{Y}$ (original units) $= 4316.75$

$s^2_Y = 86.0741857$

$\dfrac{1}{n} = .0625$

$b_1 = -.44985482$

$S_{xx} = 3,355,843.75$

$\sqrt{2F} = 2.735$

$Y_c = \bar{Y} + b_1 (X - \bar{X})$

$s^2_{Y_c} = s^2_Y \left[\dfrac{1}{n} + \dfrac{(X - \bar{X})^2}{S_{xx}} \right]$

$W_1 = 2.735\, s_{Y_c}$

5-4.1.2.2   Give a $(1 - \alpha)$ Confidence Interval Estimate for a Single Point on the Line (i.e., the Mean Value of Y Corresponding to a Chosen Value of $x = x'$)

Procedure	Example

(1) Choose the desired confidence level, $1 - \alpha$

(1) Let: $1 - \alpha = .95$
$\alpha = .05$

(2) Obtain s_Y from Worksheet.

(2) $s_Y = 9.277617$
from Worksheet 5-4.1

(3) Look up $t_{1-\alpha/2}$ for $n - 2$ degrees of freedom in Table A-4.

(3) $t_{.975}(14) = 2.145$

(4) Choose X', the value of X at which we want to make an interval estimate of the mean value of Y.

(4) Let $X' = 1200$

(5) Compute:
$$W_2 = t_{1-\alpha/2}\, s_Y \left[\frac{1}{n} + \frac{(X' - \bar{X})^2}{S_{xx}}\right]^{\frac{1}{2}}$$

and

$$Y_c = \bar{Y} + b_1 (X' - \bar{X})$$

(5)

$W_2 = 2.145\ (3.2451)$
$= 6.96$

$Y_c = 4115.16$

(6) A $(1 - \alpha)$ confidence interval estimate for the mean value of Y corresponding to $X = X'$ is given by
$Y_c \pm W_2$.

(6) A 95% confidence interval estimate for the mean value of Y corresponding to $X = 1200$ is
4115.16 ± 6.96
= 4108.20 to 4122.12.

Note: An interval estimate of the intercept of the line (β_0) is obtained by setting $X' = 0$ in the above procedure.

5-4.1.2.3 Give a $(1 - \alpha)$ Confidence Interval Estimate for a Single (Future) Value (Y') of Y Corresponding to a Chosen Value (x') of x.

Procedure	Example
(1) Choose the desired confidence level, $1 - \alpha$	(1) Let: $1 - \alpha = .95$ $\alpha = .05$
(2) Obtain s_Y from Worksheet.	(2) $s_Y = 9.277617$ from Worksheet 5-4.1
(3) Look up $t_{1-\alpha/2}$ for $n - 2$ degrees of freedom in Table A-4.	(3) $t_{.975}(14) = 2.145$
(4) Choose X', the value of X at which we want to make an interval estimate of a single value of Y.	(4) Let $X' = 1200$
(5) Compute:	(5)

$$W_3 = t_{1-\alpha/2}\, s_Y \left[1 + \frac{1}{n} + \frac{(X' - \bar{X})^2}{S_{xx}}\right]^{\frac{1}{2}}$$

and

$$Y_c = \bar{Y} + b_1 (X' - \bar{X})$$

$W_3 = 2.145\ (9.8288)$
$\quad = 21.08$

$Y_c = 4115.16$

(6) A $(1 - \alpha)$ confidence interval estimate for Y' (the single value of Y corresponding to X') is

$$Y_c \pm W_3 .$$

(6) A 95% confidence interval estimate for a single value of Y corresponding to $X' = 1200$ is
4115.16 ± 21.08
$= 4094.08$ to 4136.24 .

5-4.1.3 What is the Confidence Interval Estimate for β_1, the Slope of the True Line $y = \beta_0 + \beta_1 x$?

Procedure	Example
(1) Choose the desired confidence level, $1 - \alpha$	(1) Let: $1 - \alpha = .95$ $\alpha = .05$
(2) Look up $t_{1-\alpha/2}$ for $n - 2$ degrees of freedom in Table A-4.	(2) $t_{.975}(14) = 2.145$
(3) Obtain s_{b_1} from Worksheet.	(3) $s_{b_1} = .005064$ from Worksheet 5.4.1
(4) Compute $W_4 = t_{1-\alpha/2}\, s_{b_1}$	(4) $W_4 = 2.145\ (.005064)$ $= .010862$

(5) A $(1 - \alpha)$ confidence interval estimate for β_1 is

$$b_1 \pm W_4 .$$

(5) $b_1 = -.449855$
$W_4 = .010862$
A 95% confidence interval for β_1 is the interval $-.449855 \pm .010862$, i.e., the interval from $-.460717$ to $-.438993$.

5-4.1.4 If We Observe n' New Values of Y (with Average $\bar{Y}'$), How Can We Use the Fitted Regression Line to Obtain an Interval Estimate of the Value of x that Produced These Values of Y?

Example: Suppose that we obtain 10 new measurements of Young's modulus (with average, $\bar{Y}' = 4500$) and we wish to use the regression line to make an interval estimate of the temperature (x) at which the measurements were made.

Procedure	**Example**

(1) Choose the desired confidence level, $1 - \alpha$

(1) Let: $1 - \alpha = .95$
$$\alpha = .05$$

(2) Look up $t_{1-\alpha/2}$ for $n - 2$ degrees of freedom in Table A-4.

(2) $t_{.975}(14) = 2.145$

(3) Obtain b_1 and $s_{b_1}^2$ from Worksheet.

(3) From Worksheet 5-4.1,
$$b_1 = -.449855$$
$$s_{b_1}^2 = .0000256490$$

(4) Compute
$$C = b_1^2 - (t_{1-\alpha/2})^2 \, s_{b_1}^2$$

(4)
$$C = .202370 - .000118$$
$$= .202252$$

(5) A $(1 - \alpha)$ confidence interval estimate for the X corresponding to $\bar{Y}'$ is computed from

$$X' = \bar{X} + \frac{b_1 (\bar{Y}' - \bar{Y})}{C}$$
$$\pm \frac{t_{1-\alpha/2} \, s_Y}{C} \sqrt{\frac{(\bar{Y}' - \bar{Y})^2}{S_{xx}} + \left(\frac{1}{n} + \frac{1}{n'}\right) C}$$

(5) A 95% confidence interval would be computed as follows:

$$X' = 751.875 - \frac{.449855 \, (4500 - 4316.75)}{.202252}$$
$$\pm \frac{2.145 \, (9.277617)}{.202252} \times$$
$$\sqrt{\frac{(183.25)^2}{3,355,843.75} + (.1625)(.202252)}$$
$$= 751.875 - 407.590$$
$$\pm 98.39452 \sqrt{.0100066 + .0328660}$$
$$= 344.285 \pm 98.39452 \sqrt{.0428726}$$
$$= 344.285 \pm 98.39452 \, (.20706)$$
$$= 344.285 \pm 20.374$$

The interval from $X = 323.911$ to $X = 364.659$ is a 95% confidence interval for the value of temperature which produced the 10 measurements whose mean Young's modulus was 4500.

5-4.1.5 Using the Fitted Regression Line, How Can We Choose a Value (x') of x Which We May Expect with Confidence (1 − α) Will Produce a Value of Y Not Less Than Some Specified Value Q?

Example: What value (x') of temperature (x) can be expected to produce a value of Young's modulus not less than 4300?

Procedure	**Example**

(1) Choose the desired confidence level, $1 - \alpha$; and choose Q

(1) Let: $1 - \alpha = .95$
$\qquad \alpha = .05$
$\qquad Q = 4300$

(2) Look up $t_{1-\alpha}$ for $n - 2$ degrees of freedom in Table A-4.

(2) $\quad t_{.95}(14) = 1.761$

(3) Obtain b_1 and $s_{b_1}^2$ from Worksheet.

(3) From Worksheet 5-4.1,
$$b_1 = -.449855$$
$$s_{b_1}^2 = .0000256490$$

(4) Compute
$$C = b_1^2 - (t_{1-\alpha})^2 \, s_{b_1}^2$$

(4)
$$C = .202370 - .000080$$
$$= .202290$$

(5) Compute
$$X' = \bar{X} + b_1 \left(\frac{Q - \bar{Y}}{C} \right)$$
$$\pm \frac{t_{1-\alpha} \, s_Y}{C} \sqrt{ \frac{(Q - \bar{Y})^2}{S_{xx}} + \left(\frac{n+1}{n} \right) C }$$

where the sign before the last term is $+$ if b_1 is positive or $-$ if b_1 is negative. We have confidence $(1 - \alpha)$ that a value of $X = X'$ will correspond to (produce) a value of Y not less than Q. (See discussion of "confidence" in straight-line prediction in Paragraph 5-4.1.2).

(5) The value of X' is computed as follows:

$$X' = 751.875$$
$$+ \frac{-.449855 \, (4300 - 4316.75)}{.202290}$$
$$- \frac{1.761 \, (9.277617)}{.202290} \times$$
$$\sqrt{ \frac{(4300 - 4316.75)^2}{3{,}355{,}843.75} + \left(\frac{17}{16} \right) C }$$

$$= 751.875 + 37.249$$
$$- 80.764662 \sqrt{.000084 + .214933}$$

$$= 751.875 + 37.249$$
$$- 80.764662 \sqrt{.215017}$$

$$= 751.875 + 37.249 - 37.450$$

$$= 751.674 \ .$$

5-4.1.6 Is the Assumption of Linear Regression Justified?

This involves a test of the assumption that the mean Y values ($\bar{Y}_x$) for given x values do lie on a straight line (we assume that for any given value of x, the corresponding individual Y values are normally distributed with variance σ_Y^2, which is independent of the value of x). A simple test is available provided that we have more than one observation on Y at one or more values of x. Assume that there are n pairs of values (x_i, Y_i), and that among these pairs there occur only k values of x (where k is less than n).

For example, see the data recorded in Table 5-3 which shows measurements of Young's modulus (coded) of sapphire rods as a function of temperature.

Each x is recorded in Column 1, and the corresponding Y values (varying in number from 1 to 3 in the example) are recorded opposite the appropriate x. The remaining columns in the table are convenient for the required computations.

TABLE 5-3. COMPUTATIONAL ARRANGEMENT FOR TEST OF LINEARITY

X = Temperature	Y = Young's Modulus Minus 3000			ΣY	$(\Sigma Y)^2$	ΣY^2	n_i	$n_i X_i$	$n_i X_i^2$	ΣXY	$\dfrac{(\Sigma Y)^2}{n_i}$
500	328			328	107584	107584	1	500	250000	164000	107584
550	296			296	87616	87616	1	550	302500	162800	87616
600	266			266	70756	70756	1	600	360000	159600	70756
603	260	244		504	254016	127136	2	1206	727218	303912	127008
650	240	232	213	685	469225	156793	3	1950	1267500	445250	156408.3
700	204	203	184	591	349281	116681	3	2100	1470000	413700	116427
750	174	175	154	503	253009	84617	3	2250	1687500	377250	84336.3
800	152	146	124	422	178084	59796	3	2400	1920000	337600	59361.3
850	117	94		211	44521	22525	2	1700	1445000	179350	22260.5
900	97	61		158	24964	13130	2	1800	1620000	142200	12482
950	38			38	1444	1444	1	950	902500	36100	1444
1000	30	5		35	1225	925	2	2000	2000000	35000	612.5
TOTAL				4037 $= T_1$		849003 $= T_2$	24 $= n$	18006 $= T_3$	13952218 $= T_4$	2756762 $= T_5$	846296 $= T_6$

Procedure	Example

(1) Choose α, the significance level of the test.

(1) Let: $\alpha = .05$
$1 - \alpha = .95$

(2) Compute:

$$\bar{Y} = \frac{T_1}{n}$$

$$\bar{X} = \frac{T_3}{n}, \quad \text{the weighted average of } X.$$

(2)

$$\bar{Y} = \frac{4037}{24}$$
$$= 168.21$$

$$\bar{X} = \frac{18006}{24}$$
$$= 750.25$$

(3) Compute

$$S_1 = T_6 - \frac{(T_1)^2}{n}$$

(3)

$$\frac{(T_1)^2}{n} = 679057.04$$
$$S_1 = 846296 - 679057.04$$
$$= 167238.96$$

(4) Compute

$$b = \frac{T_5 - \frac{T_3 T_1}{n}}{T_4 - \frac{(T_3)^2}{n}}$$

(4)

$$b = \frac{2756762 - 3028759.25}{13952218 - 13509001.5}$$
$$= \frac{-271997.25}{443216.5}$$
$$= -0.6136894$$

(5) Compute

$$S_2 = b\left(T_5 - \frac{T_3 T_1}{n}\right)$$

(5)

$$S_2 = -0.6136894\,(-271997.25)$$
$$= 166921.83$$

(6) Compute

$$S_3 = T_2 - \frac{(T_1)^2}{n}$$

(6)

$$S_3 = 849003 - 679057.04$$
$$= 169945.96$$

(7) Look up $F_{1-\alpha}$ for $(k - 2, n - k)$ degrees of freedom in Table A-5.

(7) $n = 24$
$k = 12$
$F_{.95}$ for $(10, 12)$ degrees of freedom $= 2.75$

(8) Compute

$$F = \left(\frac{S_1 - S_2}{S_3 - S_1}\right)\left(\frac{n - k}{k - 2}\right)$$

(8)

$$F = \left(\frac{317.13}{2707}\right)\left(\frac{24 - 12}{10}\right)$$
$$= (.11715)\,(1.2)$$
$$= 0.14$$

(9) If $F > F_{1-\alpha}$, decide that the "array means" $\bar{Y}_x$ do not lie on a straight line. If $F < F_{1-\alpha}$, the hypothesis of linearity is not disproved.

(9) Since F is less than $F_{1-\alpha}$, the hypothesis of linearity is not disproved.

5-4.2   FI RELATIONSHIPS WHEN THE INTERCEPT IS KNOWN TO BE EQUAL TO ZERO (LINES THROUGH THE ORIGIN)

In Paragraph 5-4.1, we assumed:

(a) that there is an underlying linear functional relationship between x and y of the form $y = \beta_0 + \beta_1 x$, with intercept β_0 and slope β_1 both different from zero;

(b) that our data consist of observed values $Y_1, Y_2, \ldots, Y_n$ of y, corresponding to accurately-known values $x_1, x_2, \ldots, x_n$ of x; and,

(c) that the Y's can be regarded as being independently and normally distributed with means equal to their respective *true* values (i.e, mean of $Y_i = \beta_0 + \beta_1 x_i$, $i = 1, 2, \ldots, n$) and constant variance $\sigma^2_{Y \cdot x} = \sigma^2$ for all x.

Furthermore, we gave: a procedure (Paragraph 5-4.1.2.2 with $X' = 0$) for determining confidence limits for β_0, and hence for testing the hypothesis that $\beta_0 = 0$, in the absence of prior knowledge of the value of β_1; and a procedure that is independent of the value of β_0 (Paragraph 5-4.1.3) for determining confidence limits for β_1, and hence for testing the hypothesis that $\beta_1 = 0$.

We now consider the analysis of data corresponding to an FI structural relationship when it is known that $y = 0$ when $x = 0$, so that the line must pass through the origin, i.e., *when it is known that $\beta_0 = 0$.* To begin with, we assume as in (b) and (c) above, that our data consist of observed values $Y_1, Y_2, \ldots, Y_n$, of a *dependent* variable y corresponding to accurately-known values $x_1, x_2, \ldots, x_n$ of the *independent* variable x and that these Y's can be regarded as being *independently* and normally distributed with means $\beta_1 x_1, \beta_1 x_2, \ldots, \beta_1 x_n$, respectively, and variances $\sigma^2_{Y \cdot x}$ that may depend on x. We consider explicitly the cases of constant variance $(\sigma^2_{Y \cdot x} = \sigma^2)$, variance proportional to x $(\sigma^2_{Y \cdot x} = x\sigma^2)$, and standard deviation proportional to x $(\sigma_{Y \cdot x} = x\sigma)$. Finally, we consider briefly the case of *cumulative data* where $x_1 < x_2 < \ldots < x_n$ and the error in Y_i is of the form $e_1 + e_2 + \ldots + e_{i-1} + e_i$, that is, is the sum of the errors of all preceding Y's plus a "private error" e_i of its own. Following Mandel,[3] we assume that the errors (e_i) are independently and normally distributed with zero means and with variances proportional to the length of their generation intervals, i.e.,

$\sigma^2_{e_i} = (x_i - x_{i-1})\sigma^2$. Under these circumstances, the Y's will be normally distributed with means $\beta_1 x_1, \beta_1 x_2, \ldots, \beta_1 x_n$, respectively, as before; and with variances $\sigma^2_{Y_i} = x_i \sigma^2$, respectively; but will not be independent owing to the overlap among their respective errors.

5-4.2.1   Line Through Origin, Variance of Y's Independent of x.

The slope of the best-fitting line of the form $Y = b_1 x$ is given by

$$b_1 = \frac{\sum\limits_{i=1}^{n} x_i Y_i}{\sum\limits_{i=1}^{n} x_i^2}$$

and the estimated variance of b_1 is

$$s_{b_1}^2 = \frac{s_Y^2}{\sum\limits_{i=1}^{n} x_i^2}$$

where

$$s_Y^2 = \frac{\sum\limits_{i=1}^{n} (Y_i - b_1 x_i)^2}{n - 1}$$

$$= \frac{\sum\limits_{i=1}^{n} Y_i^2 - \dfrac{\left(\sum\limits_{1}^{n} x_i Y_i\right)^2}{\sum\limits_{1}^{n} x_i^2}}{n - 1}$$

Consequently, we may effect a simplification of our Basic Worksheet—see Worksheet 5-4.2.1.

Using the values of b_1 and s_{b_1} so obtained, confidence limits for β_1, the slope of the true line through the origin, $y = \beta_1 x$, can be obtained by following the procedure of Paragraph 5-4.1.3 using $t_{1-\alpha/2}$ for $n - 1$ degrees of freedom. Confidence limits for the line as a whole then are obtained simply by plotting the lines $y = \beta_1^U x$ and $y = \beta_1^L x$, where β_1^U and β_1^L are the upper and lower confidence limits for β_1 obtained in the manner just described. The limiting lines, in this instance, also furnish confidence limits for the value y' of y corresponding to a particular point on the line, say for $x = x'$, so that an additional procedure is unnecessary. Confidence limits for a single future observed Y corresponding to $x = x'$ are given by

$$b_1 x' \pm t_{1-\alpha/2} \sqrt{s_Y^2 + (x')^2 s_{b_1}^2} \, ,$$

where s_Y^2 and s_{b_1} are from our modified worksheet and $t_{1-\alpha/2}$ corresponds to $n - 1$ degrees of freedom.

WORKSHEET 5-4.2.1

**WORKSHEET FOR FI RELATIONSHIPS WHEN THE INTERCEPT IS KNOWN TO BE ZERO
AND THE VARIANCES OF THE Y's IS INDEPENDENT OF x**

X denotes _____ Y denotes _____

$\Sigma X =$ _____ $\Sigma Y =$ _____

$\bar{X} =$ _____ $\bar{Y} =$ _____

Number of points: $n =$ _____

Step (1) ΣXY = _____

(2) ΣX^2 = _____   (5) $\dfrac{(\Sigma XY)^2}{\Sigma X^2}$ = _____

(3) ΣY^2 = _____   (6) $(n-1)\,s_Y^2 =$ Step (3) − Step (5)

(4) $b_1 = \dfrac{\Sigma XY}{\Sigma X^2} =$ Step (1) ÷ Step (2)   (7) s_Y^2 =   Step (6) ÷ (n − 1)

s_Y = _____

Estimated variance of the slope:

Equation of the Line:

$Y = b_1 X$

_____

$s_{b_1}^2 = \dfrac{s_Y^2}{\Sigma X^2}$ =   Step (7) ÷ Step (2)

$s_{b_1} =$ _____

5-4.2.2 Line Through Origin, Variance Proportional to x ($\sigma_{Y \cdot x}^2 = x\sigma^2$). The slope of the best-fitting line of form $Y = b_1 x$ is given by

$$b_1 = \frac{\displaystyle\sum_{i=1}^{n} Y_i}{\displaystyle\sum_{i=1}^{n} x_i} = \frac{\bar{Y}}{\bar{x}} \; ,$$

the *ratio of the averages*, and the estimated variance of b_1 is

$$s_{b_1}^2 = \frac{s^2}{\displaystyle\sum_{i=1}^{n} x_i}$$

where

$$(n-1)\,s^2 = \sum_{i=1}^{n} \left(\frac{Y_i^2}{x_i}\right) - \frac{\left(\displaystyle\sum_{i=1}^{n} Y_i\right)^2}{\displaystyle\sum_{i=1}^{n} x_i}$$

Using the values of b_1 and s_{b_1} so obtained, confidence limits for β_1, the slope of the true line through the origin, $y = \beta_1 x$, can be obtained by following the procedure of Paragraph 5-4.1.3 using $t_{1-\alpha/2}$ for $n-1$ degrees of freedom. Confidence limits for the line as a whole then are obtained simply by plotting the lines $y = \beta_1^U x$ and $y = \beta_1^L x$ where β_1^U and β_1^L are the upper and lower confidence limits for β_1 obtained in the manner just described. The limiting lines, in this instance, also furnish confidence limits for the value y' corresponding to a particular point on the line, say for $x = x'$. Confidence limits for a single future observed Y corresponding to $x = x'$, are given by

$$b_1 x' \pm t_{1-\alpha/2} \sqrt{x' s^2 + (x')^2 s_{b_1}^2},$$

where s_{b_1} is computed as shown above and $t_{1-\alpha/2}$ corresponds to $n-1$ degrees of freedom.

5-4.2.3 Line Through Origin, Standard Deviation Proportional to x ($\sigma_{Y \cdot x} = x\sigma$).

The slope of the best-fitting line of form $Y = b_1 x$ is given by

$$b_1 = \sum_{i=1}^{n} \left(\frac{Y_i}{x_i} \right) / n,$$

the average of the ratios $\left(\dfrac{Y_i}{x_i} \right)$,

and the estimated variance of b_1 is

$$s_{b_1}^2 = \frac{s^2}{n}$$

where

$$(n-1) \, s^2 = \sum_{i=1}^{n} \left(\frac{Y_i}{x_i} \right)^2 - \frac{\left[\sum_{i=1}^{n} \left(\frac{Y_i}{x_i} \right) \right]^2}{n}$$

that is,

$$s^2 = \frac{\sum_{i=1}^{n} R_i - \dfrac{(\Sigma R_i)^2}{n}}{n \, (n-1)}$$

for $R_i = \dfrac{Y_i}{x_i}$

Using the values of b_1 and s_{b_1} so obtained, confidence limits for β_1, the slope of the true line through the origin, $y = \beta_1 x$, can be obtained by following the procedure of Paragraph 5-4.1.3 using $t_{1-\alpha/2}$ for $n-1$ degrees of freedom. Confidence limits for the line as a whole are then obtained simply by plotting the lines $y = \beta_1^U x$ and $y = \beta_1^L x$ where β_1^U and β_1^L are the upper and lower confidence limits for β_1 obtained in the manner just described. The limiting lines, in this instance, also furnish confidence limits for the value y' of y corresponding to a particular point on the line, say for $x = x'$. Confidence limits for a single future observed Y corresponding to $x = x'$, are given by

$$b_1 x' \pm t_{1-\alpha/2} \, x' \, \sqrt{s^2 + s_{b_1}^2} \;,$$

where s_{b_1} is computed as shown above and $t_{1-\alpha/2}$ corresponds to $n-1$ degrees of freedom.

5-4.2.4 Line Through Origin, Errors of Y's Cumulative (Cumulative Data).

In many engineering tests and laboratory experiments the observed values $Y_1, Y_2, \ldots, Y_i, \ldots$, of a dependent variable y represent the cumulative magnitude of some effect at successive values $x_1 < x_2 < x_3 < \ldots$ of the independent

variable x. Thus, $Y_1, Y_2, \ldots$, may denote: the total weight loss of a tire under road test, measured at successive mileages $x_1, x_2, \ldots$; or the weight gain of some material due to water absorption at successive times $x_1, x_2, \ldots$; or the total deflection of a beam (or total compression of a spring) under continually increasing load, measured at loads $x_1, x_2, \ldots$; and so forth. In such cases, even though the underlying functional relationship takes the form of a line through the origin, $y = \beta x$, none of the procedures that we have presented thus far will be applicable, because of the cumulative effect of errors of technique on the successive Y's; the deviation of Y_i from its true or expected value y_i will include the deviation $(Y_{i-1} - y_{i-1})$ of Y_{i-1} from its true or expected value, plus an individual "private deviation or error" e_i of its own. Hence, the total error of Y_i will be the sum $(e_1 + e_2 + \ldots + e_{i-1} + e_i)$ of the individual error contributions of $Y_1, Y_2, \ldots, Y_{i-1}$, and its own additional deviation.

If the test or experiment starts at $x_0 = 0$, and the x's form an uninterrupted sequence $0 < x_1 < x_2 < \ldots < x_n$, and if we may regard the individual error contributions $e_1, e_2, \ldots$, as independently and normally distributed with zero means and variances proportional to the lengths of the x-intervals over which they accrue, i.e., if $\sigma_{e_i}^2 = (x_i - x_{i-1}) \, \sigma^2$, then the best estimate of the slope of the underlying linear functional relation $y = \beta_1 x$ is given by

$$b_1 = \frac{Y_n}{x_n}$$

and estimated variance of b_1

$$s_{b_1}^2 = \frac{1}{(n-1) \, x_n} \left\{ \sum_{i=1}^{n} \frac{(Y_i - Y_{i-1})^2}{x_i - x_{i-1}} - \frac{Y_n^2}{x_n} \right\}$$

in which $x_0 = 0$ and $Y_0 = 0$ by hypothesis.

Using the values of b_1 and s_{b_1} so obtained, confidence limits for β_1, the slope of the true line through the origin, $y = \beta_1 x$, can be obtained by following the procedure of Paragraph 5-4.1.3 using $t_{1-\alpha/2}$ for $n-1$ degrees of freedom. Confidence limits for the line as a whole then are obtained simply by plotting the lines $y = \beta_1^U x$ and $y = \beta_1^L x$, where β_1^U and β_1^L are the upper and lower confidence limits for β_1 obtained in the manner just described. These limit lines also provide confidence limits for a particular point on the line, say the value y' corresponding to $x = x'$. For the fitting of lines of this sort to cumulative data under more general conditions, and for other related matters, see Mandel's article.[3]

5-4.3 FII RELATIONSHIPS

Distinguishing Features. There is an underlying mathematical (functional) relationship between the two variables, of the form

$$y = \beta_0 + \beta_1 x.$$

Both X and Y are subject to errors of measurement. Read Paragraph 5-3.1 and Table 5-1.

The full treatment of this case depends on the assumptions we are willing to make about error distributions. For complete discussion of the problem, see Acton.[4]

5-4.3.1 A Simple Method of Fitting the Line In the General Case.

There is a quick and simple method of fitting a line of the form $Y = b_0 + b_1 X$ which is generally applicable when both X and Y are subject to errors of measurement. This method is described in Bartlett,[5] and is illustrated in this paragraph. Similar methods had been used previously by other authors.

(a) For the location of the fitted straight line, use as the pivot point the center of gravity of all n observed points (X_i, Y_i), that is, the point with the mean coordinates $(\bar{X}, \bar{Y})$. In consequence, the fitted line will be of the form $Y = b_0 + b_1 X$ with $b_0 = \bar{Y} - b_1 \bar{X}$, just as in the least-squares method in Paragraph 5-4.1.

(b) For the slope, divide the n plotted points into three non-overlapping groups when considered in the X direction. There should be an equal number of points, k, in each of the two extreme groups, with k as close to $\frac{n}{3}$ as possible.

Take, as the slope of the line,

$$b_1 = \frac{\bar{Y}_3 - \bar{Y}_1}{\bar{X}_3 - \bar{X}_1} ,$$

where

$\bar{Y}_3 = $ average Y for 3rd group
$\bar{Y}_1 = $ average Y for 1st group
$\bar{X}_3 = $ average X for 3rd group
$\bar{X}_1 = $ average X for 1st group.

Data Sample 5-4.3.1—Relation of Two Colorimetric Methods

The following data are coded results of two colorimetric methods for the determination of a chemical constituent. (The data have been coded for a special purpose which has nothing to do with this illustration). The interest here, of course, is in the relationship between results given by the two methods, and it is presumed that there is a functional relationship with both methods subject to errors of measurement.

Sample	Method I X	Method II Y
1	3720	5363
2	4328	6195
3	4655	6428
4	4818	6662
5	5545	7562
6	7278	9184
7	7880	10070
8	10085	12519
9	11707	13980

(a) The fitted line must pass through the point $(\bar{X}, \bar{Y})$, where

$\bar{X} = 6668.4$
$\bar{Y} = 8662.6$

(b) To determine the slope, divide the points into 3 groups. Since there are 9 points, exactly 3 equal groups are obtained.

$\bar{Y}_3 = 12190$
$\bar{Y}_1 = 5995$
$\bar{X}_3 = 9891$
$\bar{X}_1 = 4234$

$$b_1 = \frac{\bar{Y}_3 - \bar{Y}_1}{\bar{X}_3 - \bar{X}_1}$$

$$= \frac{12190 - 5995}{9891 - 4234}$$

$$= \frac{6195}{5657}$$

$$= 1.0951$$

$$b_0 = \bar{Y} - b_1 \bar{X}$$

$$= 8662.6 - \frac{6195}{5657}(6668.4)$$

$$= 1360.0$$

The fitted line

$$Y = 1360.0 + 1.0951\ X$$

is shown in Figure 5-9.

Procedures are given in Bartlett[5] for determining $100\ (1 - \alpha)\ \%$ confidence limits for the true slope β_1; and for determining a $100\ (1 - \alpha)\ \%$ confidence ellipse for β_0 and β_1 jointly, from which $100\ (1 - \alpha)\ \%$ confidence limits for the line as a whole can be derived. For strict validity, they require that the measurement errors affecting the observed X_i be sufficiently small in comparison with the spacing of their true values x_i that the allocation of the observational points (X_i, Y_i) to the three groups is unaffected. These procedures are formally

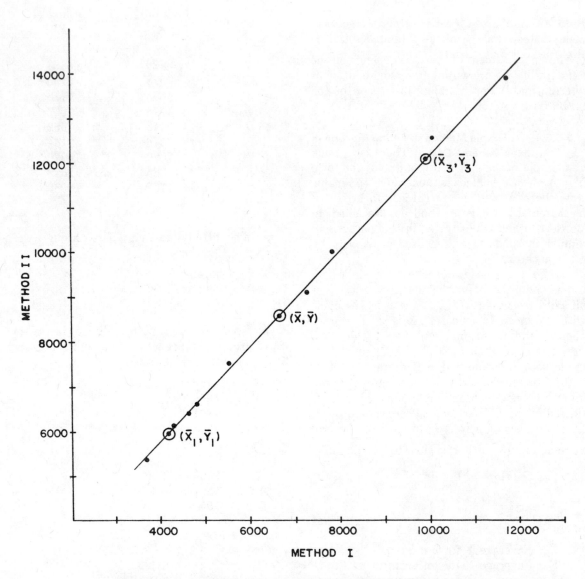

Figure 5-9.   Relationship between two methods of determining
a chemical constituent—an FII relationship.

5-28

similar to those appropriate to the least-squares method in FI situations, but involve more complex calculations. We do not consider them further here.

5-4.3.2 An Important Exceptional Case.

Until comparatively recently it was not realized that there is a broad class of controlled experimental situations in which both X and Y are subject to errors of measurement, yet all of the techniques appropriate to the FI case (x's accurately known, measurement errors affect the Y's only) are strictly applicable without change.

As an example, let us consider the case of an analytical chemist who, in order to obtain an accurate determination of the concentration of a potassium sulphate solution, decides to proceed as follows: From a burette he will draw off 5, 10, 15, and 20 ml samples of the solution. Volume of solution is his independent variable x, and his target values are $x_1 = 5$, $x_2 = 10$, $x_3 = 15$, and $x_4 = 20$, respectively. The volumes of solution that he actually draws off $X_1, X_2, X_3,$ and X_4 will, of course, differ from the nominal or target values as a result of errors of technique, and he will not attempt to measure their volumes accurately. These four samples of the potassium sulphate solution then will be treated with excess barium chloride, and the precipitated barium sulphate dried and weighed. Let $Y_1, Y_2, Y_3,$ and Y_4 denote the corresponding yields of barium sulphate. These yields actually will correspond, of course, to the actual inputs $X_1, X_2, X_3,$ and X_4, respectively; and will differ from the true yields associated with these inputs, say $y_1(X_1), y_2(X_2), y_3(X_3),$ and $y_4(X_4)$, respectively, as a result of errors of weighing and analytical technique. The sulphate concentration of the original potassium sulphate solution then will be determined by evaluating the slope b_1 of the best fitting straight line $Y = b_0 + b_1x$, relating the observed barium sulphate yields ($Y_1, Y_2, Y_3,$ and Y_4) to the nominal or target volumes of solution ($x_1, x_2, x_3,$ and x_4)—the intercept b_0 of the line making appropriate allowance for the possibility of bias of the analytical procedure resulting in a non-zero blank.

Without going into the merits of the foregoing as an analytical procedure, let us note a number of features that are common to *controlled experi-*

ments: First, the experimental program involves a number of *preassigned* nominal or target values ($x_1, x_2, \ldots$) of the independent variable x, to which the experimenter equates the independent variable in his experiment as best he can, and then observes the corresponding yields ($Y_1, Y_2, \ldots$) of the dependent variable y; Second, the experimenter, in his notebook, records the *observed* yields ($Y_1, Y_2, \ldots$) as corresponding to, and treats them as if they were produced by, the *nominal* or *target* values ($x_1, x_2, \ldots$) of the independent variable—whereas, strictly they correspond to, and were produced by, the actual input values ($X_1, X_2, \ldots$), which ordinarily will differ somewhat from the nominal or target values ($x_1, x_2, \ldots$) as a result of errors of technique. Furthermore, the *effective values* ($X_1, X_2, \ldots$) of the independent variable actually realized in the experiment are not recorded at all—nor even measured!

It is surprising but nevertheless true that an underlying linear structural relationship of the form $y = \beta_0 + \beta_1x$ can be estimated validly from the results of such experiments, by fitting a line of the form $Y = b_0 + b_1x$ in accordance with the procedures for FI situations (x's known accurately, Y's only subject to error). This fact was emphatically brought to the attention of the scientific world by Joseph Berkson in a paper[6] published in 1950, and for its validity requires only the usual assumptions regarding the randomness and independence of the errors of measurement and technique affecting both of the variables (i.e., causing the deviations of the actual *inputs* $X_1, X_2, \ldots$, from their target values $x_1, x_2, \ldots$, and the deviations of the observed *outputs* $Y_1, Y_2, \ldots$, from their *true values* of $y_1(X_1), y_2(X_2), \ldots$). The conclusion also extends to the many-variable case considered in Chapter 6, *provided that* the relationship is linear, i.e., that

$$y = \beta_0 + \beta_1x + \beta_2u + \beta_3v + \ldots.$$

If the underlying relationship is a polynomial in x (e.g., $y = \beta_0 + \beta_1x + \beta_2x^2 + \beta_3x^3$), then Geary[7] has found that Berkson's conclusion carries over to the extent that the usual least-squares estimates (given in Chapter 6) of the coefficients of the two highest powers of x (i.e., of β_2 and β_3 here) retain their optimum properties of unbiasedness and minimum variance, but the confidence-interval and tests-of-significance procedures require modification.

5-4.4 SOME LINEARIZING TRANSFORMATIONS

If the form of a non-linear relationship between two variables is known, it is sometimes possible to make a transformation of one or both variables such that the relationship between the transformed variables can be expressed as a straight line. For example, we might know that the relationship is of the form $Y = ab^X$. If we take logs of both sides of this equation, we obtain

$$\log Y = \log a + X \log b,$$

which will be recognized to be a straight line whose intercept on the $\log Y$ scale is equal to $\log a$, and whose slope is equal to $\log b$. The procedure for fitting the relationship is given in the following steps.

(1) Make the transformation $Y_T = \log Y$ (i.e., take logs of all the observed Y values).

(2) Use the procedure of Paragraph 5-4.1.1 to fit the line $Y_T = b_0 + b_1 X$, substituting Y_T everywhere for Y.

(3) Obtain the constants of the original equation by substituting the calculated values of b_0 and b_1 in the following equations:

$$b_0 = \log a$$
$$b_1 = \log b,$$

and taking the required antilogs.

Some relationships between X and Y which can easily be transformed into straight-line form are shown in Table 5-4. This table gives the appropriate change of variable for each relationship, and gives the formulas to convert the constants of the resulting straight line to the constants of the relationship in its original form. In addition to the ones given in Table 5-4, some more-complicated relationships can be handled by using special tricks which are not described here, but can be found in Lipka,[8] Rietz,[9] and Scarborough.[10]

It should be noted that the use of these transformations is certain to accomplish one thing only—i.e., to yield a relationship in straight-line form. The transformed data will not necessarily satisfy certain assumptions which are theoretically necessary in order to apply the procedures of Paragraph 5-4.1.1, for example, the assumption that the variability of Y given X is the same for all X. However, for practical purposes and within the range of the data considered, the transformations often do help in this regard.

Thus far, our discussion has centered on the use of transformations to convert a *known* relationship to linear form. The existence of such linearizing transformations also makes it possible to determine the form of a relationship empirically. The following possibilities, adapted from Scarborough,[10] are suggested in this regard:

(1) Plot Y against $\dfrac{1}{X}$ on ordinary graph paper. If the points lie on a straight line, the relationship is

$$Y = a + \frac{b}{X} .$$

(2) Plot $\dfrac{1}{Y}$ against X on ordinary graph paper. If the points lie on a straight line, the relationship is

$$Y = \frac{1}{a + bX}, \quad \text{or}$$
$$\frac{1}{Y} = a + bX .$$

(3) Plot X against Y on semilog paper (X on the arithmetic scale, Y on the logarithmic scale). If the points lie on a straight line, the variables are related in the form

$$Y = ae^{bX}, \text{ or}$$
$$Y = ab^X .$$

(4) Plot Y against X on log-log paper. If the points lie on a straight line, the variables are related in the form

$$Y = aX^b .$$

TABLE 5-4. SOME LINEARIZING TRANSFORMATIONS

If the Relationship Is of the Form:	Plot the Transformed Variables		Fit the Straight Line $Y_T = b_0 + b_1 X_T$	Convert Straight Line Constants (b_0 and b_1) To Original Constants:	
	$Y_T =$	$X_T =$		$b_0 =$	$b_1 =$
$Y = a + \dfrac{b}{X}$	Y	$\dfrac{1}{X}$	Use the procedures of Paragraph 5-4.1.1. In all formulas given there, substitute values of Y_T for Y and values of X_T for X, as appropriate.	a	b
$Y = \dfrac{1}{a + bX}$, or $\dfrac{1}{Y} = a + bX$	$\dfrac{1}{Y}$	X		a	b
$Y = \dfrac{X}{a + bX}$	$\dfrac{X}{Y}$	X		a	b
$Y = ab^X$	$\log Y$	X		$\log a$	$\log b$
$Y = ae^{bX}$	$\log Y$	X		$\log a$	$b \log e$
$Y = aX^b$	$\log Y$	$\log X$		$\log a$	b
$Y = a + bX^n$, where n is known	Y	X^n		a	b

5-5 PROBLEMS AND PROCEDURES FOR STATISTICAL RELATIONSHIPS

5-5.1 SI RELATIONSHIPS

In this case, we are interested in an association between two variables. See Paragraph 5-3.2 and Table 5-1.

We usually make the assumption that for any fixed value of X, the corresponding values of Y form a normal distribution with means $\bar{Y}_X = \beta_0 + \beta_1 X$ and variance $\sigma^2_{Y \cdot X}$ (read as "variance of Y given X") which is constant for all values of X.* Similarly, we usually assume that for any fixed value of Y, the corresponding values of X form a normal distribution with mean $\bar{X}_Y = \beta'_0 + \beta'_1 Y$ and variance $\sigma^2_{X \cdot Y}$, (vari-

ance of X given Y) which is constant for all values of Y.* Taken together, these two sets of assumptions imply that X and Y are jointly distributed according to the bivariate normal distribution. In practical situations, we usually have only a sample from all the possible pairs of values X and Y, and therefore we cannot determine either of the *true* regression lines, $\bar{Y}_X = \beta_0 + \beta_1 X$ or $\bar{X}_Y = \beta'_0 + \beta'_1 Y$, exactly. If we have a random sample of n pairs of values $(X_1, Y_1), (X_2, Y_2), \ldots, (X_n, Y_n)$, we can estimate either line, or both. Our method of fitting the line gives us best predictions in the sense that, for a given $X = X'$ our estimate of the corresponding value of $Y = Y'$ will:

(a) on the average equal $\bar{Y}_{X'}$ the mean value of Y for $X = X'$ (i.e., it will be on the *true* line $\bar{Y}_X = \beta_0 + \beta_1 X$); and

(b) have a smaller variance than had we used any other method for fitting the line.

---

* Strictly, we should write

$$m_{Y \cdot X} = \beta_0 + \beta_1 X$$

and

$$m_{X \cdot Y} = \beta'_0 + \beta'_1 Y .$$

See Footnote in Paragraph 5-3.2.

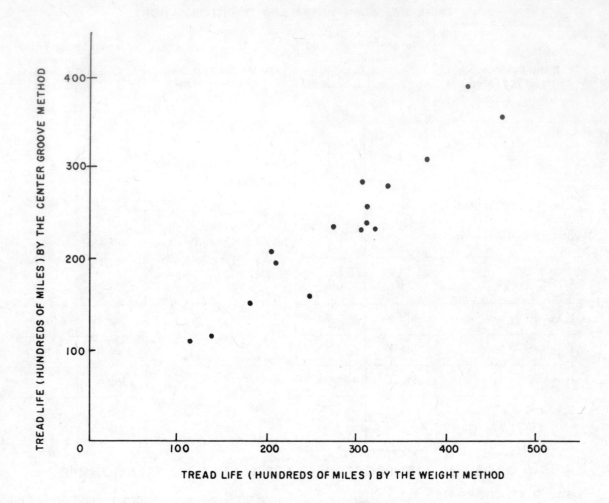

Figure 5-10.　Relationship between the weight method and the center groove method of estimating tread life— an SI relationship.

Data Sample 5-5.1—Estimated Tread Wear of Tires

The data used for illustration are from a study of two methods of estimating tread wear of commercial tires (Stiehler and others[11]). The data are shown here and plotted in Figure 5-10. The variable which is taken as the independent variable X is the estimated tread life in hundreds of miles by the *weight-loss* method. The associated variable Y is the estimated tread life by the *groove-depth* method (center grooves). The plot seems to indicate a relationship between X and Y, but the relationship is statistical rather than functional or exact. The scatter of the points stems primarily from product variability and variation of tread wear under normal operating conditions, rather than from errors of measurement of weight loss or groove depth. Descriptions and predictions are applicable only "on the average."

X = Tread Life (Hundreds of Miles) Estimated By Weight Method	Y = Tread Life (Hundreds of Miles) Estimated By Center Groove Method
459	357
419	392
375	311
334	281
310	240
305	287
309	259
319	233
304	231
273	237
204	209
245	161
209	199
189	152
137	115
114	112

5-5.1.1   What is the Best Line To Be Used for Estimating $\bar{Y}_X$ for Given Values of X?

Procedure

The procedure is identical to that of Paragraph 5-4.1.1. Using Basic Worksheet (see Worksheet 5-5.1), compute the line

$$Y = b_0 + b_1 X.$$

This is an estimate of the true regression line

$$\bar{Y}_X = \beta_0 + \beta_1 X.$$

Using Data Sample 5-5.1, the equation of the fitted line is

$$Y = 13.506 + 0.790212\, X.$$

In Figure 5-11, the line is drawn, and confidence limits for the line (see Paragraph 5-5.1.2) are shown.

WORKSHEET 5-5.1

EXAMPLE OF SI RELATIONSHIP

X denotes Tread Life Estimated by Weight Method

Y denotes Tread Life Estimated by Center Groove Method

$\Sigma X = $ ___4505___

$\Sigma Y = $ ___3776___

$\bar{X} = $ ___281.5625___

$\bar{Y} = $ ___236___

Number of points: $n = $ ___16___

Step (1) ΣXY = ___1,170,731___

(2) $(\Sigma X)(\Sigma Y)/n = $ ___1,063,180___

(3) S_{xy} = ___107551___

(4) ΣX^2 = ___1,404,543___

(5) $(\Sigma X)^2/n$ = ___1,268,439.0625___

(6) S_{xx} = ___136103.9375___

(7) ΣY^2 = ___985740___

(8) $(\Sigma Y)^2/n$ = ___891136___

(9) S_{yy} = ___94604___

(10) $b_1 = \dfrac{S_{xy}}{S_{xx}}$ = ___.790212___

(11) $\bar{Y}$ = ___236___

(12) $b_1 \bar{X}$ = ___222.494___

(13) $b_0 = \bar{Y} - b_1 \bar{X} = $ ___13.506___

(14) $\dfrac{(S_{xy})^2}{S_{xx}}$ = ___84988.119___

(15) $(n-2) s_Y^2$ = ___9615.881___

(16) s_Y^2 = ___686.849___

     s_Y = ___26.21___

Equation of the line:

$Y = b_0 + b_1 X$

   = ___13.506 + .790212 \, X___

$s_{b_1} = $ ___0.0710387___

$s_{b_0} = $ ___21.048___

Estimated variance of the slope:

$s_{b_1}^2 = \dfrac{s_Y^2}{S_{xx}}$ = ___.005046504___

Estimated variance of intercept:

$s_{b_0}^2 = s_Y^2 \left\{ \dfrac{1}{n} + \dfrac{\bar{X}^2}{S_{xx}} \right\}$ = ___443.002___

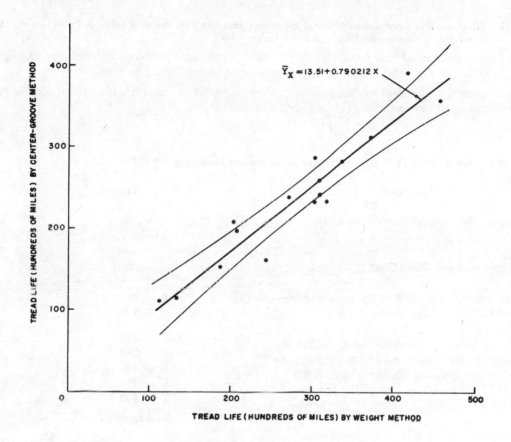

Figure 5-11.   Relationship between weight method and center groove method—the line shown with its confidence band is for estimating tread life by center groove method from tread life by weight method.

Using the Regression Line for Prediction.   The equation of the fitted line may be used to predict $\bar{Y}_x$, the average value of Y associated with a value of X.   For example, using the fitted line, $Y = 13.506 + 0.790212 \, X$, the following are some predicted values for $\bar{Y}_x$.

X	$\bar{Y}_X$
200	172
250	211
300	251
350	290
400	330
450	369

5-5.1.2 **What are the Confidence Interval Estimates for: the Line as a Whole; a Point on the Line; a Single Y Corresponding to a New Value of X?**

Read the discussion of the interpretation of three types of confidence intervals in Paragraph 5-4.1.2, in order to decide which is the appropriate kind of confidence interval.

The solutions are identical to those given in Paragraph 5-4.1.2, and are illustrated for the tread wear of commercial tires example (Data Sample 5-5.1).

5-5.1.2.1 **What Is the $(1 - \alpha)$ Confidence Band for the Line as a Whole?**

Procedure	Example

(1) Choose the desired confidence level, $1 - \alpha$

(1) Let: $1 - \alpha = .95$
$\alpha = .05$

(2) Obtain s_Y from Worksheet.

(2) $s_Y = 26.21$

(3) Look up $F_{1-\alpha}$ for $(2, n - 2)$ degrees of freedom in Table A-5.

(3) $n = 16$
$F_{.95} (2, 14) = 3.74$

(4) Choose a number of values of X (within the range of the data) at which to compute points for drawing the confidence band.

(4) Let: $X = 200$
$X = 250$
$X = 300$
$X = 350$
$X = 400,$
for example.

(5) At each selected value of X, compute:

$$Y_c = \bar{Y} + b_1 (X - \bar{X})$$

and

$$W_1 = \sqrt{2F} \, s_Y \left[\frac{1}{n} + \frac{(X - \bar{X})^2}{S_{xx}} \right]^{\frac{1}{2}}$$

(5) See Table 5-5 for a convenient computational arrangement, and the example calculations.

(6) A $(1 - \alpha)$ confidence band for the whole line is determined by

$$Y_c \pm W_1 .$$

(6) See Table 5-5.

(7) To draw the line and its confidence band, plot Y_c at two of the extreme selected values of X. Connect the two points by a straight line. At each selected value of X, plot also $Y_c + W_1$ and $Y_c - W_1$. Connect the upper series of points, and the lower series of points, by smooth curves.

(7) See Figure 5-11.

If more points are needed for drawing the curves, note that, because of symmetry, the calculation of W_1 at n values of X actually gives W_1 at $2n$ values of X.

For example: W_1 (but not Y_c) has the same value at $X = 250$ (i.e., $\bar{X} - 31.56$) as at $X = 313.12$ (i.e., $\bar{X} + 31.56$).

TABLE 5-5.   COMPUTATIONAL ARRANGEMENT FOR PROCEDURE 5-5.1.2.1

X	$(X - \bar{X})$	Y_c	$\frac{1}{n} + \frac{(X - \bar{X})^2}{S_{xx}}$	$s_{Y_c}^2$	s_{Y_c}	W_1	$Y_c + W_1$	$Y_c - W_1$
200	−81.56	171.6	0.111375	76.50	8.746	23.9	195.5	147.7
250	−31.56	211.1	0.069818	47.95	6.925	18.9	230.0	192.2
300	+18.44	250.6	0.064998	44.64	6.681	18.3	268.9	232.3
350	68.44	290.1	0.096915	66.57	8.159	22.3	312.4	267.8
400	118.44	329.6	0.165569	113.72	10.66	29.2	358.8	300.4

$\bar{X} = 281.5625$

$\bar{Y} = 236$

$s_Y^2 = 686.849$

$\frac{1}{n} = .0625$

$b_1 = 0.790212$

$S_{xx} = 136103.9375$

$Y_s = \bar{Y} + b_1 (X - \bar{X})$

$s_{Y_c}^2 = s_Y^2 \left[\frac{1}{n} + \frac{(X - \bar{X})^2}{S_{xx}} \right]$

$\sqrt{2F} = \sqrt{7.48}$
$\qquad = 2.735$

$W_1 = \sqrt{2F}\, s_{Y_c}$

5-5.1.2.2   Give a $(1 - \alpha)$ Confidence Interval Estimate For a Single Point On the Line, i.e., the Mean Value of Y Corresponding to $X = X'$.

Procedure

(1) Choose the desired confidence level, $1 - \alpha$

(2) Obtain s_Y from Worksheet.

(3) Look up $t_{1-\alpha/2}$ for $n - 2$ degrees of freedom in Table A-4.

(4) Choose X', the value of X at which we want to make an interval estimate of the mean value of Y.

(5) Compute:

$$W_2 = t_{1-\alpha/2}\, s_Y \left[\frac{1}{n} + \frac{(X' - \bar{X})^2}{S_{xx}} \right]^{\frac{1}{2}}$$

and

$$Y_c = \bar{Y} + b_1 (X' - \bar{X})$$

(6) A $(1 - \alpha)$ confidence interval estimate for the mean value of Y corresponding to $X = X'$ is given by

$$Y_c \pm W_2 .$$

Example

(1)   Let: $1 - \alpha = .95$
$\qquad \alpha = .05$

(2) $s_Y = 26.21$

(3) $n = 16$
$t_{.975}$ for 14 d.f. $= 2.145$

(4) Let $X' = 250$,
for example.

(5)

$W_2 = (2.145)\,(26.21)\,(.2642)$
$\quad = 14.85$

$Y_c = 211.1$

(6) A 95% confidence interval estimate for the mean value of Y corresponding to $X = 250$ is

211.1 ± 14.8 ,

the interval from 196.3 to 225.9 .

5-5.1.2.3   Give a $(1 - \alpha)$ Confidence Interval Estimate For a Single (Future) Value of Y Corresponding to a Chosen Value of $X = X'$.

Procedure	Example

(1) Choose the desired confidence level, $1 - \alpha$

(2) Obtain s_Y from Worksheet.

(3) Look up $t_{1-\alpha/2}$ for $n - 2$ degrees of freedom in Table A-4.

(4) Choose X', the value of X at which we want to make an interval estimate of a single value of Y.

(5) Compute:

$$W_3 = t_{1-\alpha/2}\, s_Y \left[1 + \frac{1}{n} + \frac{(X' - \bar{X})^2}{S_{xx}} \right]^{\frac{1}{2}}$$

and

$$Y_c = \bar{Y} + b_1 (X' - \bar{X})$$

(6) A $(1 - \alpha)$ confidence interval estimate for Y' (the single value of Y corresponding to X') is

$$Y_c \pm W_3 .$$

Example

(1) Let: $1 - \alpha = .95$
$\alpha = .05$

(2) $s_Y = 26.21$

(3) $n = 16$
$t_{.975}$ for 14 d.f. $= 2.145$

(4) Let $X' = 250$, for example.

(5)
$$W_3 = (2.145)\,(26.21)\,(1.0343)$$
$$= 58.1$$

$$Y_c = 211.1 .$$

(6) A 95% confidence interval estimate for a single value of Y corresponding to $X' = 250$ is 211.1 ± 58.1, the interval from 153.0 to 269.2 .

5-5.1.3   Give a Confidence Interval Estimate For β_1, the Slope of the True Regression Line, $\bar{Y}_X = \beta_0 + \beta_1 X$.

The solution is identical to that of Paragraph 5-4.1.3 and is illustrated here for Data Sample 5-5.1.

Procedure	Example

(1) Choose the desired confidence level, $1 - \alpha$

(2) Look up $t_{1-\alpha/2}$ for $n - 2$ degrees of freedom in Table A-4.

(3) Obtain s_{b_1} from Worksheet.

(4) Compute

$$W_4 = t_{1-\alpha/2}\, s_{b_1}$$

(5) A $(1 - \alpha)$ confidence interval estimate for β_1 is

$$b_1 \pm W_4 .$$

Example

(1) Let: $1 - \alpha = .95$
$\alpha = .05$

(2) $n = 16$
$t_{.975}$ for 14 d.f. $= 2.145$

(3) $s_{b_1} = 0.0710387$

(4)
$$W_4 = (2.145)\,(.0710387)$$
$$= 0.152378$$

(5) $b_1 = 0.790212$
$W_4 = 0.152378$

A 95% confidence interval estimate for β_1 is the interval 0.790212 ± 0.152378, i.e., the interval from 0.637834 to 0.942590 .

5-5.1.4 What Is the Best Line For Predicting $\bar{X}_Y$ From Given Values of Y?

For this problem, we fit a line $X = b_0' + b_1' Y$ (an estimate of the true line $\bar{X}_Y = \beta_0' + \beta_1' Y$). To fit this line we need to interchange the roles of the X and Y variables in the computations outlined in Worksheet 5-5.1 and proceed as in Paragraph 5-5.1.1.

That is, the fitted line will be:

$$X = b_0' + b_1' Y ,$$

where

$$b_0' = \bar{X} - b_1' \bar{Y}$$

and

$$b_1' = \frac{S_{xy}}{S_{yy}} .$$

From Data Sample 5-5.1:

$$b_1' = \frac{107551}{94604}$$

$$= 1.136855$$

$$b_0' = 281.5625 - (1.136855)(236)$$
$$= 13.26$$

The equation of the fitted line is:

$$X = 13.26 + 1.136855 Y ,$$

and this line is shown in Figure 5-12, along with the line for predicting Y from X.

In order to obtain confidence intervals, we need the following formulas:

$$s_X^2 = \frac{S_{xx} - \dfrac{(S_{xy})^2}{S_{yy}}}{n - 2}$$

$$s_{b_1'}^2 = \frac{s_X^2}{S_{yy}}$$

$$s_{b_0'}^2 = s_X^2 \left\{ \frac{1}{n} + \frac{(\bar{Y})^2}{S_{yy}} \right\} .$$

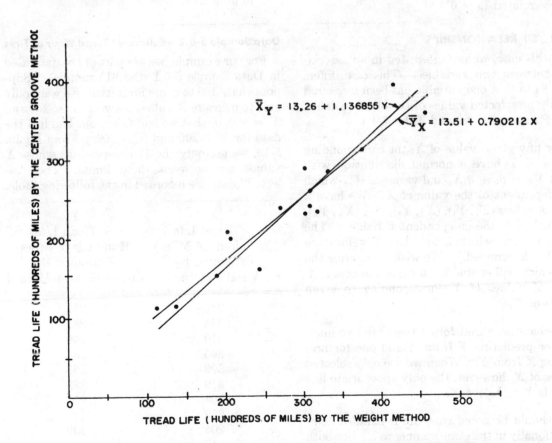

$$\bar{X}_Y = 13.26 + 1.136855 Y$$

$$\bar{Y}_X = 13.51 + 0.790212 X$$

Figure 5-12.   Relationship between weight method and center groove method—showing the two regression lines.

5-5.1.5 What is the Degree of Relationship of the Two Variables X and Y as Measured by ρ, the Correlation Coefficient?

Procedure	Example
(1) Compute	(1) Using Worksheet 5-5.1,

$$r = \frac{S_{xy}}{\sqrt{S_{xx}} \sqrt{S_{yy}}}$$

$$r = \frac{107551}{\sqrt{136103.94} \sqrt{94604}}$$

$$= \frac{107551}{(368.92)(307.58)}$$

$$= 0.95$$

(2) A 95% confidence interval for ρ can be obtained from Table A-17, using the appropriate n and r.   If the confidence interval does not include $\rho = 0$, we may state that the data give reason to believe that there is a relationship (measured by $\rho \neq 0$) between the two variables; otherwise, we may state that the data are consistent with the possibility that the two variables are uncorrelated ($\rho = 0$).

(2) $n = 16$
$r = 0.95$

From Table A-17, the 95% confidence interval estimate of ρ is the interval from 0.85 to 0.98.   Since this interval does not include $\rho = 0$, we may state that the data give reason to believe that there is a relationship between the two methods of estimating tread wear of tires.

5-5.2 SII RELATIONSHIPS

In this case, we are interested in an association between two variables. This case differs from SI in that one variable has been measured at only preselected values of the other variable. (See Paragraph 5-3.2 and Table 5-1.)

For any given value of X, the corresponding values of Y have a normal distribution with mean $\bar{Y}_X = \beta_0 + \beta_1 X$, and variance $\sigma^2_{Y \cdot X}$ which is independent of the value of X. We have n pairs of values $(X_1, Y_1), (X_2, Y_2), \ldots, (X_n, Y_n)$, in which X is the independent variable. (The X values are selected, and the Y values are thereby determined.) We wish to describe the line which will enable us to make the best estimate of values of Y corresponding to given values of X.

We have seen that for SI there are two lines, one for predicting Y from X and one for predicting X from Y. When we use only selected values of X, however, the only appropriate line to fit is $Y = b_0 + b_1 X$.

It should be noted that SII is handled computationally in the same manner as FI, but both the underlying assumptions and the interpretation of the end results are different.

Data Sample 5-5.2—Estimated Tread Wear of Tires

For our example, we use part of the data used in Data Sample 5-5.1 (the SI example). Suppose that, due to some limitation, we were only able to measure X values between $X = 200$ and $X = 400$, or that we had taken but had lost the data for $X < 200$ and $X > 400$. From Figure 5-10, we use only the 11 observations whose X values are between these limits. The "selected" data are recorded in the following table.

X = Tread Life (Hundreds of Miles) Estimated By Weight Method	Y = Tread Life (Hundreds of Miles) Estimated By Center Groove Method
375	311
334	281
310	240
305	287
309	259
319	233
304	231
273	237
204	209
245	161
209	199

5-5.2.1 What Is the Best Line To Be Used for Estimating $\bar{Y}_X$ From Given Values of X?

Procedure

Using Basic Worksheet (see Worksheet 5-5.2), compute the line $Y = b_0 + b_1 X$. This is an estimate of the true line $\bar{Y}_X = \beta_0 + \beta_1 X$.

Using Data Sample 5-5.2, the fitted line is

$$Y = 48.965 + 0.661873\ X.$$

The fitted line is shown in Figure 5-13, and the confidence band for the line (see the procedure of Paragraph 5-5.2.2.1) also is shown.

WORKSHEET 5-5.2

EXAMPLE OF SII RELATIONSHIP

X denotes Tread Life Estimated by Weight Method

$\Sigma X = $ 3187

$\bar{X} = $ 289.727

Y denotes Tread Life Estimated by Center Groove Method

$\Sigma Y = $ 2648

$\bar{Y} = $ 240.727

Number of points: $n = $ 11

Step (1) ΣXY	=	785369
(2) $(\Sigma X)(\Sigma Y)/n$	=	767197.818
(3) S_{xy}	=	18171.182

(4) ΣX^2	=	950815	(7) ΣY^2	=	655754
(5) $(\Sigma X)^2/n$	=	923360.818	(8) $(\Sigma Y)^2/n$	=	637445.818
(6) S_{xx}	=	27454.182	(9) S_{yy}	=	18308.182
(10) $b_1 = \dfrac{S_{xy}}{S_{xx}}$	=	0.661873	(14) $\dfrac{(S_{xy})^2}{S_{xx}}$	=	12027.015
(11) $\bar{Y}$	=	240.727	(15) $(n-2)s_Y^2$	=	6281.167
(12) $b_1 \bar{X}$	=	191.762	(16) s_Y^2	=	697.9074
(13) $b_0 = \bar{Y} - b_1 \bar{X}$	=	48.965	s_Y	=	26.418

Equation of the line:

$Y = b_0 + b_1 X$

$= \quad$ 48.965 + 0.661873 X

$s_{b_1} = \quad$ 0.159439

$s_{b_0} = \quad$ 46.88

Estimated variance of the slope:

$$s_{b_1}^2 = \frac{s_Y^2}{S_{xx}} = \quad .0254208$$

Estimated variance of intercept:

$$s_{b_0}^2 = s_Y^2 \left\{ \frac{1}{n} + \frac{\bar{X}^2}{S_{xx}} \right\} = \quad 2197.313$$

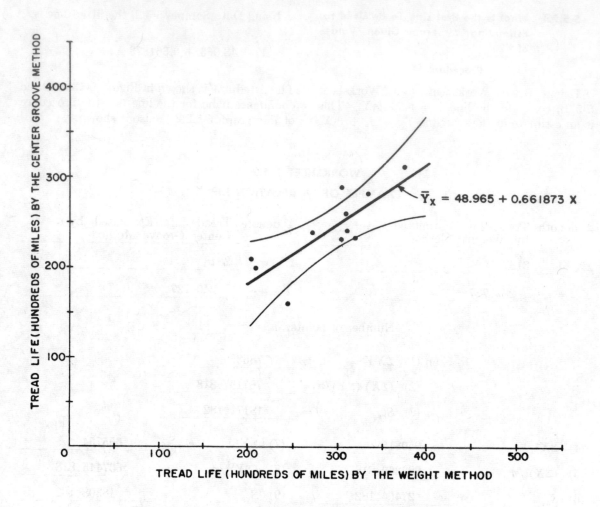

$$\bar{Y}_X = 48.965 + 0.661873\ X$$

*Figure 5-13. Relationship between weight method and center
groove method when the range of the weight method
has been restricted—an SII relationship.*

**5-5.2.2 What are the Confidence Interval Estimates for: the Line as a Whole; a Point on the Line;
a Single Y Corresponding to a New Value of X?**

Read the discussion of the interpretation of these three types of confidence intervals in Paragraph
5-4.1.2 in order to decide which is the appropriate kind of confidence interval.

5-5.2.2.1 What Is the $(1 - \alpha)$ Confidence Band For the Line as a Whole?

The solution is identical to that of Procedure 5-4.1.2.1 and is illustrated here for Data Sample 5-5.2.

Procedure	Example
(1) Choose the desired confidence level, $1 - \alpha$	(1) Let: $1 - \alpha = .95$ $\alpha = .05$
(2) Obtain s_Y from Worksheet.	(2) From Worksheet 5-5.2 $s_Y = 26.418$
(3) Look up $F_{1-\alpha}$ for $(2, n - 2)$ degrees of freedom in Table A-5.	(3) $n = 11$ $F_{.95}(2, 9) = 4.26$
(4) Choose a number of values of X (within the range of the data) at which to compute points for drawing the confidence band.	(4) Let. $\quad X = 200$ $X = 250$ $X = 300$ $X = 350$ $X = 400$, for example.
(5) At each selected value of X, compute: $$Y_c = \bar{Y} + b_1 (X - \bar{X})$$ and $$W_1 = \sqrt{2F}\, s_Y \left[\frac{1}{n} + \frac{(X - \bar{X})^2}{S_{xx}} \right]^{\frac{1}{2}}$$	(5) See Table 5-6 for a convenient computational arrangement and the example calculations.
(6) A $(1 - \alpha)$ confidence band for the whole line is determined by $$Y_c \pm W_1 .$$	(6) See Table 5-6.
(7) To draw the line and its confidence band, plot Y_c at two of the extreme selected values of X. Connect the two points by a straight line. At each selected value of X, also plot $Y_c + W_1$ and $Y_c - W_1$. Connect the upper series of points, and the lower series of points, by smooth curves.	(7) See Figure 5-13.

If more points are needed for drawing the curves for the band, note that, because of symmetry the calculation of W_1 at n values of X actually gives W_1 at $2n$ values of X.

For example: W_1 (but not Y_c) has the same value at $X = 250$ (i.e., $\bar{X} - 39.73$) as at $X = 329.5$ (i.e., $\bar{X} + 39.73$).

TABLE 5-6. COMPUTATIONAL ARRANGEMENT FOR PROCEDURE 5-5.2.2.1

X	$(X - \bar{X})$	Y_c	$\dfrac{1}{n} + \dfrac{(X - \bar{X})^2}{S_{xx}}$	$s^2_{Y_c}$	s_{Y_c}	W_1	$Y_c + W_1$	$Y_c - W_1$
200	-89.73	181.3	0.384179	268.12	16.37	47.8	229.1	133.5
250	-39.73	214.4	0.148404	103.57	10.18	29.7	244.1	184.7
300	$+10.27$	247.5	0.094751	66.127	8.132	23.7	271.2	223.8
350	60.27	280.6	0.223219	155.79	12.48	36.4	317.0	244.2
400	110.27	313.7	0.533810	372.55	19.30	56.3	370.0	257.4

$\bar{X} = 289.727$

$\bar{Y} = 240.727$

$s^2_Y = 697.9074$

$\dfrac{1}{n} = 0.0909091$

$b_1 = 0.661873$

$S_{xx} = 27454.182$

$Y_c = \bar{Y} + b_1 (X - \bar{X})$

$s^2_{Y_c} = s^2_Y \left[\dfrac{1}{n} + \dfrac{(X - \bar{X})^2}{S_{xx}} \right]$

$\sqrt{2F} = \sqrt{8.52} = 2.919$

$W_1 = \sqrt{2F}\, s_{Y_c}$

5-5.2.2.2 Give a $(1 - \alpha)$ Confidence Interval For a Single Point On the Line, i.e., the Mean Value of Y Corresponding To a Chosen Value of X (X').

Procedure

(1) Choose the desired confidence level, $1 - \alpha$

(2) Obtain s_Y from Basic Worksheet.

(3) Look up $t_{1-\alpha/2}$ for $n - 2$ degrees of freedom in Table A-4.

(4) Choose X', the value of X at which we want to make an interval estimate of the mean value of Y.

(5) Compute:

$$W_2 = t_{1-\alpha/2}\, s_Y \left[\dfrac{1}{n} + \dfrac{(X' - \bar{X})^2}{S_{xx}} \right]^{\frac{1}{2}}$$

and

$$Y_c = \bar{Y} + b_1 (X' - \bar{X})$$

(6) A $(1 - \alpha)$ confidence interval estimate for the mean value of Y corresponding to $X = X'$ is given by

$$\bar{Y} + b_1 (X - \bar{X}) \pm W_2$$
$$= Y_c \pm W_2 .$$

Example

(1) Let: $1 - \alpha = .95$
$\alpha = .05$

(2) From Worksheet 5-5.2
$s_Y = 26.418$

(3) $n = 11$
$t_{.975}$ for 9 d.f. $= 2.262$

(4) Let $X' = 300$,
for example.

(5)

$W_2 = (2.262)\,(26.418)\,(0.3078)$
$= 18.4$

$Y_c = 247.5$

(6) A 95% confidence interval estimate for the mean value of Y at $X = 300$ is the interval 247.5 ± 18.4, i.e., the interval from 229.1 to 265.9

5-5.2.2.3   Give a $(1 - \alpha)$ Confidence Interval Estimate For a Single (Future) Value of Y Corresponding To a Chosen Value of $X = X'$.

Procedure	Example

(1) Choose the desired confidence level, $1 - \alpha$

(1)   Let: $1 - \alpha = .95$
$\alpha = .05$

(2) Obtain s_Y from Worksheet.

(2)   From Worksheet 5-5.2
$s_Y = 26.418$

(3) Look up $t_{1-\alpha/2}$ for $n - 2$ degrees of freedom in Table A-4.

(3) $t_{.975}$ for 9 d.f. $= 2.262$

(4) Choose X', the value of X at which we want to make an interval estimate of a single value of Y.

(4)   Let $X' = 300$,
for example.

(5) Compute:

$$W_3 = t_{1-\alpha/2}\, s_Y \left[1 + \frac{1}{n} + \frac{(X' - \bar{X})^2}{S_{xx}} \right]^{\frac{1}{2}}$$

and

$$Y_c = \bar{Y} + b_1 (X' - \bar{X})$$

(5)

$$W_3 = (2.262)\,(26.418)\,(1.0463)$$
$$= 62.5$$

$$Y_c = 247.5$$

(6) A $(1 - \alpha)$ confidence interval estimate for Y' (the single value of Y corresponding to X') is given by

$$\bar{Y} + b_1 (X' - \bar{X}) \pm W_3$$
$$= Y_c \pm W_3$$

(6)   A 95% confidence interval estimate for Y at $X = 300$ is the interval 247.5 ± 62.5, i.e., the interval from 185.0 to 310.0

5-5.2.3   What Is the Confidence Interval Estimate for β_1, the Slope of the True Line, $\bar{Y}_X = \beta_0 + \beta_1 X$?

Procedure	Example

(1) Choose the desired confidence level, $1 - \alpha$

(1)   Let: $1 - \alpha = .95$
$\alpha = .05$

(2) Look up $t_{1-\alpha/2}$ for $n - 2$ degrees of freedom in Table A-4.

(2) $n = 11$
$t_{.975}$ for 9 d.f. $= 2.262$

(3) Obtain s_{b_1} from Worksheet.

(3)   From Worksheet 5-5.2
$s_{b_1} = 0.159439$

(4) Compute

$$W_4 = t_{1-\alpha/2}\, s_{b_1}$$

(4)

$$W_4 = 2.262\,(0.159439)$$
$$= 0.360651$$

(5) A $(1 - \alpha)$ confidence interval estimate for β_1 is

$$b_1 \pm W_4$$

(5) $b_1 = 0.661873$
$W_4 = 0.360651$

A 95% confidence interval estimate for β_1 is the interval 0.661873 ± 0.360651, i.e., the interval from 0.301222 to 1.022524

REFERENCES

1. C. Eisenhart, "The Interpretation of Certain Regression Methods and Their Use in Biological and Industrial Research," *Annals of Mathematical Statistics*, Vol. 10, No. 2, pp. 162-186, June, 1939.
2. M. Ezekiel, *Methods of Correlation Analysis* (2d edition), Chapter 20, John Wiley & Sons, Inc., New York, N.Y., 1941.
3. J. Mandel, "Fitting a Straight Line to Certain Types of Cumulative Data," *Journal of the American Statistical Association*, Vol. 52, pp. 552-566, 1957.
4. F. S. Acton, *Analysis of Straight-Line Data*, John Wiley & Sons, Inc., New York, N.Y., 1959.
5. M. S. Bartlett, "Fitting a Straight Line When Both Variables are Subject to Error," *Biometrics*, Vol. 5, No. 3, pp. 207-212, 1949.
6. J. Berkson, "Are There Two Regressions?",
7. R. C. Geary, "Non-linear Functional Relationships Between Two Variables When One is Controlled," *Journal of the American Statistical Association*, Vol. 48, pp. 94-103, 1953.
8. J. Lipka, *Graphical and Mechanical Computation*, John Wiley & Sons, Inc., New York, N.Y., 1918.
9. H. L. Rietz, (ed.), *Handbook of Mathematical Statistics*, Houghton Mifflin Company, Boston, Mass., 1924.
10. J. B. Scarborough, *Numerical Mathematical Analysis* (2d edition), The Johns Hopkins Press, Baltimore, Md., 1950.
11. R. D. Stiehler, G. G. Richey, and J. Mandel, "Measurement of Treadwear of Commercial Tires," *Rubber Age*, Vol. 73, No. 2, May, 1953.

Journal of the American Statistical Association, Vol. 45, pp. 164-180, 1950.

CHAPTER 6

POLYNOMIAL AND MULTIVARIABLE RELATIONSHIPS
ANALYSIS BY THE METHOD OF LEAST SQUARES

6-1 INTRODUCTION

In this Chapter, we give methods for estimating the coefficients of, and for answering various questions about, multivariable functional relationships of the form

$$y = \beta_0 x_0 + \beta_1 x_1 + \ldots + \beta_{k-1} x_{k-1} \qquad (6\text{-}1)$$

between a *dependent variable y* and a number of *independent variables* $x_0, x_1, \ldots, x_{k-1}$. We restrict our discussion, however, to the case in which the values of the independent variables $x_0, x_1, \ldots, x_{k-1}$, are known exactly, and errors of measurement affect only the *observed* values Y of y, that is, to many-variable analogs of the FI functional relationships considered in Paragraphs 5-3.1 and 5-4.1.

Methods for the analysis of many-variable relationships in which errors of measurement affect the values of the x's involved as well as the *observed Y*'s, i.e., the multivariable analogs of the FII structural relationships considered in Paragraphs 5-3.1 and 5-4.3, are not discussed *per se* in this Chapter. If, however, the *errors* that affect the x's are not errors of measurement, but rather are errors of control in the sense of Paragraph 5-4.3.2, i.e., are errors made in attempting to set $X_0, X_1, \ldots, X_{k-1}$, equal to their respective *nominal values* $x_0', x_1', \ldots, x_{k-1}'$, then the methods of this Chapter are applicable, *provided that* the errors made in adjusting $X_0, X_1, \ldots, X_{k-1}$, to their respective nominal values are mutually independent (or, at least, are uncorrelated).

The techniques presented in this Chapter are general. They are applicable whenever we know the functional form of the relation between y and the x's, and are primarily concerned with estimating the unknown values of the coefficients of the respective terms of the relationship. Thus, taking $x_0 = 1, x_1 = x, x_2 = x^2, \ldots, x_m = x^m$, the methods of this Chapter enable us to estimate the coefficients of, and to answer various questions about, an mth degree polynomial relationship

$$y = \beta_0 + \beta_1 x + \beta_2 x^2 + \ldots + \beta_m x^m \qquad (6\text{-}2)$$

between a *dependent variable y* and a single *independent variable x*. Alternatively, taking $x_0 = 1$, $x_1 = x, x_2 = z, x_3 = x^2, x_4 = xz$, and $x_5 = z^2$, the techniques of this Chapter can be used to investigate the nature of a quadratic *surface* relationship

$$y = \beta_0 + (\beta_1 x + \beta_2 z) + (\beta_3 x^2 + \beta_4 xz + \beta_5 z^2) \qquad (6\text{-}3)$$

between a *dependent variable y* and two *independent variables x* and *z*. For example, we may wish to test the hypothesis that the *surface* actually is a plane, i.e., that β_3, β_4, and β_5, in Equation (6-3) are equal to zero, and so forth.

Multivariate* statistical relationships analogous to the SI and SII situations considered in Paragraphs 5-3.2 and 5-5.1 are not considered *per se* in this Chapter. If, however, Y and X_1, $X_2, \ldots, X_{k-1}$, have a joint multivariate frequency (probability) distribution in some definite population, and if a sample of size n is drawn from this population, with or without selection or restrictions on the values of the X's but *without selection or restriction on the Y's*, then the methods of this Chapter, taking $X_0 \equiv 1$ throughout, are directly applicable to estimating the coefficients of, and to answering various questions about, the *multivariate regression* of Y on $X_1, X_2, \ldots,$ and X_{k-1}, namely,

$$\bar{Y}_{\{x\}} = \beta_0 + \beta_1 X_1 + \beta_2 X_2 + \ldots + \beta_{k-1} X_{k-1}, \tag{6-4}$$

where $\bar{Y}_{\{x\}}$ is *shorthand* for $m_{Y \cdot x_1 x_2 \ldots x_{k-1}}$, the mean value of all of the Y's that are associated in the population with the particular indicated combination $X_1, X_2 \ldots X_{k-1}$, of values of the X's (see footnote of Par. 5-3.2)—and, where

$$\beta_0 = m_Y - \beta_1 m_{X_1} - \beta_2 m_{X_2} - \ldots - \beta_{k-1} m_{X_{k-1}}, \tag{6-5}$$

$m_y, m_{x_1}, \ldots, m_{x_{k-1}}$, are the population means of $Y_1, X_1, \ldots, X_{k-1}$, respectively. The *fitted regression*, yielded by the application of the methods of this Chapter to observational data of this kind, will be of the form

$$\bar{Y}_{\{x\}} = b_0 + b_1 X_1 + b_2 X_2 + \ldots + b_{k-1} X_{k-1} \tag{6-6}$$

with $b_0 = \bar{Y} - b_1 \bar{X}_1 - b_2 \bar{X}_2 - \ldots - b_{k-1} \bar{X}_{k-1}$ \hfill (6-7)

where $\bar{Y}, \bar{X}_1, \bar{X}_2, \ldots, \bar{X}_{k-1}$, are the means of $Y, X_1, X_2, \ldots,$ and X_{k-1}, *in the sample;* and each b will be a *best* (i.e., minimum variance unbiased) estimate of the corresponding *true β*.

When, as in all of the previously mentioned situations, the relationship between y and the x's is *linear in the coefficients* whose values are to be determined from the data in hand, the Method of Least Squares is the most generally accepted procedure for estimating the unknown values of the coefficients, and for answering questions about the relationship as a whole. A widely applicable Least Squares Theorem is given in Paragraph 6-2; and its application to a general linear situation is presented in detail in Paragraph 6-3, with worked examples. Special applications to polynomial and other situations are discussed in subsequent paragraphs of this Chapter.

The numerical calculations required for least-squares analysis of multivariable relationships often are lengthy and tedious. Hence, this Chapter is directed toward arrangement of the work for automatic computation on modern electronic computers. Consequently, basic equations called for in the calculations are written both in traditional and in matrix forms. This Chapter concludes with a discussion of matrix operations that are useful both in formulating and in carrying out the requisite calculations, Paragraph 6-9.

In most instances, related Procedures and Examples appear on facing pages in this Chapter.

---

* The important distinction in statistical work between a *variable* and a *variate* is drawn in the Kendall-Buckland *Dictionary of Statistical Terms*[1] as follows:

Variable—Generally, any quantity which varies. More precisely, a variable in the mathematical sense, i.e., a quantity which may take any one of a specified set of values. It is convenient to apply the same word to denote non-measurable characteristics, e.g., "sex" is a variable in this sense, since any human individual may take one of two "values", male or female.

It is useful, but far from being the general practice, to distinguish between a variable as so defined and a random variable or variate (q.v.).

Variate—In contradistinction to a variable (q.v.) a variate is a quantity which may take any of the values of a specified set with a specified relative frequency or probability. The variate is therefore often known as a random variable. It is to be regarded as defined, not merely by a set of permissible values like an ordinary mathematical variable, but by an associated frequency (probability) function expressing how often those values appear in the situation under discussion.

6-2   LEAST SQUARES THEOREM

If the n measurements $Y_1, Y_2, \ldots, Y_n$ are statistically independent with common variance σ^2 and have expected values $E(Y_i)$,

$$E(Y_1) = \beta_0 x_{01} + \beta_1 x_{11} + \beta_2 x_{21} + \ldots + \beta_{k-1} x_{k-1,1}$$
$$E(Y_2) = \beta_0 x_{02} + \beta_1 x_{12} + \beta_2 x_{22} + \ldots + \beta_{k-1} x_{k-1,2} \tag{6-8}$$
$$\ldots$$
$$E(Y_n) = \beta_0 x_{0n} + \beta_1 x_{1n} + \beta_2 x_{2n} + \ldots + \beta_{k-1} x_{k-1,n}$$

then the best linear unbiased estimates $\hat{\beta}_0, \hat{\beta}_1, \hat{\beta}_2, \ldots, \hat{\beta}_{k-1}$, of the unknown coefficients are given by the solution of k simultaneous equations, called the *normal equations*,

$$\hat{\beta}_0 \Sigma x_0^2 + \hat{\beta}_1 \Sigma x_0 x_1 + \ldots + \hat{\beta}_{k-1} \Sigma x_0 x_{k-1} = \Sigma x_0 Y$$
$$\hat{\beta}_0 \Sigma x_1 x_0 + \hat{\beta}_1 \Sigma x_1^2 + \ldots + \hat{\beta}_{k-1} \Sigma x_1 x_{k-1} = \Sigma x_1 Y \tag{6-9}*$$
$$\ldots$$
$$\hat{\beta}_0 \Sigma x_{k-1} x_0 + \hat{\beta}_1 \Sigma x_{k-1} x_1 + \ldots + \hat{\beta}_{k-1} \Sigma x_{k-1}^2 = \Sigma x_{k-1} Y$$

where the summation is over all of the n values of the variables involved; e.g.,

$$\Sigma x_1 x_2 = \sum_{i=1}^{n} x_{1i} x_{2i},$$

and the estimate of σ^2 is given by

$$s^2 = \frac{1}{n-k} \sum_{1}^{n} [Y_i - (\hat{\beta}_0 x_{0i} + \hat{\beta}_1 x_{1i} + \ldots + \hat{\beta}_{k-1} x_{k-1,i})]^2 \tag{6-10}$$
$$= \frac{1}{n-k} \left\{ \sum_{1}^{n} Y_i^2 - \sum_{1}^{k} \hat{\beta}_j \, (\Sigma x_j Y) \right\}.$$

If no unique solution to Equation (6-9) exists (which will occur when one or more of the x's are linearly dependent, for example, if $x_1 = ax_2 + bx_3$), then not all k coefficients can be estimated from the data.   Variables may be deleted or several variables may be replaced by a linear function of those variables so that a solvable system involving fewer equations results.

In situations where the variance of the Y's is not the same for all Y's and/or there is correlation among the Y's, a transformation of variables is required.   The methods for these cases are discussed later in this Chapter.

This theorem can be restated using matrix notation as follows:*

Let, $Y = \begin{bmatrix} Y_1 \\ Y_2 \\ \cdot \\ Y_n \end{bmatrix}$, $X = \begin{bmatrix} x_{01} \; x_{11} \ldots x_{k-1,1} \\ x_{02} \; x_{12} \ldots x_{k-1,2} \\ \cdot \quad \cdot \qquad \cdot \\ x_{0n} \; x_{1n} \ldots x_{k-1,n} \end{bmatrix}$, and $\beta = \begin{bmatrix} \beta_0 \\ \beta_1 \\ \cdot \\ \beta_{k-1} \end{bmatrix}$

The expected values of the Y's then is expressed as

$$E(Y) = X\beta, \tag{6-8M}$$

and the condition of independence and common variance is expressed by

$$\text{Var}\,(Y) = V = \sigma^2 I.$$

Under these conditions, the minimum variance unbiased estimates $\hat{\beta}$ of β are given by the solution of the normal equations

$$X'X\hat{\beta} = X'Y. \tag{6-9M}$$

The estimate of σ^2 is given by

$$s^2 = \frac{1}{n-k} \{(Y - X\hat{\beta})' \, (Y - X\hat{\beta})\}$$

$$= \frac{1}{n-k} (Y'Y - \hat{\beta}'X'Y).$$
(6-10M)

Equations (6-8), (6-9), and (6-10) are given in the usual algebraic notation, and the corresponding equations in matrix notation are (6-8M), (6-9M), and (6-10M).

6-3 MULTIVARIABLE FUNCTIONAL RELATIONSHIPS

6-3.1 USE AND ASSUMPTIONS

Least-squares methods for estimating the coefficients of a functional relation of the form

$$y = \beta_0 x_0 + \beta_1 x_1 + \beta_2 x_2 + \ldots + \beta_{k-1} x_{k-1}$$
(6-1)

are used in a number of situations:

(a) when it is known from theoretical considerations in the subject matter field that the relationship *is* of this form;

(b) when the exact expression relating y and the x's either is unknown or is too complicated to be used directly and it is assumed that an approximation of this type will be satisfactory.

In the latter case, the approximation often can be justified on the grounds that, for the limited range of the x's considered, the surface representing y as a function of the x's is very nearly the hyperplane given by Equation (6-1). The method is strictly valid in (a), but in (b) there is danger of obtaining misleading results, analogous to the bias arising in the straight-line case from the assumption that the functional relation involved is *linear* when in fact it is not linear.

In addition to the validity of Equation (6-1), the following assumptions must be satisfied:*

(a) the random errors in the Y's have mean zero and a common variance σ^2;

(b) the random errors in the Y's are mutually independent in the statistical sense.

For strict validity of the usual tests of significance, and confidence interval estimation procedures in Paragraph 6-3.3 (Steps 8 and 9), an additional assumption must be satisfied:

(c) the random errors affecting the Y's are normally distributed.

The x variables may be powers or other functions of some basic variables, and several different functions of the same x variable may be used. (See, for example, Equation (6-2) or (6-3)).

The data for analysis consist of the *n points* $(x_{01}, x_{11}, \ldots, x_{k-1,1}, Y_1) \, (x_{02}, x_{12}, \ldots, x_{k-1,2} \, Y_2) \ldots,$ $(x_{0n}, x_{1n}, \ldots, x_{k-1,n}, Y_n)$, and usually are represented in tabular form as:

X_0	X_1	X_2	.	.	.	X_{k-1}	Y
x_{01}	x_{11}	x_{21}				$x_{k-1,1}$	Y_1
x_{02}	x_{12}	x_{22}				$x_{k-1,2}$	Y_2
.						.	
.						.	
.						.	
x_{0n}	x_{1n}	x_{2n}	.	.	.	$x_{k-1,n}$	Y_n

---

* When these assumptions are not satisfied, see Paragraph 6-6 for the case of inequality of variance, and Paragraph 6-7 for the case of correlation among the Y's.

Alternatively, the data may be expressed in the form of *observational equations,*

$$\beta_0 x_{01} + \beta_1 x_{11} + \beta_2 x_{21} + \ldots + \beta_{k-1} x_{k-1,1} = Y_1 = y_1 + e_1$$
$$\beta_0 x_{02} + \beta_1 x_{12} + \beta_2 x_{22} + \ldots + \beta_{k-1} x_{k-1,2} = Y_2 = y_2 + e_2$$

.

.   (6-11)

.

$$\beta_0 x_{0n} + \beta_1 x_{1n} + \beta_2 x_{2n} + \ldots + \beta_{k-1} x_{k-1,n} = Y_n = y_n + e_n$$

where $e_1, e_2, \ldots, e_n$ denote the *errors* of the Y's as measured values of the corresponding true y's. When the number of observational equations exceeds the number of unknown coefficients, i.e., when $n > k$, the observational equations ordinarily are mutually contradictory; that is, the values of $\beta_0, \beta_1, \ldots,$ and β_{k-1} implied by any chosen solvable selection of k of the equations do not satisfy one or more of the remaining $n - k$ equations. Hence, there is a need for *best* estimates of the β's based on the data as a whole.

For a unique least-squares solution, n must not be less than k, and the normal equations (6-9) must be uniquely solvable. If not, some variables must be deleted or suitably combined with other variables.

6-3.2 DISCUSSION OF PROCEDURES AND EXAMPLES

In setting forth the steps in the solution, the formulas are given in the usual algebraic notation and also in matrix notation where appropriate.

Data Sample 6-3.2, selected for arithmetical simplicity, serves to illustrate the worked examples of numerical procedures involved in estimating the coefficients of, and in answering various questions about, multivariable functional relationships.

Data Sample 6-3.2

x_1	x_2	x_3	Y
1	8	1	2
2	8	7	4
2	6	0	4
3	1	2	4
4	2	7	8
4	5	1	3

We assume that these data correspond to a situation in which the functional dependence of y on x_1, x_2, and x_3, is of the form

$$y = \beta_1 x_1 + \beta_2 x_2 + \beta_3 x_3,$$ (6-12)

which is a special case of Equation (6-1) with the term $\beta_0 x_0$ omitted; i.e., with β_0 taken equal to zero. Equation (6-12) implies that the functional dependence of y on x_1, x_2, and x_3, takes the form of a hyperplane* that passes through the origin (0, 0, 0, 0) of the four-dimensional Euclidean *space*

---

* A flat surface in four or more dimensions is termed a *hyperplane* when it is the locus of points that vary in more than two dimensions.

whose coordinates are x_1, x_2, x_3, and y.   If we wished to allow for the possibility that the dependence of y on x_1, x_2, and x_3, may take the form of a hyperplane that intersects the y-axis at some point $(0, 0, 0, \beta_0)$, not necessarily the origin, then we would substitute

$$y = \beta_0 x_0 + \beta_1 x_1 + \beta_2 x_2 + \beta_3 x_3$$

for Equation (6-12), and take $x_0 \equiv 1$; i.e., amend Data Sample 6-3.2 by adding an x_0 column of 1's.

By analogy with Equations (6-11), Data Sample 6-3.2 and the assumed functional relationship Equation (6-12) can be summarized *symbolically* by *observational equations* of the form

$$\beta_1 x_{11} + \beta_2 x_{21} + \beta_3 x_{31} = Y_1$$
$$\beta_1 x_{12} + \beta_2 x_{22} + \beta_3 x_{32} = Y_2$$
$$\cdot$$
$$\cdot$$
$$\cdot$$
$$\beta_1 x_{16} + \beta_2 x_{26} + \beta_3 x_{36} = Y_6$$

$$(6\text{-}13)$$

Substitution of the values of the x's and Y's of Data Sample 6-3.2 in Equation (6-13) gives

$$\beta_1 \cdot 1 + \beta_2 \cdot 8 + \beta_3 \cdot 1 = 2$$
$$\beta_1 \cdot 2 + \beta_2 \cdot 8 + \beta_3 \cdot 7 = 4$$
$$\beta_1 \cdot 2 + \beta_2 \cdot 6 + \beta_3 \cdot 0 = 4$$
$$\beta_1 \cdot 3 + \beta_2 \cdot 1 + \beta_3 \cdot 2 = 4$$
$$\beta_1 \cdot 4 + \beta_2 \cdot 2 + \beta_3 \cdot 7 = 3$$
$$\beta_1 \cdot 4 + \beta_2 \cdot 5 + \beta_3 \cdot 1 = 3$$

$$(6\text{-}14)$$

as the observational equations corresponding to Data Sample 6-3.2.

6-3.3 PROCEDURES AND EXAMPLES

Step 1 Procedure—Formation of Normal Equations. The *normal equations* are formed from the sums of squares and cross products as follows:

$$\beta_0 \Sigma x_0^2 + \beta_1 \Sigma x_0 x_1 + \ldots + \beta_{k-1} \Sigma x_0 x_{k-1} = \Sigma x_0 Y$$
$$\beta_0 \Sigma x_1 x_0 + \beta_1 \Sigma x_1^2 + \ldots + \beta_{k-1} \Sigma x_1 x_{k-1} = \Sigma x_1 Y$$

$$\ldots$$

$$\beta_0 \Sigma x_{k-1} x_0 + \beta_1 \Sigma x_{k-1} x_1 + \ldots + \beta_{k-1} \Sigma x_{k-1}^2 = \Sigma x_{k-1} Y$$

$$(6\text{-}9)$$

or in matrix form

$$X'X\hat{\beta} = X'Y = Q$$

$$(6\text{-}9M)$$

where $Q' = (q_1, q_2, \ldots, q_r)$,

and $q_j = \sum_{i=1}^{n} x_{ji} Y_i$, $(j = 0, 1, \ldots, k - 1)$.

Step 1 Example—Formation of Normal Equations. The *normal equations* (See Equations (6-9)) corresponding to the observational equations (6-13) are

$$\beta_1 \, \Sigma x_1^2 + \beta_2 \, \Sigma x_1 x_2 + \beta_3 \, \Sigma x_1 x_3 = \Sigma x_1 Y$$
$$\beta_1 \, \Sigma x_1 x_2 + \beta_2 \, \Sigma x_2^2 + \beta_3 \, \Sigma x_2 x_3 = \Sigma x_2 Y \qquad\qquad (6\text{-}15)$$
$$\beta_1 \, \Sigma x_1 x_3 + \beta_2 \, \Sigma x_2 x_3 + \beta_3 \, \Sigma x_3^2 = \Sigma x_3 Y$$

or in matrix form

$$X' \, X \, \beta = X'Y \qquad\qquad (6\text{-}15\text{M})$$

where
$$\beta = \begin{bmatrix} \beta_1 \\ \beta_2 \\ \beta_3 \end{bmatrix}$$

Numerical evaluation of the requisite sums of squares and sums of cross products for Data Sample 6-3.2 and substitution in Equation (6-15), yields

$$\beta_1 \cdot 50 + \beta_2 \cdot 67 \ + \beta_3 \cdot 53 \ = 54$$
$$\beta_1 \cdot 67 + \beta_2 \cdot 194 + \beta_3 \cdot 85 \ = 97 \qquad\qquad (6\text{-}16)$$
$$\beta_1 \cdot 53 + \beta_2 \cdot 85 \ + \beta_3 \cdot 104 = 62$$

and the matrices involved in Equation (6-15M) become

$$(X'X) = \begin{bmatrix} \Sigma x_1^2 & \Sigma x_1 x_2 & \Sigma x_1 x_3 \\ \Sigma x_1 x_2 & \Sigma x_2^2 & \Sigma x_2 x_3 \\ \Sigma x_1 x_3 & \Sigma x_2 x_3 & \Sigma x_3^2 \end{bmatrix} = \begin{bmatrix} 50 & 67 & 53 \\ 67 & 194 & 85 \\ 53 & 85 & 104 \end{bmatrix}$$

$$(X'Y) = \begin{bmatrix} \Sigma x_1 Y \\ \Sigma x_2 Y \\ \Sigma x_3 Y \end{bmatrix} = \begin{bmatrix} 54 \\ 97 \\ 62 \end{bmatrix} = \begin{bmatrix} q_1 \\ q_2 \\ q_3 \end{bmatrix} = Q \qquad (6\text{-}16\text{M})$$

Step 2 Procedure—Solution of Normal Equations. Equations (6-9) can be solved by a number of methods giving values for $\hat{\beta}_0$, $\hat{\beta}_1$, $\hat{\beta}_2$, ..., which can be expressed as

$$\hat{\beta}_0 = c_{00}q_0 + c_{01}q_1 + \ldots + c_{0,k-1}q_{k-1}$$
$$\hat{\beta}_1 = c_{10}q_0 + c_{11}q_1 + \ldots + c_{1,k-1}q_{k-1} \qquad\qquad (6\text{-}17)$$
$$\ldots$$
$$\hat{\beta}_{k-1} = c_{k-1,0}q_0 + c_{k-1,1}q_1 + \ldots + c_{k-1,k-1}q_{k-1}.$$

A solution for the $\hat{\beta}_i$'s can be arrived at without explicitly computing the c_{ij}'s, of course, but in the following computations the c_{ij}'s are needed. The values of the c_{ij}'s depend only on the sums of squares and cross products of the *independent* variables $x_0, x_1, \ldots, x_k$, so that the estimates of the β_i's can be expressed as a linear function of the Y's.

In matrix notation, this step is given by computing the inverse of the matrix of normal equations, i.e.,

$$(X'X)^{-1} = \begin{bmatrix} c_{00} & c_{01} & \cdot & \cdot & \cdot & c_{0,k-1} \\ c_{10} & c_{11} & \cdot & \cdot & \cdot & c_{1,k-1} \\ \cdot & \cdot & \cdot & & & \\ c_{k-1,0} & c_{k-1,1} & \cdot & \cdot & \cdot & c_{k-1,k-1} \end{bmatrix}$$

and Equations (6-17) become

$$\hat{\beta} = (X'X)^{-1}X'Y \qquad\qquad (6\text{-}17\text{M})$$
$$= (X'X)^{-1}Q.$$

Step 2 Example—Solution of Normal Equations.   The values $\hat{\beta}_1$, $\hat{\beta}_2$, and $\hat{\beta}_3$, that constitute the solutions of the normal equations can be expressed (See Equations (6-17)) in the form

$$
\begin{aligned}
\hat{\beta}_1 &= c_{11}\, q_1 + c_{12}\, q_2 + c_{13}\, q_3 \\
&= c_{11}\cdot 54 + c_{12}\cdot 97 + c_{13}\cdot 62 \\
\hat{\beta}_2 &= c_{21}\, q_1 + c_{22}\, q_2 + c_{23}\, q_3 \\
&= c_{21}\cdot 54 + c_{22}\cdot 97 + c_{23}\cdot 62 \\
\hat{\beta}_3 &= c_{31}\, q_1 + c_{32}\, q_2 + c_{33}\, q_3 \\
&= c_{31}\cdot 54 + c_{32}\cdot 97 + c_{33}\cdot 62
\end{aligned}
\qquad (6\text{-}18)
$$

where the c's are the elements of the inverse matrix

$$
(X'X)^{-1} = \begin{bmatrix} c_{11} & c_{12} & c_{13} \\ c_{21} & c_{22} & c_{23} \\ c_{21} & c_{32} & c_{33} \end{bmatrix}
$$

$(X'X)^{-1}$ may be computed in many ways.*   The exact inverse of the matrix $(X'X)$ determined by

the first equation of Equations (6-16M) is

$$
(X'X)^{-1} = \frac{1}{239418} \begin{bmatrix} 12951 & -2463 & -4587 \\ -2463 & 2391 & -699 \\ -4587 & -699 & 5211 \end{bmatrix}
\qquad (6\text{-}18M)
$$

where the factor in front of the matrix is to be applied to the individual terms in the matrix.

Using the first equation of Equations (6-18), we get

$$
\begin{aligned}
\hat{\beta}_1 &= \frac{1}{239418} \{(12951)\,(54) + (-2463)\,(97) + (-4587)\,(62)\} \\
&= \frac{1}{239418} \{699354 - 238911 - 284394\} \\
&= \frac{176049}{239418} \\
&= 0.735\ 320\ 652.
\end{aligned}
$$

The other coefficients are obtained similarly:

$$
\hat{\beta}_2 = 0.232\ 175\ 526
$$
$$
\hat{\beta}_3 = 0.031\ 664\ 286.
$$

The prediction equation, therefore, is

$$
\hat{Y} = 0.735\ 320\ 652\ x_1 + 0.232\ 175\ 526\ x_2 + 0.031\ 664\ 286\ x_3.
$$

---

* The advent of automatic electronic digital computers has reduced the inversion of matrices of even moderate size to a matter of seconds.   Routines for matrix inversion are standard tools of automatic computation.   In contrast, matrix inversion by desk calculators is a time-consuming and tedious affair.   Detailed illustration at this juncture of any one of the common methods of matrix inversion by desk calculator would not only constitute a distractive interruption to the orderly presentation of the essential features of this Chapter, but would lengthen it considerably.   The two most common methods of matrix inversion by desk calculator—the *Doolittle method*, and the *abbreviated Doolittle method* (also called the *Gauss-Doolittle method*)—are described and illustrated by numerical examples in various statistical textbooks, e.g., in Chapter 15 of Anderson and Bancroft.[2]   Details of the square-root method, favored by some computers, are given, with a numerical illustration, in Appendix 11A of O. L. Davies' book.[3]   All of the common methods of matrix inversion by desk calculators are described in considerable detail, illustrated by numerical examples, and compared with respect to advantages and disadvantages in a paper by L. Fox, *Practical Solution of Linear Equations and Inversion of Matrices*, included in Taussky.[4]   Reference also may be made to the book of Dwyer.[5]   The reader of this Handbook who is faced with matrix inversion by desk calculator is referred to these standard sources for guidance and details.

Step 3 Procedure—Calculation of Deviation Between Predicted and Observed Value of the Y's. The predicted value $\hat{Y}_i$ at a given point $(x_{0i}, x_{1i}, \ldots, x_{k-1,i}, Y_i)$ is given by substituting the values of x in the prediction equation, i.e.,

$$\hat{Y}_i = \hat{\beta}_0 x_{0i} + \hat{\beta}_1 x_{1i} + \hat{\beta}_2 x_{2i} + \ldots + \hat{\beta}_{k-1} x_{k-1,i},$$

and the *residuals* $r_i = Y_i - \hat{Y}_i$ are given by

$$\begin{aligned}
r_1 &= Y_1 - \hat{Y}_1 = Y_1 - (\hat{\beta}_0 x_{01} + \hat{\beta}_1 x_{11} + \ldots + \hat{\beta}_{k-1} x_{k-1,1}) \\
r_2 &= Y_2 - \hat{Y}_2 = Y_2 - (\hat{\beta}_0 x_{02} + \hat{\beta}_1 x_{12} + \ldots + \hat{\beta}_{k-1} x_{k-1,2}) \\
&\;\;\vdots \\
r_n &= Y_n - \hat{Y}_n = Y_n - (\hat{\beta}_0 x_{0n} + \hat{\beta}_1 x_{1n} + \ldots + \hat{\beta}_{k-1} x_{k-1,n})
\end{aligned}$$

(6-19)

or in matrix notation

$$r = Y - X\hat{\beta} \tag{6-19M}$$

where

$$r = \begin{bmatrix} r_1 \\ r_2 \\ \cdot \\ \cdot \\ \cdot \\ r_n \end{bmatrix}$$

In classical least-squares analysis, $\hat{Y}_i$ is termed the *adjusted value* of the observed value Y_i. It is important to distinguish between the *errors* of the Y_i with respect to the corresponding *true* values y_i, and the *residuals* of the Y_i with respect to their *adjusted* or *predicted* values $\hat{Y}_i$; that is, between the e_i of Equations (6-11) and the r_i of Equations (6-19).

Step 4 Procedure—Estimation of σ^2. The estimate s^2 of σ^2 is computed from

$$\begin{aligned}
s^2 &= \frac{1}{n-k} \Sigma r^2 \\
&= \frac{1}{n-k} \left\{ \Sigma Y^2 - \sum_0^{k-1} \hat{\beta}_j q_j \right\}
\end{aligned} \tag{6-20}$$

or in matrix notation

$$\begin{aligned}
s^2 &= \frac{1}{n-k} (r'r) \\
&= \frac{1}{n-k} \{ Y'Y - \beta'Q \}.
\end{aligned} \tag{6-20M}$$

Step 3 Example—Calculation of Deviation Between Predicted and Observed Value of the Y's.   The *predicted* or *adjusted* values $\hat{Y}_i$ corresponding to the observations Y_i are obtained by substituting the values of the x's into the prediction equation.   For the first observation, substituting $x_{11} = 1$, $x_{21} = 8$, $x_{31} = 1$ leads to

$$\hat{Y}_1 = 0.735\ 320\ 652\ (1) + 0.232\ 175\ 526\ (8) + 0.031\ 664\ 286\ (1)$$
$$= 2.624\ 389\ 146.$$

The corresponding residual is

$$r_1 = Y_1 - \hat{Y}_1$$
$$= 2 - 2.624\ 389\ 146$$
$$= -.624\ 389\ 146.$$

The full data, the corresponding predicted values ($\hat{Y}_i$) and their residuals (r_i), are:

i	x_{1i}	x_{2i}	x_{3i}	Y_i	$\hat{Y}_i$	Residuals r_i
1	1	8	1	2	2.624 389 146	−.624 389 146
2	2	8	7	4	3.549 695 514	.450 304 486
3	2	6	0	4	2.863 694 460	1.136 305 540
4	3	1	2	4	2.501 466 054	1.498 533 946
5	4	2	7	3	3.627 283 662	−.627 283 662
6	4	5	1	3	4.133 824 524	−1.133 824 524

Step 4 Example—Estimation of σ^2.   The estimate s^2 of σ^2 may be computed directly from the sum of squared residuals.   Thus,

$$s^2 = \frac{1}{n-k}\ \Sigma r^2$$
$$= \frac{1}{3}\ (5.808\ 473\ 047)$$
$$= 1.936\ 157\ 682$$

where n is the number of observational points (here 6) and k is the number of coefficients estimated from the data (here 3).   Alternatively, s^2 may be evaluated from

$$s^2 = \frac{1}{n-k}\left\{\Sigma Y^2 - \sum_1^3 \hat{\beta}_j\ q_j\right\}$$
$$= \frac{1}{6-3}\ \{70 - (0.735\ 320\ 652)\ (54) - (0.232\ 175\ 526)\ (97) - (0.031\ 664\ 286)\ (62)\}$$
$$= \frac{1}{3}\ (5.808\ 473\ 038)$$
$$= 1.936\ 157\ 679.$$

Extracting the square root gives

$$s = 1.391\ 4588.$$

Step 5 Procedure—Estimated Standard Deviations of the Coefficients. The estimated standard deviation of $\hat{\beta}_i$ is given by $s\sqrt{c_{ii}}$, where c_{ii} is the ith diagonal term of the inverse of the matrix of normal equations

$$\text{est. s.d. of } \hat{\beta}_0 = s\sqrt{c_{00}}$$
$$\text{est. s.d. of } \hat{\beta}_1 = s\sqrt{c_{11}}$$
$$\text{est. s.d. of } \hat{\beta}_2 = s\sqrt{c_{22}}$$

.
.
.   (6-21)

$$\text{est. s.d. of } \hat{\beta}_{k-1} = s\sqrt{c_{k-1,k-1}}.$$

Step 6 Procedure—Standard Deviation of a Linear Function of the $\hat{\beta}$'s. The standard deviation of $\hat{L} = a_0\hat{\beta}_0 + a_1\hat{\beta}_1 + a_2\hat{\beta}_2 + \ldots + a_{k-1}\hat{\beta}_{k-1}$ is estimated by

$$\text{est. s.d. of } \hat{L} = s\sqrt{\sum_{i=0}^{k-1}\sum_{j=0}^{k-1} a_i a_j c_{ij}} \tag{6-22}$$

or in matrix form

$$\text{est. s.d. of } \hat{L} = s\sqrt{l'(X'X)^{-1}l} \tag{6-22M}$$

where $l' = (a_0, a_1, \ldots, a_{k-1})$.

Cases of special interest are:

(a) estimate of a single coefficient, i.e., $\hat{L} = \hat{\beta}_i$, in which case Equation (6-22) reduces to Equation (6-21);

(b) estimate of the difference of two coefficients, i.e., $\hat{L} = \hat{\beta}_i - \hat{\beta}_j$, in which case Equation (6-22) becomes

$$\text{est. s.d. of } (\hat{\beta}_i - \hat{\beta}_j) = s\sqrt{c_{ii} + c_{jj} - 2c_{ij}}. \tag{6-23}$$

Step 7 Procedure—Standard Deviation of a Predicted Point. Using the results of Step 6, the predicted *yield* $\hat{Y}_h$, at any chosen point $(x_{0h}, x_{1h}, \ldots, x_{k-1,h})$, is given by

$$\hat{Y}_h = \hat{\beta}_0 x_{0h} + \hat{\beta}_1 x_{1h} + \ldots + \hat{\beta}_{k-1} x_{k-1,h}$$

which is a linear function of the $\hat{\beta}$'s. Application of Equation (6-22) leads to

$$\text{est. s.d. of } \hat{Y}_h = s\sqrt{\sum_{i=0}^{k-1}\sum_{j=0}^{k-1} x_{ih} x_{jh} c_{ij}} \tag{6-24}$$

or in matrix notation

$$\text{est. s.d. of } \hat{Y}_h = s\sqrt{l'(X'X)^{-1}l} \tag{6-24M}$$

where $l' = (x_{0h}, x_{1h}, \ldots, x_{k-1,h})$.

Step 5 Example—Estimated Standard Deviations of the Coefficients. The values of the estimated standard deviations of the $\hat{\beta}$'s are:

Coefficient	$\sqrt{c_{ii}}$	Estimated Standard Error of Coefficient, $s\sqrt{c_{ii}}$
$\hat{\beta}_1$	.232 581	.323 627
$\hat{\beta}_2$	.099 934	.139 054
$\hat{\beta}_3$	.147 531	.205 283

Step 6 Example—Standard Deviation of a Linear Function of the Coefficients. For illustrative purposes, consider $\hat{L} = \hat{\beta}_2 - 10\,\hat{\beta}_3$.

By Equation (6-22), or Equations (6-22M),

$$\text{est. s.d. of } \hat{L} = s\sqrt{c_{22} + 100\,c_{33} - 20\,c_{23}}$$

in matrix notation

$$\text{est. s.d. of } \hat{L} = s\sqrt{l'(X'X)^{-1}l}$$

with $l' = (0, 1, -10)$.

Numerical evaluation in this instance gives

$$\text{est. s.d. of } \hat{L} = 1.391\ 4588\left(\frac{537471}{239418}\right)^{\frac{1}{2}}$$

$$= 2.0848.$$

Step 7 Example—Standard Deviation of a Predicted Point. By Equation (6-24), or Equation (6-24M), the estimated standard deviation of the predicted *yield* $\hat{Y}_h$, corresponding to any chosen point (x_{1h}, x_{2h}, x_{3h}), is given by

$$\text{est. s.d. of } \hat{Y}_h = s\sqrt{\sum_{i=1}^{3}\sum_{j=1}^{3} x_{ih}x_{jh}c_{ij}}$$

or in matrix notation

$$\hat{Y}_h = s\sqrt{l'(X'X)^{-1}l}$$

where $l' = (x_{1h}, x_{2h}, x_{3h})$.

Thus, the estimated standard error of $\hat{Y}_1$, the predicted or adjusted *yield* corresponding to the first observational point $(1, 8, 1)$, is

$$\text{est. s.d. of } \hat{Y}_1 = s[c_{11} + 8c_{12} + c_{13} + 8c_{21} + 64c_{22} + 8c_{23} + c_{31} + 8c_{32} + c_{33}]^{\frac{1}{2}}$$

$$= 1.391\ 4588\left(\frac{111420}{239418}\right)^{\frac{1}{2}}$$

$$= 0.949\ 235.$$

Step 8 Procedure—Analysis of Variance Test of Significance of a Group of p < k of the Coefficients. To test the statistical significance of a set of p of the β's (for simplicity the last p), start with a reduced set of normal equations, omitting the last p rows and columns, and repeat Steps 2, 3, and 4, as a problem with $(k - p)$ variables:

(a) The equations in Step 2 then are reduced to

$$\Sigma x_0^2 \hat{\beta}_0 + \ldots + \Sigma x_0 x_{k-p-1} \hat{\beta}_{k-p-1} = q_0$$

.

.

.

$$\Sigma x_0 x_{k-p-1} \hat{\beta}_0 + \ldots + \Sigma x_{k-p-1}^2 \hat{\beta}_{k-p-1} = q_{k-p-1}$$

(6-25)

and its solution becomes

$$\hat{\beta}_0^* = c_{00}^* q_0 + \ldots + c_{0,k-p-1}^* q_{k-p-1}$$

.

.

.

$$\hat{\beta}_{k-p-1}^* = c_{1,k-p-1}^* q_0 + \ldots + c_{k-p-1,k-p-1}^* q_{k-p-1}.$$

(6-26)

(b) These values c_{ij}^* will, in general, be different from the c_{ij} for the original equations, so that new coefficients

$$\hat{\beta}_0^*, \hat{\beta}_1^*, \hat{\beta}_2^*, \ldots, \hat{\beta}_{k-p-1}^*$$

will result.

(c) A new value of s^2, say s^{*2}, is computed from

$$s^{*2} = \frac{1}{n - (k - p)} \left\{ \Sigma Y^2 - \sum_0^{k-p-1} \hat{\beta}_i^* q_i \right\}.$$

(6-27)

These operations can be handled conveniently by matrix methods. Paragraph 6-9 contains a further discussion of "Matrix Methods."

An *Analysis of Variance* table is formed as follows:

	d.f.	Sum of Squares	Mean Square
Total	n	ΣY^2	
Reduction due to k constants	k	$\sum_0^{k-1} \hat{\beta}_i q_i$	K
Residual (after k constants)	$n - k$	$\Sigma Y^2 - \sum_0^{k-1} \hat{\beta}_i q_i$	s^2
Reduction due to $k - p$ constants	$k - p$	$\sum_0^{k-p-1} \hat{\beta}_i^* q_i$	A
*Residuals after $k - p$ constants	$n - (k - p)$	$\Sigma Y^2 - \sum_0^{k-p-1} \hat{\beta}_i^* q_i$	s^{*2}
Reduction due to additional p constants	p	$\sum_0^{k-1} \hat{\beta}_i q_i - \sum_0^{k-p-1} \hat{\beta}_i^* q_i$	P

If the y's are normally distributed about their expected values, then

Step 8 Example—Analysis of Variance Test of Significance of Last Coefficient. The required *Analysis of Variance* table is:

	d.f.	Sums of Squares	Mean Square
Total	6	70.000 000	
Reduction due to 3 constants ($\hat{\beta}_1$, $\hat{\beta}_2$, and $\hat{\beta}_3$)	3	64.191 527	$21.397\ 176 = K$
Residuals (after 3 constants)	3	5.808 473	$1.936\ 158 = s^2$
Reduction due to $\hat{\beta}_1$ and $\hat{\beta}_2$ only	2	64.145 461	$32.072\ 730 = A$
Residuals (after $\hat{\beta}_1$ and $\hat{\beta}_1$)	4	5.854 539	$1.463\ 635 = s^{*2}$
Reduction due to $\hat{\beta}_3$	1	.046 066	$.046\ 066 = P$

As implied by Equation (6-27), the *sum of squares for the reduction due to $\hat{\beta}_1$ and $\hat{\beta}_2$ only* $= \hat{\beta}_1^* q_1 + \hat{\beta}_2^* q_2$, where $\hat{\beta}_1^*$ and $\hat{\beta}_2^*$ are the estimates of β_1 and β_2 that are obtained when β_3 is taken equal to zero; i.e., when the underlying functional relation is taken to be $y = \beta_1 x_1 + \beta_2 x_2$.

The steps required to evaluate $\hat{\beta}_1^*$ and $\hat{\beta}_2^*$ are

$$(X_1'X_1) = \begin{bmatrix} 50 & 67 \\ 67 & 194 \end{bmatrix}$$

$$(X'X)^{-1} = \frac{1}{5211} \begin{bmatrix} 194 & -67 \\ -67 & 50 \end{bmatrix}$$

$$[X_1'Y] = \begin{bmatrix} 54 \\ 97 \end{bmatrix} = \begin{bmatrix} q_1 \\ q_2 \end{bmatrix}$$

$$\begin{bmatrix} \beta_1^* \\ \beta_2^* \end{bmatrix} = (X'X)^{-1} [X_1'Y]$$

$$= \frac{1}{5211} \begin{bmatrix} 194 & -67 \\ -67 & 50 \end{bmatrix} \begin{bmatrix} 54 \\ 97 \end{bmatrix}.$$

They yield

$$\hat{\beta}_1^* = 0.763\ 193\ 245$$
$$\hat{\beta}_2^* = 0.236\ 422\ 951.$$

Hence, reduction due to $\hat{\beta}_1^*$ and $\hat{\beta}_2^*$ only is given by

$$(0.763\ 193\ 245)\ (54) + (0.236\ 422\ 951)\ (97) = 64.145\ 461$$

as shown in the *Analysis of Variance* table.

Step 8 Procedure (Cont)

(a) $F = \dfrac{K}{s^2}$ is distributed as F with d.f. $= k, n - k$, and serves as a test of whether all k constants account for a significant reduction in the error variance.

(b) $F = \dfrac{P}{s^2}$ is distributed as F with d.f. $= p, n - k$, and serves as a test of whether the addition of the p coefficients accounts for a significant reduction in the error variance over that accounted for by the first $k - p$ constants.

NOTE: In cases where a constant term is involved (i.e., $x_{01} = 1$) we would use

$$F = \frac{\left\{ \sum_0^{k-1} \hat{\beta}_i \, q_i - \dfrac{(\Sigma Y)^2}{n} \right\} / (k - 1)}{s^2}$$

which is distributed as F with $(k - 1)$ and $(n - k)$ degrees of freedom as a test for the efficacy of the prediction equation.

Step 9 Procedure—Confidence Interval Estimates. L_1 and L_2 constitute a $100 (1 - \alpha)$ % confidence interval estimate for:

(a) a coefficient β_i,

when $L_1 = \hat{\beta}_i - t_{n-k, \alpha}$ (est. s.d. of $\hat{\beta}_i$)

$L_2 = \hat{\beta}_i + t_{n-k, \alpha}$ (est. s.d. of $\hat{\beta}_i$);

(b) a predicted point on the curve $\hat{Y}_i$,

when $L_1 = \hat{Y}_i - t_{n-k, \alpha}$ (est. s.d. of $\hat{Y}_i$)

$L_2 = \hat{Y}_i + t_{n-k, \alpha}$ (est. s.d. of $\hat{Y}_i$);

(c) a difference of two coefficients $\hat{\beta}_i - \hat{\beta}_j$,

when $L_1 = (\hat{\beta}_i - \hat{\beta}_j) - t_{n-k, \alpha}$ (est. s.d. of $\hat{\beta}_i - \hat{\beta}_j$)

$L_2 = (\hat{\beta}_i - \hat{\beta}_j) + t_{n-k, \alpha}$ (est. s.d. of $\hat{\beta}_i - \hat{\beta}_j$).

In the above, $t_{n-k, \alpha}$ is the value of Student's t for $(n - k)$ degrees of freedom exceeded with probability $\dfrac{\alpha}{2}$.

Step 8 Example (Cont)

The test of significance for $\hat{\beta}_3$ is

$$F = \frac{P}{s^2}$$

$$= \frac{.046\ 060}{1.936\ 158}$$

$$= .024, \text{ d.f.} = 1, 3.$$

The value of $F(1, 3)$ exceeded with probability .05 is 10.13. The observed F does not exceed this critical value, so that β_3 is not regarded as being statistically significantly different from zero.

Step 9 Example—Confidence Interval Estimates. For β_1, the 95% confidence interval estimate $L_1 \leq \beta_1 \leq L_2$ is determined by

$$L_1 = \hat{\beta}_1 - t_{3, .05} \text{ (est. s.d. of } \hat{\beta}_1)$$

$$= 0.735\ 320\ 652 - 3.182\ (.323\ 627)$$

$$= -.294\ 460$$

$$L_2 = \hat{\beta}_1 + t_{3, .05} \text{ (est. s.d. of } \hat{\beta}_1)$$

$$= 0.735\ 320\ 652 + 3.182\ (.323\ 627)$$

$$= 1.765\ 102$$

where $t_{3, .05} = 3.182$ is the value of Student's t distribution for three degrees of freedom exceeded with probability .025 (or exceeded in absolute value with probability .05).

6-4 MULTIPLE MEASUREMENTS AT ONE OR MORE POINTS

More than one measurement may be made at some or at all of the values of the independent variable x. This usually is done when the random errors are suspected of being composed of two components—one component associated with the variation of the points about the curve, and the other component associated with the variation of repeat determinations. The jth measurement at the ith point then can be represented as

$$Y_{ij} = \beta_0 x_{0i} + \beta_1 x_{1i} + \ldots + \beta_{k-1} x_{k-1,i} + \epsilon_i + \eta_{ij} \tag{6-28}$$

where the ϵ's and η's are independent and have variances σ^2 and σ_0^2, respectively.

If a number p_i of repeat determinations are made at each of the n points, the estimation of σ^2 and σ_0^2 follows from a modification of the *Analysis of Variance* table:

	Sum of Squares	d.f.	Mean Square
Total	$\sum\limits_{i=1}^{n} \sum\limits_{j=1}^{p_i} Y_{ij}^2 = T$	$\sum\limits_{1}^{n} p_i$	
Reduction due to fitted constants	$\sum\limits_{i=0}^{k-1} \hat{\beta}_i (\Sigma x_i Y) = C$	k	C/k
Residual (after fitted constants)	$T - C = R$	$\Sigma p_i - k$	$R/(\Sigma p_i - k)$
Repeat determinations	$\sum\limits_{i=1}^{n} \sum\limits_{j=1}^{p_i} (Y_{ij} - \bar{Y}_i)^2 = E_0$	$\Sigma p_i - n$	$E_0/(\Sigma p_i - n)$
Variations of averages about the curve	$R - E_0 = E_1$	$n - k$	$E_1/(n - k)$

*The expected value of $E_0/(\Sigma p_i - n)$ is σ_0^2, and the expected value of $E_1/(n - k)$ is $\sigma_0^2 + p\sigma^2$, when all the p_i are equal to p.

The quantity $[E_1/(n - k)]/[E_0/\Sigma p_i - n] = F$ is (under the assumption of a normal distribution for the ϵ's and η's) distributed as F, if $\sigma^2 = 0$, with $n - k$ and $\Sigma p_i - n$ degrees of freedom, and may be used to test the statistical significance of the component of variance associated with the ϵ's by comparing the observed F value with tables of the F distribution.

If all the p_i are equal, the proper variance estimate to use in calculating the standard errors, or confidence intervals of the estimated constants, is $E_1/(n - k)$.

6-5 POLYNOMIAL FITTING

If it can be assumed that the relation between the *dependent variable* Y and the *independent variable* x is

$$Y_i = \beta_0 + \beta_1 x_i + \beta_2 x_i^2 + \ldots + \beta_{k-1} x_i^{k-1} + \epsilon_i \qquad (6\text{-}29)$$

and that the errors of measurement ϵ_i are independent and have the same variance σ^2, then the techniques for multiple regression carry over without change, by setting:

$$x_{0i} = 1; \; x_{1i} = x_i; \; x_{2i} = x_i^2; \; \ldots ; \; x_{k-1,i} = x_i^{k-1}.$$

The normal equations are

$$n\beta_0 + \Sigma x \beta_1 + \Sigma x^2 \beta_2 + \ldots + \Sigma x^{k-1} \beta_{k-1} = \Sigma Y$$
$$\Sigma x \beta_0 + \Sigma x^2 \beta_1 + \Sigma x^3 \beta_2 + \ldots + \Sigma x^k \beta_{k-1} = \Sigma x Y \qquad (6\text{-}30)$$
$$\ldots$$
$$\Sigma x^{k-1} \beta_0 + \Sigma x^k \beta_1 + \Sigma x^{k+1} \beta_2 + \ldots + \Sigma x^{2k-2} \beta_{k-1} = \Sigma x^{k-1} Y.$$

Note that if the constant term is assumed to be zero, variable x_0 is dropped, and the first row and column are dropped from the normal equations.

In using a polynomial as an approximation to some unknown function, or as an interpolation formula, the correct degree for the polynomial usually is not known. The following procedure usually is applied:

(a) Carry through the steps in fitting polynomials of 2nd, 3rd, 4th, 5th, . . . , degrees.

(b) If the reduction in the error sum of squares due to fitting the kth degree term is statistically significant on the basis of the F-test, whereas the similar test for the $(k + 1)$ degree term is not, then the kth degree polynomial is accepted as the *best* fitting polynomial.

In this procedure, the degree of the polynomial is a random variable, and repetitions of the experiment will lead to different degree polynomials. When the law is *truly polynomial*, the computed curve will either be of correct degree and hence will give unbiased estimates of the coefficients or, *if not* of correct degree, will lead to biased estimates.

When the law is not exactly a polynomial, the error distribution for the Y's will be centered around a value off the curve, and it will be difficult to assess the effect of such systematic errors. In the limiting case, where the variance of the Y's is nearly zero, these systematic errors will be treated as the random error in the measurements. Usually, it will not be valid to assume that these systematic errors are uncorrelated. On the other hand, if these systematic errors are small relative to the measurement error, their effect probably can be neglected.

6-6 INEQUALITY OF VARIANCE

6-6.1 DISCUSSION OF PROCEDURES AND EXAMPLES

When the measurements Y_i have different precision, i.e., when $V(Y_i) = \sigma_i^2$ and $\sigma_{i_1} \neq \sigma_{i_2}$ for at least one pair of subscripts $1 \leq i_1 < i_2 \leq n$, the conditions of the least squares theorem of Paragraph 6-2 are not satisfied. However, the transformed variates

$$Y_i' = \frac{Y_i}{\sigma_i}$$

have a common variance $V(Y_i') = 1$. Often, we have information on the relative magnitudes of the variances σ_i^2 only, and not on their absolute magnitudes. If the variances σ_i^2 are expressed in the form

$$\sigma_i^2 = \frac{\sigma_0^2}{w_i}, \tag{6-31}$$

then w_i is termed the *relative weight** of the measurement Y_i, and the quantities $Y_i^* = \sqrt{w_i}\, Y_i$ have common variance σ_0^2, the magnitude of which may be unknown. In other words, equality of variance is achieved through *weighting* the observations by quantities proportional to the reciprocals of their standard deviations.

---

* The *absolute weight* of a measurement is, by definition, the reciprocal of its variance.

6-6.2 PROCEDURES AND EXAMPLES

Procedures—The equations representing the expected values of the Y_i^* are

$$
\begin{aligned}
E(Y_i^*) &= \sqrt{w_i}\, E(Y_i) \\
&= \beta_0 \sqrt{w_i}\, x_{0i} + \beta_1 \sqrt{w_i}\, x_{1i} + \ldots + \beta_{k-1} \sqrt{w_i}\, x_{k-1,i} \\
&= \beta_0 x_{0i}^* + \beta_1 x_{1i}^* + \ldots + \beta_{k-1} x_{k-1,i}^*
\end{aligned}
\tag{6-32}
$$

where $\quad x_{ij}^* = \sqrt{w_i}\, x_{ij}.$

The normal equations for the estimation of the β's are

$$
\begin{aligned}
\Sigma\, w\, x_0^2\, \beta_0 + \Sigma\, w\, x_0 x_1 \beta_1 + \ldots + \Sigma\, w\, x_0 x_{k-1} \beta_{k-1} &= \Sigma\, w\, x_0 Y \\
\Sigma\, w\, x_0 x_1 \beta_0 + \Sigma\, w\, x_1^2 \beta_1 + \ldots + \Sigma\, w\, x_1 x_{k-1} \beta_{k-1} &= \Sigma\, w\, x_1 Y \\
\ldots \\
\Sigma\, w\, x_0 x_{k-1} \beta_0 + \Sigma\, w\, x_1 x_{k-1} \beta_1 + \ldots + \Sigma\, w\, x_{k-1}^2 \beta_{k-1} &= \Sigma\, w\, x_{k-1} Y
\end{aligned}
\tag{6-33}
$$

The estimate s^2 of σ_0^2 is given by the usual formula

$$
s^2 = \frac{\displaystyle\sum_{i=1}^{n} Y_i^{*2} - \sum_{j=1}^{k-1} \hat{\beta}_j \left(\sum_{i=1}^{n} x_{ji}^* Y_i^* \right)}{n-k}
\tag{6-34}
$$

which may be written, in terms of the original variables, as

$$
\begin{aligned}
s^2 &= \frac{\Sigma\, r_i^2\, w_i}{n-k} \\
&= \frac{\Sigma\, w_i Y_i^2 - \Sigma\, \hat{\beta}_j \left(\displaystyle\sum_{i=1}^{n} w_i x_{ij} Y_i \right)}{n-k}.
\end{aligned}
\tag{6-35}
$$

Note that in the case where the value of σ_0^2 is known, we may perform a test of significance of the closeness of the observed estimate to the known value by forming the ratio $F = \dfrac{s^2}{\sigma_0^2}$ and comparing this value with the $100\,(1 - \alpha)$ percentage point of the F distribution for $n - k$ and ∞ degrees of freedom; or, equivalently, we may compare $\chi^2 = \dfrac{(n-k)\, s^2}{\sigma_0^2}$ with the $100\,(1 - \alpha)$ percentage point of the χ^2 distribution for $n - k$ degrees of freedom. Restatement of the foregoing, using matrix notation, goes as follows:

If $\mathrm{Var}\,(Y_i) = \mathrm{Diag}\,(\sigma_1^2,\ \sigma_2^2,\ \ldots,\ \sigma_n^2)$

$$
= \sigma_0^2 \,\mathrm{Diag} \left(\frac{1}{w_1},\ \frac{1}{w_2},\ \ldots,\ \frac{1}{w_n} \right),
$$

then the transformed variates

$$
\begin{aligned}
Y^* &= \mathrm{Diag}\,(\sqrt{w_1}\ \sqrt{w_2}\ \ldots\ \sqrt{w_n})\, Y = W Y \quad \text{and} \\
X^* &= \mathrm{Diag}\,(\sqrt{w_1}\ \sqrt{w_2}\ \ldots\ \sqrt{w_n})\, X = W X
\end{aligned}
$$

satisfy the requirements of the least squares theorem of Paragraph 6-2, and the normal equations are

$$
\begin{aligned}
(X^*)'(X^*)\hat{\beta} &= (X^*)' Y^* \quad \text{or,} \\
X'\, W^2\, X\, \hat{\beta} &= X'\, W^2\, Y.
\end{aligned}
\tag{6-33M}
$$

The estimate of σ_0^2 is given by

$$s^2 = \frac{1}{n - k} \{Y^{*\prime} Y^* - \hat{\beta}' (X^*)'Y^*\} \quad \text{or,}$$

$$s^2 = \frac{r' W^2 r}{n - k} \tag{6-34M}$$

Examples—Fitting Straight Line Relation (Variance of Y Proportional to Abscissa). Consider the estimation of the coefficients of a line where

$$y = \alpha + \beta x_i,$$

and where $\text{Var}(Y_i) = \sigma^2 x_i$, $i = 1, 2, \ldots, n$. The equations of expectation are

$$
\begin{aligned}
E(Y_1) &= \alpha + \beta x_1 \\
E(Y_2) &= \alpha + \beta x_2 \\
&\cdots \\
E(Y_n) &= \alpha + \beta x_n
\end{aligned}
\tag{6-36}
$$

Transforming to $Y_i^* = Y_i/\sqrt{x_i}$, gives

$$
\begin{aligned}
E(Y_1^*) &= \frac{\alpha}{\sqrt{x_1}} + \beta\sqrt{x_1} \\[6pt]
E(Y_2^*) &= \frac{\alpha}{\sqrt{x_2}} + \beta\sqrt{x_2} \\[6pt]
&\cdots \\[6pt]
E(Y_n^*) &= \frac{\alpha}{\sqrt{x_n}} + \beta\sqrt{x_n}
\end{aligned}
\tag{6-37}
$$

and the normal equations for estimating α and β become

$$
\begin{aligned}
\hat{\alpha} \Sigma \frac{1}{x_i} + \hat{\beta} n &= \Sigma Y_i/x_i \\[4pt]
\hat{\alpha} n + \hat{\beta} \Sigma x &= \Sigma Y_i
\end{aligned}
\tag{6-38}
$$

Direct solution of these equations gives

$$\hat{\beta} = \frac{n \Sigma \dfrac{Y_i}{x_i} - \Sigma Y_i \left(\Sigma \dfrac{1}{x_i}\right)}{n^2 - (\Sigma x_i) \left(\Sigma \dfrac{1}{x_i}\right)} \tag{6-39}$$

$$\hat{\alpha} = \frac{n \Sigma Y_i - \Sigma x_i \Sigma Y_i/x_i}{n^2 - (\Sigma x_i) \Sigma \left(\dfrac{1}{x_i}\right)} \tag{6-40}$$

and for the estimate of σ^2,

$$s^2 = \frac{1}{n - 2} \left\{ \Sigma \frac{1}{x_i} (Y - \hat{\alpha} - \hat{\beta} x_i)^2 \right\}. \tag{6-41}$$

6-7 CORRELATED MEASUREMENT ERRORS

6-7.1 DISCUSSION OF PROCEDURES AND EXAMPLES

If the errors of measurement are not independent but instead are correlated so that they have covariances

$$\text{Covar } (Y_i, Y_j) = \sigma_{ij} = \sigma_{ji} \tag{6-42}$$

and variances

$$\text{Var } (Y_i) = \sigma_i^2,$$

then a transformation of the variables $Y_1, Y_2, \ldots, Y_n$, to new variables $Y_1^*, Y_2^*, \ldots, Y_n^*$, is required so that the method of least squares may be applied. In some simple cases, a transformation in the form of sums and differences of the original variables immediately suggests itself, and the expected values of the new variables are computed easily. The example used to illustrate the techniques presented in this Paragraph is such a case.

6-7.2 PROCEDURES AND EXAMPLES

Procedures—The variances and covariances may be represented by the $n \times n$ variance-covariance matrix

$$V = \begin{bmatrix} \sigma_1^2 & \sigma_{12} & . & . & . & \sigma_{1n} \\ \sigma_{12} & \sigma_2^2 & . & . & . & \sigma_{2n} \\ . & . & . & & & \\ \sigma_{n1} & \sigma_{n2} & . & . & . & \sigma_n^2 \end{bmatrix} \tag{6-42M}$$

Assuming V to be of full rank, i.e., determinant of V is not zero, it is possible to factor V into the product

$$V = T\, T' \tag{6-43M}$$

where T is lower triangular and T' is the transpose of T. The required transformation then is given by

$$Y^* = T^{-1}\, Y \qquad \text{and} \qquad X^* = T^{-1}\, X \tag{6-44M}$$

where $(Y^*)' = (Y_1^*, Y_2^*, \ldots, Y_n^*)$ is the vector of transformed variables and $Y' = (Y_1, Y_2, \ldots, Y_n)$ is the vector of original variables. X^* and X are the matrices representing the equations of expected values of the transformed variables and of the original variables, respectively. (See Paragraph 6-9 for the method of computing T and T^{-1}).

The normal equations then are

$$(X^*)'(X^*)\, \hat{\beta} = (X^*)'\, Y^* \tag{6-45M}$$

or, in terms of the original variables,

$$X'V^{-1}X\, \hat{\beta} = X'V^{-1}\, Y, \tag{6-46M}$$

and the estimates of the β's are given by

$$\begin{aligned} \hat{\beta} &= [(X^*)'(X^*)]^{-1}(X^*)'Y^* \\ &= (X'V^{-1}X)^{-1}X'V^{-1}Y. \end{aligned} \tag{6-47M}$$

The variance estimate

$$s^2 = \frac{1}{n-k} \left\{ \Sigma\, Y^{*2} - \sum_{i=1}^{k} \hat{\beta}_i \left(\sum_{j=1}^{n} x_{ij}^*\ Y_j^* \right) \right\} \tag{6-48}$$

Procedures (Cont)

is an estimate of unity when the variances and covariances are known.   This may be written as

$$s^2 = \frac{1}{n-k} \{Y'V^{-1}Y - \hat{\beta}'X'V^{-1}Y\}$$

$$= \frac{1}{n-k} \{r'V^{-1}r\}$$

(6-48M)

where r is the column vector of deviations, $r = Y - X\hat{\beta}$.

If, instead of V, a matrix with entries proportional to the variances and covariances is used, say $W = \frac{1}{\sigma_0^2} V$, then s^2 is an estimate of σ_0^2.

Examples—Parabolic Relationship with Cumulative Errors.   If the errors of measurements of Y at successive x values in a case of a parabolic law $Y = \beta_0 + \beta_1 x + \beta_2 x^2$ are cumulative, i.e.,

$$Y_1 = \beta_0 + \beta_1 x_1 + \beta_2 x_1^2 + \epsilon_1$$
$$Y_2 = \beta_0 + \beta_1 x_2 + \beta_2 x_2^2 + \epsilon_1 + \epsilon_2$$
$$\cdot \quad \cdot \quad \cdot$$
$$Y_n = \beta_0 + \beta_1 x_n + \beta_2 x_n^2 + \sum_1^n \epsilon_i$$

then $E(Y) = \begin{bmatrix} 1 & x_1 & x_1^2 \\ 1 & x_2 & x_2^2 \\ \cdot & \cdot & \cdot \\ \cdot & \cdot & \cdot \\ \cdot & \cdot & \cdot \\ 1 & x_n & x_n^2 \end{bmatrix} \begin{bmatrix} \beta_0 \\ \beta_1 \\ \beta_2 \end{bmatrix} = X\beta.$

If all the ϵ's are from the same distribution,

then $\text{Var}(Y_i) = i \cdot \sigma^2$

$$\text{Covar}(Y_i Y_j) = \begin{cases} i \cdot \sigma^2 & i < j \\ j \cdot \sigma^2 & j < i \end{cases}$$

and the variance covariance matrix becomes

$$V = \sigma^2 \begin{bmatrix} 1 & 1 & 1 & \cdot & \cdot & \cdot & 1 \\ 1 & 2 & 2 & & & & 2 \\ 1 & 2 & 3 & & & & 3 \\ \cdot & & & & & & \\ \cdot & & & & & & \\ \cdot & & & & & & \\ 1 & 2 & 3 & & & & n \end{bmatrix}.$$

Taking $W = \frac{1}{\sigma^2} V$, the necessary transformation is given by factoring W into $W = T\,T'$.

6-7.2 PROCEDURES AND EXAMPLES (CONT)

Examples (Cont)

A little computation gives

$$
W = \begin{bmatrix} 1 & & & & \\ 1 & 1 & & & \\ 1 & 1 & 1 & & \\ & & & \ddots & \\ 1 & 1 & 1 & \cdots & 1 \end{bmatrix} \begin{bmatrix} 1 & 1 & 1 & \cdots & 1 \\ & 1 & 1 & & 1 \\ & & 1 & & 1 \\ & & & \ddots & \\ & & & & 1 \end{bmatrix} = T\,T'
$$

$$
W^{-1} = (T')^{-1} T^{-1} = \begin{bmatrix} 1 & -1 & 0 & 0 & 0 \\ & 1 & -1 & 0 & 0 \\ & & 1 & -1 & 0 \\ & & & \ddots & \\ & & & 1 & -1 \\ & & & & 1 \end{bmatrix} \begin{bmatrix} 1 & & & & \\ -1 & 1 & & & \\ 0 & -1 & 1 & & \\ & & & \ddots & \\ 0 & 0 & 0 & 1 & \\ 0 & 0 & 0 & -1 & 1 \end{bmatrix}
$$

$$
= \begin{bmatrix} 2 & -1 & & & & & \\ -1 & 2 & -1 & & & & \\ & -1 & 2 & -1 & & & \\ & & & \cdot & & & \\ & & & & \cdot & & \\ & & & & & \cdot & \\ & & & & -1 & 2 & -1 \\ & & & & & -1 & 1 \end{bmatrix}
$$

which, for the transformed variate, gives

$$
Y^* = T^{-1} Y = \begin{bmatrix} 1 & & & & \\ -1 & 1 & & & \\ 0 & -1 & 1 & & \\ \cdot & \cdot & & & \\ 0 & 0 & 0 & \cdots & -1 & 1 \end{bmatrix} \begin{bmatrix} Y_1 \\ Y_2 \\ Y_3 \\ \cdot\cdot \\ Y_n \end{bmatrix} = \begin{bmatrix} Y_1 \\ Y_2 - Y_1 \\ Y_3 - Y_2 \\ \cdot\quad\cdot\quad\cdot \\ Y_n - Y_{n-1} \end{bmatrix}
$$

Examples (Cont)

and

$$X^* = T^{-1}X = \begin{bmatrix} 1 & & & & & \\ -1 & 1 & & & & \\ 0 & -1 & 1 & & & \\ \cdot & \cdot & \cdot & & & \\ 0 & 0 & 0 & \cdots & -1 & 1 \end{bmatrix} \begin{bmatrix} 1 & x_1 & x_1^2 \\ 1 & x_2 & x_2^2 \\ 1 & x_3 & x_3^2 \\ \cdot & \cdot & \cdot \\ 1 & x_n & x_n^2 \end{bmatrix}$$

$$= \begin{bmatrix} 1 & x_1 & x_1^2 \\ 0 & x_2 - x_1 & x_2^2 - x_1^2 \\ 0 & x_3 & x_3 & x_3^2 - x_2^2 \\ \cdot & \cdot & \cdot \\ 0 & x_n - x_{n-1} & x_n^2 - x_{n-1}^2 \end{bmatrix}.$$

Note that $Y_i^* = Y_i - Y_{i-1}$
$$= (x_i - x_{i-1})\beta_0 + (x_i^2 - x_{i-1}^2)\beta_1 + \epsilon_i \text{ for } i \geq 2$$

and $\qquad Y_1^* = Y_1;$

hence, the Y^*'s have the same variance, and have zero covariances.

The normal equations become

$$X^{*\prime}X^*\beta = \begin{bmatrix} 1 & x_1 & x_1^2 \\ x_1 & x_1^2 + \sum_1^n (x_i - x_{i-1})^2 & x_1^3 + \sum_2^n (x_i - x_{i-1})(x_i^2 - x_{i-1}^2) \\ x_1^2 & x_1^3 + \sum_2^n (x_i - x_{i-1})(x_i^2 - x_{i-1}^2) & x_1^4 + \sum_2^n (x_i^2 - x_{i-1}^2)^2 \end{bmatrix} \beta$$

$$= \begin{bmatrix} Y_1 \\ x_1 Y_1 + \sum_2^n (x_i - x_{i-1})(Y_i - Y_{i-1}) \\ x_1^2 Y_1 + \sum_2^n (x_i^2 - x_{i-1}^2)(Y_i - Y_{i-1}) \end{bmatrix}$$

6-7.2 PROCEDURES AND EXAMPLES (CONT)

Examples (Cont)

or, in terms of the original matrices $X'W^{-1}X\beta = X'W^{-1}Y$, give

$$
\begin{bmatrix}
1 & 1 & . & . & . & 1 \\
x_1 & x_2 & . & . & . & x_n \\
x_1^2 & x_2^2 & . & . & . & x_n^2
\end{bmatrix}
\begin{bmatrix}
2 & -1 & & & & \\
-1 & 2 & -1 & & & \\
 & -1 & 2 & -1 & & \\
 & . & . & . & . & \\
 & & & -1 & 2 & -1 \\
 & & & & -1 & 1
\end{bmatrix}
\begin{bmatrix}
1 & x_1 & x_1^2 \\
1 & x_2 & x_2^2 \\
1 & x_3 & x_3^2 \\
. & . & . \\
1 & x_n & x_n^2
\end{bmatrix}\beta
$$

$$
=
\begin{bmatrix}
1 & 1 & . & . & . & 1 \\
x_1 & x_2 & & & & x_n \\
x_1^2 & x_2^2 & & & & x_n^2
\end{bmatrix}
\begin{bmatrix}
2 & -1 & & & \\
-1 & 2 & -1 & & \\
 & . & . & . & \\
 & & & -1 & 1
\end{bmatrix}
\begin{bmatrix}
Y_1 \\
Y_2 \\
Y_3 \\
. \\
. \\
. \\
Y_n
\end{bmatrix}
$$

which, upon multiplication, will be seen to give the same normal equations as above. If the analysis is carried out in terms of the transformed variables, σ^2 is estimated by

$$
s^2 = \frac{\Sigma Y^{*2} - \Sigma \hat{\beta}_i \left(\sum_j x_{ji}^* Y_j^* \right)}{n - 3}
$$

or equivalently, in terms of the original variables, by

$$
s^2 = \frac{1}{n - 3} \{ Y'W^{-1}Y - \hat{\beta}'X'W^{-1}Y \}.
$$

6-8 USE OF ORTHOGONAL POLYNOMIALS WITH EQUALLY SPACED x VALUES

6-8.1 DISCUSSION OF PROCEDURES AND EXAMPLES

The fitting of a polynomial

$$
Y = \beta_0 + \beta_1 x + \beta_2 x^2 + \ldots + \beta_{k-1} x^{k-1} \tag{6-49}
$$

to observations at n equally-spaced values of x (spaced a distance D apart) can be simplified by transforming the x's to new variables $\xi_0', \xi_1', \ldots, \xi_{k-1}'$, which are orthogonal to each other.

The variables then become

$$\xi_0' = \xi_0 = 1$$

$$*\xi_1' = \lambda_1\xi_1 \text{ where } \xi_1 = \frac{x_i - \bar{x}}{D}$$

$$*\xi_2' = \lambda_2\xi_2 \text{ where } \xi_2 = \left(\frac{x_i - \bar{x}}{D}\right)^2 - \frac{n^2 - 1}{12}$$

$$*\xi_3' = \lambda_3\xi_3 \text{ where } \xi_3 = \left(\frac{x_i - \bar{x}}{D}\right)^3 - \left(\frac{x_i - \bar{x}}{D}\right)\left(\frac{3n^2 - 7}{20}\right) \qquad (6\text{-}50)$$

$$*\xi_4' = \lambda_4\xi_4 \text{ where } \xi_4 = \left(\frac{x_i - \bar{x}}{D}\right)^4 - \left(\frac{x_i - \bar{x}}{D}\right)^2\left(\frac{3n^2 - 13}{14}\right) + \frac{3}{560}(n^4 - 10n^2 + 9)$$

$$*\xi_5' = \lambda_5\xi_5 \text{ where } \xi_5 = \left(\frac{x_i - \bar{x}}{D}\right)^5 - \left(\frac{x_i - \bar{x}}{D}\right)^3 \frac{5(n^2 - 7)}{18} + \left(\frac{x_i - \bar{x}}{D}\right)\left(\frac{15n^4 - 230n^2 + 407}{1008}\right)$$

. . .

$$\text{where} \qquad \xi_{k+1} = \xi_1\xi_k - \frac{k^2(n^2 - k^2)}{4(4k^2 - 1)}\xi_{k-1}.$$

The λ_i are chosen so that the elements of ξ_i are integers.

By fitting Y as a function

$$*Y = \alpha_0\xi_0' + \alpha_1\xi_1' + \ldots + \alpha_{k-1}\xi_{k-1}', \qquad (6\text{-}51)$$

the estimation of the α's and the analysis of variance are simplified because the normal equations are in diagonal form.

In order to obtain the estimates of the β's and their associated standard errors, or to use Equation (6-51) for predicting a value for a point not in the original data, an extra calculation but no matrix inversion is required.

Tables of ξ', λ, and $\Sigma(\xi')^2$ are given by Fisher and Yates[6] for $n \leq 75$, and by Anderson and Houseman[7] for $n \leq 104$ for up to 5th degree polynomials; in DeLury[8] for $n \leq 26$ for all powers; and in Pearson and Hartley[9] for $n \leq 52$ for up to 6th degree polynomials. Table 6-1 is a sample from Fisher and Yates.[6]

To illustrate the calculations, consider the fitting of a cubic to the following (x, Y) points:

x	Y
10	3.4
20	11.7
30	37.2
40	80.1
50	151.4
60	253.2
70	392.6

TABLE 6-1. SAMPLE TABLE OF ORTHOGONAL POLYNOMIALS

n = 3

ξ'_1	ξ'_2
−1	+1
0	−2
+1	+1
Σ(ξ')² 2	6
λ 1	3

n = 4

ξ'_1	ξ'_2	ξ'_3
−3	+1	−1
−1	−1	+3
+1	−1	−3
+3	+1	+1
Σ(ξ')² 20	4	20
λ 2	1	10/3

n = 5

ξ'_1	ξ'_2	ξ'_3	ξ'_4
−2	+2	−1	+1
−1	−1	+2	−4
0	−2	0	+6
+1	−1	−2	−4
+2	+2	+1	+1
Σ(ξ')² 10	14	10	70
λ 1	1	5/6	35/12

n = 6

ξ'_1	ξ'_2	ξ'_3	ξ'_4	ξ'_5
−5	+5	−5	+1	−1
−3	−1	+7	−3	+5
−1	−4	+4	+2	−10
+1	−4	−4	+2	+10
+3	−1	−7	−3	−5
+5	+5	+5	+1	+1
Σ(ξ')² 70	84	180	28	252
λ 2	3/2	5/3	7/12	21/10

n = 7

ξ'_1	ξ'_2	ξ'_3	ξ'_4	ξ'_5
−3	+5	−1	+3	−1
−2	0	+1	−7	+4
−1	−3	+1	+1	−5
0	−4	0	+6	0
+1	−3	−1	+1	+5
+2	0	−1	−7	−4
+3	+5	+1	+3	+1
Σ(ξ')² 28	84	6	154	84
λ 1	1	1/6	7/12	7/20

n = 8

ξ'_1	ξ'_2	ξ'_3	ξ'_4	ξ'_5
−7	+7	−7	+7	−7
−5	+1	+5	−13	+23
−3	−3	+7	−3	−17
−1	−5	+3	+9	−15
+1	−5	−3	+9	+15
+3	−3	−7	−3	+17
+5	+1	−5	−13	−23
+7	+7	+7	+7	+7
Σ(ξ')² 168	168	264	616	2184
λ 2	1	2/3	7/12	7/10

n = 9

ξ'_1	ξ'_2	ξ'_3	ξ'_4	ξ'_5
0	−20	0	+18	0
+1	−17	−9	+9	+9
+2	−8	−13	−11	+4
+3	+7	−7	−21	−11
+4	+28	+14	+14	+4
Σ(ξ')² 60	2,772	990	2,002	468
λ 1	3	5/6	7/12	3/20

n = 10

ξ'_1	ξ'_2	ξ'_3	ξ'_4	ξ'_5
+1	−4	−12	+18	+6
+3	−3	−31	+3	+11
+5	−1	−35	−17	+1
+7	+2	−14	−22	−14
+9	+6	+42	+18	+6
Σ(ξ')² 330	132	8,580	2,860	780
λ 2	1/2	5/3	7/12	3/10

n = 11

ξ'_1	ξ'_2	ξ'_3	ξ'_4	ξ'_5
0	−10	0	+6	0
+1	−9	−14	+4	+4
+2	−6	−23	−1	+4
+3	−1	−22	−6	−1
+4	+6	−6	−6	−6
+5	+15	+30	+6	+3
Σ(ξ')² 110	858	4,290	286	156
λ 1	1	5/6	7/12	7/10

n = 12

ξ'_1	ξ'_2	ξ'_3	ξ'_4	ξ'_5
+1	−35	−7	+28	+20
+3	−29	−19	+12	+44
+5	−17	−25	−13	+29
+7	+1	−21	−33	−21
+9	+25	−3	−27	−57
+11	+55	+33	+33	+33
Σ(ξ')² 572	12,012	5,148	8,008	15,912
λ 2	3	2/3	7/24	3/20

n = 13

ξ'_1	ξ'_2	ξ'_3	ξ'_4	ξ'_5
0	−14	0	+84	0
+1	−13	−4	+64	+20
+2	−10	−7	+11	+26
+3	−5	−8	−54	+11
+4	+2	−6	−96	−18
+5	+11	0	−66	−33
+6	+22	+11	+99	+22
Σ(ξ')² 182	2,002	572	68,068	6,188
λ 1	1	1/6	7/12	7/120

n = 14

ξ'_1	ξ'_2	ξ'_3	ξ'_4	ξ'_5
+1	−8	−24	+108	+60
+3	−7	−67	+63	+145
+5	−5	−95	−13	+139
+7	−2	−98	−92	+28
+9	+2	−66	−132	−132
+11	+7	+11	−77	−187
+13	+13	+143	+143	+143
Σ(ξ')² 910	728	97,240	136,136	235,144
λ 2	1/2	2/3	7/12	7/10

n = 15

ξ'_1	ξ'_2	ξ'_3	ξ'_4	ξ'_5
0	−56	0	+756	0
+1	−53	−27	+621	+675
+2	−44	−49	+251	+1000
+3	−29	−61	−249	+751
+4	−8	−58	−704	−44
+5	+19	−35	−869	−979
+6	+52	+13	−429	−1144
+7	+91	+91	+1001	+1001
Σ(ξ')² 280	37,128	39,780	6,466,460	10,581,480
λ 1	3	5/6	35/12	11/12

TABLE 6-1. SAMPLE TABLE OF ORTHOGONAL POLYNOMIALS (Continued)

	16					17					18			
ξ'_1	ξ'_2	ξ'_3	ξ'_4	ξ'_5	ξ'_1	ξ'_2	ξ'_3	ξ'_4	ξ'_5	ξ'_1	ξ'_2	ξ'_3	ξ'_4	ξ'_5
+1	−21	−63	+189	+45	0	−24	0	+36	0	+1	−40	−8	+44	+220
+3	−19	−179	+129	+115	+1	−23	−7	+31	+55	+3	−37	−23	+33	+583
+5	−15	−265	+23	+131	+2	−20	−13	+17	+88	+5	−31	−35	+13	+733
+7	−9	−301	−101	+77	+3	−15	−17	−3	+83	+7	−22	−42	−12	+588
+9	−1	−267	−201	−33	+4	−8	−18	−24	+36	+9	−10	−42	−36	+156
+11	+9	−143	−221	−143	+5	+1	−15	−39	−39	+11	+5	−33	−51	−429
+13	+21	+91	−91	−143	+6	+12	−7	−39	−104	+13	+23	−13	−47	−871
+15	+35	+455	+273	+143	+7	+25	+7	−13	−91	+15	+44	+20	−12	−676
					+8	+40	+28	+52	+104	+17	+68	+68	+68	+884

	16					17					18			
$\Sigma(\xi')^2$	1,360	1,007,760		201,552	408	3,876		100,776		1,938	23,256		6,953,544	
	5,712	470,288			7,752	16,796				23,256	28,424			
λ	2	1	$\frac{10}{3}$	$\frac{7}{12}$	$\frac{7}{6}$	1	1	$\frac{1}{6}$	$\frac{7}{12}$	$\frac{7}{6}$	2	$\frac{3}{?}$	$\frac{1}{?}$	$\frac{7}{12}$	$\frac{7}{6}$

*Note: In Table 6-1, only the values for positive $\xi'_1 = \dfrac{x-\bar{x}}{D}$ are given for $n > 8$. The missing values ($n/2$ rows for n even and $(n-1)/2$ rows for n odd) must be supplied by using the given rows in reverse order, changing the sign for odd-numbered ξ'. See $n=7$ and $n=8$ for example of this rule.

Excerpt reproduced with permission from *Statistical Tables for Biological, Agricultural and Medical Research* (5th ed.), by R. A. Fisher and F. Yates. Copyright, 1957, Oliver and Boyd Ltd., Edinburgh.

From Table 6-1, for $n = 7$ we copy out:

ξ'_0	ξ'_1	ξ'_2	ξ'_3	Y
1	−3	5	−1	3.4
1	−2	0	1	11.7
1	−1	−3	1	37.2
1	0	−4	0	80.1
1	1	−3	−1	151.4
1	2	0	−1	253.2
1	3	5	1	392.6

where

$$\xi'_0 = 1 \qquad \lambda_0 = 1$$

$$\xi'_1 = \frac{x - \bar{x}}{10} \qquad \lambda_1 = 1$$

$$\xi'_2 = \xi_1^2 - 4 \qquad \lambda_2 = 1$$

$$\xi'_3 = \frac{\xi_1^3 - 7\xi_1}{6} \qquad \lambda_3 = 1/6$$

with $\bar{x} = 40$, $D = 10$.

6-8.2 PROCEDURES AND EXAMPLES

Step 1 Procedure—Form the quantities

$$\Sigma Y$$
$$\Sigma \xi_1' Y$$
$$\Sigma \xi_2' Y$$
$$.$$
$$.$$
$$.$$
$$\Sigma \xi_{k-1}' Y$$

$$(6\text{-}52)$$

*and, using the values of $\Sigma \xi_1'^2$, $\Sigma \xi_2'^2$, . . . , given in Table 6-1 form the estimates of the parameters, $\alpha_0, \alpha_1, \ldots$, as follows:

$$\hat{\alpha}_0 = \frac{\Sigma Y}{n} = \bar{y}$$

$$\hat{\alpha}_1 = \frac{\Sigma \xi_1' Y}{\Sigma \xi_1'^2}$$

$$\hat{\alpha}_2 = \frac{\Sigma \xi_2' Y}{\Sigma \xi_2'^2}$$

$$. \quad . \quad .$$

$$\hat{\alpha}_{k-1} = \frac{\Sigma \xi_{k-1}' Y}{\Sigma \xi_{k-1}'^2}$$

$$(6\text{-}53)$$

Step 2 Procedure—Calculate the deviations r_i from

$$r_i = Y_i - \bar{y} - \hat{\alpha}_1 \xi_{1,i}' - \hat{\alpha}_2 \xi_{2,i}' - \ldots - \hat{\alpha}_{k-1} \xi_{k-1,i}'. \qquad (6\text{-}54)$$

Step 1 Example—Using the values copied from Table 6-1, the following calculations are made:

$$\Sigma \xi_0' Y = 929.6 \qquad \Sigma \xi_0'^2 = 7$$
$$\Sigma \xi_1' Y = 1764.8 \qquad \Sigma \xi_1'^2 = 28$$
$$\Sigma \xi_2' Y = 1093.8 \qquad \Sigma \xi_2'^2 = 84$$
$$\Sigma \xi_3' Y = 33.5 \qquad \Sigma \xi_3'^2 = 6.$$

The estimates of the coefficients in the representation of y as a function of the ξ_i', i.e., as

$$y = \alpha_0 \xi_0' + \alpha_1 \xi_1' + \alpha_2 \xi_2' + \alpha_3 \xi_3'$$

are given by

$$\hat{\alpha}_0 = \Sigma \xi_0' Y / \Sigma \xi_0'^2 = 929.6/7 = 132.8$$

$$\hat{\alpha}_1 = \Sigma \xi_1' Y / \Sigma \xi_1'^2 = 1764.8/28 = 63.0285\ 7143$$

$$\hat{\alpha}_2 = \Sigma \xi_2' Y / \Sigma \xi_2'^2 = 1093.8/84 = 13.0214\ 2857$$

$$\hat{\alpha}_3 = \Sigma \xi_3' Y / \Sigma \xi_3'^2 = 33.5/6 = 5.5833\ 3333.$$

Step 2 Example—The predicted value for the point $x = 10$ is given by substituting its corresponding values of the ξ's ($\xi_0' = 1$, $\xi_1' = -3$, $\xi_2' = 5$, and $\xi_3' = -1$) in the equation

$$\hat{Y}_x = 132.8 + 63.028\ 5714\ \xi_1' + 13.021\ 4286\ \xi_2' + 5.583\ 3333\ \xi_3',$$

i.e., $\hat{Y}_{10} = 132.8 + 63.028\ 5714(-3) + 13.021\ 4286(5) + 5.583\ 3333(-1)$

$$= 3.238\ 0955$$

leading to a deviation between observed and calculated of

$$r_{10} = 3.4 - 3.238\ 0955$$
$$= 0.161\ 9045.$$

For the entire set of points, we get:

Observed Y	Calculated $\hat{Y}$	Residual $r = Y - \hat{Y}$
3.4	3.238 0955	0.161 9045
11.7	12.326 1905	−0.626 1905
37.2	36.290 4761	0.909 5239
80.1	80.714 2856	−0.614 2856
151.4	151.180 9523	0.219 0477
253.2	253.273 8095	−0.073 8095
392.6	392.576 1905	0.023 8095

Step 3 Procedure—The estimate of σ^2 is given by

$$s^2 = \frac{1}{n-k} \{ \Sigma Y^2 - \hat{\alpha}_0 \Sigma Y - \hat{\alpha}_1 \Sigma \xi_1' Y - \ldots - \hat{\alpha}_{k-1} \Sigma \xi_{k-1}' Y \}. \tag{6-55}$$

Step 4 Procedure—The estimate of the standard deviations of the $\hat{\alpha}$'s is given by

$$\text{s.d. } (\hat{\alpha}_j) = \frac{s}{\sqrt{\displaystyle\sum_{i=1}^{n} \xi_{ji}^2}}. \tag{6-56}$$

Step 5 Procedure—The *Analysis of Variance* table becomes:

	d.f.	Sum of Squares
Total	n	ΣY^2
Reduction due to fitting α_0	1	$\hat{\alpha}_0 (\Sigma Y) = R_0$
Deviations from fit with α_0	$n-1$	$\Sigma Y^2 - R_0$
Reduction due to fitting α_1	1	$\hat{\alpha}_1 (\Sigma \xi_1' Y) = R_1$
Deviations from fit with α_0, α_1	$n-2$	$\Sigma Y^2 - R_0 - R_1$
. . .		
Reduction due to fit of α_{k-1}	1	$\hat{\alpha}_{k-1} (\Sigma \xi_{k-1}' Y) = R_{k-1}$
Deviations from fit with $\alpha_0, \alpha_1, \ldots, \alpha_{k-1}$	$n-k$	$\Sigma Y_0 - R_0 - R_1 \ldots - R_{k-1}$

Step 3 Example—The estimate of σ^2 is given by

$$s^2 = \frac{1}{7-4} \Sigma r^2$$

$$= \frac{1}{3}(1.676\ 9048)$$

$$= .558\ 9683$$

$$s = \sqrt{.558\ 9683}$$

$$= .7476.$$

Step 4 Example—The standard deviations of the coefficients are given by

$$\text{s.d. }(\hat{\alpha}_i) = s/\sqrt{\Sigma \xi_i'^2}$$

$$\text{s.d. }(\hat{\alpha}_0) = .7476/\sqrt{7}\ = .2826$$

$$\text{s.d. }(\hat{\alpha}_1) = .7476/\sqrt{28} = .1413$$

$$\text{s.d. }(\hat{\alpha}_2) = .7476/\sqrt{84} = .0816$$

$$\text{s.d. }(\hat{\alpha}_3) = .7476/\sqrt{6}\ = .3052.$$

Step 5 Example—The Analysis of Variance table becomes:

	d.f.	Sum of Squares	Mean Square
Total	7	249 115.26	
Reduction due to coef. of ξ_0'	1	123 450.88	123 450.88
Residuals from $\hat{\alpha}_0\xi_0'$	6	125 664.38	20 944.06
Reduction due to coef. of ξ_1'	1	111 232.822 86	111 232.82
Residuals from $\hat{\alpha}_0\xi_0' + \hat{\alpha}_1\xi_1'$	5	14 431.557 14	2 886.31
Reduction due to coef. of ξ_2'	1	14 242.838 57	14 242.84
Residuals from $\hat{\alpha}_0\xi_0' + \hat{\alpha}_1\xi_1' + \hat{\alpha}_2\xi_2'$	4	188.718 57	47.18
Reduction due to coef. of ξ_3'	1	187.041 67	187.04
Residuals from $\hat{\alpha}_0\xi_0' + \ldots + \hat{\alpha}_3\xi_3'$	3	1.676 90	.5590

Step 6 Procedure—Convert to an equation in the original x units by substituting the expressions in Equations (6-50) into Equation (6-51). By writing the $\hat{\beta}$'s as linear functions of the $\hat{\alpha}$'s, say

$$\hat{\beta}_k = \sum_{i=0}^{k} b_i \, \hat{\alpha}_i,$$

the standard deviation can be computed from

$$\text{s.d. of } \hat{\beta}_k = \sqrt{\sum_0^k b_i^2 \, (\text{s.d. of } \hat{\alpha}_i)^2}.$$

The following Equations (6-57) show the $\hat{\beta}$'s as a function of the $\hat{\alpha}$'s for polynomials up to 5th degree. (If a polynomial of 4th degree is used, simply disregard the terms involving $\hat{\alpha}_5$; if 3rd degree, disregard the terms involving $\hat{\alpha}_4$ and $\hat{\alpha}_5$; etc.)

As an example, if a 4th degree polynomial is fitted, the estimate $\hat{\beta}_3$ is given by

$$\hat{\beta}_3 = \frac{\lambda_3}{D^3} \hat{\alpha}_3 - 4 \frac{\lambda_4}{D^3} \left(\frac{\bar{x}}{D}\right) \hat{\alpha}_4$$

and the s.d. of $\hat{\beta}_3$ is estimated by

$$s\sqrt{\left(\frac{\lambda_3}{D^3}\right)^2 \frac{1}{\Sigma \, (\xi_3')^2} + \left(\frac{4\lambda_4}{D^3}\right)^2 \left(\frac{\bar{x}}{D}\right)^2 \frac{1}{\Sigma \, (\xi_4')^2}}.$$

See Equations (6-57) on page 6-36.

Step 6 Example—To obtain the equation in terms of the original x variable, i.e., expressing y as $y = \beta_0 + \beta_1 x + \beta_2 x^2 + \beta_3 x^3$, we substitute as follows:

$$y = \alpha_0 (1) + \alpha_1 \left(\frac{x - 40}{10} \right) + \alpha_2 \left[\left(\frac{x - 40}{10} \right)^2 - 4 \right] + \frac{\alpha_3}{6} \left[\left(\frac{x - 40}{10} \right)^3 - 7 \left(\frac{x - 40}{10} \right) \right]$$

$$= (\alpha_0 - 4\alpha_1 + 12\alpha_2 - 6\alpha_3) + \left(\frac{\alpha_1}{10} - \frac{8}{10} \alpha_2 + \frac{41}{60} \alpha_3 \right) x + \left(\frac{\alpha_2}{100} - \frac{2\alpha_3}{100} \right) x^2 + \frac{\alpha_3}{6000} x^3.$$

Substituting the estimated values for the α's gives

$$Y = 3.4428\ 5714 - .299\ 007\ 9375\ x + .018\ 547\ 6191\ x^2 + .000\ 930\ 5556\ x^3.$$

The standard deviations of the $\hat{\beta}$'s are given by

$$\text{s.d. of } \hat{\beta}_0 = \text{s.d. of } (\hat{\alpha}_0 - 4\hat{\alpha}_1 + 12\hat{\alpha}_2 - 6\hat{\alpha}_3)$$

$$= s \sqrt{\frac{1}{7} + \frac{(-4)^2}{28} + \frac{(12)^2}{84} + \frac{(-6)^2}{6}}$$

$$= s \sqrt{\frac{59}{7}}$$

$$= 2.170$$

$$\text{s.d. of } \hat{\beta}_1 = \frac{s}{60} \sqrt{\frac{(6)^2}{28} + \frac{(-48)^2}{84} + \frac{(41)^2}{6}}$$

$$= .2190$$

$$\text{s.d. of } \hat{\beta}_2 = \frac{s}{100} \sqrt{\frac{1}{84} + \frac{(-2)^2}{6}}$$

$$= .006\ 158$$

$$\text{s.d. of } \hat{\beta}_3 = \frac{s}{6000} \frac{1}{\sqrt{6}}$$

$$= .0000\ 5087.$$

$$* \quad \hat{\beta}_0 = \hat{a}_0 - \lambda_1\left[\frac{l}{D}\right]\hat{a}_1 + \lambda_2\left[\left(\frac{l}{D}\right)^2 - \frac{n^2-1}{12}\right]\hat{a}_2 - \lambda_3\left[\left(\frac{l}{D}\right)^3 - \left(\frac{l}{D}\right)\left(\frac{3n^2-7}{20}\right)\right]\hat{a}_3 + \lambda_4\left[\left(\frac{l}{D}\right)^4 - \left(\frac{l}{D}\right)^2\left(\frac{3n^2-13}{14}\right) + \frac{3}{560}(n^4-10n^2+9)\right]\hat{a}_4 - \lambda_5\left[\left(\frac{l}{D}\right)^4 - \left(\frac{l}{D}\right)^2\frac{5(n^2-7)}{18} + \left(\frac{l}{D}\right)\left(\frac{15n^4-230n^2+407}{1008}\right)\right]\hat{a}_5$$

$$(6\text{-}57)$$

$$\hat{\beta}_1 = \frac{\lambda_1}{D}\hat{a}_1 - \frac{2\lambda_2}{D}\left(\frac{l}{D}\right)\hat{a}_2 + \frac{\lambda_3}{D}\left[3\left(\frac{l}{D}\right)^2 - \frac{3n^2-7}{20}\right]\hat{a}_3 - \frac{\lambda_4}{D}\left[4\left(\frac{l}{D}\right)^3 - 2\left(\frac{l}{D}\right)\left(\frac{3n^2-13}{14}\right)\right]\hat{a}_4 + \frac{\lambda_5}{D}\left[5\left(\frac{l}{D}\right)^4 - 3\left(\frac{l}{D}\right)^2\frac{5(n^2-7)}{18} + \frac{15n^4-230n^2+407}{1008}\right]\hat{a}_5$$

$$\hat{\beta}_2 = \frac{\lambda_2}{D^2}\hat{a}_2 - \frac{3\lambda_3}{D^2}\left(\frac{l}{D}\right)\hat{a}_3 + \frac{\lambda_4}{D^2}\left[6\left(\frac{l}{D}\right)^2 - \left(\frac{3n^2-13}{14}\right)\right]\hat{a}_4 - \frac{\lambda_5}{D^2}\left[10\left(\frac{l}{D}\right)^3 - 3\left(\frac{l}{D}\right)\frac{5(n^2-7)}{18}\right]\hat{a}_5$$

$$\hat{\beta}_3 = \frac{\lambda_3}{D^3}\hat{a}_3 - \frac{4\lambda_4}{D^3}\left(\frac{l}{D}\right)\hat{a}_4 + \frac{\lambda_5}{D^3}\left[10\left(\frac{l}{D}\right)^2 - \frac{5(n^2-7)}{18}\right]\hat{a}_5$$

$$\hat{\beta}_4 = \frac{\lambda_4}{D^4}\hat{a}_4 - \frac{5\lambda_5}{D^4}\left(\frac{l}{D}\right)\hat{a}_5$$

$$\hat{\beta}_5 = \frac{\lambda_5}{D^5}\hat{a}_5$$

6-9 MATRIX METHODS

6-9.1 FORMULAS USING TRIANGULAR FACTORIZATION OF NORMAL EQUATIONS

The matrix for the left-hand side of normal equations can be factored into $(X'X) = TT'$ where T is lower triangular, so that $(X'X)^{-1} = (T')^{-1} T^{-1} = (T^{-1})' T^{-1}$.

Thus, $\hat{\beta} = (T^{-1})' (T^{-1}Q)$ where $Q = X'Y$.

Denote the column vector $T^{-1}Q$ by

$$g = T^{-1}Q = \begin{bmatrix} g_1 \\ g_2 \\ \cdot \\ \cdot \\ \cdot \\ g_k \end{bmatrix}.$$

Therefore, $\hat{\beta} = (T^{-1})'g$.

This representation leads to certain simplifications, e.g.:

(a) The estimate of σ^2 is given by

$$s^2 = \frac{1}{n-k} (Y'Y - \hat{\beta}'Q)$$

$$= \frac{1}{n-k} (Y'Y - g'T^{-1}Q)$$

$$= \frac{1}{n-k} (Y'Y - g'g)$$

$$= \frac{1}{n-k} \left(\Sigma Y_i^2 - \sum_1^k g_i^2 \right).$$

(b) The variance of a linear function, $L = a'\hat{\beta}$ of the $\hat{\beta}$'s is given by

$$s^2 \{a' (T^{-1})' T^{-1} a\} = s^2 (T^{-1}a)' (T^{-1}a)$$
$$= s^2 \Sigma h_i^2$$

when $h = \begin{bmatrix} h_1 \\ h_2 \\ \cdot \\ \cdot \\ \cdot \\ h_k \end{bmatrix} = T^{-1}a.$

(c) The reduction in sum of squares due to fitting the last p constants is

$$\sum_{k-p+1}^k g_i^2.$$

This formulation also permits us to make a detailed *Analysis of Variance* table. An important caution is in order. The reduction due to the addition of $\hat{\beta}_i$ is the reduction *given that* $\hat{\beta}_1, \hat{\beta}_2, \ldots, \hat{\beta}_{i-1}$, *have been fitted to the data*. The reduction due to $\hat{\beta}_i$ given that any other set of coefficients have been fitted will be different.

The *Analysis of Variance* table becomes:

	d.f.	Sum of Squares
Reduction due to fitting $\hat{\beta}_1$	1	g_1^2
Residual (after fitting $\hat{\beta}_1$)	$n - 1$	$\Sigma Y^2 - g_1^2$
Additional reduction fitting $\hat{\beta}_2$	1	g_2^2
Reduction due to fitting $\hat{\beta}_1$ and $\hat{\beta}_2$	2	$g_1^2 + g_2^2$
Residual (after fitting $\hat{\beta}_1$ and $\hat{\beta}_2$)	$n - 2$	$\Sigma Y^2 - g_1^2 - g_2^2$
.		
.		
.		
Additional reduction due to fitting $\hat{\beta}_k$	1	g_k^2
Reduction due to fitting $\hat{\beta}_1, \hat{\beta}_2, \ldots, \hat{\beta}_k$	k	$\sum_1^k g_i^2$
Residual (after fitting $\hat{\beta}_1, \hat{\beta}_2, \ldots, \hat{\beta}_k$)	$n - k$	$\Sigma Y^2 - \sum_1^k g_i^2$

This form of analysis is especially useful in the analysis for polynomials where the ordering is by powers of x. In the multiple regression case, the reduction attributed to $\hat{\beta}_i$ is dependent upon the ordering of the parameters $\hat{\beta}_1, \hat{\beta}_2, \ldots, \hat{\beta}_{i-1}$, and will be different for different orders.

6-9.2 TRIANGULARIZATION OF MATRICES

The real symmetric matrix

$$N = \begin{bmatrix} a_{11} & a_{12} & . & . & . & a_{1n} \\ a_{21} & a_{22} & . & . & . & a_{2n} \\ . & . & . & & & \\ a_{n1} & a_{n2} & & & & a_{nn} \end{bmatrix}$$

can, if N is non-singular (i.e., if $|N| \neq 0$), be factored into the product of two triangular matrices so that $N = TT'$, i.e.,

$$\begin{bmatrix} a_{11} & a_{12} & . & . & . & a_{1n} \\ a_{21} & a_{22} & . & . & . & a_{2n} \\ . & . & . & & & \\ a_{n1} & a_{n2} & & & & a_{nn} \end{bmatrix} = \begin{bmatrix} c_{11} & & & & & \\ c_{21} & c_{22} & & & & \\ . & . & . & & & \\ c_{n1} & c_{n2} & . & . & . & c_{nn} \end{bmatrix} \begin{bmatrix} c_{11} & c_{21} & . & . & . & c_{n1} \\ & c_{22} & & & & c_{n2} \\ & & . & . & . & . \\ & & & & & c_{nn} \end{bmatrix}$$

The elements c_{ij} are computed from the following (note that $c_{ij} = 0$ for $j > i$):

$$c_{11} = \sqrt{a_{11}}$$
$$c_{21} = a_{21}/c_{11}$$
.
.
.
$$c_{n1} = a_{n1}/c_{11}$$
$$c_{22} = \sqrt{a_{22} - c_{21}^2}$$
$$c_{32} = (a_{32} - c_{31} c_{21})/c_{22}$$
.
.
.
$$c_{n2} = (a_{n2} - c_{n1} c_{21})/c_{22}$$
- - - - - - - -
$$c_{jj} = \sqrt{a_{jj} - c_{j,j-1}^2 - c_{j,j-2}^2 - \ldots - c_{j,1}^2}$$
.
.
.
$$c_{ij} = (a_{ij} - c_{i,j-1}c_{j,j-1} - c_{i,j-2}c_{j,j-2} - \ldots - c_{i,1}c_{j,1})/c_{jj}.$$

As an example, consider

$$N = \begin{bmatrix} 4 & 6 & 8 & 10 \\ 6 & 25 & 20 & 27 \\ 8 & 20 & 36 & 30 \\ 10 & 27 & 30 & 36 \end{bmatrix}$$

Applying the formulas for c_{ij}, we get

$$c_{11} = \sqrt{4} = 2$$
$$c_{21} = 6/2 = 3$$
$$c_{31} = 8/2 = 4$$
$$c_{41} = 10/2 = 5$$
$$c_{22} = \sqrt{25 - (3)^2} = 4$$
$$c_{32} = [20 - 4(3)]/4 = 2$$
$$c_{42} = [27 - 5(3)]/4 = 3$$
$$c_{33} = \sqrt{36 - 2^2 - 4^2} = 4$$
$$c_{43} = [30 - 3(2) - 5(4)]/4 = 1$$
$$c_{44} = \sqrt{36 - 1^2 - 3^2 - 5^2} = 1.$$

This gives

$$N = \begin{bmatrix} 2 & & & \\ 3 & 4 & & \\ 4 & 2 & 4 & \\ 5 & 3 & 1 & 1 \end{bmatrix} \begin{bmatrix} 2 & 3 & 4 & 5 \\ & 4 & 2 & 3 \\ & & 4 & 1 \\ & & & 1 \end{bmatrix}$$

The inverse of a triangular matrix

$$T = \begin{bmatrix} c_{11} & & & & \\ c_{21} & c_{22} & & & \\ . & & & & \\ . & & & & \\ . & & & & \\ c_{n1} & c_{n2} & . & . & . & c_{nn} \end{bmatrix}$$

is given by

$$T^{-1} = \begin{bmatrix} b_{11} & & & & \\ b_{21} & b_{22} & & & \\ . & & & & \\ . & & & & \\ . & & & & \\ b_{n1} & b_{n2} & . & . & . & b_{nn} \end{bmatrix}$$

where

$$b_{11} = \frac{1}{c_{11}}$$

$$b_{21} = - \, (b_{11} \, c_{21})/c_{22}$$

$$b_{31} = - \, (c_{31} \, b_{11} + c_{32} \, b_{21})/c_{33}$$

.

.

.

$$b_{n1} = - \, (c_{n1} \, b_{11} + c_{n2} \, b_{21} + \ldots + c_{n,n-1} \, b_{n-1,1})/c_{nn}$$

$$b_{22} = \frac{1}{c_{22}}$$

$$b_{32} = - \, c_{32} \, b_{22}/c_{33}$$

$$b_{42} = - \, (c_{42} \, b_{22} + c_{43} \, b_{32})/c_{44}$$

.

.

.

$$b_{n2} = - \, (c_{n2} \, b_{22} + c_{n3} \, b_{32} + \ldots + c_{n,n-1} \, b_{n-1,2})/c_{nn}$$

. . .

$$b_{jj} = \frac{1}{c_{jj}}$$

.

.

.

$$b_{ij} = - \, (c_{ij} \, b_{jj} + c_{i,j+1} \, b_{j+1,j} + \ldots + c_{i,i-1} \, b_{i-1,j})/c_{ii}.$$

Example:

For $T = \begin{bmatrix} 2 & & & \\ 3 & 4 & & \\ 4 & 2 & 4 & \\ 5 & 3 & 1 & 1 \end{bmatrix}$.

The elements of T^{-1} are

$$b_{11} = \frac{1}{2}$$

$$b_{21} = -\frac{1}{2} \cdot \frac{3}{4} = -\frac{3}{8}$$

$$b_{31} = -\left[4\left(\frac{1}{2}\right) + 2\left(-\frac{3}{8}\right)\right]/4 = -\frac{5}{16}$$

$$b_{41} = -\left[5\left(\frac{1}{2}\right) + 3\left(-\frac{3}{8}\right) + 1\left(-\frac{5}{16}\right)\right]/1 = -\frac{17}{16}$$

$$b_{22} = \frac{1}{4}$$

$$b_{32} = -2\left(\frac{1}{4}\right)/4 = -\frac{1}{8}$$

$$b_{42} = -\left[3\left(\frac{1}{4}\right) + 1\left(-\frac{1}{8}\right)\right]/1 = -\frac{5}{8}$$

$$b_{33} = \frac{1}{4}$$

$$b_{43} = -1\left(\frac{1}{4}\right) = -\frac{1}{4}$$

$$b_{44} = 1.$$

Thus, $T^{-1} = \dfrac{1}{16} \begin{bmatrix} 8 & & & \\ -6 & 4 & & \\ -5 & -2 & 4 & \\ -17 & -10 & -4 & 16 \end{bmatrix}$

and $N^{-1} = (TT')^{-1} = (T'^{-1})(T^{-1})$ gives

$$N^{-1} = \frac{1}{16}\begin{bmatrix} 8 & -6 & -5 & -17 \\ & 4 & -2 & -10 \\ & & 4 & -4 \\ & & & 16 \end{bmatrix} \frac{1}{16}\begin{bmatrix} 8 & & & \\ -6 & 4 & & \\ -5 & -2 & 4 & \\ -17 & -10 & -4 & 16 \end{bmatrix} = \frac{1}{256}\begin{bmatrix} 414 & 156 & 48 & -272 \\ 156 & 120 & 32 & -160 \\ 48 & 32 & 32 & -64 \\ -272 & -160 & -64 & 256 \end{bmatrix}$$

6-9.3   REMARKS

By forming the matrix product

$$\begin{bmatrix} X' \\ Y' \end{bmatrix} (X,Y) = \begin{bmatrix} X'X & X'Y \\ Y'X & Y'Y \end{bmatrix}$$

and replacing $Y'X$ by 0 (a null matrix) and $Y'Y$ by I (the identity matrix), we obt.

$$N = \begin{bmatrix} X'X & X'Y \\ 0 & I \end{bmatrix}.$$

In this form, Y may be a single vector of observations $Y' = (Y_1 Y_2 \ldots Y_n)$, or a set of p vectors

$$Y = \begin{bmatrix} Y_{11} & \cdot & \cdot & \cdot & Y_{1p} \\ Y_{21} & & & & Y_{2p} \\ \cdot & & & & \\ \cdot & & & & \\ \cdot & & & & \\ Y_{n1} & & & & Y_{np} \end{bmatrix}.$$

Then,

$$N^{-1} = \begin{bmatrix} (X'X)^{-1} & -\beta \\ 0 & I \end{bmatrix},$$

where I is $p \times p$ and 0 is $p \times k$, gives all the values needed for the computations of this Paragraph.

REFERENCES

1. M. G. Kendall and W. R. Buckland, *A Dictionary of Statistical Terms*, Oliver and Boyd, Ltd., Edinburgh, 1954.

2. R. L. Anderson and T. A. Bancroft, *Statistical Theory in Research*, McGraw-Hill Book Company, Inc., New York, N.Y., 1952.

3. O. L. Davies, (ed.), *The Design and Analysis of Industrial Experiments*, Oliver and Boyd, Ltd., Edinburgh, 1954.

4. O. Taussky, (ed.), *Contributions to the Solution of Systems of Linear Equations and the Determination of Eigenvalues*, (National Bureau of Standards Applied Mathematics Series, No. 39), U. S. Government Printing Office, Washington, D. C., 1954.

5. P. S. Dwyer, *Linear Computations*, John Wiley & Sons, Inc., New York, N.Y., 1951.

6. R. A. Fisher and F. Yates, *Statistical Tables for Biological, Agricultural and Medical Research* (5th edition), Oliver and Boyd, Ltd., Edinburgh, 1957.

7. R. L. Anderson and E. E. Houseman, *Tables of Orthogonal Polynomial Values Extended to N = 104*, Research Bulletin No. 297, Agricultural Experiment Station, Iowa State College, Ames, Iowa, 1942.

8. D. B. DeLury, *Values and Integrals of the Orthogonal Polynomials up to n = 26*, University of Toronto Press, 1950.

9. E. S. Pearson and H. O. Hartley, (eds.), *Biometrika Tables for Statisticians*, Vol. I (2d edition), Cambridge University Press, Cambridge, England, 1958.

SECTION 2

STANDARD TECHNIQUES FOR ANALYSIS

AND INTERPRETATION OF

ENUMERATIVE AND CLASSIFICATORY DATA

DISCUSSION OF TECHNIQUES IN CHAPTERS 7 THROUGH 10

For some kinds of tests, it may be impossible to obtain actual measurements. An item may be subjected to a test and the result of that particular test can be expressed only in terms of a pre-established classification of possible results. The simplest kind of classification, and the one most widely used in practice, consists of just two mutually exclusive categories. For example, the results of the test on each item may be recorded as pass or fail, hit or miss, fires or does not fire, larger than specification limit or less than specification limit, etc. Some other problems call for classification into more than two categories. In classifying types of metal fractures, we might establish such classes as smooth, rough, jagged, and splintery. Glass or plastic material after exposure to radiation might be classified as transparent, translucent, or opaque. In screening inspection, for example, we may have three established categories — accept, reject, or rework.

Once these qualitative observations have been recorded in the established categories of the classification scheme, we may count the number in any category, or we may compute the proportion of the total which falls in any category. In most of the analytical procedures given in these Chapters, we work with proportions, not with percentages, even though final presentation of results may be made in percentages.

The methods given in these Chapters also may be used for tests where exact measurements could have been obtained, but actually were not obtained because of the expense or inconvenience involved. For example, one always can measure a dimension; but, in large-scale production, go-no-go gauges may be used for routine checks. Whenever it is possible to obtain actual measurements, analysis of the measurements does provide more information than does analysis of counts. In planning experimental programs, various factors may contribute to the decision of whether to measure or to gauge — e.g., the availability of time, funds, and experienced personnel. When *measurements* are analyzed, the methods of these Chapters do not apply; the appropriate methods are given in ORDP 20-110, Chapters 2 through 6.

The problems considered in these Chapters parallel those of Chapters 2 through 6, as much as possible. Chapter 7 gives methods for making single estimates and interval estimates of a proportion. Instead of estimating the true average of a lot with respect to some property, we estimate the true proportion of items in the lot which have a particular property. Comparisons may be made between a new product and a standard product, or between any two products, with regard to the proportion of items which exhibit the characteristic in question. Chapter 8 gives methods for making such comparisons when the classification scheme consists of two categories. Chapter 9 gives methods for making such comparisons when the classification scheme consists of three or more categories. Chapter 10 gives methods of analysis for a particular experimental situation which has generally been called "sensitivity testing."

All A-Tables referenced in these Chapters are contained in ORDP 20-114, Section 5.

CHAPTER 7

CHARACTERIZING THE QUALITATIVE PERFORMANCE
OF A MATERIAL, PRODUCT, OR PROCESS

7-1 GENERAL

The problem is that of estimating the true proportion (or percentage) of items that have a given quality characteristic. The tested items have been classified into two previously established categories of classification. Methods are given for obtaining:

(a) the best single estimate; and,

(b) confidence interval estimates* of the proportion which is of interest.

The following data will serve to illustrate the application of the procedures.

Data Sample 7-1 — Proportion of Defective Fuzes

Form: A sample of n items is selected at random from a much larger group. Upon examination or test, r of the n items show the characteristic of interest.

Example: Ten fuzes are taken at random from a production line, and are tested under a specified set of conditions. Four of the ten fail to function.

In general, what can we say on the basis of our sample about the larger group with regard to the proportion of defective items contained therein? We show how to answer two questions:

(a) What is the true proportion P of the fuzes produced that would be expected to fail under the specified conditions?

(b) What is an interval which we can expect, with prescribed confidence, to bracket the true proportion of defective fuzes?

7-2 BEST SINGLE ESTIMATE OF THE TRUE PROPORTION P

The best single estimate of the true proportion of items having a given characteristic in some well defined population is the observed proportion of items having this characteristic in a random sample from the population, i.e., the number of sample items which have the characteristic divided by the total number of items in the sample.

The best estimate from Data Sample 7-1 of the true proportion of fuzes that will fail is

equal to the number of defective fuzes in the sample, divided by the total number of fuzes in the sample.

Procedure

(1) Compute the estimated proportion p, as follows:

$$p = \frac{r}{n}$$

Example

(1) From Data Sample 7-1,

$$p = 4/10$$
$$= .4$$

---

* The reader who is not familiar with the meaning and interpretation of confidence intervals should refer to Chapter 1 and to Paragraph 2-1.3 of ORDP 20-110.

7-3   CONFIDENCE INTERVAL ESTIMATES OF THE TRUE PROPORTION P

7-3.1   TWO-SIDED CONFIDENCE INTERVALS

Although the best single estimate of the true proportion of items having a given characteristic is the proportion of such items in a random sample, an interval estimate may be preferred. A two-sided confidence interval is an interval expected to give upper and lower limits for the true proportion with prescribed confidence.

7-3.1.1   Exact Limits for $n \leq 30$. For $n \leq 30$, two-sided confidence limits are given in Table A-22. For example, using Data Sample 7-1, where $n = 10$ and $r = 4$, a two-sided 95% confidence interval for the true proportion is the interval from .150 to .733.

7-3.1.2   Exact Limits for $n > 30$. For $n > 30$, use the charts of Table A-24 for 90%, 95%, and 99% confidence intervals, as desired. On the charts, there are two curves for each of a number of values of n.   The upper and lower curve for a particular n constitute a confidence belt for the true proportion P.   First, locate the observed proportion $p = r/n$, on the horizontal scale.   From this point, travel up to the curves for the sample size n, and read off the upper and lower limits for the population proportion P. For example, in a sample of $n = 100$, where the observed proportion is .4, the interval from .31 to .51 gives 95% confidence limits for the true proportion P.

The three charts in Table A-24 give $(1 - \alpha)$ confidence interval estimates for $\alpha = .10$, $\alpha = .05$, and $\alpha = .01$.   If we use these charts a large number of times to make interval estimates of the true proportion P, we can expect $100(1 - \alpha)\%$ of these intervals to contain P. If the appropriate sample size requires interpolation on the charts, the procedure of Paragraph 7-3.1.3 should be used instead of the charts of Table A-24.

7-3.1.3   Approximate Limits for $n > 30$. This method should be used in lieu of interpolation on the charts (Table A-24).

Procedure	**Example**
(1) Choose the desired confidence level, $1 - \alpha$.	(1) Let $1 - \alpha = .90$ $\alpha = .10$
(2) Look up $z_{1-\alpha/2}$ in Table A-2.	(2) $z_{.95} = 1.645$
(3) Compute:	(3) Using $n = 150$, $p = .40$, for example,

$$p_1 = p - z_{1-\alpha/2} \sqrt{\frac{p(1 - p)}{n}}$$

$$p_2 = p + z_{1-\alpha/2} \sqrt{\frac{p(1 - p)}{n}}$$

$$\begin{aligned} p_1 &= .40 - 1.645 \sqrt{.0016} \\ &= .40 - 1.645\,(.04) \\ &= .40 - .07 \\ &= .33 \\ p_2 &= .40 + .07 \\ &= .47 \end{aligned}$$

(4) The interval from p_1 to p_2 is a two-sided $100(1 - \alpha)\%$ confidence interval estimate of the true proportion P.

(4) The interval from .33 to .47 is a 90% two-sided confidence interval estimate of P.

7-3.2 ONE-SIDED CONFIDENCE INTERVALS

A one-sided confidence interval estimate states that the true proportion P is less than a calculated proportion p_2' (or alternatively, that P is larger than p_1') and the statement is made at a prescribed confidence level.

7-3.2.1 Exact Limits for $n \leq 30$.   For $n \leq 30$, one-sided confidence limits are given in Table A-23. For example, using Data Sample 7-1, where $n = 10$ and $r = 4$, the upper 90% one-sided confidence limit is .646.   (The lower 90% one-sided confidence limit would be .188 in this case.)

7-3.2.2 Exact Limits for $n > 30$.   Use the charts of Table A-24 to obtain .95, .975, or .995 one-sided confidence intervals, by using only the upper curve, or only the lower curve, of the belt for a given sample size.   When used in this way, the chart labelled "Confidence Coefficient .90" yields one-sided 95% confidence intervals, the chart labelled "confidence coefficient .95" yields one-sided 97.5% confidence intervals, and the chart labelled "confidence coefficient .99" yields one-sided 99.5% confidence intervals.

If the appropriate sample size requires interpolation on the charts, the procedure of Paragraph 7-3.2.3 should be used instead of the charts of Table A-24.

7-3.2.3 Approximate Limits for $n > 30$.   This method should be used in lieu of interpolation on the charts (Table A-24).

Procedure	Example
(1) Choose the desired confidence level, $1 - \alpha$.	(1) Let $1 - \alpha = .90$ $\alpha = .10$
(2) Look up $z_{1-\alpha}$ in Table A-2.	(2) $z_{.90} = 1.282$
(3) If a lower one-sided confidence limit is desired, compute $$p_1' = p - z_{1-\alpha}\sqrt{\frac{p(1-p)}{n}}$$	(3) Using $n = 150$, $p = .40$, for example, $p_1' = .40 - 1.282\sqrt{.0016}$ $= .40 - 1.282\,(.04)$ $= .40 - .05$ $= .35$; this is the lower 90% confidence limit for P, the true proportion defective.
(4) Alternatively, if an upper one-sided confidence limit is desired, compute $$p_2' = p + z_{1-\alpha}\sqrt{\frac{p(1-p)}{n}}$$	(4) Using $n = 150$, $p = .40$, for example, $p_2' = .40 + 1.282\,(.04)$ $= .40 + .05$ $= .45$; this is the upper 90% confidence limit for P, the true proportion defective.

7-4 SAMPLE SIZE REQUIRED TO ESTIMATE THE TRUE PROPORTION

We shall discuss two problems:

(a) Determining the sample size required to estimate the true proportion *with a specified limit of error in both directions;* i.e., when it is required to estimate P within $\pm\delta$. (See Paragraph 7-4.1.)

(b) Determining the sample size required to estimate the true proportion *with a specified limit of error in only one direction;* i.e., when it is required to estimate P within $+\delta$ (or to estimate P within $-\delta$). (See Paragraph 7-4.2.)

In (a), we are indifferent as to whether our estimate is too high or too low. In (b), we wish to protect ourselves against an overestimate, but do not worry about an underestimate (or vice versa).

7–4.1 DETERMINING THE SAMPLE SIZE REQUIRED TO ESTIMATE THE TRUE PROPORTION *WITH A SPECIFIED LIMIT OF ERROR IN BOTH DIRECTIONS,* i.e., WHEN IT IS REQUIRED TO ESTIMATE *P* WITHIN $\pm\delta$

7-4.1.1 Graphical Method. For the graphical method, the problem may be restated as follows: we wish to make a two-sided confidence interval estimate of P and the width of the interval should be not greater than 2δ. It, therefore, is possible to use the charts of Table A-24 in reverse; that is, to find the sample size belt whose maximum width (vertical distance on the charts) is equal to 2δ. The maximum width of confidence interval for a particular n will occur when the observed proportion is equal to 0.5. (If past records on the particular process indicate an upper or lower limit for the observed proportion, e.g., "the observed proportion always has been less than 0.1", one may use the widths of the intervals for this value of p rather than the maximum widths.)

Procedure

Problem: What is the sample size n required to estimate the true proportion P within $\pm\delta$?

(1) Choose $1 - \alpha$, the confidence coefficient to be associated with the resulting estimate. (The charts of Table A-24 can be used for confidence coefficients $.90$, $.95$, and $.99$).

(2) Specify δ, the error permitted in the estimate.

(3) Lacking knowledge of a safe upper or lower bound for P, look at the vertical line for $p = .50$. (If a safe upper or lower bound can be assumed, use this value of p.)

(4) Find the pair of n curves whose separation on this vertical line is not more than 2δ.

(5) n is the required sample size.

Example

Problem: What is the sample size n required to estimate the true proportion P within $\pm.10$?

(1) Let $1 - \alpha = .90$

Use Table A-24,
confidence coefficient $= .90$.

(2) Let $\delta = .10$

(3) Locate, on Table A-24, the vertical line for $p = .50$.

(4) At $p = .50$, n $= 100$ is the smallest n for which the interval is less than $.20$.

(5) $n = 100$ is the required sample size.

Note: $n = 50$ gives an interval approximately equal to $.25$, and $n = 100$ gives an interval approximately equal to $.16$, so that a sample somewhat less than 100 would be sufficient. The exact n, however, cannot be determined from the charts of Table A-24.

7-4.1.2 Numerical Method. The formula for sample size is

$$n = \frac{z^2_{1-\alpha/2} \, P(1 - P)}{\delta^2} \, .$$

A sample of size n guarantees a probability not greater than α that our estimate of P is in error by more than δ.

Since the true proportion P is unknown, we must substitute for it a value P' which is obtained as follows:

(a) If no prior information about P is available, or if P is believed to be in the neighborhood of 0.5, use $P' = 0.5$. The formula then simplifies to

$$n = \frac{z^2_{1-\alpha/2}}{4\delta^2} \, .$$

(b) If the true proportion P can safely be assumed to be less than 0.5, let P' be the *largest* reasonable guess for P.

(c) If the true proportion P can safely be assumed to be greater than 0.5, let P' be the *smallest* reasonable guess for P.

It is obvious that the largest sample size will be required when the true P is 0.5, and the purpose of these three rules is to be as conservative as possible.

Procedure	**Example**
Problem: What is the sample size n required to estimate the true proportion P within $\pm\delta$?	*Problem:* What is the sample size n required to estimate the true proportion P within $\pm.10$?
(1) Choose $1 - \alpha$, the confidence coefficient to be associated with the resulting estimate.	(1) Let $1 - \alpha = .90$ $\alpha = .10$
(2) Specify δ, the error permitted in the estimate.	(2) Let $\delta = .10$
(3) Look up $z_{1-\alpha/2}$ in Table A-2.	(3) $z_{.95} = 1.645$
(4a) If there is no prior information about the true proportion P, compute $n = \dfrac{z^2_{1-\alpha/2}}{4\delta^2}$	(4a) $n = \dfrac{(1.645)^2}{.04}$ $= \dfrac{2.706}{.04}$ $= 68,$ which is the required sample size.
(4b) If it is safe to assume that the true proportion P is less than some value P', compute $n = \dfrac{z^2_{1-\alpha/2} \, P'(1 - P')}{\delta^2}$	(4b) If it is safe to assume that the true proportion P is less than .40, for example, $n = \dfrac{(1.645)^2 \, (0.4) \, (0.6)}{.01}$ $= 65,$ which is the required sample size.

7-4.2 DETERMINING THE SAMPLE SIZE REQUIRED TO ESTIMATE THE TRUE PROPORTION *WITH A SPECIFIED LIMIT OF ERROR IN ONLY ONE DIRECTION*, i.e., WHEN IT IS REQUIRED TO ESTIMATE *P* WITHIN +δ (OR TO ESTIMATE *P* WITHIN −δ)

In some problems, we would be unconcerned if our estimate of P was too large, but would wish to be protected against an underestimate. Alternatively, in other problems, an underestimate is tolerable, but not an overestimate.   The error in the estimate is to be only in the direction that we choose.

The formula for sample size is

$$n = \frac{z_{1-\alpha}^2 \, P(1 - P)}{\delta^2} \, .$$

A sample of size n guarantees a probability not greater than α that our estimate of P is in error by more than $+\delta$ (or more than $-\delta$, as we choose).

Since the true proportion P is unknown, we must substitute for it a value P' which is obtained as follows:

(a) If no prior information about P is available, or if P is believed to be in the neighborhood of 0.5, use $P' = 0.5$.   The formula then simplifies to

$$n = \frac{z_{1-\alpha}^2}{4\delta^2} \, .$$

(b) If the true proportion P can safely be assumed to be less than 0.5, let P' be the *largest* reasonable guess for P.

(c) If the true proportion P can safely be assumed to be greater than 0.5, let P' be the *smallest* reasonable guess for P.

The largest sample size will be required when $P = 0.5$, and the purpose of the rules is to be as conservative as possible.

Procedure	Example
Problem: What is the sample size n required to estimate the true proportion P within $+\delta$ (or, within $-\delta$)?	*Problem:* What is the required sample size? In estimating P, we wish to be protected against making an estimate that is too small by more than 0.05.
(1) Choose $1 - \alpha$, the confidence coefficient to be associated with the resulting estimate.	(1) Let $1 - \alpha = .90$ $\alpha = .10$
(2) Specify $+\delta$ (or $-\delta$) the error permitted in the estimate.	(2) Let $\delta = -.05$
(3) Look up $z_{1-\alpha}$ in Table A-2.	(3) $z_{.90} = 1.282$
(4a) If there is no prior information about P, compute $$n = \frac{z_{1-\alpha}^2}{4\delta^2}$$	(4a) $$n = \frac{(1.282)^2}{.01}$$ $$= 164,$$ which is the required sample size.
(4b) If it is safe to assume that the true proportion P is less than some value P', compute $$n = \frac{z_{1-\alpha}^2 \, P'(1 - P')}{\delta^2}$$	(4b) If it is safe to assume that the true proportion P is less than .40, for example, $$n = \frac{(1.282)^2 \, (.4)\,(.6)}{.0025}$$ $$= 158,$$ which is the required sample size.

CHAPTER 8

COMPARING MATERIALS OR PRODUCTS WITH
RESPECT TO A TWO-FOLD CLASSIFICATION
OF PERFORMANCE
(COMPARING TWO PERCENTAGES)

In some situations, we are faced with the problem of comparing proportions or percentages. For example, the specification for a given kind of ammunition may prescribe the maximum allowable percentage of duds. Production lots of this ammunition will not be acceptable if they exceed this specified percent defective. The percentage of duds in a sample will provide an estimate of the percentage of duds in the lot, which then may be compared with the specified tolerance. When comparing an observed proportion with a specification or standard value, the procedures of Paragraph 8-1 are appropriate. The reader will note that the comparison is made by computing a confidence interval for the observed proportion and then looking to see whether the standard value is contained within this interval. This is a slightly different approach to answering the posed questions than was used in ORDP 20-110, Chapter 3, for example. Amplification of the relationship between confidence intervals and tests of significance of differences is given in ORDP 20-113, Chapter 21.

A different kind of comparison is involved when we compare two percentages with each other, without regard to any standard value — for example, in comparing two production processes with regard to the percentages of defective items produced. When two percentages are compared with each other, the methods of Paragraph 8-2 are appropriate.

8-1 COMPARING AN OBSERVED PROPORTION WITH A STANDARD PROPORTION

8-1.1 DOES THE NEW PRODUCT DIFFER FROM THE STANDARD WITH REGARD TO THE PROPORTION OF ITEMS WHICH SHOW THE CHARACTERISTIC OF INTEREST? (DOES P DIFFER FROM P_0?)

8-1.1.1 Procedure for $n \leq 30$.

Data Sample 8-1.1.1 — Defectives in Sample of New Product

Form: A sample of n items is selected at random from a much larger group. On examination, r of the n items show the presence of the pertinent characteristic. $p = r/n$ is the observed proportion, and is an estimate of P, the true proportion for the new product. P_0 is the known proportion of individual items in the standard product that show the pertinent characteristic.

Example: A sample of 20 components is taken from a production lot after a slight change in the process has been made. Three of the 20 items are classified as defectives. The observed proportion, therefore, is $p = 3/20 = 0.15$. The proportion defective for this item with the standard process is known to be $P_0 = 0.10$.

The question to be answered is: Does the proportion defective in this lot, P, *differ* from the standard proportion defective (either an increase or a decrease being of interest)?

Procedure	Example
(1) Choose α, the significance level of the test. Table A-22 gives 90%, 95%, and 99% two-sided confidence limits, appropriate to $\alpha = .10$, $\alpha = .05$, and $\alpha = .01$, respectively.	(1) Let $\quad \alpha = .10$ $\quad\quad\quad 1 - \alpha = .90$ Use the 90% confidence limits in Table A-22.
(2) Enter Table A-22 with observed n and r. Select appropriate column and read the limits.	(2) From Data Sample 8-1.1.1, $\quad n = 20$ $\quad r = 3$ From Table A-22, the 90% two-sided confidence limits for P are 0.056 to 0.328.
(3) If the tabled limits *do not* include P_0, conclude that P differs from P_0. If the tabled limits *do* include P_0, there is no reason to believe that P differs from P_0.	(3) Since the tabled limits *do* include $P_0 = 0.10$, there is no reason to believe that the proportion defective in the lot differs from the standard.

8-1.1.2 Procedure for n > 30.

Data Sample 8-1.1.2 — Performance of a New Type of Mine Fuze

Form: A sample of n items is selected at random from a much larger group. On examination, r of the n items show the presence of the pertinent characteristic. $p = r/n$ is the observed proportion, and is an estimate of P, the true proportion for the new product. P_0 is the known proportion of individual items in the standard product that show the pertinent characteristic.

Example: In a program of testing mine fuzes, 216 fuzes of a new type are buried, simulated "tanks" are run over them, and 160 "proper hits" are recorded. The observed proportion, p, of proper hits is $160/216 = 0.74$. The specified value for proportion of proper hits is $P_0 = 0.85$.

The question to be answered is: Does the proportion of proper hits for this fuze *differ* from the standard proportion (either an increase or a decrease being of interest)?

Procedure	**Example**
(1) Choose α, the significance level of the test. Table A-24 gives two-sided 90%, 95%, and 99% confidence limits appropriate to $\alpha = .10$, $\alpha = .05$, and $\alpha = .01$, respectively.	(1) Let $\alpha = .10$ $1 - \alpha = .90$ Use the Chart for confidence coefficient .90 in Table A-24.
(2) Compute $p = r/n$ and locate p on the horizontal scale. Locate curves for appropriate n.	(2) From Data Sample 8-1.1.2, $n = 216$ $r = 160$ $p = 160/216$ $= 0.74$
(3) Read off upper and lower limits for P. If these limits *do not* include P_0, conclude that P differs from P_0. If the limits *do* include P_0, there is no reason to believe that P differs from P_0.	(3) The chart does not show $n = 216$. Look at the belt for the next lower n, in this case $n = 100$. The belt for $n = 100$ will be wider than the belt for $n = 216$. Since the belt for $n = 100$ does not include $P_0 = 0.85$, the belt for $n = 216$ would not include P_0, and we conclude that the proportion of hits for this fuze does differ from the standard $P_0 = 0.85$.

8-1.2   DOES THE CHARACTERISTIC PROPORTION FOR THE NEW PRODUCT *EXCEED* THAT FOR THE STANDARD?   (IS $P > P_0$?)

8-1.2.1   Procedure for $n \leq 30$.   In terms of Data Sample 8-1.1.1, let us suppose that — in advance of looking at the data — the important question is: Does the characteristic proportion of defectives in this lot *exceed* that for the standard?

Procedure	**Example**
(1) Choose α, the significance level of the test. Table A-23 gives 90%, 95%, and 99% one-sided confidence limits appropriate to $\alpha = .10$, $\alpha = .05$, and $\alpha = .01$, respectively.	(1) Let $\alpha = .05$ $1 - \alpha = .95$ Use the 95% confidence limits in Table A-23.
(2) In Table A-23, follow directions at the beginning of the table to obtain p_1', a *lower* one-sided confidence limit for P.	(2) From Data Sample 8-1.1.1, $n = 20$ $r = 3$ $P_0 = 0.10$ is specified. The value in Table A-23, for $n = 20$, $n - r = 17$, is 0.958. The lower 95% limit for P is equal to $1 - 0.958 = 0.042$.

Procedure	Example

(3) If the *lower* limit p_1' obtained in Step (2) *exceeds* P_0, so that P_0 lies *outside* the confidence interval $p_1' \leq P \leq 1$, conclude that the characteristic proportion for the new product P exceeds that for the standard P_0.

If the *lower* limit obtained in Step (2) is *not larger* than P_0, so that P_0 lies *within* the confidence interval $p_1' \leq P \leq 1$, there is no reason to believe that the proportion for the new product P exceeds that for the standard P_0.

(3)

Since 0.042 is less than $P_0 = 0.10$, there is no reason to believe that the proportion of defectives in the lot exceeds the standard proportion.

8-1.2.2 Procedure for $n > 30$. In terms of Data Sample 8-1.1.2, let us suppose that — in advance of looking at the data — the important question is: Does the characteristic proportion of proper hits for this fuze *exceed* that for the standard?

Procedure	Example

(1) Choose α, the significance level of the test.

By using only the lower curve of the confidence belt, Table A-24 gives 95%, 97.5%, and 99.5% one-sided confidence limits appropriate to $\alpha = .05$, $\alpha = .025$, and $\alpha = .005$, respectively.

(1) Let $\quad \alpha = .05$
$\qquad 1 - \alpha = .95$
Use lower curves of the Chart labeled "confidence coefficient .90", in Table A-24.

(2) Compute $p = r/n$, and locate p on the horizontal scale. Locate lower curve for appropriate n.

(2) From Data Sample 8-1.1.2,
$$n = 216$$
$$r = 160$$
$$p = 160/216$$
$$= 0.74$$
$$P_0 = 0.85 \text{ is specified.}$$

(3) Read off the *lower* confidence limit for P.

If P_0 is *less* than this limit, p_1', so that P_0 lies *outside* the confidence interval $p_1' \leq P \leq 1$, conclude that the proportion for the new product exceeds that for the standard product.

If P_0 is *larger* than p_1', and therefore is *included* in the confidence interval $p_1' \leq P \leq 1$, there is no reason to believe that P is larger than P_0.

(3) From Table A-24, confidence coefficient .90, for $p = 0.74$ and $n = 216$, the lower 95% confidence limit for P is seen to be approximately 0.68.

Since $P_0 = 0.85$ is larger than 0.68, there is no reason to believe that P is larger than P_0.

8-1.3 IS THE CHARACTERISTIC PROPORTION FOR THE NEW PRODUCT LESS THAN THAT FOR THE STANDARD?   (IS $P < P_0$?)

8-1.3.1 Procedure for $n \leq 30$. In terms of Data Sample 8-1.1.1, let us suppose that — in advance of looking at the data — the important question is: Is the characteristic proportion of defectives in this lot *less* than that for the standard?

Procedure	Example
(1) Choose α, the significance level of the test. Table A-23 gives 90%, 95%, and 99% one-sided confidence limits appropriate to $\alpha = .10$, $\alpha = .05$, and $\alpha = .01$, respectively.	(1) Let $\alpha = .10$ $1 - \alpha = .90$ Use the 90% confidence limits in Table A-23.

(2) Enter Table A-23 with n and r and chosen confidence. Read the upper one-sided limit p_2' for P.	(2) From Data Sample 8-1.1.1,
	       $n = 20$
	       $r = 3$
	       $P_0 = 0.10$ is specified.
	The upper 90% limit for P is 0.304.

(3) If the tabled *upper* limit p_2' is *less* than P_0, so that P_0 lies *outside* the confidence interval $0 \leq P \leq p_2'$, conclude that the characteristic proportion for the new product is less than that for the standard. If the tabled limit is *larger* than P_0, so that P_0 lies *inside* the confidence interval $0 < P \leq p_2'$, there is no reason to believe that the proportion for the new product is less than the standard.	(3) Since the tabled limit (0.304) is larger than $P_0 = 0.10$, there is no reason to believe that the proportion of defectives in the lot is less than the standard.

8-1.3.2 Procedure for $n > 30$. In terms of Data Sample 8-1.1.2, let us suppose that — in advance of looking at the data — the important question is: Is the proportion of proper hits for this fuze *less than* that for the standard?

Procedure	Example
(1) Choose α, the significance level of the test. By using only the upper curve of the confidence belt, Table A-24 gives 95%, 97.5%, and 99.5% one-sided confidence limits appropriate to $\alpha = .05$, $\alpha = .025$, and $\alpha = .005$, respectively.	(1) Let $\alpha = .025$ $1 - \alpha = .975$ Use the upper curve of the Chart labeled "confidence coefficient .95", in Table A-24.

(2) Compute $p = r/n$, and locate p on the horizontal scale. Locate upper curve for appropriate n.	(2) From Data Sample 8-1.1.2,
	       $n = 216$
	       $r = 160$
	       $p = 160/216$
	         $= 0.74$
	       $P_0 = 0.85$ is specified.

Procedure	**Example**
(3) Read off upper confidence limit p_2' for P.	(3) From Table A-24, confidence coefficient .95, for $p = 0.74$ and $n = 216$, the upper 97.5% confidence limit for P is seen to be approximately 0.81.
If P_0 is *larger* than this limit, so that P_0 lies *outside* the confidence interval $0 \leq P \leq p_2'$, conclude that the proportion for the new product is less than that for the standard product.	Since $P_0 = 0.85$ is larger than this limit, we conclude that the proportion of proper hits for this fuze is less than for the standard.
If P_0 is *less* than this limit, and therefore is *included in* the one-sided confidence limit $0 \leq P \leq p_2'$, there is no reason to believe that P is less than P_0.	

8-1.4 SAMPLE SIZE REQUIRED TO DETECT A DIFFERENCE OF PRESCRIBED MAGNITUDE FROM A STANDARD PROPORTION WHEN THE SIGN OF THE DIFFERENCE IS NOT IMPORTANT

Given:

P_0 = the known proportion of the population of standard items which exhibit the pertinent characteristic. P_0 may be known from the process history, or may be given by the requirements of a specification or a standard.

To be Specified for This Problem:

δ = the absolute magnitude of the difference which is considered important to detect.

α = the significance level, or the risk of announcing a difference when in fact there is none.

β = the risk of failing to detect a difference when in fact P, the true proportion for the new product, differs from the standard by an amount δ (i.e., $\delta = |P - P_0|$).

Tables to be Used:

Table A-25 gives the required sample size for a number of values of P_0 and P for $\alpha = .05$ and $1 - \beta = .50, .80, .90, .95,$ and $.99$. This table is given largely for illustration, to demonstrate how the required sample size is affected by the magnitude of the P_0 and δ involved, and also by different choices of β. For desired values of α and β which are not included in Table A-25, use Table A-27, a table to convert the difference between the proportions into the form necessary for use with Table A-8.

Procedure	**Example**
(1) Specify δ, the absolute magnitude of the difference considered important to detect.	(1) Assume $P_0 = .30$ Specify $\delta = .10$
(2) Choose α and β.	(2) Let $\alpha = .05$ $\beta = .20$
(3) For $\alpha = .05$, and $1 - \beta = .50, .80, .90, .95,$ and $.99$, go to Table A-25.	(3) Use Table A-25 with $1 - \beta = .80$
(4) Let $P = P_0 + \delta$, or $P = P_0 - \delta$, whichever makes P closer to 0.5.	(4) $P = .30 + .10$ $= .40$

Procedure	**Example**
(5) If *either* P or P_0 is less than 0.5, enter Table A-25 with P and P_0. If neither P nor P_0 is less than 0.5, enter Table A-25 with $1 - P$ and $1 - P_0$. In either case, the smaller of the two proportions determines the column and the larger determines the row in Table A-25.	(5) Enter Table A-25 in column .30 and row .40 .
Read off n directly. n is the required sample size for the new product.	The required sample size is $n = 178$.

---

(6) For values of α, β, and P which are not included in Table A-25, go to Table A-27. Look up:

$\theta_0 = \theta$ corresponding to P_0
$\theta = \theta$ corresponding to P

(7) Compute $d = |\theta - \theta_0|$

(8) Enter Table A-8 with chosen α, $1 - \beta$, and d (from Step (7)).

The tabled n is the required sample size for the new product. (The footnote to Table A-8 should be ignored.)

For values of d not given in Table A-8, the sample size may be computed using the formula

$$n = \frac{(z_{1-\alpha/2} + z_{1-\beta})^2}{d^2}$$

(6) Assume that we had wished to specify $\alpha = .01$, $\beta = .20$, $P_0 = .30$, and $P = .40$. From Table A-27,

$\theta_0 = 1.16$
$\theta = 1.37$

(7) $d = 0.21$

(8) From Table A-8, the sample size for $d = 0.2$ is $n = 292$.

In this area of the table, interpolation is not recommended.

To obtain the sample size for $d = 0.21$, compute

$$n = \frac{(2.576 + 0.84)^2}{(0.21)^2}$$
$$= 265$$

8-1.5 SAMPLE SIZE REQUIRED TO DETECT A DIFFERENCE OF PRESCRIBED MAGNITUDE FROM A STANDARD PROPORTION WHEN THE SIGN OF THE DIFFERENCE IS IMPORTANT

Given:

P_0 = the known proportion of the population of standard items which exhibit the pertinent characteristic. P_0 may be known from the process history, or may be given by the requirements of a specification or a standard.

To be Specified for This Problem:

δ = the absolute magnitude of the difference which is considered important to detect.
P = $P_0 + \delta$, if we wish to distinguish between P_0 and a proportion larger than P_0;
or,
P = $P_0 - \delta$, if we wish to distinguish between P_0 and a proportion smaller than P_0.
α = the significance level, or the risk of announcing a difference when in fact there is none.
β = the risk of failing to detect a difference when in fact the true proportion for the new product is P, where $P = P_0 + \delta$ or $P = P_0 - \delta$, depending on the choice made above.

Tables to be Used:

Table A-26 gives the required sample size for a number of values of P_0 and P for $\alpha = .05$ and $1 - \beta = .50, .80, .90, .95$, and $.99$. The Table is given largely for illustration, to demonstrate how the required sample size is affected by the magnitude of the P_0 and δ involved, and also by different choices of β. For desired values of α and β which are not included in Table A-26, use Table A-27, a table to convert the difference between the proportions into the form necessary for use with Table A-9.

Procedure	**Example**
(1) Choose α and β.	(1) Let $\qquad \alpha = .05$ $\qquad\qquad \beta = .10$
(2) For $\alpha = .05$, and $1 - \beta = .50, .80, .90, .95,$ and $.99$, go to Table A-26.	(2) Use Table A-26, with $1 - \beta = .90$
(3) Let $P = P_0 + \delta$, or $\qquad P = P_0 - \delta$, as specified.	(3) Assume $P_0 = 0.70$ Specify $P = 0.70 + 0.10$ $\qquad\qquad = 0.80$
(4) If either P or P_0 is less than 0.5, enter Table A-26 with P and P_0. If neither P nor P_0 is less than 0.5, enter Table A-26 with $1 - P$ and $1 - P_0$.	(4) Since neither P nor P_0 is less than 0.5, take $1 - P = 0.20$ $\qquad\qquad 1 - P_0 = 0.30$.
In either case, the smaller of the two proportions determines the column and the larger determines the row in Table A-26.	Use column 0.20 and row 0.30 in Table A-26.
Read off n directly. n is the required sample size for the new product.	The required sample size is $n = 160$.

---

(5) For values of α, β, and P not included in Table A-26, go to Table A-27. Look up: $\qquad \theta_0 = \theta$ corresponding to P_0 $\qquad \theta = \theta$ corresponding to P	(5) Assume that we had specified $\alpha = .01$, $\beta = .10$, $P_0 = .10$, and $P = .40$. From Table A-27, $\qquad \theta_0 = .64$ $\qquad \theta = 1.37$
(6) Compute $d = |\theta - \theta_0|$	(6) $\qquad d = 0.73$
(7) Enter Table A-9 with chosen α, $1 - \beta$, and d (from Step (6)). The tabled n is the required sample size for the new product.	(7) From Table A-9, the sample size for $d = 0.6$ is $n = 37$, and for $d = 0.8$, is $n = 21$, so that the required sample size for $d = 0.73$ is greater than 21 and less than 37. In this area of the table, interpolation is not recommended. To obtain the sample size for $d = 0.73$, compute
For values of d not given in Table A-9, the sample size may be computed using the formula $$n = \frac{(z_{1-\alpha} + z_{1-\beta})^2}{d^2}$$	$$n = \frac{(2.326 + 1.282)^2}{(0.73)^2}$$ $$= \frac{13.018}{.5329}$$ $$= 24.4$$ As is conventional in sample size calculations, we round up to $n = 25$.

8-2 COMPARING TWO OBSERVED PROPORTIONS

We assume that n_A and n_B items are taken from products A and B, respectively. The items are to be examined or tested, and then classified into one of two mutually-exclusive categories. Some examples of two-category classifications are: hit or miss; pass or fail; white or black; damaged or not damaged; within tolerance or outside tolerance; etc. For purposes of illustration, we call the two categories Class I and Class II.

After examination of the n_A items, a number r_A are classified as Class I, and after examination of the n_B items, a number r_B are classified as Class I. The observed classification of the items is recorded in a two-row, two-column table (often called a 2×2 table) as shown in Table 8-1. Since there are just two mutually-exclusive classes, the entries for Class II can be filled in by subtracting the number recorded for Class I from the total number for each sample.

TABLE 8-1. OBSERVED FREQUENCIES FROM TWO SAMPLES IN TWO MUTUALLY EXCLUSIVE CATEGORIES (A 2 X 2 TABLE)

	Class I	Class II	Total
Sample from A	r_A	s_A	$n_A = r_A + s_A$
Sample from B	r_B	s_B	$n_B = r_B + s_B$
Total	r	s	n

The rows in the Table represent the two samples, and the columns are the two classes into which the observed items have been classified. Entries in the Table are counts — e.g., in the A sample (consisting of n_A items), r_A items are found to be Class I and s_A items ($s_A = n_A - r_A$) are Class II.

Although the problems will be posed in terms of proportions, and final results presented in terms of proportions, most of the techniques given use the observed *counts*. In terms of Table 8-1, if Class I is the property of interest, the observed proportions are $p_A = r_A/n_A$ and $p_B = r_B/n_B$.

Since the selection of available techniques depends on the sample sizes involved, this section is organized in three subparagraphs:

8-2.1 Comparing two proportions when the sample sizes are equal ($n_A = n_B$).

8-2.2 Comparing two proportions when the sample sizes are unequal and small ($n_A \neq n_B$; both less than 20).

8-2.3 Comparing two proportions when the sample sizes are unequal and large.

In each paragraph, procedures will be given for answering two questions:

(a) Does the characteristic proportion for product A differ from that for product B?

(b) Does the characteristic proportion for product A exceed that for product B?

As always, it is important to decide which question is appropriate before taking the observations. If this is not done, and if the choice of the problem is influenced by the observations, both the significance level of the test and the operating characteristics of the test may differ considerably from their nominal values.

8-2.1 COMPARING TWO PROPORTIONS WHEN THE SAMPLE SIZES ARE EQUAL

The solution involves three operations:

(a) Recording the observed counts in the form shown in Table 8-1;

(b) Selecting the proper pair of entries from among the four entries in the table; and,

(c) Comparing that pair with the "minimum contrast" pair given in Table A-28, to determine whether or not the observed contrast is significant at the chosen level. The procedure is detailed in Paragraphs 8-2.1.1 and 8-2.1.2; and, with a little practice, can be done quickly by eye.

Table A-28 gives "minimum contrasts" for $n_A = n_B = 1(1)20(10)100(50)200(100)500$ corresponding to significance levels $\alpha = .05$ and $\alpha = .01$ for two-sided tests (see Paragraph 8-2.1.1); or to $\alpha = .025$ and $\alpha = .005$ for one-sided tests (see Paragraph 8-2.1.2). By "minimum contrast" is meant the "least different" pair which is significant at the chosen significance level. A "more different" pair is of course significant also. For example, look at the entries in Table A-28 for $n_A = n_B = 17$. The "minimum contrasts required" at significance level $\alpha = .05$ for the two-sided test (Does P_A differ from P_B?) are (0, 5), (1, 7), (2, 9), (3, 10), etc. Since (0, 5) is significant, so also is (0, 6), (0, 7), etc. Since (1, 7) is significant, so also is (1, 8), (1, 9), etc.

It is worth noting that Table A-28 can be used to give satisfactory answers for values of n intermediate to those tabulated (see *Note* to Table A-28).

Data Sample 8-2.1 — Small-scale Comparison Test of Two Types of Mine Fuzes

Seventeen impact fuzes of each of two different types are tested, and the number of successful firings are recorded, as follows:

Fuze Type	Success (Class I)	Failure (Class II)	Total
Type A	$r_A = 15$	$s_A = 2$	$n_A = 17$
Type B	$r_B = 7$	$s_B = 10$	$n_B = 17$
Total	$r = 22$	$s = 12$	$n = 34$

8-2.1.1 Does the Characteristic Proportion for Product A Differ From That for Product B? (Does P_A Differ From P_B?) In terms of Data Sample 8-2.1, we wish to compare the proportion of successful firings for the two types of fuzes. The question to be answered is: Does Type A *differ* from Type B with regard to the proportion of successful firings?

Procedure	**Example**
(1) Choose α, the significance level of the test. Table A-28 provides "minimum contrasts" corresponding to $\alpha = .05$ and $\alpha = .01$ for this two-sided test.*	(1) Let $\alpha = .01$
(2) Record the observed counts as in Table 8-1.	(2) See Data Sample 8-2.1.
(3) Let: a_1 = smallest of all four entries a_2 = entry in the same class as a_1 from the other sample. The "observed contrast" pair is the ordered pair (a_1, a_2). If $a_1 = a_2$, no further analysis is necessary. The data give no reason to believe that the two proportions differ.	(3) $a_1 = 2$ $a_2 = 10$ The "observed contrast" pair is (2, 10).
(4) Enter Table A-28 with sample size $n_A = n_B$.	(4) $n_A = n_B = 17$
(5) Call the tabled pairs (A_1, A_2). Find the tabled pair where $A_1 = a_1$; this is the "least different" pair which is significant at the chosen level.	(5) From Table A-28, with $\alpha = .01$ and $a_1 = 2$, the "least different" pair $(A_1, A_2) = (2, 11)$.
(6) If a_2 is equal to or larger than A_2, the observed contrast is significant at the chosen level, and we conclude that the two products differ with regard to the characteristic proportion considered. If a_2 is smaller than A_2, there is no reason to believe that the two proportions differ.	(6) Since $a_2 = 10$ is less than $A_2 = 11$, the observed contrast is not significant at the .01 level, and we conclude that there is no reason to believe that the two fuze types differ with regard to the proportion of successful firings.

---

* Table A-29 and the more complicated procedure of Paragraph 8-2.2.1 can be used to conduct equivalent two-sided tests corresponding to $\alpha = \underline{.10}$, .05, $\underline{.02}$, and .01, when $n_A = n_B \leq 20$, thus extending the present two-sided test procedure to the underscored values of α for equal sample sizes up to 20.

8-2.1.2   Does the Characteristic Proportion for Product A Exceed That for Product B?   (Is P_A Larger Than P_B ?)   In terms of Data Sample 8-2.1, let us suppose that — in advance of looking at the data — the important question is: Does the proportion of successful firings for Type A exceed the proportion of successes for Type B?

Procedure	**Example**
(1) Choose α, the significance level of the test. Table A-28 provides "minimum contrasts" corresponding to $\alpha = .025$ and $\alpha - .005$ for this one-sided test.*	(1) Let $\alpha = .025$
(2) Record the observed counts as in Table 8-1.	(2) See Data Sample 8-2.1
(3) Compute p_A, the observed proportion for Product A, and p_B, the observed proportion for Product B. If Class I is the class of interest, $p_A = r_A/n_A$ and $p_B = r_B/n_B$. If Class II is the class of interest, $p_A = s_A/n_A$ and $p_B = s_B/n_B$.	(3) $p_A = 15/17$ $= 0.88$ $p_B = 7/17$ $= 0.41$
(4) If p_A is not larger than p_B, conclude at once that there is no reason to believe that the true proportion P_A is larger than P_B; otherwise, proceed to Step (5).	(4) Since p_A is larger than p_B, proceed to Step (5).
(5) If p_A is larger than p_B, let: a_1 = smallest of all four entries a_2 = entry in the same class as a_1 from the other sample. The "observed contrast" pair is the ordered pair (a_1, a_2).	(5) $a_1 = 2$ $a_2 = 10$ The "observed contrast" pair is $(2, 10)$.
(6) Enter Table A-28 with sample size $n_A = n_B$.	(6) $n_A = n_B = 17$
(7) Call the tabled pairs (A_1, A_2). Find the tabled pair where $A_1 = u_1$; this is the "least different" pair which is significant at the chosen level.	(7) From Table A-28, with $\alpha = .025$ and $a_1 = 2$, the "least different" pair $(A_1, A_2) = (2, 9)$.
(8) If a_2 is equal to or is larger than A_2, the observed contrast is significant at the chosen level, and we conclude that the proportion for Product A exceeds that for Product B. If a_2 is smaller than A_2, there is no reason to believe that the two proportions differ.	(8) Since $a_2 = 10$ is larger than $A_2 = 9$, we conclude that the proportion of successes for type A exceeds that for type B.

* Table A-29 and the more complicated procedure of Paragraph 8-2.2.2 can be used to conduct equivalent one-sided tests corresponding to $\alpha = .05, .025, .01$, and .005, when $n_A - n_B \leq 20$, thus extending the present one-sided test procedure to the underscored values of α for equal sample sizes up to 20.

8-2.2 COMPARING TWO PROPORTIONS WHEN THE SAMPLE SIZES ARE UNEQUAL AND SMALL ($n_A \neq n_B$; BOTH NO GREATER THAN 20)

8-2.2.1 Does the Characteristic Proportion for Product A Differ From That for Product B?

Data Sample 8-2.2.1 — Small-scale Comparison Test of Two Types of Artillery Fuzes

The following data are recorded from an artillery fuze-testing program:

Fuze Type	Fires (Class I)	Does Not Fire (Class II)	Total
Type A	$r_A = 4$	$s_A = 2$	$n_A = 6$
Type B	$r_B = 8$	$s_B = 2$	$n_B = 10$
Total	$r = 12$	$s = 4$	$n = 16$

Procedure

(1) Choose α, the significance level of the test. Table A-29 provides a listing of "significant contrasts" corresponding to $\alpha = .10, .05, .02$, and $.01$ for this two-sided test. *

(2) Record the observed counts as in Table 8-1.

(3) In order to use Table A-29 for this problem, we must have the data arranged in a special way. Arrange the data as shown in Table 8-2 so that the results from the larger sample are in the first row, and re-label the entries r_1, r_2, etc., as shown in Table 8-2. Retain the original product identification of the samples.

Example

(1) Let $\alpha = .02$

(2) See Data Sample 8-2.2.1

(3) See Rearranged Data Sample 8-2.2.1A

TABLE 8-2. REARRANGEMENT OF TABLE 8-1 FOR CONVENIENT USE IN TESTING SIGNIFICANCE WITH TABLE A-29

	Class I	Class II	Total
Larger Sample	r_1	s_1	n_1
Smaller Sample	r_2	s_2	n_2
Total	r	s	n

* It should be noted that Table A-29 also could be used for equal sample sizes up to 20. For equal samples and $\alpha = .05$ or $.01$, however, the method of Paragraph 8-2.1.1 is recommended because of simplicity.

Rearranged Data Sample 8-2.2.1A

Fuze Type	Fires (Class I)	Does Not Fire (Class II)	Total
Larger sample (Type B)	$r_1 = 8$	$s_1 = 2$	$n_1 = 10$
Smaller sample (Type A)	$r_2 = 4$	$s_2 = 2$	$n_2 = 6$
Total	$r = 12$	$s = 4$	$n = 16$

Procedure	**Example**

(4) Compute the four proportions:

$$p_1 = r_1/n_1$$

$$p_2 = r_2/n_2$$

$$q_1 = s_1/n_1$$

$$q_2 = s_2/n_2$$

(4)

$$p_1 = 8/10$$
$$= .80$$

$$p_2 = 4/6$$
$$= .67$$

$$q_1 = 2/10$$
$$= .20$$

$$q_2 = 2/6$$
$$= .33$$

(5) If p_1 is larger than or is equal to p_2, focus attention on Class I.
For use with Table A-29, take

$$a_1 = r_1$$

$$a_2 = r_2$$

If q_1 is larger than or is equal to q_2, focus attention on Class II.
For use with Table A-29, take
$$a_1 = s_1$$
$$a_2 = s_2$$

(5) Since p_1 is larger than p_2, focus on Class I.

$$a_1 = r_1$$
$$= 8$$
$$a_2 = r_2$$
$$= 4$$

(6) Enter Table A 29 with n_1, n_2, and a_1 (determined from Step (5)).

The observed a_2 (from Step (5)) must be equal to or smaller than the tabled a_2 (bold-face in Table A-29) for significance at the chosen level. Therefore, if the observed a_2 is equal to or is smaller than bold-face a_2 in Table A-29, conclude that the two products differ with regard to the proportion of interest.
If the observed a_2 is larger than the tabled a_2, there is no reason to believe that the two products differ.

(6) From Table A-29, for $n_1 = 10$, $n_2 = 6$, $a_1 = 8$, and $\alpha = .02$, the tabled a_2 is 0.

Since the observed $a_2 = 4$ is larger than the tabled a_2, there is no reason to believe that the two fuzes differ in regard to the proportion which fire.

8-2.2.2   Does the Characteristic Proportion for Product A Exceed That for Product B?   (Is P_A Larger Than P_B?)

Data Sample 8-2.2.2 — Small-scale Comparison Test of Two Types of Impact Fuzes

The following data are recorded from an impact fuze-testing program:

Fuze Type	Fires (Class I)	Does Not Fire (Class II)	Total
Type A	$r_A = 4$	$s_A = 2$	$n_A = 6$
Type B	$r_B = 0$	$s_B = 10$	$n_B = 10$
Total	$r = 4$	$s = 12$	$n = 16$

Procedure

(1) Record the observed counts as shown in Table 8-1.

(2) Focus on the class of interest.   If this is Class I, compute:

$$p_A = r_A/n_A$$

$$p_B = r_B/n_B$$

(If Class II were the class of interest p_A would equal s_A/n_A, and p_B would equal s_B/n_B).

If p_A is larger than p_B, proceed to Step (3). If p_A is not larger than p_B, conclude at once that the data give no reason to believe that the true proportion P_A is larger than P_B.

(3) Choose α, the significance level of the test. Table A-29 is used for this one-sided test*for $\alpha = .05, .025, .01$, and $.005$.

(4) In order to use Table A-29 for this problem, we must have the data arranged in a special way.   Arrange the data as shown in Table 8-2 so that the results from the larger sample are in the first row, and relabel the entries r_1, r_2, etc., as shown in Table 8-2. Retain the original product identification of the samples.

Example

(1) See Data Sample 8-2.2.2.

(2) Since we are interested in comparing the proportions of fuzes which do fire, compute:

$$p_A = r_A/n_A$$
$$= 4/6$$
$$= .67$$
$$p_B = r_B/n_B$$
$$= 0/10$$
$$= 0$$

Since p_A is larger than p_B, proceed to Step (3).

(3) Let $\alpha = .01$

(4) See Rearranged Data Sample 8-2.2.2A.

---

* It should be noted that Table A-29 also could be used for equal sample sizes up to 20.   For equal sample sizes and $\alpha = .025$ and $\alpha = .005$, however, the method of Paragraph 8-2.1.2 is recommended because of simplicity.

Rearranged Data Sample 8-2.2.2A

Fuze Type	Fires (Class I)	Does Not Fire (Class II)	Total
Larger sample (Type B)	$r_1 = 0$	$s_1 = 10$	$n_1 = 10$
Smaller sample (Type A)	$r_2 = 4$	$s_2 = 2$	$n_2 = 6$
Total	$r = 4$	$s = 12$	$n = 16$

Procedure	**Example**

(5) Compute the four proportions:

$$p_1 = r_1/n_1$$

$$p_2 = r_2/n_2$$

$$q_1 = s_1/n_1$$

$$q_2 = s_2/n_2$$

(5)

$p_1 = 0/10$
$\quad = 0$

$p_2 = 4/6$
$\quad = .67$

$q_1 = 10/10$
$\quad = 1.00$

$q_2 = 2/6$
$\quad = .33$

Note that:

$p_1 = p_A$ if n_A is the larger sample;

$p_1 = p_B$ if n_B is the larger sample.

(6) If p_1 is larger than or is equal to p_2, focus attention on Class I.
For use with Table A-29, take

$\quad a_1 = r_1$

$\quad a_2 = r_2$.

If q_1 is larger than or is equal to q_2, focus attention on Class II.
For use with Table A-29, take

$\quad a_1 = s_1$

$\quad a_2 = s_2$

(6)

Since q_1 is larger than q_2, focus attention on Class II.

$a_1 = s_1$
$\quad = 10$

$a_2 = s_2$
$\quad = 2$

(7) Enter Table A-29 with n_1, n_2, and the a_1 (determined from Step (6)).
The observed a_2 (from Step (6)) must be equal to or smaller than the tabled a_2 (bold face in Table A-29) for significance at the chosen level.
Therefore, if observed a_2 is equal to or is smaller than bold-face a_2 in Table A-29, conclude that the proportion of interest for product A exceeds the proportion for product B.
If the observed a_2 is larger than the tabled a_2, there is no reason to believe that the two proportions differ.

(7) From Table A-29, for $n_1 = 10$, $n_2 = 6$, $a_1 = 10$, and $\alpha = .01$, the tabled a_2 is 2.

Since the observed a_2 is equal to the tabled a_2, we conclude that the proportion of successful fuzes of type A exceeds that for type B.

8-2.3   COMPARING TWO PROPORTIONS WHEN THE SAMPLE SIZES ARE LARGE*

8-2.3.1   Does the Characteristic Proportion for Product A Differ From That for Product B?   (Does P_A Differ From P_B?)

Data Sample 8-2.3.1 — Field Trials of Two Types of Mine Fuzes

In field trials of mine fuzes, 216 of each of two new types of fuze were buried, simulated tanks run over them, and the number of "proper hits" recorded.   The results are as follows:

Fuze Type	Hit	Not Hit	Total
Type A	$r_A = 181$	$s_A = 35$	$n_A = 216$
Type B	$r_B = 160$	$s_B = 56$	$n_B = 216$
Total	$r = 341$	$s = 91$	$n = 432$

Let us assume with respect to Data Sample 8-2.3.1 that the important question is: Is the proportion of hits for Type A different from the proportion of hits for Type B?

Procedure	**Example**
(1) Choose α, the significance level of the test.	(1) Let $\alpha = .10$
(2) Look up $\chi^2_{1-\alpha}$ for one degree of freedom in Table A-3.	(2) $\chi^2_{.90}$ for 1 d.f. = 2.71
(3) Compute $$\chi^2 = \frac{n\left(|r_A s_B - r_B s_A| - \dfrac{n}{2}\right)^2}{n_A\, r\, n_B\, s}$$ (See *Note* below.)	(3) $$\chi^2 = \frac{432\,(4536 - 216)^2}{(73656)\,(19656)}$$ $$= 5.57$$
(4) If $\chi^2 \geq \chi^2_{1-\alpha}$, decide that the two products differ with regard to the proportion having the given characteristic; otherwise, there is no reason to believe that the products differ in this respect.	(4) Since χ^2 is larger than $\chi^2_{.90}$, we conclude that the two types of fuzes do differ with regard to the proportion of "proper hits".

---

* The procedures of this paragraph *must be used* for large samples of unequal size, and *may be used* for samples of equal size.   If the sample sizes are equal and are included in Table A-28, the procedures of Paragraph 8-2.1 are to be preferred because of simplicity.

Procedure	Example

Note: The computation of x^2 is most conveniently done in terms of the actual counts in the table, as given in Step (3) above. The formula can be expressed in terms of the observed proportions as follows:

Note: Using Data Sample 8-2.3.1 with this formula:

$$x^2 = \frac{\left(n' |p_A - p_B| - \frac{1}{2}\right)^2}{n'p(1-p)}$$

$$x^2 = \frac{(108\,(.097) - 1/2)^2}{108\,(.789)\,(.211)}$$
$$= \frac{(9.976)^2}{17.980}$$
$$= 5.54$$

where

$$p_A = r_A/n_A$$

$$p_A = 181/216$$
$$= .838$$

$$p_B = r_B/n_B$$

$$p_B = 160/216$$
$$= .741$$

$$p = \frac{r_A + r_B}{n_A + n_B}$$

$$p = 341/432$$
$$= .789$$
$$1 - p = .211$$

and

$$n' = \frac{n_A n_B}{n_A + n_B}$$

$$n' = 46656/432$$
$$= 108$$

This formula and the formula in Step (3) are algebraically equivalent, but use of the form given in the *Note* requires extra arithmetic and rounding. In spite of the fact that the question is put in terms of the difference between proportions, the answer is obtained more easily and more accurately using observed *counts,* i.e., the formula of Step (3) is preferred. Furthermore, using the formula in terms of counts (Step (3)) highlights the fact that one *cannot* judge the difference between two proportions without knowing the sample sizes involved.

8-2.3.2   **Is the Characteristic Proportion for Product A Larger Than That for Product B?**   **(Is P_A Larger Than P_B?)**   In terms of Data Sample 8-2.3.1, let us suppose that — in advance of looking at the data — the important question is: Is the proportion of hits for type A larger than the proportion of hits for type B?

Procedure	Example

(1) Choose α, the significance level of the test.

(1) Let $\alpha = .025$

(2) Look up $\chi^2_{1-2\alpha}$ for one degree of freedom in Table A-3.

(2) $\chi^2_{.95}$ for 1 d.f. = 3.84

(3) Compute:

$$\chi^2 = \frac{n\left(\left|r_A s_B - r_B s_A\right| - \dfrac{n}{2}\right)^2}{n_A \, r \, n_B \, s}$$

(3)

$$\chi^2 = \frac{432\,(4536 - 216)^2}{(73656)\,(19656)}$$
$$= 5.57$$

and

$$p_A = r_A/n_A$$

$$p_B = r_B/n_B$$

$$p_A = 181/216$$
$$= .84$$

$$p_B = 160/216$$
$$= .74$$

(See *Note* at end of procedure of Paragraph 8-2.3.1)

(4) If $\chi^2 \geq \chi^2_{1-2\alpha}$ *and* p_A is larger than p_B, decide that P_A exceeds P_B; otherwise, there is no reason to believe the proportions differ.

(4) Since χ^2 is larger than $\chi^2_{.95}$ and $p_A = .84$ is larger than $p_B = .74$, conclude that the proportion of hits for type A is larger than the proportion of hits for type B.

8-2.4   SAMPLE SIZE REQUIRED TO DETECT A DIFFERENCE BETWEEN TWO PROPORTIONS

8-2.4.1   **Sample Size Required to Detect a Difference of Prescribed Magnitude Between Two Proportions When the Sign of the Difference Is Not Important.**   Unfortunately, the sample size required depends on the true but unknown values of the two proportions involved. Very often, the experimenter has some idea of the magnitude of (or an upper bound for) one of these values, and then must specify the size of the difference which the experiment should be designed to detect. For a fixed difference to be detected, the largest sample sizes will be required if the true proportions are in the neighborhood of 0.5. A look at Table A-25, however, will show that over-conservatism may not pay. Suppose, for example, that one of the proportions can *safely* be assumed to be less than 0.4. The most conservative assumption would be that it is equal to 0.4 (this being the closest reasonable guess to 0.5). Attempting to be over-cautious by using the value 0.45 will extract a heavy price in the number of tests to be run.

Given:

For this problem there is nothing given, but —

Assumed:

P' = an estimate of one of the two proportions.
     To be conservative, make this estimate as close to 0.5 as is reasonable.

To be Specified for This Problem:

α = the significance level, or the risk of announcing a difference when in fact there is none.

β = the risk of failing to detect a difference when in fact the true proportions differ by an amount δ (i.e., $|P' - P''| = \delta$).

δ = the absolute magnitude of the difference which is considered important to detect.

Tables to be Used:

Table A-25 can be used for α = .05 and $1 - \beta$ = .50, .80, .90, .95, and .99, and for certain values of the proportions. The entry in Table A-25 must be doubled to give n'; and n' is the required sample size to be taken from each product.

For other desired values of α and β, use Table A-27, a table to convert the difference between the proportions into the form necessary for use with Table A-8.

The question to be answered by the experiment is: Does P_A differ from P_B?

Procedure	**Example**
(1) Specify δ, the absolute magnitude of the difference considered important to detect.	(1) Specify δ = .10
(2) Choose α and β.	(2) Let $\quad \alpha = .05$ $\qquad \beta = .20$
(3) For α = .05 and $1 - \beta$ = .50, .80, .90, .95, or .99, go to Table A-25.	(3) Use Table A-25 with $1 - \beta$ = .80
(4) Let P' = an estimate of one of the proportions. Let $P'' = P' + \delta$ or $P' - \delta$, *whichever* makes P'' closer to 0.5.	(4) Let $\quad P' = .20$ Let $\quad P'' = .20 + .10$ $\qquad = .30$
(5) If *either* P' or P'' is less than 0.5, enter Table A-25 with P' and P''. If *neither* P' nor P'' is less than 0.5, enter Table A-25 with $1 - P'$ and $1 - P''$. In either case, the smaller of the two proportions determines the column and the larger of the two determines the row in Table A-25.	(5) Enter Table A-25 in column .20 and row .30.
Read off n, and double it to obtain n'. n' is the required sample size to be taken from each product.	$n = 146$ $n' = 292$, the required sample size to be taken from each product.
(6) For other values of α and β, and for values of P' and P'' not included in Table A-25, go to Table A-27. Look up: $\theta' = \theta$ corresponding to P' $\theta'' = \theta$ corresponding to P''	(6) Assume that we had specified α = .01, β = .20, P' = .34, and P'' = .44. From Table A-27, $\theta' = 1.25$ $\theta'' = 1.45$
(7) Compute $d = |\theta' - \theta''|$	(7) $d = |1.25 - 1.45|$ $\qquad = .20$

Procedure	Example

(8) Enter Table A-8 with α, β, and d (from Step (7)).

(8) From Table A-8 with $\alpha = .01$, $1 - \beta = .80$, and $d = .20$, $n = 292$.

Read off n and double it to obtain n'. Then, n' is the required sample size to be taken from each product.
(Rounding two-decimal values of d to the nearest value considered in Table A-8 may lead to excessively high (or low) values of n, and thence of n'. Interpolation for values of n corresponding to values of d not considered in Table A-8 is *not* recommended. For values of d not given in Table A-8, the sample size may be computed using the formula

$$n = \frac{(z_{1-\alpha/2} + z_{1-\beta})^2}{d^2}$$

$n' = 584$, the required sample size to be taken from each product.

8-2.4.2 Sample Size Required to Detect a Difference of Prescribed Magnitude Between Two Proportions When the Sign of the Difference Is Important. Read the general discussion at the beginning of Paragraph 8-2.4.1.

Given:

For this problem, there is nothing given, but —

Assumed:

P' = an estimate of one of the two proportions. P' may be P_A', an estimate of P_A, or P_B', an estimate of P_B.
To be conservative, make this estimate as close to 0.5 as is reasonable.

To be Specified for This Problem:

α = the significance level, or the risk of announcing a difference when in fact there is none.
β = the risk of failing to detect a difference when in fact the true proportion for the other product is $P'' = P' + \delta$ or is $P'' = P' - \delta$.
δ = the absolute magnitude of the difference considered important to detect.

Tables to be Used:

Table A-26 can be used for $\alpha = .05$ and $1 - \beta = .50$, .80, .90, .95, and .99; and for certain values of the proportions.

For other desired values of α and β, use Table A-27, a table to convert the difference between the proportions into the form necessary for use with Table A-9.

The question to be answered by the experiment is: Is P_A larger than P_B?

Procedure	Example

(1) Specify δ, the absolute magnitude of the difference considered important to detect.
If the estimate P_A' is available, then $P'' = P_A' - \delta$.
If the estimate P_B' is available, then $P'' = P_B' + \delta$.

(1) Specify $\delta = .05$

Let P_A', the estimate of P_A, = .10
Then, $P'' = .10 - .05$
$\qquad = .05$

Procedure	**Example**

(2) Choose α and β.

(2) Let $\alpha = .05$
           $\beta = .10$

(3) For $\alpha = .05$, $1 - \beta = .50$, $.80$, $.90$, $.95$, or $.99$, go to Table A-26.

(3) Use Table A-26 with $1 - \beta = .90$

(4) If either P' or P'' is less than 0.5, enter Table A-26 with P' and P''.

If neither P' nor P'' is less than 0.5, enter Table A-26 with $1 - P'$ and $1 - P''$.

In either case, the smaller of the two proportions determines the column and the larger determines the row in Table A-26.

(4) Since both P' and P'' are less than 0.5, enter Table A-26 in column .05 and row .10.

(5) Read off n, and double it to obtain n'. n' is the required sample size to be taken from each product.

(5) $n = 232$
      $n' = 464$, the required sample size to be taken from each product.

---

(6) For other values of α and β, and for values of P' and P'' not included in Table A-26, go to Table A-27.
Look up:
    $\theta' = \theta$ corresponding to P'
    $\theta'' = \theta$ corresponding to P''

(6) Assume that we had specified $\alpha = .01$, $1 - \beta = .90$, $P' = .70$, and $P'' = .50$.

From Table A-27
      $\theta' = 1.98$
      $\theta'' = 1.57$

(7) Compute $d = |\theta' - \theta''|$

(7) $d = |1.98 - 1.57|$
        $= .41$

(8) Enter Table A-9 with α, β, and d (from Step (7)).

Read off n, and double it to obtain n'. n' is the required sample size to be taken from each product.

Rounding two-decimal values of d to the nearest value considered in Table A-9 may lead to excessively high (or low) values of n, and thence of n'.

Interpolation for values of n corresponding to values of d not considered in Table A-9 is *not* recommended.

For values of d not given in Table A-9, the sample size may be computed using the formula

$$n = \frac{(z_{1-\alpha} + z_{1-\beta})^2}{d^2}$$

(8) From Table A-9, for $d = .4$, $n = 82$.

$n' = 164$ is an upper bound to the required sample size to be taken from each product.

In the present instance,

$$n = \frac{(2.326 + 1.282)^2}{(.41)^2}$$

$$= \frac{13.018}{.1681}$$

$$= 78$$

and $n' = 156$ is the required sample size to be taken from each product.

CHAPTER 9

COMPARING MATERIALS OR PRODUCTS WITH RESPECT TO SEVERAL CATEGORIES OF PERFORMANCE (CHI-SQUARE TESTS)

In some inspection and testing procedures, a two-category classification of performance (e.g., success or failure) is not sufficient. In inspection work, the classification scheme might consist of *three* categories; for example, (1) acceptable, (2) reworkable, and (3) unusable. In process control, we might wish to record occurrences of each of a number of types of defects, and to make comparisons between shifts or between time periods with regard to the distribution of the types of defects. Similarly, reports of types of failures of machinery, or of records of repairs, may call for a classification scheme with more than two categories. Classifications by size, color, and structure are other possible examples of classifications likely to require three or more categories.

Where the classification scheme provides for three or more categories, the procedures of this Chapter are appropriate. (The methods of Chapter 8 could be used only if we were to consider a single class as, for example, *success*, with all the other classes lumped together as *failure*.)

If the classification scheme has a large number of categories, and if we are interested in a special group of these classes, the individual classes in the group may be combined and considered as one grand category. For example, in records of the causes of aircraft accidents, we may consider the one large category *collision*, or we may have this information broken down into several classes, e.g., *between two in air, with ground, with water*, and *other types of collision*.

9-1 COMPARING A MATERIAL OR PRODUCT WITH A STANDARD

9-1.1 WHEN THE COMPARISON IS WITH A STANDARD MATERIAL OR PRODUCT

Data Sample 9-1.1 — Inspections and Tests of Clinical Thermometers

Form: A sample of n items is selected at random from a much larger group. After inspection or test, each sample item (or observation) is classified into one of k categories, according to some established classification scheme. The result is that n_1 items are observed to be in category 1, n_2 items in category 2, n_i items in the ith category, etc., and

$$n_1 + n_2 + \ldots + n_k = n.$$

Let: P_1 equal the known proportion of *standard* items that are classified in category 1; P_2 equal the known proportion in category 2; and P_i equal the known proportion of standard items in the ith category.

The relevant question to be asked is: "Does the new product differ from the standard with regard to the proportions in each category?"

Example: The inspection and testing of clinical thermometers provides an illustrative example. Clinical thermometers are classified into one of the following four categories, on the basis of inspection and test:

1. Non-defective;

2. Defective — class A (Defects in glass, defective markings, dimensional nonconformance, etc.);

3. Defective — class B (Defects in mercury column);

4. Defective — class C (Nonconformance to precision and accuracy requirements).

Over a period of time, it has been found that thermometers produced by a certain manufacturer are distributed among the four categories in the following average proportions:

1. Non-defective — 87 percent ($P_1 = 0.87$);

2. Class A — 9 percent ($P_2 = 0.09$);

3. Class B — 3 percent ($P_3 = 0.03$);

4. Class C — 1 percent ($P_4 = 0.01$).

A new lot of 1336 thermometers is submitted by the manufacturer for inspection and test, and the following distribution into the four categories results:

Category	No. of Thermometers Reported
1	1188 (n_1)
2	91 (n_2)
3	47 (n_3)
4	10 (n_4)
	$n = 1336$

The question asked is: "Does this new lot of thermometers differ from previous experience with regard to proportions of thermometers in each category?"

Procedure*	Example

(1) Choose α, the significance level of the test.

(2) Look up $x^2_{1-\alpha}$ for $k - 1$ degrees of freedom in Table A-3.

(3) Compute nP_i, the theoretical value for each category.

(4) Compute

$$x^2 = \sum_{i=1}^{k} (n_i^2/nP_i) - n$$

(5) If $x^2 \geq x^2_{1-\alpha}$, conclude that the material, product, or process differs from the standard with regard to the proportions in the categories; otherwise, there is no reason to believe that they differ.

(1) Let $\alpha = .05$
$1 - \alpha = .95$

(2) $k - 1 = 3$
$x^2_{.95}$ for 3 d.f. = 7.81

(3) For a convenient computational arrangement, see Table 9-1.

(4) See Table 9-1,

$$x^2 = 9.72$$

(5) Since x^2 is larger than $x^2_{.95}$, we conclude that the new lot of thermometers is different from previous lots submitted by the same manufacturer with regard to the proportions in the respective inspection-test categories.

TABLE 9-1. COMPUTATIONAL ARRANGEMENT FOR DATA SAMPLE 9-1.1

Thermometer Class	No. of Thermometers in Each Category (n_i)	Known Proportion for Standard Product (P_i)	Expected No. (nP_i)	$\dfrac{n_i^2}{nP_i}$
1. Non-defective	1188	.87	1162.32	1214.25
2. Class A	91	.09	120.24	68.87
3. Class B	47	.03	40.08	55.11
4. Class C	10	.01	13.36	7.49
Total	$n = 1336$	1.00	1336.00	1345.72

$$x^2 = \Sigma(n_i^2/nP_i) - n = 1345.72 - 1336 = 9.72$$

* This x^2 procedure is based on a *large-sample* approximation, but if $nP_i \geq 5.0$ for all categories, the approximation ordinarily is very good. If $nP_i < 5$ for several categories, these categories may be pooled to obtain a theoretical frequency of at least 5 for the combined cells, and a corresponding improvement in the accuracy of the approximate solution, but at the price of some loss of resolution.

9-1.2 WHEN THE COMPARISON IS WITH A THEORETICAL "STANDARD"

The following example illustrates an application of the foregoing procedure in which the "standard" is of a theoretical nature.

Data Sample 9-1.2 — Breakdowns of Electricity Meters

Form: There are k different types of meters in current use. The total number of each type in service at the beginning of the service period under consideration was $N_1, N_2, \ldots, N_k$, respectively. If the probability of a meter breaking down during the service period is the same for all k types, then we would expect the total number of breakdowns during this period to be distributed among the k types in proportion to their respective numbers in service. For example, suppose that a total of n meters break down. Among these n, we would expect to find the proportion

$$P_1 = \frac{N_1}{N_1 + N_2 + \ldots + N_k}$$

of them to be of type 1; the proportion

$$P_2 = \frac{N_2}{N_1 + N_2 + \ldots + N_k}$$

to be of type 2; etc. The actual number of each type that are found in the n breakdowns are $n_1, n_2, \ldots, n_k$ (and $n_1 + n_2 + \ldots + n_k = n$). The actual proportions $n_1/n, n_2/n, \ldots, n_k/n$, rarely will conform to the theoretical values, $P_1, P_2, \ldots, P_k$, even when the hypothesis that all types are equally likely to break down is true. The relevant question is: Are the differences between the observed and theoretical proportions sufficient to cast doubt on the supposition that the probability of a breakdown is the same for all k types of meters?

Example: There are (approximately) equal numbers of four different types of meters in service. If all types are equally likely to break down, the reported failures during a given period should be distributed (approximately) equally among the four types — i.e.,

$$P_1 = P_2 = P_3 = P_4 = \frac{1}{4}.$$

The actual number of breakdowns reported are given in the following list. Have we evidence to conclude that the chances of failure of the four types are not all equal?

Type of Meter	No. of Breakdowns Reported n_i
1	30
2	40
3	33
4	47
	$n = 150$

Procedure	**Example**
(1) Choose α, the significance level of the test.	(1) Let $\alpha = .10$ $1 - \alpha = .90$
(2) Look up $\chi^2_{1-\alpha}$ for $k - 1$ degrees of freedom in Table A-3.	(2) $k - 1 = 3$ $\chi^2_{.90}$ for 3 d.f. $= 6.25$
(3) Compute nP_i, the theoretical frequency for each category.	(3) For a convenient computational arrangement, see Table 9-2.
(4) Compute $$\chi^2 = \sum_{i=1}^{k} (n_i^2/nP_i) - n$$	(4) See Table 9-2, $$\chi^2 = 4.62$$
(5) If $\chi^2 \geq \chi^2_{1-\alpha}$, conclude that the probabilities of failure are not the same for all of the types*; otherwise, that there is no reason to believe that they differ.	(5) Since χ^2 is not larger than $\chi^2_{.90}$, we have no reason to discard the hypothesis that the probability of failure is the same for each type.

TABLE 9-2. COMPUTATIONAL ARRANGEMENT FOR DATA SAMPLE 9-1.2

Type of Meter	No. of Breakdowns Reported (n_i)	Expected No. of Breakdowns (nP_i)	$\dfrac{n_i^2}{nP_i}$
1	30	37.5	24.00
2	40	37.5	42.67
3	33	37.5	29.04
4	47	37.5	58.91
Total	$n = 150$		154.62

P_i = the theoretical proportion for each category. In Data Sample 9-1.2, $P_i = .25$ for all categories.
$\chi^2 = \Sigma(n_i^2/nP_i) - n = 154.62 - 150 = 4.62$.

---

* In reaching this conclusion on the basis of evidence that the P's are not all equal to their theoretical values, we are assuming, of course, that our information on the numbers of meters of each type in service is correct. In practice, this assumption should be checked before accepting the conclusion that the probabilities of failure are not the same for all of the types.

9-2 COMPARING TWO OR MORE MATERIALS OR PRODUCTS

Data Sample 9-2 — Causes of Rejection of Metal Castings

Form: There are m things to be compared with regard to the percentage of items distributed among several categories.   The m things may be materials, products, processes, shifts, time periods (days, weeks, months, etc.) or any other such groups of interest.   From each of the m groups, a sample is available, and each item in the sample is classified into one of k categories.   The data is tabulated conveniently in the following form:

Material, Product, or Process	Category				Total
	1	2	. . .	k	
1	f_{11}	f_{12}	. . .	f_{1k}	n_1
2	f_{21}	f_{22}	. . .	f_{2k}	n_2
.	.	.		.	.
.	.	.		.	.
.	.	.		.	.
m	f_{m1}	f_{m2}	. . .	f_{mk}	n_m
Total	C_1	C_2	. . .	C_k	n

where:
  m = number of materials, products, processes, etc., to be compared;
  k = number of categories of classification;
  n_i = size of sample for the ith material, product, or process;
  f_{ij} = number of items of the ith kind which are classified in the jth category;
  C_j = total number in the jth category;
  n = total number of items.

The relevant question to be asked is: "Do the materials, products, etc., *differ* with regard to the proportion of items in the categories?"

Example: Rejects of metal castings were classified by cause of rejection for three different weeks, as given in the following tabulation.   The question to be answered is: Does the distribution of rejects differ from week to week?

	Cause of Rejection							
	Sand	Misrun	Shift	Drop	Corebreak	Broken	Other	Total
Week 1	97	8	18	8	23	21	5	180
Week 2	120	15	12	13	21	17	15	213
Week 3	82	4	0	12	38	25	19	180
Total	299	27	30	33	82	63	39	573

Data adapted with permission from *Industrial Quality Control*, Vol. IV, No. 4, p. 26, 1948, from article entitled "A Training Program Becomes a Clinic," by George A. Hunt.

Procedure*	**Example**

(1) Choose α, the significance level of the test.

(2) Look up $\chi^2_{1-\alpha}$ for $(k-1)(m-1)$ degrees of freedom in Table A-3.

(3) Compute

$$\chi^2 = n\left(\sum_{i=1}^{m}\sum_{j=1}^{k}\frac{f_{ij}^2}{n_i C_j} - 1\right)$$

That is, compute each column total C_j. Compute each row total n_i. For each cell in the table, square the number f_{ij} and divide by the product $n_i C_j$. Sum the resulting values for all cells in the table; subtract one, and multiply by n.

(4) If $\chi^2 \geq \chi^2_{1-\alpha}$, decide that the materials, products, or processes differ with regard to the proportions in the categories; otherwise, that there is no reason to believe that they differ in this regard.

(1) Let
$$\alpha = .10$$
$$1 - \alpha = .90$$

(2)
$$k = 7$$
$$m = 3$$
$$(k-1)(m-1) = 12$$
$$\chi^2_{.90} \text{ for 12 d.f.} = 18.55$$

(3) See Table 9-3 for a convenient computational arrangement.
$$\chi^2 = 45.84$$

(4) Since χ^2 is larger than $\chi^2_{.90}$, we conclude that the weeks differ with regard to proportions of various types of rejections.

TABLE 9-3. TABLE OF $\frac{f_{ij}^2}{n_i C_j}$ — COMPUTATIONAL ARRANGEMENT FOR DATA SAMPLE 9-2

	Sand	Misrun	Shift	Drop	Corebreak	Broken	Other	Total
Week 1	$\frac{9409}{53820}$ = 0.175	$\frac{64}{4860}$ = 0.013	$\frac{324}{5400}$ = 0.060	$\frac{64}{5940}$ = 0.011	$\frac{529}{14760}$ = 0.036	$\frac{441}{11340}$ = 0.039	$\frac{25}{7020}$ = 0.004	0.338
Week 2	$\frac{14400}{63687}$ = 0.226	$\frac{225}{5751}$ = 0.039	$\frac{144}{6390}$ = 0.023	$\frac{169}{7029}$ = 0.024	$\frac{441}{17466}$ = 0.025	$\frac{289}{13419}$ = 0.022	$\frac{225}{8307}$ = 0.027	0.386
Week 3	$\frac{6724}{53820}$ = 0.125	$\frac{16}{4860}$ = 0.003	0	$\frac{144}{5940}$ = 0.024	$\frac{1444}{14760}$ = 0.098	$\frac{625}{11340}$ = 0.055	$\frac{361}{7020}$ = 0.051	0.356
Total	0.526	0.055	0.083	0.059	0.159	0.116	0.082	1.080

$$\chi^2 = n\left(\sum_{i=1}^{m}\sum_{j=1}^{k}\frac{f_{ij}^2}{n_i C_j} - 1\right)$$
$$= 573\,(1.080 - 1)$$
$$= 573\,(.080)$$
$$= 45.84$$

---

* The solution is approximate, but should be quite accurate if the smallest $n_i C_j/n \geq 5$.

Simplified Computation for the Special Case $m = 2$. In this case, the tabulation would consist of only the first two rows of the schematic table shown in Data Sample 9-2, and

$$\chi^2 = \sum_{j=1}^{k} \left[\frac{n_1 n_2}{f_{1j} + f_{2j}} \left(\frac{f_{1j}}{n_1} - \frac{f_{2j}}{n_2} \right)^2 \right].$$

The degrees of freedom for χ^2 is $k - 1$.

This form is convenient if the data are given in terms of proportions.

Further Simplification for $m = 2$ When $n_1 = n_2$. When there are only two rows, and the row totals are equal, then,

$$\chi^2 = \sum_{j=1}^{k} \frac{(f_{1j} - f_{2j})^2}{f_{1j} + f_{2j}}$$

with $k - 1$ degrees of freedom.

Note: This shortcut has an analog for $m = 3$ when $n_1 = n_2 = n_3$. For each category, take all three possible differences, sum the squares of the three differences, and divide by the sum of the three observations. Finally, sum this quantity over all of the categories, to obtain

$$\chi^2 = \sum_{j=1}^{k} \frac{(f_{1j} - f_{2j})^2 + (f_{1j} - f_{3j})^2 + (f_{2j} - f_{3j})^2}{f_{1j} + f_{2j} + f_{3j}}.$$

9-3   A TEST OF ASSOCIATION BETWEEN TWO METHODS OF CLASSIFICATION

There are situations in which individual items are classified into categories in terms of two different criteria. For example, in a study of tire wear, see Swan,[1] records of scrapping of tires were kept and tires were classified as front and rear, left and right. In another study of the cause of failure of vacuum tubes, see Day,[2] the two criteria of classification were position in shell and type of failure. In each study the question was: Is there any association or relation between the criteria of classification?

Basically, this is a different problem than the problem of Paragraph 9-2, but it is discussed here because of the similarity in analysis.

We assume that we have a total of n individual items, and that each item is classified by criteria A and B into k and m categories, respectively. Let f_{ij} be the number of individuals in the ith category of A *and* the jth category of B. Let R_i and C_j be the total numbers of individuals classified in the ith category of A and the jth category of B, respectively.

We tabulate these data as follows:

		Criterion B				Total
		1	2	...	k	
Criterion A	1	f_{11}	f_{12}	...	f_{1k}	R_1
	2	f_{21}	f_{22}	...	f_{2k}	R_2
	.	.	.		.	.
	.	.	.		.	.
	.	.	.		.	.
	m	f_{m1}	f_{m2}	...	f_{mk}	R_m
Total		C_1	C_2	...	C_k	n

The relevant question to be asked is: "Is there a relation or association between the two criteria of classification?"

Data Sample 9-3 — Vacuum Tube Failures

In the development of the VT fuze during World War II, a study was made of the causes of failure of vacuum tubes. The criteria of classification were: position in shell and type of failure. The following entries are the number of tubes that failed.

Position in Shell	Type of Failure			Total
	A	B	C	
Top block	75	10	15	$100 = R_1$
Bottom block	40	30	10	$80 = R_2$
Total	115	40	25	$180 = n$

Adapted with permission from *Review of the International Statistical Institute*, Vol. 17, Nos. 3 and 4, pp. 129-155, 1949, from article entitled "Application of Statistical Methods to Research and Development in Engineering" by Besse B. Day.

The question to be asked is: Is the type of tube failure associated with the position in the shell?

Procedure*	Example
(1) Choose α, the level of significance of the test.	(1) Let $\alpha = .10$ $1 - \alpha = .90$
(2) Look up $\chi^2_{1-\alpha}$ for $(k - 1)(m - 1)$ degrees of freedom in Table A-3.	(2) $k = 3$ $m = 2$ $(k - 1)(m - 1) = (2)(1)$ $= 2$ $\chi^2_{.90}$ for 2 d.f. $= 4.61$

---

* The solution is approximate, but should be quite accurate if the smallest of $R_i C_j / n \geq 5.0$.

Procedure	Example

Procedure

(3) Compute

$$\chi^2 = n \left(\sum_{i=1}^{m} \sum_{j=1}^{k} \frac{f_{ij}^2}{R_i C_j} - 1 \right)$$

That is, compute each row total R_i. Compute each column total C_j. For each cell in the table, square the number f_{ij} and divide by the product $R_i C_j$. Sum the resulting values for all cells in the table; subtract one, and multiply by n.

(4) If $\chi^2 \geq \chi_{1-\alpha}^2$, conclude that there is an association between the two criteria of classification; otherwise, that there is no reason to believe that such an association exists.

Example

(3) See Table 9-4 for a computational arrangement.

$$\chi^2 = 180 \,(1.1092 - 1)$$
$$= 19.66$$

(4) Since χ^2 is greater than $\chi_{.90}^2$, we conclude that the type of failure is associated with the position in the shell.

TABLE 9-4. TABLE OF $\dfrac{f_{ij}^2}{R_i C_j}$ — COMPUTATIONAL ARRANGEMENT FOR DATA SAMPLE 9-3

Position in Shell	Type of Failure			Total
	A	**B**	**C**	
Top block	5625/11500 = .4891	100/4000 = .0250	225/2500 = .0900	.6041
Bottom block	1600/9200 = .1739	900/3200 = .2812	100/2000 = .0500	.5051
Total	.6630	.3062	.1400	1.1092

$$\chi^2 = n \left(\sum_{i=1}^{m} \sum_{j=1}^{k} \frac{f_{ij}^2}{R_i C_j} - 1 \right)$$
$$= 180 \,(1.1092 - 1)$$
$$= 180 \,(.1092)$$
$$= 19.66$$

REFERENCES

1. A. W. Swan, "The χ^2 Significance Test — Expected vs. Observed Results," *The Engineer*, Vol. 186, No. 4849, p. 679, December 31, 1948.
2. B. B. Day, "Application of Statistical Methods to Research and Development in Engineering," *Review of the International Statistical Institute*, Vol. 17, Nos. 3 and 4, pp. 129-155, 1949.

CHAPTER 10

SENSITIVITY TESTING

10-1 EXPERIMENTAL SITUATION

The term "sensitivity test" is commonly applied to the following situation:

1. A test item will *respond* or *not respond* to a certain level of test stimulus (e.g., a shell will explode or will not explode when subjected to a certain shock).

2. The test is *destructive* to the item being tested, no matter what the outcome of the test. Either the item is destroyed completely, or the characteristics of the item are so changed that further tests are meaningless.

3. The percentage of items expected to *respond* (fail, explode, die) increases as the severity of the test is increased.

In this general situation, there are variable (and usually controllable) levels of test which can be applied; e.g., height of drop in a shock test, dosage of a poison in tests of insecticides, etc. We assume that each object has an associated critical level or threshold value. If the test stimulus applied equals or exceeds this critical level, the object responds (fails, explodes, dies). If the test stimulus applied does not equal or exceed this critical level, the object does not respond. For any particular object, the *exact* critical level cannot be determined. More than one object may be tested at a given test level, however, and inferences may be made about the distribution of critical levels in a population of objects from which the tested samples came.

The experimenter obtains data of the following type: objects were tested at the k stimulus levels $x_1, x_2, \ldots, x_k$; of the n_i objects tested at level x_i, r_i responded and $n_i - r_i$ did not respond.

An ordnance example might involve the detonation of samples of an explosive in powder form by dropping a specified weight on them from various heights. If the weight is dropped from a height below the sample's critical level (in this case, the lowest height at which the weight will cause the sample to explode), the sample does not explode, but the powder may be packed more tightly than before and, therefore, the test cannot be repeated at increased height. If the weight is dropped from above the sample's critical level, the sample is destroyed.

A partial list of the many ordnance problem areas in which tests of increased severity can be used is as follows.

1. Sensitivity to mechanical shock:
   a. Impact tests of high explosives;
   b. Impact tests of artillery fuzes;
   c. Izod impact test of metals;
   d. Izod impact test of plastics;
   e. Impact or drop test of packing cases.

2. High explosives sensitivity to setback pressures.

3. Missile components sensitivity to acceleration.

4. Explosives sensitivity to friction.

5. Fuzes and explosives sensitivity to velocity.

6. Artillery fuzes and missile components sensitivity to voltage.

7. Pyrotechnic materials sensitivity to electric spark.

8. Explosives and missile components sensitivity to temperature.

The following ordnance example is used to illustrate the computational techniques.

Data Sample 10-1 — Peak-Voltage Test of Fuzes

Groups of fuzes are subjected to specified values of peak voltage.

For each group we observe the number which fire in less than a specified time. The observations are summarized as follows:

Peak Voltage	n	r	$p = r/n$
10.0	12	0	0
15.0	12	0	0
17.5	12	1	.08
20.0	13	2	.15
22.5	10	3	.30
25.0	13	6	.46
30.0	12	8	.67
35.0	13	9	.69
40.0	13	11	.85
50.0	11	10	.91
60.0	11	11	1.00

Several methods for collecting and analyzing such data are described and illustrated in this Chapter. Paragraphs 10-2 and 10-3 detail methods of analysis for the usual testing situation, where the levels of test are assigned before the test begins. Paragraph 10-4 details a special method applicable when the test levels can be different for each successive object tested, and can be changed easily during the course of the experiment. Paragraph 10-5 discusses the situation where the test levels cannot be completely controlled.

Most of the methods involve assumptions about the distribution of the critical levels such as, for example, that the distribution is *normal*. The distribution of critical levels as measured in the original units (or *natural* units) may not meet these assumptions, but there may exist a transformation such that the distribution of the transformed values does meet the assumption. The logarithm of the original value is perhaps the most frequently used transformation.

When a transformation is used, all comments on the selection of testing levels and all computational instructions refer to the transformed values, not the original ones. Usually, however, it is desirable to state the final results of the analysis in terms of the original units. For most transformations (including the logarithmic), the percentile estimates* and their associated confidence intervals are converted into the original units easily. Suppose that the stimulus levels are originally measured in "y" units, and transformed values, e.g., $x = \log y$, are used in the computations. If $\hat{x}_P$ is an estimate of x_P, as here defined,* and [a, b] is a $1 - \alpha$ confidence interval estimate of x_P, then antilog $\hat{x}_P$ and [antilog a, antilog b] give, respectively, a point estimate and a $1 - \alpha$ confidence interval estimate of y_P, the $(100\,P)$th percentile of the distribution of y values. This relationship does *not* hold for the means and standard deviations of the distributions. If m and s are estimates of the mean and standard deviation of the distribution of the x values, antilog m and antilog s should not be considered estimates of the (arithmetic) mean and standard deviation of the distributions of y's.†

Note: In this Chapter, *normal* means that the expected proportion of items responding at a stimulus level x is given by

$$P(x) = \frac{1}{\sigma\sqrt{2\pi}} \int_{-\infty}^{x} e^{-(x-\mu)^2/2\sigma^2}\, dx,$$

i.e., the probability that an individual item has a critical level or threshold value $\leq x$.

---

* For any random variable X, the "$(100\,P)$th percentile" of its distribution is the value x_P such that the probability that X is $\leq x_P$ is equal to P.

† If $x = \log y$, then

$$\bar{x} = \frac{1}{n} \sum_{i=1}^{n} \log y_i$$

$$= \log (y_1 y_2 \ldots y_n)^{\frac{1}{n}}$$

= log (geometric mean of the y's).

Hence, antilog m will be an estimate of the *geometric mean* of the distribution of the y's. Since the geometric mean of a set of different numbers always is less than their arithmetic mean, it follows that antilog m will tend to underestimate the population mean of the y's.

10-2 KÄRBER METHOD OF ANALYSIS

This method gives simple nonparametric estimates of the mean and standard deviation of the distribution of critical levels. There are three situations for which this method might be chosen:

(1) the shape or mathematical form of the distribution is unknown;

(2) quick and easy procedures for routine laboratory calculations are desired; and,

(3) good *initial estimates* or *first approximations* are needed for iterative computational procedures; for example, the Exact Probit Solution given in Paragraph 10-3.2.

The Kärber method provides very good estimates of the mean and standard deviation of the distribution of critical levels in most laboratory situations. It must be remembered that the Kärber method gives an estimate of the mean of the distribution; the mean of the distribution is not equal to the 50th percentile (that level x_0

such that half the objects have critical levels less than x_0 and half have critical levels greater than x_0) unless it is known that the distribution is symmetrical about its mean.

For further discussion of the Kärber method, see Cornfield and Mantel.[1]

Selection of Stimulus Levels. Order the stimulus levels to be used in the test by their magnitude — in other words, let $x_1 < x_2 < \ldots < x_k$. For the Kärber method to be applicable, x_1 must be sufficiently low that there are no responses among the objects tested ($r_1 = 0$), and x_k must be sufficiently high that all objects tested respond ($r_k = n_k$). In other words, x_1 and x_k are to be chosen so that they are likely to cover the entire range of critical levels in the population. In addition, it is preferable to have more (and consequently, more closely spaced) test levels with fewer objects tested at each level than to have only a few test levels and a large number of objects tested at each level.

Note: The following segments of Chapter 10 are paged and spaced as necessary to allow a facing-page arrangement of Procedures and Examples. Thus, Procedure steps appear on left-hand pages, and their associated Example steps appear on facing right-hand pages. The only exception is in Paragraph 10-3.3, where both the Procedure and Example are complete on the same page.

10-2.1 GENERAL SOLUTION FOR THE KÄRBER METHOD

10-2.1.1 Procedure. Prepare a table with nine columns headed x, n, r, p, $(p_{i+1} - p_i)$, a, a^2, d, and d^2. (See Table 10-1.)

(1) In column 1, enter the stimulus levels used in the test from lowest to highest — that is, enter $x_1, x_2, \ldots, x_k$ where $x_1 < x_2 < \ldots < x_k$.

(2) In columns 2 and 3, for each x_i, enter the corresponding n_i (number of objects tested at that level) and r_i (number of responses).

(3) Corresponding to each x, compute $p_i = \dfrac{r_i}{n_i}$ and enter this in column 4. (Remember that p_1 must equal 0 and p_k must equal 1 if this solution is to be used.)

(4) Corresponding to each x_i (except x_k), compute $p_{i+1} - p_i$ and enter in column 5. There is no entry in this column corresponding to x_k.

(5) Corresponding to each x_i (except x_k), compute $a_i = \dfrac{x_{i+1} + x_i}{2}$, the midpoint of the interval from x_i to x_{i+1}. Tabulate the a_i values in column 6. There is no entry in this column corresponding to x_k.

(6) Corresponding to each a_i, enter a_i^2 in column 7.

(7) Corresponding to each x_i (except x_k), compute $d_i = x_{i+1} - x_i$, the length of the interval from x_i to x_{i+1}. Tabulate the d_i values in column 8. There is no entry in this column corresponding to x_k.

(8) Corresponding to each d_i, enter d_i^2 in column 9.

(9) Compute $m = \Sigma(p_{i+1} - p_i)a_i$, the sum of products of corresponding entries in the 5th and 6th columns. m is our estimate of the mean of the distribution of critical levels.

(10) Compute:

$S_1 = \Sigma(p_{i+1} - p_i)a_i^2$, the sum of products of corresponding entries in the 5th and 7th columns;

$S_2 = \Sigma(p_{i+1} - p_i)d_i^2$, the sum of products of corresponding entries in the 5th and 9th columns;

$$s^2 = S_1 - m^2 - \frac{S_2}{12}.$$

s is our estimate of the standard deviation of the distribution of critical levels.

10-2.1.2 Example. The observations of Data Sample 10-1 are used to illustrate the Procedure. The problem is to estimate the mean and standard deviation of the distribution of critical values of peak voltage. In this example, we assume that nothing is known about the distribution of critical levels, and the computations are performed in natural units. If the distribution of critical levels were known or presumed to be log-normal, and if the Kärber method were being used to provide a quick and easy answer, or to provide initial estimates for the exact probit solution (Paragraph 10-3.2), then the computations would have been performed on the transformed values $x = \log$ (peak voltage).

The entries and calculations of Steps (1) through (8) of the Procedure are shown in columns 1 through 9 of Table 10-1. The calculations of Steps (9) and (10) are shown at the bottom of Table 10-1.

TABLE 10-1. KÄRBER METHOD OF ANALYSIS FOR FUZE PEAK VOLTAGE TEST DATA (SEE DATA SAMPLE 10-1)

Level of Stimulus, Peak Voltage x	Number of Objects Tested n	Number of Objects Responding r	r/n = p	$p_{i+1} - p_i$	a	a^2	d	d^2
Col. (1)	(2)	(3)	(4)	(5)	(6)	(7)	(8)	(9)
10.0	12	0	0	0	12.50	156.25	5.0	25.00
15.0	12	0	0	.08	16.25	264.06	2.5	6.25
17.5	12	1	.08	.07	18.75	351.56	2.5	6.25
20.0	13	2	.15	.15	21.25	451.56	2.5	6.25
22.5	10	3	.30	.16	23.75	564.06	2.5	6.25
25.0	13	6	.46	.21	27.50	756.25	5.0	25.00
30.0	12	8	.67	.02	32.50	1056.25	5.0	25.00
35.0	13	9	.69	.16	37.50	1406.25	5.0	25.00
40.0	13	11	.85	.06	45.00	2025.00	10.0	100.00
50.0	11	10	.91	.09	55.00	3025.00	10.0	100.00
60.0	11	11	1.00					

Step (9): $m = \Sigma (p_{i+1} - p_i) a_i$
= 29.68
= mean value of critical peak voltage.

Step (10): $S_1 = \Sigma (p_{i+1} - p_i) a_i^2$
= 1002.4051

$S_2 = \Sigma (p_{i+1} - p_i) d_i^2$
= 27.6250

$s^2 = S_1 - m^2 - (S_2/12)$
= 1002.4051 - 880.9024 - 2.3021
= 119.2006

$s = 10.92$
= estimated standard deviation of critical peak voltage.

10-5

10-2.2 SIMPLIFIED SOLUTION (KÄRBER METHOD) FOR THE SPECIAL CASE WHEN TEST LEVELS ARE EQUALLY SPACED AND EQUAL NUMBERS OF ITEMS ARE TESTED AT EACH LEVEL

10-2.2.1 Procedure. Prepare a table with columns headed x, r, p, and cumulative p. (See Table 10-2.)

(1) In the x column, enter the test levels from lowest to highest, i.e., enter x_1, x_2, $\ldots$, x_k, where $x_1 < x_2 < \ldots < x_k$.

(2) Enter r_i, the number of objects responding at each x_i.

(3) Corresponding to each x_i, compute $p_i = r_i/n$. (n is the number of objects tested at each level and is the same for all levels). Remember that p_1 must equal 0 and p_k must equal 1 for this solution to be used.

(4) In the last column, enter the cumulative p, i.e., at x_i, the sum of all p up to and including p_i.

(5) Let: x_k = highest test level.
　　　　d = interval between successive test levels.
　　　　S_1 = sum of column p.
　　　　S_2 = sum of column cumulative p.

(6) Compute $m = x_k - d(S_1 - \tfrac{1}{2})$.

(7) Compute $s^2 = d^2(2S_2 - S_1 - S_1^2 - \tfrac{1}{12})$.

10-2.2.2 Example. In order to demonstrate the computing procedure, the fuze data (Data Sample 10-1) have been changed arbitrarily, to have equal spacing in x and equal numbers of objects at each level. Assume that 12 objects were tested at each level, and that the responses were as shown in Table 10-2. Steps (1) through (4) of the Procedure consist of preparing and filling out the four columns of Table 10-2. Steps (5) through (7) are shown at the bottom of Table 10-2.

TABLE 10-2. SIMPLIFIED SOLUTION FOR THE KÄRBER METHOD OF ANALYSIS WHEN THE TEST LEVELS (x) ARE EQUALLY SPACED AND EQUAL NUMBERS OF OBJECTS (n) ARE TESTED AT EACH LEVEL

Peak Voltage x	Number of Objects Responding r	Proportion of Objects Responding $p = r/12$	Cumulative Proportion
10.0	0	0	0
15.0	0	0	0
20.0	2	.17	.17
25.0	6	.50	.67
30.0	8	.67	1.34
35.0	9	.75	2.09
40.0	10	.83	2.92
45.0	10	.83	3.75
50.0	11	.92	4.67
55.0	12	1.00	5.67
		$S_1 = 5.67$	$S_2 = 21.28$

Step (5) x_k = highest test level
   = 55
   d = interval in x
   = 5
   S_1 = sum of p
   = 5.67
   S_2 = sum of cumulative p
   = 21.28

Step (6) $m = x_k - d(S_1 - \frac{1}{2})$
   $= 55 - 5(5.67 - .50)$
   $= 29.15$
   = mean value of critical peak voltage.

Step (7) $s^2 = d^2(2S_2 - S_1 - S_1^2 - \frac{1}{12})$
   $= 25(42.56 - 5.67 - 32.15 - .08)$
   $= 116.50$
   $s = 10.79$
   = estimated standard deviation of critical peak voltage.

10-3 PROBIT METHOD OF ANALYSIS

When it is assumed that the distribution of critical levels is of a particular type, methods for estimating the properties of the distribution are tailored to it. There are three types of distributions for sensitivity data that have been studied extensively in the statistical literature — the *normal*, the *logistic*, and the *angular*. Only the *normal* will be discussed in detail here because it is most frequently used in ordnance sensitivity testing. For the *logistic*, see Berkson[2] and Hodges,[3] for the *angular*, see Knudsen and Curtis[4] and Fisher and Yates.[5] When the stimulus levels used in the test are between the levels which cut off the lower and upper 10% of the distribution (most testing is performed in this range), any one of these types will fit the data nearly as well (or as poorly) as another, no matter what the true distribution of critical levels is. However, estimates of the parameters of the *logistic* or the *angular* distributions involve simpler computations than are given here for the *normal*; for example, see the technique described in Hodges[3] for the logistic curve.

The procedures described here assume that the distribution of critical values is *normal* — that is, for all x the proportion of objects which have critical levels between x and $x + dx$ is equal to the area of some *normal* curve between x and $x + dx$. In general, the procedures are not very sensitive to moderate departures from normality, provided one does not extrapolate beyond the range of the data.

The problem may be summarized as follows: k different levels $x_1, x_2, \ldots, x_k$ of a stimulus are applied to $n_1, n_2, \ldots, n_k$ objects, with $r_1, r_2, \ldots, r_k$ responses, respectively. Let $p_i = r_i/n_i$. The questions to be answered are:

(1) At what level m of the stimulus would half of similar objects be expected to respond? Or equivalently, under the assumption of normality, what is the mean of the critical levels of all such objects?

(2) Estimate the relation between the level of the stimulus and the proportion of objects responding.

Selection of Stimulus Levels.   There are no simple cut-and-dried rules. A general guide can be given in terms of the purpose of the experiment:

(1) If the experimenter is interested in estimating a specific percentage point, the stimulus levels to be used in the test should be fairly close to that point, and should bracket the point. It is pertinent here to emphasize that extrapolations may lead to serious error, particularly if the experimenter attempts to estimate an extreme percentage point (say, the 5% or 99% point) from observations at stimulus levels which all lie to one side of that point.

(2) The test levels should cover a range sufficiently wide so that the proportion responding p_i varies from near 0 to near 1, if:

(a) One is interested in the relation between stimulus level and percentage response over the entire range; or,

(b) One is interested in estimating the standard deviation of the distribution of critical levels (or equivalently, the slope of the regression line in the probit solution); or,

(c) One is interested in testing the assumption of *normality*.

Basis of the Method.   If the critical levels are normally distributed (with unknown mean μ and standard deviation σ), then Y_i', which can be determined from tables of the normal integral, is a linear function of the corresponding stimulus level x_i.

Y_i' is determined from:

$$p_i = \int_{-\infty}^{Y_i'-5} \frac{1}{\sqrt{2\pi}} \, e^{-v^2/2} \, dy \, .$$

The "5" in the upper limit of the integral is introduced for computational convenience.

Least squares procedures are used to estimate the best straight line passing through the k points (Y_i', x_i).   The formulas take account of the fact that the points do not have equal weights.   The line will be expressed as

$$Y_p = 5 + b(x - m)$$

where m and b are estimated from the data, x is the stimulus level, and Y_p is related to p, the probability that an object's critical level is $\leq x$, by the formula

$$\int_{-\infty}^{Y_p-5} \frac{1}{\sqrt{2\pi}} \, e^{-v^2/2} \, dy = p \, .$$

m is an estimate of μ (the mean and 50th percentile of the underlying *normal* distribution), and b is an estimate of $1/\sigma$ (the reciprocal of the standard deviation of the critical values).

Solutions Described.   We describe two methods of solution: the graphical probit method in Paragraph 10-3.1; and the computational (*exact*) probit method in Paragraph 10-3.2.   The graphical method is much simpler, and is sufficiently precise for many purposes.   When a more accurate solution is desired, the graphical method furnishes a first approximation for the exact probit method.

10-3.1 GRAPHICAL PROBIT SOLUTION

10-3.1.1 Procedure. To facilitate the calculations, prepare a table with nine columns, headed respectively, x, n, r, p, Y', Y, W, nW, nWx. (See Table 10-3.)

(1) In column x, enter the levels x_1, x_2, ..., x_k used in the experiment.

(2) In columns n and r, record the values of n_i and r_i, corresponding to x_i.

(3) In column p, compute the respective proportions responding, $p_i = r_i/n_i$.

(4) Use Table A-2 to obtain z_p corresponding to p. In column Y', enter $Y' = z_p + 5$ corresponding to each p.

(5) Plot Y' as ordinate against x as abscissa, on ordinary rectangular coordinate graph paper. See Figure 10-1. If probit paper * is available, it can be used, and the column Y' is omitted from the table. The percentages responding at each x (% response $= 100\ p_i$) are plotted on probit paper, using the left vertical scale; the right vertical scale gives the corresponding z_p, and hence the corresponding Y minus 5.

(6) Whichever graph paper is used, draw a straight line by eye to fit the k points. Only vertical deviations from the line are to be considered in fitting; and points for which the value of Y' is outside the interval 2.5 to 7.5 may almost be disregarded unless n_i for those points is much larger than for points inside the interval. (Points outside this interval are beyond the range of the probit paper).

(7) For each value of x plotted on the graph, read the ordinate Y of the line (on probit scale if on probit paper), and record the values in the Y column of the table.†

---

* "Probit paper" also is called "normal deviate paper", "normal ruling", etc.

† Instead of reading the Y values from the graph, we may complete step (8), and use the equation thus obtained to compute Y.

10-3.1.2 Example. The observations of Data Sample 10-1 were plotted on normal probability paper, using both x = peak voltage and x = $\log_{10}$ (peak voltage), as abscissa. The data plot more nearly as a straight line when transformed using the equation x = $\log_{10}$ (peak voltage); therefore, all of the probit method calculations are done on the transformed variable.   (See Table 10-3.)

Steps (1) through (4) of the Procedure result in filling in the first 5 columns of Table 10-3 (through Y').

TABLE 10-3. GRAPHICAL PROBIT SOLUTION USING DATA SAMPLE 10-1

Level of Stimulus = $\log_{10}$peak Voltage x	Number of Objects Tested n	Number of Objects Responding r	Proportion of Objects Responding $p = r/n$	Y'	Y	W	nW	nWx
1.0000	12	0	0	—	2.0	.015	0.180	0.180
1.1761	12	0	0	—	3.2	.180	2.160	2.540
1.2430	12	1	.08	3.59	3.7	.336	4.032	5.012
1.3010	13	2	.15	3.96	4.1	.471	6.123	7.966
1.3522	10	3	.30	4.48	4.5	.581	5.810	7.856
1.3979	13	6	.46	4.90	4.8	.627	8.151	11.394
1.4771	12	8	.67	5.44	5.3	.616	7.392	·10.919
1.5441	13	9	.69	5.50	5.8	.503	6.539	10.097
1.6021	13	11	.85	6.04	6.2	.370	4.810	7.706
1.6990	11	10	.91	6.34	6.9	.154	1.694	2.878
1.7782	11	11	1.00	—	7.4	˙.062	0.682	1.213

$$\Sigma\, nW = 47.573$$
$$\Sigma\, nWx = 67.761$$

Steps (5) through (7) — Plot Y' against x on ordinary graph paper, as shown in Figure 10-1. A straight line is fitted to the plotted points by eye.   The ordinate Y of the line is read off at each observed x, and is entered in the Y column of Table 10-3.*

---

* Or, complete step (8), and use the equation $Y = 5 + b(x - m)$ to obtain the Y values.

10-3.1.1 Procedure (Cont)

Note: Before proceeding further, it is often desirable to determine whether the line is an adequate representation of the data. The procedure given in Paragraph 10-3.3 may be used for this purpose.

(8) Calculate b, the slope of the fitted line, as the increase in Y for a unit increase in x. Mark two convenient points, c and d, on the line. Read off the corresponding values for both x and Y.

$$x_c = \qquad\qquad\qquad Y_c =$$
$$x_d = \qquad\qquad\qquad Y_d =$$

Then $b = \dfrac{Y_d - Y_c}{x_d - x_c}$. Read off m, the value of x corresponding to $Y = 5$. (Probit $= 5$, on probit paper). We may then write the equation of the line as $Y = 5 + b(x - m)$.

(9) The relation between a given level of stimulus x' and the proportion of individuals responding p' is estimated by the relationship $z_{p'} = b(x' - m)$ where the p corresponding to $z_{p'}$ is given in Table A-1. (Or, this relationship can be read directly from the straight line drawn on probit paper.)

10-3.1.2   Example (Cont)

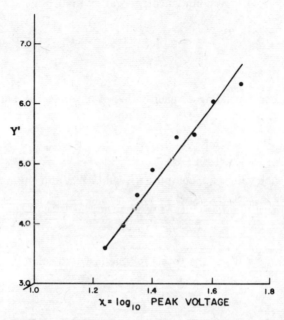

Figure 10-1. Probit regression line (fitted by eye).

Step (8) — The slope b of the line is calculated as follows:

$$x_c = 1.3 \qquad\qquad Y_c = 4.0$$
$$x_d = 1.6 \qquad\qquad Y_d = 6.0$$

$$b = \frac{Y_d - Y_c}{x_d - x_c}$$

$$= \frac{6.0 - 4.0}{0.3}$$

$$= 7$$

m (the value of x at $Y = 5$) $= 1.43$.

Equation of the line:

$$Y = 5 + b(x - m)$$
$$= 5 + 7x - 10.01$$
$$= -5.01 + 7x.$$

Step (9) — If we wish to estimate the proportion of individuals responding at a peak voltage $= 18$, for example, then:

$$x' = \log_{10} 18$$
$$= 1.255$$
$$z_{p'} = b(x' - m)$$
$$= 7(1.255 - 1.43)$$
$$= 8.785 - 10.01$$
$$= -1.22$$

$p' = .11$, the proportion which may be expected to respond at $PV = 18$.

10-3.1.1 Procedure (Cont)

m is our estimate of μ, the stimulus level at which we would expect half of similar individuals to respond.   A $(1 - \alpha)$ confidence interval estimate of μ may be computed as follows:

(10) Look up $z_{1-\alpha/2}$ in Table A-2.

(11) In the column W, corresponding to each value of Y, enter the value of W obtained from Table A-18.

(12) Corresponding to each value of x, compute nW and nWx, and enter them in the last columns of the table.

(13) Compute $\Sigma n_i W_i$ and $\Sigma n_i W_i x_i$, the totals for the last two columns.

(14) Compute $s_m^2 = \dfrac{1}{b^2} \left(\dfrac{1}{\Sigma nW} \right)$, the estimate of the variance of m.   This estimate is slightly too small on the average, but the bias is negligible provided that $\bar{x} = \Sigma nWx/\Sigma nW$ is approximately equal to m.   If the two differ considerably, then the quantity

$$S_{xx} = \Sigma n_i W_i x_i^2 - (\Sigma nWx)^2/\Sigma nW$$

should be computed, and our estimate of the variance of m becomes

$$s_m^2 = \frac{1}{b^2} \left(\frac{1}{\Sigma nW} \right) + \frac{(m - \bar{x})^2}{S_{xx}} .$$

(15) A $(1 - \alpha)$ confidence interval estimate of μ is the interval from $m - z_{1-\alpha/2}\, s_m$ to $m + z_{1-\alpha/2}\, s_m$.

10-3.1.2   Example (Cont)

Steps (10) through (15) — A 95% confidence interval estimate of μ (the level at which we would expect half of the individuals to respond) is obtained as follows:

Columns W, nW, and nWx, are computed and entered in Table 10-3.

Compute:

$$\Sigma nW = 47.573$$
$$\Sigma nWx = 67.761$$
$$\bar{x} = \frac{\Sigma nWx}{\Sigma nW}$$
$$= \frac{67.761}{47.573}$$
$$= 1.424$$
$$s_m^2 = \frac{1}{b^2}\frac{1}{\Sigma nW}$$
$$= \frac{1}{49}\left(\frac{1}{47.573}\right)$$
$$= \frac{1}{2331.077}$$
$$= .000429$$
$$s_m = .0207$$

(Since $\bar{x} = 1.424$, approximately equal to m ($= 1.43$), we do not bother to use the more complicated formula for s_m^2.)

Let. $\alpha = .05$
    $z_{1-\alpha/2} = 1.96$

A 95% confidence interval estimate of μ is the interval $m \pm 1.96\, s_m = 1.43 \pm .04$, the interval from 1.39 to 1.47.

10-3.2 EXACT PROBIT SOLUTION

The graphical solution very often is adequate, but complications in the data may make this solution less satisfactory in some cases and an arithmetic technique may be necessary. For example, the points may be too irregular for us to place any confidence in a line drawn by eye; or, the weights (nW), that should be attached to each point, may be so different as to make it difficult to adjust for them visually.

10-3.2.1 Procedure. The probit solution given here involves a series of successive approximations, the first of which is given by the graphical probit solution or by the Kärber method described in Paragraph 10-2. For the exact solution, we need a table with ten columns headed, respectively, x, n, r, p, Y, W, nW, nWx, y, nWy. (See Table 10-4).

(1) In column x, enter the levels x_1, x_2, ..., x_k used in the experiment.
(2) In columns n and r, record the values of n_i and r_i, corresponding to x_i.
(3) In column p, compute the respective proportions responding $p_i = r_i/n_i$.
(4) Obtain values for column Y by either method (a) or (b):
    (a) Follow instructions (1) through (7) of the graphical probit solution in Paragraph 10-3.1 to obtain the Y-values. These then are tabulated in the table for the exact solution.
    (b) Follow instructions (1) through (10) of the Kärber method described in Paragraph 10-2 to compute m and s. For initial estimates, take $m_0 = m$, $b_0 = \dfrac{1}{s}$; and corresponding to each x_i, use the equation $Y_i = 5 + b_0(x_i - m_0)$ to compute the values for the Y column of the table for the exact solution. Unless n is very large, 1 decimal in Y is sufficient. If 2 decimals in Y should be required, Tables A-18 and A-19 in ORDP 20-114 of this Handbook are not convenient; consult Finney[6] for more extensive tables.
(5) In column W, corresponding to each value of Y, enter the value of W obtained from Table A-18.
(6) Corresponding to each value of x, compute n_iW_i and $n_iW_ix_i$, and enter them in the nW and nWx columns, respectively, of the table.
(7) Corresponding to each "expected probit" Y in the Y column, use Table A-19 to compute the "working probit" y, as follows:

$$\text{For } Y \leq 5.0, \, y = y_0 + p\left(\frac{1}{Z}\right);$$

$$\text{For } Y \geq 5.0, \, y = y_{100} - (1 - p)\left(\frac{1}{Z}\right);$$

where, for each Y, p is the corresponding entry in the p column of the Table, and Table A-19 gives the values for y_0 (or y_{100}) and $\dfrac{1}{Z}$. Tabulate the values in column y.

(8) For each value of y, calculate the value $n_iW_iy_i$, and enter it in column nWy.
(9) Compute:

$$\Sigma \, n_iW_i, \text{ the sum of column } nW$$
$$\Sigma \, n_iW_ix_i, \text{ the sum of column } nWx$$
$$\Sigma \, n_iW_iy_i, \text{ the sum of column } nWy$$
$$S_1 = \Sigma \, n_iW_ix_i^2, \text{ the sum of the products of elements in columns } x \text{ and } nWx.$$
$$S_2 = \Sigma \, n_iW_ix_iy_i, \text{ the sum of products of corresponding elements in columns } nWx \text{ and } y.$$
$$S_3 = \Sigma \, nWy^2$$
$$S_{xx} = S_1 - (\Sigma \, nWx)^2/\Sigma \, nW$$
$$S_{xy} = S_2 - (\Sigma \, nWx)(\Sigma \, nWy)/\Sigma \, nW$$
$$S_{yy} = S_3 - (\Sigma \, nWy)^2/\Sigma \, nW$$

10-3.2.2 Example. The observations of Data Sample 10-1 are used for illustration, and the line fitted graphically in Paragraph 10-3.1 is used as the first approximation.

Steps (1) through (3) consist of filling in the first four columns of Table 10-4.
Step (4) — The Y values entered are copied from the Y column of the graphical probit solution (Table 10-3). These are the ordinates of the line at each observed x.
Step (5) through (8) — fill in the remaining columns of Table 10-4.

TABLE 10-4. EXACT PROBIT SOLUTION

$\log_{10}PV$ x	No. of Objects Tested n	No. of Objects Responding r	Proportion of Objects Responding $p = r/n$	Expected Probit Y	W	nW	nWx	Working Probit y	nWy
1.0000	12	0	0	2.0	.015	0.180	0.180	1.695	0.305
1.1761	12	0	0	3.2	.180	2.160	2.540	2.745	5.929
1.2430	12	1	.08	3.7	.336	4.032	5.012	3.602	14.523
1.3010	13	2	.15	4.1	.471	6.123	7.966	3.972	24.321
1.3522	10	3	.30	4.5	.581	5.810	7.856	4.476	26.006
1.3979	13	6	.46	4.8	.627	8.151	11.394	4.900	39.940
1.4771	12	8	.67	5.3	.616	7.392	10.919	5.436	40.183
1.5441	13	9	.69	5.8	.503	6.539	10.097	5.461	35.709
1.6021	13	11	.85	6.2	.370	4.810	7.706	6.020	28.956
1.6990	11	10	.91	6.9	.154	1.694	2.878	5.966	10.106
1.7782	11	11	1.00	7.4	.062	0.682	1.213	7.766	5.296

Step (9) —
$$\Sigma nW = 47.573$$
$$\Sigma nWx = 67.761$$
$$\Sigma nWy = 231.274$$
$$S_1 = \Sigma nWx^2 = 97.4232$$
$$S_2 = \Sigma nWxy = 335.4415$$
$$S_{xx} = S_1 - (\Sigma nWx)^2/\Sigma nW = 0.9073$$
$$S_{xy} = S_2 - (\Sigma nWx)(\Sigma nWy)/\Sigma nW = 6.0244$$

10-17

10-3.2.1   Procedure (Cont)

(10) Compute:

$$b = S_{xy}/S_{xx}$$
$$\bar{x} = \Sigma\, nWx/\Sigma\, nW$$
$$\bar{y} = \Sigma\, nW_y/\Sigma\, nW$$

The equation of the probit regression line is

$$Y = \bar{y} + b(x - \bar{x}).$$

The procedure for obtaining the *best* line is an iterative one, and in theory we should repeat the above procedure until the same equation is obtained for two successive iterations.   Practically, we often may be able to see that an additional iteration will not change the equation materially.

Next Iteration:

The procedure for obtaining an additional iteration is as follows: Make a table with nine columns headed x, n, p, Y, W, nW, nWx, y, nWy.   (See Table 10-5.)

(11) Copy the three columns, x, n, p from Table 10-4.

(12) For each value of x, compute the corresponding value of Y, using the equation

$$Y = \bar{y} + b(x - \bar{x})$$

calculated in the previous iteration.

(13) Follow instructions of steps (5) through (10).

To test whether the line is a good fit to the data, use the test procedure outlined in Paragraph 10.3.3, using the $\bar{y}$, $\bar{x}$, and b obtained from the *last* iteration performed, to compute a new

$$Y = \bar{y} + b(x - \bar{x})$$

for each value of x used in the test.

10-18

10-3.2.2   Example (Cont)

Step (10) — $\bar{x} = \Sigma\, nWx/\Sigma\, nW = 1.4244$

$\bar{y} = \Sigma\, nWy/\Sigma\, nW = 4.8615$

$b = S_{xy}/S_{xx} = 6.640$

The equation of the probit regression line is

$$Y = \bar{y} + b(x - \bar{x}) = -4.5965 + 6.640\, x .$$

Next Iteration.   An additional iteration is shown in Table 10-5.   The first three columns (x, n, p) of Table 10-5 are copied from Table 10-4.   The Y column is calculated by substituting observed values of x in the equation shown in Step (10) above.   The remaining columns of Table 10-5 are filled in as described in Steps (5) through (8) of the Procedure.

TABLE 10-5.   EXACT PROBIT SOLUTION (SECOND ITERATION)

$\log_{10}PV$ x	No. of Objects Tested n	Proportion of Objects Responding $p = r/n$	Y	W	nW	nWx	y	nWy
1.0000	12	0	2.0	.015	0.180	0.180	1.695	0.305
1.1761	12	0	3.2	.180	2.160	2.540	2.745	5.929
1.2430	12	.08	3.7	.336	4.032	5.012	3.602	14.523
1.3010	13	.15	4.0	.439	5.707	7.425	3.964	22.623
1.3522	10	.30	4.4	.558	5.580	7.545	4.477	24.982
1.3979	13	.46	4.7	.616	8.008	11.194	4.904	39.271
1.4771	12	.67	5.2	.627	7.524	11.114	5.432	40.870
1.5441	13	.69	5.7	.532	6.916	10.679	5.482	37.914
1.6021	13	.85	6.0	.439	5.707	9.143	6.036	34.447
1.6990	11	.91	6.7	.208	2.288	3.887	6.217	14.224
1.7782	11	1.00	7.2	.092	1.012	1.800	7.592	7.683

Step (9) — $\Sigma\, nW = 49.114$

$\Sigma\, nWx = 70.519$

$\Sigma\, nWy = 242.771$

$S_1 = \Sigma\, nWx^2 = 102.2663$

$S_2 = \Sigma\, nWxy = 355.3694$

$S_3 = \Sigma\, nWy^2 = 1247.7433$

$S_{xx} = 1.0135$

$S_{xy} = 6.7983$

$S_{yy} = 47.7238$

Step (10) — $\bar{x} = \Sigma\, nWx/\Sigma\, nW$

$= 1.4358$

$\bar{y} = \Sigma\, nWy/\Sigma\, nW$

$= 4.943$

$b = S_{xy}/S_{xx}$

$= 6.703$

The equation of the probit regression line is:

$$Y = \bar{y} + b(x - \bar{x}) = -4.6812 + 6.703\, x .$$

Using this equation to calculate values of Y, the Y values obtained differ very little from those obtained on the first iteration, and no further iterations are considered necessary.

10-3.3 TESTING WHETHER THE LINE IS AN ADEQUATE REPRESENTATION OF THE DATA

10-3.3.1 Procedure. To facilitate the calculations, we require a table with ten columns: x, n, r, Y, P, nP, $1 - P$, $nP(1 - P)$, $r - nP$, and $\dfrac{(r - nP)^2}{nP(1 - P)}$. See Table 10-6.

(1) Choose α, the level of significance of the test. In columns x, n, r, copy the values from the probit solution table. If the graphical probit solution was used, copy the Y column of that table as the Y column here. If the exact probit solution was used, use the $\bar{y}$, $\bar{x}$, and b obtained from the last iteration performed to compute, corresponding to each x,

$$Y = \bar{y} + b(x - \bar{x})$$

and tabulate these values in the Y column here.

(2) Look up $\chi^2_{1-\alpha}$ for $k - 2$ degrees of freedom in Table A-3. k = number of rows in the table (see Table 10-6).

(3) Put $z_P = Y - 5$, and for each Y, using Table A-1, obtain the value of P corresponding to z_P.

(4) Compute the required quantities in the last columns of the table.

(5) Obtain $\chi^2 = \displaystyle\sum_{i=1}^{k} \frac{(r_i - n_i P_i)^2}{n_i P_i (1 - P_i)}$, the sum of the values in the last column.

(6) If $\chi^2 \leq \chi^2_{1-\alpha}$, decide that there is no reason to believe that the line does not adequately represent the data. If $\chi^2 > \chi^2_{1-\alpha}$, decide that the straight line does not adequately describe the relation between stimulus and response. If a significant value of χ^2 is obtained, check to see whether an unusually large contribution to χ^2 comes from one class or from a few classes with very small expected values, i.e., small nP or $n(1 - P)$. If this is the case, several such classes may be combined (for details, see Finney[6]).

10-3.3.2 Example. The test of the final probit equation is shown in Table 10-6. If $\alpha = .05$, we find in Step (2) that $\chi^2_{.95}$ for 9 d.f. $= 16.92$. In Step (5), the calculated $\chi^2 = 2.37$. Since this is not larger than $\chi^2_{.95}$, we accept the fitted line.

TABLE 10-6. TEST OF LINEARITY — FINAL PROBIT EQUATION

$\log_{10} PV$ x	n	r	Y	P	nP	$1 - P$	$nP(1 - P)$	$r - nP$	$\dfrac{(r - nP)^2}{nP(1 - P)}$
1.0000	12	0	2.02	.0014	0.02	.9986	0.02	− .02	.02
1.1761	12	0	3.20	.04	0.48	.96	0.46	− .48	.50
1.2430	12	1	3.65	.09	1.08	.91	0.98	− .08	.01
1.3010	13	2	4.04	.17	2.21	.83	1.83	− .21	.02
1.3522	10	3	4.38	.27	2.70	.73	1.97	.30	.05
1.3979	13	6	4.69	.38	4.94	.62	3.06	1.06	.37
1.4771	12	8	5.22	.59	7.08	.41	2.90	.92	.29
1.5441	13	9	5.67	.75	9.75	.25	2.44	− .75	.23
1.6021	13	11	6.06	.86	11.18	.14	1.57	− .18	.02
1.6990	11	10	6.71	.96	10.56	.04	0.42	− .56	.75
1.7782	11	11	7.24	.99	10.89	.01	0.11	+ .11	.11

$$\chi^2 = 2.37$$

10-3.4 USING THE PROBIT REGRESSION LINE FOR PREDICTION

The procedures which follow describe how to use the probit regression line for estimation, including confidence interval estimates. If a *nonsignificant value* of x^2 was obtained in the test of linearity, Paragraph 10-3.3, the formulas given here are directly applicable. If a *significant value* of x^2 was obtained, these formulas do not apply without adjustment. For details, see Finney.[6]

10-3.4.1 Level of Stimulus x′ At Which a Specified Proportion P′ of the Individuals Would Be Expected To Respond.

Single Estimate
   (1) Choose P'
   (2) Use Table A-2 to find $z_{P'}$ corresponding to P'
   (3) Let $Y' = 5 + z_{P'}$
   (4) Compute $x' = \bar{x} + (Y' - \bar{y})/b$.

This x' is the value at which we would expect a proportion P' of the individuals to respond.

Confidence Interval Estimate
   For a confidence interval estimate, see Finney.[6]

10-3.4.2 Level of Stimulus x′ At Which 50% of the Individuals Would Be Expected To Respond.

The estimate of μ, the mean and the 50th percentile of the distribution of critical levels, is

$$m = \bar{x} + \frac{1}{b}(5 - \bar{y}).$$

A $(1 - \alpha)$ confidence interval estimate of μ is computed as follows:*

   (1) Look up $z_{1-\alpha/2}$ in Table A-2.
   (2) Compute

$$s_m^2 = \frac{1}{b^2}\left[\frac{1}{\Sigma nW} + \frac{(m - \bar{x})^2}{S_{xx}}\right]$$

   (3) A $(1 - \alpha)$ confidence interval estimate of μ is the interval from $m - z_{1-\alpha/2}\, s_m$ to $m + z_{1-\alpha/2}\, s_m$.

10-3.4.3 Proportion of Individuals Which Would Be Expected To Respond At a Specified Level of Stimulus.
The probit regression equation $Y = \bar{y} + b(x - \bar{x})$ gives the expected value of $Y(Y')$ at a specified value of $x(x')$.

The variance of Y, s_Y^2, is given by the formula

$$s_Y^2 = \frac{1}{\Sigma nW} + \frac{(x' - \bar{x})^2}{S_{xx}}.$$

A $(1 - \alpha)$ confidence interval estimate for Y at a single specified value of x is given by the formula
$$Y' \pm t_{1-\alpha/2}\, s_Y.$$

If we want to make confidence interval statements for several values of x using the same fitted line, however, we must use the wider interval given by

$$Y' \pm \sqrt{2F}\, s_Y,$$

as discussed in Chapter 5 (see Paragraph 5-4.1.2), ORDP 20-110.

---

* This method is sufficiently good for most purposes. For an exact method, see Finney.[6]

10-4   THE UP-AND-DOWN DESIGN

The *up-and-down* design, sometimes called the "Bruceton" method, is one of a class of designs that are called *staircase methods* because the test level for the next trial or group of trials depends on the results of the preceding trial or group of trials.   In the up-and-down design, only one object is tested at a time.   Starting at a level where about 50% responses are expected, the test level is moved up one level after each non-response, and down one level after each response.   The experiment is concluded after a specified number of trials.

The use of the up-and-down design, of course, presumes that it is convenient to test one object at a time and all staircase methods presume that the results of test can be known immediately, and that the test level can be adjusted quickly and easily.

If x's represent responses, and o's represent non-responses, then the pattern of the experiment looks like this:

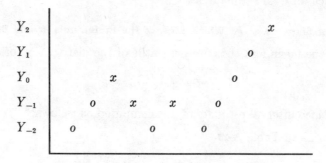

The *up-and-down* design and its analysis are described in detail here.   The Procedure assumes normal distribution of the critical levels and, in such a case, gives a more accurate estimate of the mean (which also is the 50th percentile) than any other method described in this Chapter.   For further discussion of the up-and-down method, see Brownlee, Hodges, and Rosenblatt,[7] Dixon and Massey,[8] Dixon and Mood.[9]   For a completely worked-out example of an ordnance application, see Culling.[10]   Other staircase methods are described in Anderson, McCarthy, and Tukey.[11]

The up-and-down design requires initial guesses of the mean and standard deviation of the distribution of critical levels (x_0 = guess for mean, d = guess for standard deviation).   The method of estimation makes some allowance for a poor initial guess of the mean x_0, and, in fact, is a particularly useful way of estimating the mean when the experimenter has little idea what the true mean is.   So long as the initial guess for the standard deviation is between half and twice the true standard deviation of the distribution, the method of estimation described is appropriate.

Determine equally-spaced test levels, . . . , x_{-3}, x_{-2}, x_{-1}, x_0, x_1, x_2, x_3 , . . . , so that the distance between two successive levels is d .   ($d = x_1 - x_0 = x_0 - x_{-1}$, etc.).   The first object is tested at level x_0; if it "responds," the second object is tested at level x_{-1}; if it "does not respond," the second object is tested at level x_1.   Similarly, each succeeding object is tested at the level one step below the level used in the preceding test if it resulted in a "response," or, at the level one step above the level used in the preceding test if it resulted in "no response."

Procedure. Count the total number $R = \Sigma r_i$ of responses, and let $N = \Sigma n_i$ be the total number of objects tested. If $R \leq \dfrac{N}{2}$, perform steps (1) through (6); if $R > \dfrac{N}{2}$, perform steps (1') through (6').

When $R \leq \dfrac{N}{2}$:

(1) Prepare a four-column table with columns headed y, r, j, j^2.

(2) Let: y_0 = the lowest level at which a "response" occurred
       y_1 = the level one step above y_0
       y_2 = the level two steps above y_0
       y_k = the highest level at which a "response" occurred.
     Enter $y_0, y_1, \ldots, y_k$ in column y.

(3) In column r, corresponding to each y_j, enter r_j = the number of "responses" at level y_j.

(4) Enter the numbers $0, 1, \ldots, k$, in column j.

(5) Corresponding to each entry in column j, enter its square in column j^2.

(6) Compute:
     $A = \Sigma j\, r_j$, the sum of products of corresponding entries in columns r and j.
     $B = \Sigma j^2\, r_j$, the sum of products of corresponding entries in columns r and j^2.

$$m = y_0 + d\left(\frac{A}{R} - \frac{1}{2}\right)$$

$$s = 1.620d\left(\frac{RB - A^2}{R^2} + .029\right).$$

When $R > \dfrac{N}{2}$:

(1') Prepare a four-column table with columns headed $y, n - r, j, j^2$.

(2') Let: y_0 = the lowest level at which "no response" occurred
       y_1 = the level one step above y_0
       y_2 = the level two steps above y_0
       y_k = the highest level at which "no response" occurred.
     Enter $y_0, y_1, \ldots, y_k$, in column y.

(3') In column $n - r$, corresponding to each y_j, enter $n_j - r_j$, the number of "no response" at level y_j.

(4') Enter the numbers $0, 1, \ldots, k$, in column j.

(5') Corresponding to each entry in column j, enter its square in column j^2.

(6') Compute:
     $A = \Sigma j\, (n_j - r_j)$, the sum of products of corresponding entries in columns $n - r$ and j
     $B = \Sigma j^2\, (n_j - r_j)$, the sum of products of corresponding entries in columns $n - r$ and j^2.

$$m = y_0 + d\left(\frac{A}{N - R} + \frac{1}{2}\right)$$

$$s = 1.62d\left\{\frac{(N - R)B - A^2}{(N - R)^2} + .029\right\}.$$

m is our estimate of the mean (and the 50th percentile) of the distribution of critical levels.

s is our estimate of the standard deviation of the distribution of critical levels.

10-5 SENSITIVITY TESTS WHEN THE STIMULUS LEVELS CANNOT BE CONTROLLED

The methods discussed in Paragraphs 10-2 through 10-4 assumed that the stimulus levels can be preassigned and accurately controlled. Although this is the usual case in experimental work, there are times when conditions cannot be sufficiently well controlled to insure that the level used is exactly the one that the experimenter intended to use. For example: he may intend to fire a group of 10 projectiles, each at a velocity of 2000 f/s; but, because of random variation in velocities for a fixed charge, the actual observed velocities range from 1975 to 2020 f/s.

In such a case, when the level used in the test can be measured directly, the experimenter has two choices for analyzing the data. If the actual levels used cluster so closely about the intended levels that:

(1) there is no overlapping between two of these clusters;

and,

(2) the range of any cluster is so small that the probability of "response" at any of the actual levels differs little from the probability of response at the intended level;

then the experimenter may simply assume that each test was conducted at the intended level, and use the methods already presented in Paragraphs 10-2 through 10-4. However, if one or both of these conditions are not met, none of the methods described in this Chapter are valid. Techniques for handling such data when the underlying distribution is normal are described in Golub and Grubbs.[12]

REFERENCES

1. J. Cornfield and N. Mantel, "Some New Aspects of the Application of Maximum Likelihood to the Calculation of the Dosage Response Curve," *Journal of the American Statistical Association*, Vol. 45, pp. 181-209, 1950.

2. J. Berkson, "A Statistically Precise and Relatively Simple Method of Estimating the Bio-assay with Quantal Response, Based on the Logistic Function," *Journal of the American Statistical Association*, Vol. 48, pp. 565-599, 1953.

3. J. L. Hodges, Jr., "Fitting the Logistic by Maximum Likelihood," *Biometrics*, Vol. 14, No. 4, pp. 453-461, December 1958.

4. L. F. Knudsen and J. M. Curtis, "The Use of the Angular Transformation in Biological Assays," *Journal of the American Statistical Association*, Vol. 42, pp. 282-296, 1947.

5. R. A. Fisher and F. Yates, *Statistical Tables for Biological, Agricultural, and Medical Research*, Hafner Publishing Co., New York, N.Y., 5th ed., 1957.

6. D. J. Finney, *Probit Analysis*, Cambridge University Press, 1947.

7. K. A. Brownlee, J. L. Hodges, Jr., and M. Rosenblatt, "The Up-and-Down Method with Small Samples," *Journal of the American Statistical Association*, Vol. 48, pp. 262-277, 1953.

8. W. J. Dixon and F. J. Massey, Jr., *Introduction to Statistical Analysis* (2d ed.), Chapter 19, "Sensitivity Experiments," McGraw-Hill Book Co., Inc., New York, N.Y., 1957.

9. W. J. Dixon and A. M. Mood, "A Method for Obtaining and Analyzing Sensitivity Data," *Journal of the American Statistical Association*, Vol. 43, pp. 109-126, 1948.

10. H. P. Culling, "Statistical Methods Appropriate for Evaluation of Fuze Explosive Train Safety and Reliability," *NAVORD Report 2101*, U. S. Naval Ordnance Laboratory, White Oak, Maryland, October 1953.

11. T. W. Anderson, P. J. McCarthy, and J. W. Tukey, "Staircase Method of Sensitivity Testing," *NAVORD Report 65-46*, U. S. Navy Bureau of Ordnance, Washington, D. C., March 1946.

12. A. Golub and F. E. Grubbs, "Analysis of Sensitivity Experiments When the Levels of Stimulus Cannot Be Controlled," *Journal of the American Statistical Association*, Vol. 51, pp. 257-265, 1956.

SECTION 3

THE PLANNING AND ANALYSIS OF

COMPARATIVE EXPERIMENTS

DISCUSSION OF TECHNIQUES
IN CHAPTERS 11 THROUGH 14

In this Section, we attempt to give only the following coverage:

(1) some broad consideration to the planning of experiments, in Chapter 11;

(2) some examples of the more widely used experimental designs, with appropriate methods of analysis, in Chapters 12 and 13;

(3) a brief description of new techniques that are useful when the purpose of experimentation is that of seeking maximum or optimum levels of the experimental factors, in Chapter 14.

Excellent books are available to give more extensive catalogs of experimental designs and more details regarding precautions in applying and analyzing these designs. A list of recommended books is given at the end of Chapter 11. When actually faced with the problem of planning an experiment, however, books will not be sufficient. The planning of experiments cannot be done in an ivory tower; and does not consist merely of writing down a few key words or parameters, looking them up in an index, and then selecting a specific plan. The proper experimental plan depends on: the purpose of the experiment; physical restrictions on the process of taking measurements; and other restrictions imposed by limitations of time, money, and the availability of material and personnel, etc. The novice experimenter is advised to consult a competent statistician and give him all the information available — not only what is thought to be important, but also what may be thought to be unimportant. In the words of Cochran and Cox*:

Participation in the initial stages of experiments in different areas of research leads to a strong conviction that too little time and effort is put into the planning of experiments. The statistician who expects that his contribution to the planning will involve some technical matter in statistical theory finds repeatedly that he makes a much more valuable contribution simply by getting the investigator to explain clearly why he is doing the experiment, to justify the experimental treatments whose effects he proposes to compare, and to defend his claim that the completed experiment will enable its objectives to be realized. . . .

It is good practice to make a written draft of the proposals for any experiment. This draft will in general have three parts: (i) a statement of the objectives; (ii) a description of the experiment, covering such matters as the experimental treatments, the size of the experiment, and the experimental material; and (iii) an outline of the method of analysis of the results.

In outlining the methods of conducting and analyzing an experiment, Anderson and Bancroft† give the following advice:

(i) *The experimenter should clearly set forth his objectives before proceeding with the experiment.* Is this a preliminary experiment to determine the future course of experimentation, or is it intended to furnish answers to immediate questions? Are the results to be carried into practical use at once, or are they to be used to explain aspects of theory not adequately understood before? Are you mainly interested in estimates or in tests of significance? Over what range of experimental conditions do you wish to extend your results?

(ii) *The experiment should be described in detail.* The treatments should be clearly defined. Is it necessary to use a control treatment in order to make comparisons with past results? The size of the experiment should be determined. If insufficient funds are available to conduct an experiment from which useful results can be obtained, the experiment should not be started. And above all, the necessary material to conduct the experiment should be available.

(iii) *An outline of the analysis should be drawn up before the experiment is started.*

All A-Tables referenced in these chapters are contained in ORDP 20-114, Section 5.

---

* W. G. Cochran and G. M. Cox, *Experimental Designs*, (2d edition), p. 10, John Wiley and Sons, Inc., New York, N.Y., 1957.

† R. L. Anderson and T. A. Bancroft, *Statistical Theory in Research*, p. 223, McGraw-Hill Book Co., Inc., New York, N.Y., 1952.

CHAPTER 11

GENERAL CONSIDERATIONS
IN PLANNING EXPERIMENTS

11-1 THE NATURE OF EXPERIMENTATION

An experiment has been defined, in the most general sense, as "a considered course of action aimed at answering one or more carefully framed questions." Observational programs in the natural sciences and sample surveys in the social sciences are clearly included in this general definition. In ordnance engineering, however, we are concerned with a more restricted kind of experiment in which the experimenter *does something* to at least some of the things under study and then *observes the effect of his action*.

The things under study which are being deliberately varied in a controlled fashion may be called the *factors*. These factors may be quantitative factors such as temperature which can be varied along a continuous scale (at least for practical purposes the scale may be called continuous) or they may be qualitative factors (such as different machines, different operators, different composition of charge, etc.). The use of the proper *experimental pattern* aids in the evaluation of the factors. See Paragraph 11-2.

In addition to the factors, which are varied in a controlled fashion, the experimenter may be aware of certain background variables which might affect the outcome of the experiment. For one reason or another, these background variables will not be or cannot be included as factors in the experiment, but it is often possible to plan the experiment so that:

(1) possible effects due to background variables do not affect information obtained about the factors of primary interest; and,

(2) some information about the effects of the background variables can be obtained. See Paragraph 11-3.

In addition, there may be variables of which the experimenter is unaware which have an effect on the outcome of the experiment. The effects of these variables may be given an opportunity to "balance out" by the introduction of *randomization* into the experimental pattern. See Paragraph 11-4.

Many books have been written on the general principles of experimentation, and the book by Wilson[1] is especially recommended. There are certain characteristics an experiment obviously must have in order to accomplish anything at all. We might call these *requisites of a good experiment*, and we give as a partial listing of requisites:

(1) There must be a clearly defined objective.

(2) As far as possible, the effects of the factors should not be obscured by other variables.

(3) As far as possible, the results should not be influenced by conscious or unconscious bias in the experiment or on the part of the experimenter.

(4) The experiment should provide some measure of precision.*

(5) The experiment must have sufficient precision to accomplish its purpose.

---

* This requisite can be relaxed in some situations, i.e., when there is a well-known history of the measurement process, and consequently good *a priori* estimates of precision.

To aid in achieving these requisites, statistical design of experiments can provide some *tools for sound experimentation*, which are listed in Table 11-1.

The tools given include: *experimental pattern, planned grouping, randomization*, and *replication*. Their functions in experimentation are shown in Table 11-1, and are amplified in Paragraphs 11-2 through 11-5.

--- --- --- --- --- --- --- --- --- ---

TABLE 11-1. SOME REQUISITES AND TOOLS FOR SOUND EXPERIMENTATION

Requisites	Tools
1. The experiment should have carefully defined objectives.	1. The definition of objectives requires all of the specialized subject-matter knowledge of the experimenter, and results in such things as: (a) Choice of factors, including their range; (b) Choice of experimental materials, procedure, and equipment; (c) Knowledge of what the results are applicable to.
2. As far as possible, effects of factors should not be obscured by other variables.	2. The use of an appropriate EXPERIMENTAL PATTERN** (see Par. 11-2) helps to free the comparisons of interest from the effects of uncontrolled variables, and simplifies the analysis of the results.
3. As far as possible, the experiment should be free from bias (conscious or unconscious).	3. Some variables may be taken into account by PLANNED GROUPING (see Par. 11-3). For variables not so taken care of, use RANDOMIZATION (Par. 11-4). The use of REPLICATION aids RANDOMIZATION to do a better job.
4. Experiment should provide a measure of precision (experimental error).*	4. REPLICATION (Par. 11-5) provides the measure of precision; RANDOMIZATION assures validity of the measure of precision.
5. Precision of experiment should be sufficient to meet objectives set forth in requisite 1.	5. Greater precision may be achieved by: Refinements of technique EXPERIMENTAL PATTERN (including PLANNED GROUPING) REPLICATION.

---

* Except where there is a well-known history of the measurement process.

** Capitalized words are discussed in the following paragraphs.

11-2 EXPERIMENTAL PATTERN

The term *experimental pattern* is a broad one by which we mean the planned schedule of taking the measurements. A particular pattern may or may not include the succeeding three tools (*planned grouping*, *randomization*, and *replication*). Each of these three tools can improve the experimental pattern in particular situations. The proper pattern for the experiment will aid in control of bias and in measurement of precision, will simplify the requisite calculations of the analysis, and will permit

clear estimation of the effects of the factors.

A common experimental pattern is the so-called factorial design experiment, wherein we control several factors and investigate their effects at each of two or more levels. If two levels of each factor are involved, the experimental plan consists of taking an observation at each of the 2^n possible combinations. The factorial design, with examples, is discussed in greater detail in Chapter 12.

11-3 PLANNED GROUPING

An important class of experimental patterns is characterized by *planned grouping*. This class is often called *block designs*. The use of planned grouping (blocking) arose in comparative experiments in agricultural research, in recognition of the fact that plots that were close together in a field were usually more alike than plots that were far apart. In industrial and engineering research, the tool of planned grouping can be used to take advantage of naturally homogeneous groupings in materials, machines, time, etc., and so to take account of "background variables" which are not directly "factors" in the experiment.

Suppose we are required to compare the effect of five different treatments of a plastic material. Plastic properties vary considerably within a given sheet. To get a good comparision of the five treatment effects, we should divide the plastic sheet into more or less homogeneous areas, and subdivide each area into five parts. The five treatments could then be allocated to the five parts of a given area. Each set of five parts may be termed a block. In this case, had we had four or six treatments, we could as well have had blocks of four or six units. This is not always the case — the naturally homo-

geneous area (block) may not be large enough to accommodate all the treatments of interest.

If we are interested in the wearing qualities of automobile tires, the natural block is a block of four, the four wheels of an automobile. Each automobile may travel over different terrain or have different drivers. However, the four tires on any given automobile will undergo much the same conditions, particularly if they are rotated frequently.

In testing different types of plastic soles for shoes, the natural block consists of two units, the two feet of an individual.

The block may consist of observations taken at nearly the same time or place. If a machine can test four items at one time, then each run may be regarded as a block of four units, each item being a unit.

Statisticians have developed a variety of especially advantageous configurations of *block designs*, named and classified by their structure into randomized blocks, Latin squares, incomplete blocks, lattices, etc., with a number of subcategories of each. Some of these block designs are discussed in detail in Chapter 13.

11-4 RANDOMIZATION

Randomization is necessary to accomplish Requisites 3 and 4 in Table 11-1. In order to eliminate bias from the experiment (Requisite 3), experimental variables which are not specifically controlled as factors, or "blocked out" by planned grouping, should be randomized — e.g., the allocations of specimens to treatments or methods should be made by some mechanical method of randomization.

Randomization also assures valid estimates of experimental error (Requisite 4), and makes possible the application of statistical tests of significance and the construction of confidence intervals.

There are many famous examples of experiments where failure to randomize at a crucial stage led to completely misleading results. As always, however, the coin has another side; the beneficial effects of randomization are obtained in the long run, and not in a single isolated experiment. Randomization may be thought of as insurance, and, like insurance, may sometimes be too expensive. If a variable is thought unlikely to have an effect, and if it is very difficult to randomize with respect to the variable, we may choose not to randomize.

In general, we should try to think of all variables that could possibly affect the results, select as factors as many variables as can reasonably be studied, and use planned grouping where possible. Ideally, then, we randomize with respect to everything else — but it must be recognized that the ideal cannot always be realized in practice.

The word *randomization* has been used rather than *randomness* to emphasize the fact that experimental material rarely, if ever, has a random distribution in itself, that we are never really safe in assuming that it has, and that consequently randomness has to be assured by formal or mechanical randomization.

11-5 REPLICATION

In order to evaluate the effects of factors, a measure of precision (experimental error) must be available. In some kinds of experiments, notably in biological or agricultural research, this measure must be obtained from the experiment itself, since no other source would provide an appropriate measure. In some industrial and engineering experimentation, however, records may be available on a relatively stable measurement process, and this data may provide an appropriate measure. Where the measure of precision must be obtained from the experiment itself, *replication* provides the measure. In addition to providing the measure of precision, replication provides an opportunity for the effects of uncontrolled factors to balance out, and thus aids randomization as a bias-decreasing tool. (In successive replications, the randomization features must be independent.) Replication will also help to spot gross errors in the measurements.

11-6   THE LANGUAGE OF EXPERIMENTAL DESIGN

In discussing applications of statistical design of experiments in the field of physical sciences and engineering, we are extremely handicapped by the classical language of experimental design. The early developments and applications were in the field of agriculture, where the terms used in describing the designs had real physical meaning. The *experimental area* was an area — a piece of ground. A *block* was a smaller piece of ground, small enough to be fairly uniform in soil and topography, and thus was expected to give results within a block that would be more alike than those from different blocks. A *plot* was an even smaller piece of ground, the basic unit of the design. As a unit, the plot was planted, fertilized, and harvested, and it could be *split* just by drawing a line. A *treatment* was actually a treatment (e.g., an application of fertilizer) and a *treatment combination* was a combination of treatments. A *yield* was a yield, a quantity harvested and weighed or measured.

Unfortunately for our purposes, these are the terms commonly used. Since there is no particular future in inventing a new descriptive language for a single book, we must use these terms, and we must ask the engineer or scientist to stretch his imagination to make the terms fit his experimental situation.

Experimental area can be thought of as the scope of the planned experiment. For us, a *block* can be a group of results from a particular operator, or from a particular machine, or on a particular day — any planned natural grouping which should serve to make results from one block more alike than results from different blocks. For us, a *treatment* is the factor being investigated (material, environmental condition, etc.) in a single factor experiment. In factorial experiments (where several variables are being investigated at the same time) we speak of a *treatment combination* and we mean the prescribed levels of the factors to be applied to an experimental unit. For us, a *yield* is a measured result and, happily enough, in chemistry it will sometimes be a yield.

Many good books on experimental design are available. See the following list of References and Recommended Textbooks.

REFERENCES

1. E. B. Wilson, Jr., *An Introduction to Scientific Research*, McGraw-Hill Book Co., Inc., New York, N.Y., 1952.

SOME RECOMMENDED TEXTBOOKS

R. L. Anderson and T. A. Bancroft, *Statistical Theory in Research*, McGraw-Hill Book Co., Inc., New York, N.Y., 1952.

V. Chew (ed.), *Experimental Designs in Industry*, John Wiley and Sons, Inc., New York, N.Y., 1958.

W. G. Cochran and G. M. Cox, *Experimental Designs* (2d edition), John Wiley and Sons, Inc., New York, N.Y., 1957.

D. R. Cox, *Planning of Experiments*, John Wiley and Sons, Inc., New York, N.Y., 1958.

O. L. Davies (ed.), *The Design and Analysis of Industrial Experiments*, Oliver and Boyd, Ltd., Edinburgh, and Hafner Publishing Co., New York, N.Y., 1954.

W. T. Federer, *Experimental Design*, The Macmillan Company, New York, N.Y., 1955.

R. A. Fisher, *The Design of Experiments* (7th edition), Hafner Publishing Co., New York, N.Y., 1960.

F. A. Graybill, *An Introduction to Linear Statistical Models*, Vol. I, McGraw-Hill Book Co., Inc., New York, N.Y., 1961.

O. Kempthorne, *The Design and Analysis of Experiments*, John Wiley and Sons, Inc., New York, N.Y., 1952.

M. H. Quenouille, *The Design and Analysis of Experiment*, Hafner Publishing Co., New York, N.Y., 1953.

H. Scheffé, *The Analysis of Variance*, John Wiley and Sons, Inc., New York, N.Y., 1959.

W. J. Youden, *Statistical Methods for Chemists*, John Wiley and Sons, Inc., New York, N.Y., 1951.

CHAPTER 12

FACTORIAL EXPERIMENTS

12-1 INTRODUCTION

12-1.1 SOME GENERAL REMARKS AND TERMINOLOGY

Factorial experiment is the name commonly applied to an experiment wherein we control several factors and investigate their effects at each of two or more levels. The experimental plan consists of taking an observation at each one of all possible combinations that can be formed for the different levels of the factors. Each such different combination is called a *treatment combination*.

Suppose that we are interested in investigating the effect of pressure and temperature on the yield of some chemical process. Pressure and temperature will be called the *factors* in the experiment. Each specific value of pressure to be included will be called a *level* of the pressure factor, and similarly each specific value of temperature to be included will be called a *level* of the temperature factor. In the past, one common experimental approach has been the so-called "one at a time" approach. This kind of experiment would study the effect of varying pressure at some constant temperature, and then study the effect of varying temperature at some constant pressure. Factors would be varied "one at a time." The results of such an experiment are fragmentary in the sense that we have learned about the effect of different pressures at one temperature only (and the effect of different temperatures at one pressure only). The reaction of the process to different pressures may depend on the temperature used; if we had chosen a different temperature, our observed relation of yield to pressure may have been quite different. In statistical language, there may be an *interaction* effect between the two

factors within the range of interest, and the "one at a time" procedure does not enable us to detect it.

In a factorial experiment, the levels of each factor we wish to investigate are chosen, and a measurement is made for each possible combination of levels of the factors. Suppose that we had chosen two levels, say 7cm. and 14cm. for pressure, and two levels, say, 70°F. and 100°F. for temperature. There would be four possible combinations of pressure and temperature, and the factorial experiment would consist of four trials. In our example, the term *level* is used in connection with quantitative factors, but the same term is also used when the factors are qualitative.

In the analysis of factorial experiments, we speak of *main effects* and *interaction effects* (or simply *interactions*). Main effects of a given factor are always functions of the average response or yield at the various levels of the factor. In the case where a factor has two levels, the *main effect* is the difference between the responses at the two levels averaged over all levels of the other factors. In the case where the factor has more than two levels, there are several independent components of the main effect, the number of components being one less than the number of levels. If the difference in the response between two levels of factor A is the same regardless of the level of factor B (except for experimental error), we say that there is no interaction between A and B, or that the AB interaction is zero. Figure 12-1 shows two examples of response or yield curves; one example shows the presence of an interaction, and the other shows no interaction. If we have two

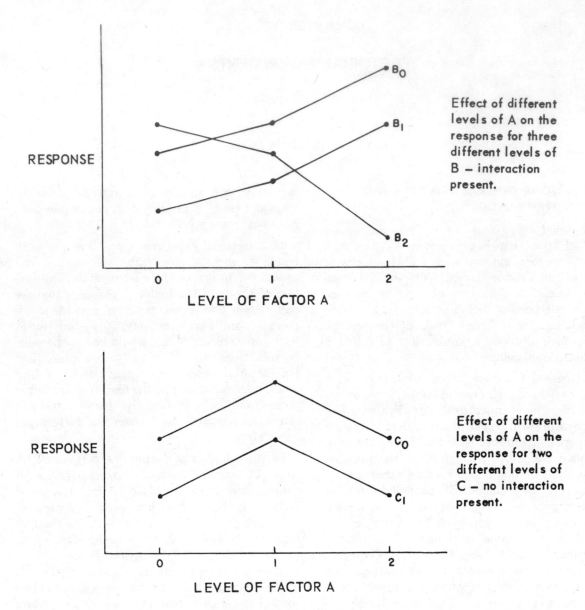

Figure 12-1. Examples of response curves showing presence or absence of interaction.

levels of each of the factors A and B, then the AB interaction (neglecting experimental error) is the difference in the yields of A at the second level of B minus the difference in the yields of A at the first level of B. If we have more than two levels of either or of both A and B, then the AB interaction is composed of more than one component. If we have a levels of the factor A and b levels of the factor B, then the AB inter-

action has $(a-1)(b-1)$ independent components.

For factorial experiments with three or more factors, interactions can be defined similarly. For instance, the ABC interaction is the interaction between the factor C and the AB interaction (or equivalently between the factor B and the AC interaction, or A and the BC interaction).

12-1.2 ESTIMATES OF EXPERIMENTAL ERROR FOR FACTORIAL-TYPE DESIGNS

12-1.2.1 Internal Estimates of Error.   As in any experiment, we must have a measure of experimental error to use in judging the significance of the observed differences in treatments. In the larger factorial designs, estimates of higher-order interactions will be available. The usual assumption is that high-order interactions are physically impossible, and that the estimates so labelled are actually estimates of experimental error. As a working rule we often use third- and higher-order interactions for error. This does not imply that third-order interactions are always nonexistent. The judgment of the experimenter will determine which interactions may reasonably be assumed to be meaningful, and which may be assumed to be nothing more than error. These latter interactions may be combined to provide an internal estimate of error for a factorial experiment of reasonable size. For very small factorials, e.g., 2^3 or smaller, there are no estimates of high-order interactions, and the experiment must be replicated (repeated) in order to obtain an estimate of error from the experiment itself.

In the blocked factorial designs (Paragraph 12-3 and Table 12-3), some of the higher-order interactions will be *confounded* with blocks, and will not be available as estimates of error (see Paragraph 12-3.1). For example, note the plan in Table 12-3 for a 2^3 factorial arranged in two blocks of four observations. The single third-order interaction provides the blocking, i.e., the means of subdividing the experiment into homogeneous groups, and therefore will estimate block effects, not error.   Here again it may be necessary to replicate the experiment in order to have an estimate of experimental error.

In the case of fractional factorials, there is obviously no point in replication of the experiment; further experimentation would probably be aimed at completing the full factorial or a larger fraction of the full factorial.   The smaller fractional factorial designs (Paragraph 12-4 and Table 12-4) do not contain high-order interactions that can suitably be assumed to be error. In fact, none of the particular plans given in Table 12-4 provides a suitable internal estimate of error. Accordingly then, an independent estimate of error will be required when using a small fractional factorial. Occasionally and cautiously we might use second-order interaction effects to test main effects, if the purpose of the experiment were to look for very large main effects (much larger than second-order effects). In using interactions as estimates of error, however, we must decide before conducting the experiment (or at least before having a knowledge of the responses or yields) which of the effects may be assumed to be zero, so that they may be used in the estimate of the variation due to experimental error.

12-1.2.2 Estimates of Error From Past Experience.   In the cases discussed in Paragraph 12-1.2.1 that do not provide adequate estimates of error from the experiment itself, we must depend on an estimate based upon past experience with the measurement process. In laboratory and industrial situations, this information is often at hand or can be found by simple analysis of previously recorded data.

12-2 FACTORIAL EXPERIMENTS (EACH FACTOR AT TWO LEVELS)

12-2.1 SYMBOLS

A factorial experiment in which we have n factors, each at two levels, is known as a 2^n factorial experiment.   The experiment consists of 2^n trials, one at each combination of levels of the factors.   To identify each of the trials, we adopt a conventional notation. A factor is identified by a capital letter, and the two levels of a factor by the subscripts *zero* and *one*. If we have three factors A, B, and C, then the corresponding levels of the factors are A_0, A_1; B_0, B_1; and C_0, C_1; respectively. By convention, the zero subscript refers to the lower level, to the normal condition, or to the absence of a condition, as appropriate. A trial is represented by a combination of small letters denoting the levels of the factors in the trial. The presence of a small letter means that the factor is at the level denoted by the subscript 1 (the higher level for quantitative factors); the absence of a letter means that the factor is at the level denoted by the subscript zero (the lower level for quantitative factors). Thus, the symbol a represents the treatment combination where A is at the level A_1, B is at B_0, and C is at C_0. The symbol bc represents the treatment combination where A is at the level A_0, B is at B_1, and C is at C_1. Conventionally, the symbol (1) represents the treatment combination with each factor at its zero level. In an experiment with three factors, each at two levels, the $2^3 = 8$ combinations, and thus the eight trials, are represented by (1), a, b, ab, c, ac, bc, abc.

The experiment has four factors, each at two levels, i.e., is a 2^4 factorial. Note that all factors are qualitative in this experiment. The experimental factors and levels are:

FACTORS	LEVELS
A — Fabric	A_0 — Sateen
	A_1 — Monks cloth
B — Treatment	B_0 — Treatment x
	B_1 — Treatment y
C — Laundering condition	C_0 — Before laundering
	C_1 — After one laundering
D — Direction of test	D_0 — Warp
	D_1 — Fill

Data Sample 12-2 — Flame Tests of Fire-Retardant Treatments

The data are taken from a larger experiment designed to evaluate the effect of laundering on certain fire-retardant treatments for fabrics.

The observations reported in Table 12-1 are *inches burned*, measured on a standard size sample after a flame test. For reference, the conventional symbol representing the treatment combination appears beside the resulting observation.

_ _

TABLE 12-1. RESULTS OF FLAME TESTS OF FIRE-RETARDANT TREATMENTS (FACTORIAL EXPERIMENT OF DATA SAMPLE 12-2)

| | | A_0 | | | | A_1 | | | |
		B_0		B_1		B_0		B_1	
C_0	D_0	4.2	(1)	4.5	b	3.1	a	2.9	ab
	D_1	4.0	d	5.0	bd	3.0	ad	2.5	abd
C_1	D_0	3.9	c	4.6	bc	2.8	ac	3.2	abc
	D_1	4.0	cd	5.0	bcd	2.5	acd	2.3	$abcd$

12-2.2 ANALYSIS

12-2.2.1 Estimation of Main Effects and Interactions.

Yates' method is a systematic method for obtaining estimates of main effects and interactions *for two-level factorials*. The method was originally described by Yates[1], and may be found in various textbooks (Cochran and Cox[2] and Davies[3]). The method as given here applies to factorials, blocked factorials (Paragraph 12-3), and fractional factorials (Paragraph 12-4), for which we have 2^n observations.* The first step in the Yates' procedure is to make a table with $n + 2$ columns, where n is the number of factors in the factorial experiment. For example, see Table 12-2, where $n + 2 = 6$. In Table 12-2, the treatment combinations are listed in a standardized order in the first column, and after following the prescribed procedure, estimated main effects and interactions result in the last column (column $n + 2$). The order in which the treatment combinations are listed in column 1 determines the order of estimated effects in column $n + 2$.

For factorials or blocked factorials, the treatment combinations should be listed in "standard order" in the first column, i.e.,

For two factors: (1), a, b, ab
For three factors: (1), a, b, ab, c, ac, bc, abc
For four factors: (1), a, b, ab, c, ac, bc, abc, d, ad, bd, abd, cd, acd, bcd, $abcd$
.
.
.
etc.

"Standard order" for five factors is obtained by listing all the treatment combinations given for four factors, followed by e, ae, be, abe, . . . , $abcde$ (i.e., the new element multiplied by all previous treatment combinations). Standard order for a higher number of factors is obtained in similar fashion, beginning with the series for the next smaller number of factors, and continuing by multiplying that series by the new element introduced.

The estimated main effects and interactions also appear in a standard order:

For two factors: T, A, B, AB
For three factors: $T, A, B, AB, C, AC, BC, ABC$
.
.
.
etc.

where T corresponds to the overall average effect, A to the main effect of factor A, AB to the interaction of factors A and B, etc.

For fractional factorials, the treatment combinations in column 1 should be listed in the order given in the plans of Table 12-4. The order of the estimated effects is also given in Table 12-4. For fractional factorial plans other than those given in Table 12-4, see Davies[3] for the necessary ordering for the Yates method of analysis.

---

* In a $\frac{1}{2^b}$ fraction of a 2^n factorial, there are $2n'$ observations, where $n' = n - b$ (See Par. 12-4).

The systematic procedure for Yates' method is as follows:

Procedure	Example
(1) Make a table with $n + 2$ columns. In the first column, list the treatment combinations in standard order.	(1) Use Data Sample 12-2, the results of which are summarized in Table 12-1. This is a 2^4 factorial $(n = 4)$. Therefore, our Table will have six columns, as shown in Table 12-2.
(2) In column 2, enter the observed yield or response corresponding to each treatment combination listed in column 1.	(2) See Table 12-2.

(3) In the top half of column 3, enter, in order, the sums of consecutive pairs of entries in column 2. In the bottom half of the column enter, in order, the differences between the same consecutive pairs of entries, i.e., second entry minus first entry, fourth entry minus third entry, etc.

(3) See Table 12-2. For example:

$$4.2 + 3.1 = 7.3$$
$$4.5 + 2.9 = 7.4$$
$$3.9 + 2.8 = 6.7$$
etc.,
and,
$$3.1 - 4.2 = -1.1$$
$$2.9 - 4.5 = -1.6$$
$$2.8 - 3.9 = -1.1$$
etc.

(4) Obtain columns 4, 5, ..., $n + 2$, in the same manner as column 3, i.e., by obtaining in each case the sums and differences of the pairs in the preceding column in the manner described in step 3.

(4) See Table 12-2.

(5) The entries in the last column (column $n + 2$) are called g_T, g_A, g_B, g_{AB}, etc., corresponding to the ordered effects T, A, B, AB, etc. Estimates of main effects and interactions are obtained by dividing the appropriate g by 2^{n-1}. g_T divided by * 2^n is the overall mean.

(5) In Table 12-2,

$$g_A = -12.9;$$

the estimated main effect of

$$A = -12.9/8$$
$$= -1.6.$$

$$g_{AD} = -2.5;$$

the estimated effect of AD interaction

$$= -2.5/8$$
$$= -0.3,$$
etc.

Note: The remaining Steps of this procedure are checks on the computation.

Note: The following Steps are checks on the computations in Table 12-2.

Procedure

Example

(6) The sum of all the 2^n individual responses (column 2) should equal the total given in the first entry of the last column (column $n + 2$).

(6) The sum of column 2 should equal g_T,
$$57.5 = 57.5$$

(7) The sum of the squares of the individual responses (column 2) should equal the sum of the squares of the entries in the last column (column $n + 2$) divided by 2^n.

(7) The sum of squares of entries in column 2 should equal the sum of squares of the entries in the last column, divided by 2^4 ($= 16$),

$$219.15 = 3506.40 \div 16$$
$$= 219.15$$

(8) For any main effect, the entry in the last column (column $n + 2$) equals the sum of the responses in which that factor is at its higher level minus the sum of the responses in which that factor is at its lower level.

(8)
$$
\begin{aligned}
g_A &= (a + ab + ac + abc + ad + abd \\
&\quad + acd + abcd) \\
&\quad - ((1) + b + c + bc + d + bd \\
&\quad + cd + bcd) \\
&= (22.3) - (35.2) \\
&= -12.9
\end{aligned}
$$

$$
\begin{aligned}
g_B &= (b + ab + bc + abc + bd + abd \\
&\quad + bcd + abcd) \\
&\quad - ((1) + a + c + ac + d + ad \\
&\quad + cd + acd) \\
&= (30.0) - (27.5) \\
&= 2.5
\end{aligned}
$$

$$
\begin{aligned}
g_C &= (c + ac + bc + abc + cd + acd \\
&\quad + bcd + abcd) \\
&\quad - ((1) + a + b + ab + d + ad \\
&\quad + bd + abd) \\
&= (28.3) - (29.2) \\
&= -0.9
\end{aligned}
$$

$$
\begin{aligned}
g_D &= (d + ad + bd + abd + cd + acd \\
&\quad + bcd + abcd) \\
&\quad - ((1) + a + b + ab + c + ac \\
&\quad + bc + abc) \\
&= (28.3) - (29.2) \\
&= -0.9
\end{aligned}
$$

TABLE 12-2.   YATES' METHOD OF ANALYSIS USING DATA SAMPLE 12-2

1 Treatment Combination	2 Response (Yield)	3	4	5	6 g		
(1)	4.2	7.3	14.7	29.2	$57.5 = g_T$		
a	3.1	7.4	14.5	28.3	$-12.9 = g_A$	, an estimate of $8A$	
b	4.5	6.7	14.5	−5.2	$2.5 = g_B$	"	$8B$
ab	2.9	7.8	13.8	−7.7	$-3.5 = g_{AB}$	"	$8AB$
c	3.9	7.0	−2.7	1.2	$-0.9 = g_C$	"	$8C$
ac	2.8	7.5	−2.5	1.3	$-0.5 = g_{AC}$	"	$8AC$
bc	4.6	6.5	−3.5	−0.8	$1.3 = g_{BC}$	"	$8BC$
abc	3.2	7.3	−4.2	−2.7	$0.5 = g_{ABC}$	"	$8ABC$
d	4.0	−1.1	0.1	−0.2	$-0.9 = g_D$	"	$8D$
ad	3.0	−1.6	1.1	−0.7	$-2.5 = g_{AD}$	"	$8AD$
bd	5.0	−1.1	0.5	0.2	$0.1 = g_{BD}$	"	$8BD$
abd	2.5	−1.4	0.8	−0.7	$-1.9 = g_{ABD}$	"	$8ABD$
cd	4.0	−1.0	−0.5	1.0	$-0.5 = g_{CD}$	"	$8CD$
acd	2.5	−2.5	−0.3	0.3	$-0.9 = g_{ACD}$	"	$8ACD$
bcd	5.0	−1.5	−1.5	0.2	$-0.7 = g_{BCD}$	"	$8BCD$
abcd	2.3	−2.7	−1.2	0.3	$0.1 = g_{ABCD}$	"	$8ABCD$
Total	57.5						
Sum of Squares	219.15				3506.40		

12-2.2.2 Testing for Significance of Main Effects and Interactions.   Before using this procedure, read Paragraph 12-1.2 and perform the computation described in Paragraph 12-2.2.1.

Procedure	Example
(1) Choose α, the level of significance.	(1) Let $\alpha = .05$
(2) If there is no available estimate of the variation due to experimental error,* find the sum of squares of the g's corresponding to interactions of three or more factors in Table 12-2.	(2) Using Table 12-2, $g^2_{ABC} + g^2_{ABD} + g^2_{ACD} + g^2_{BCD} + g^2_{ABCD}$ $= 5.17$
(3) To obtain s^2, divide the sum of squares obtained in Step 2 by $2^n \nu$, where ν is the number of interactions included. In a 2^n factorial, the number of third and higher interactions will be $2^n - (n^2 + n + 2)/2$. If an independent estimate of the variation due to experimental error *is* available, use this s^2.	(3) $n = 4$ $\nu = 5$ $2^n \nu = 16 (5)$ $= 80$ $s^2 = 5.17/80$ $= .0646$ $s = .254$

---

* See Paragraph 12-1.2.

Procedure	Example

(4) Look up $t_{1-\alpha/2}$ for ν degrees of freedom in Table A-4.

If higher order interactions are used to obtain s^2, ν is the number of interactions included.

If an independent estimate of s^2 is used, ν is the degrees of freedom associated with this estimate.

(4) $t_{.975}$ for 5 d.f. = 2.571

(5) Compute

$$w = (2^n)^{\frac{1}{2}} t_{1-\alpha/2}\, s$$

(5)

$$w = 4\,(2.571)\,(0.254)$$
$$= 2.61$$

(6) For any main effect or interaction X, if the absolute value of g_X is greater than w, conclude that X is different from zero, e.g., if $|g_A| > w$, conclude that the A effect is different from zero. Otherwise, there is no reason to believe that X is different from zero.

(6) See Table 12-2. $|g_A| = 12.9$, and $|g_{AB}| = 3.5$ are greater than w; therefore, the main effect of A and the interaction AB are believed to be significant.

12-3 FACTORIAL EXPERIMENTS WHEN UNIFORM CONDITIONS CANNOT BE MAINTAINED THROUGHOUT THE EXPERIMENT (EACH FACTOR AT TWO LEVELS)

12-3.1 SOME EXPERIMENTAL ARRANGEMENTS

When the number of factors to be investigated are more than just a few, it may be that the required number of trials 2^n is too large to be carried out under reasonably uniform conditions e.g., on one batch of raw material, or on one piece of equipment. In such cases, the design can be arranged in groups or blocks so that conditions affecting each block can be made as uniform as possible. The use of planned grouping within a factorial design (i.e., a *blocked* factorial) will improve the precision of estimation of experimental error, and will enable us to estimate the main effects free of block differences; but, the structure of the designs is such that certain interaction effects will be inextricable from block effects. In most designs, however, only three-factor and higher-order interactions will be confused ("confounded") with blocks.

Some experimental arrangements of this kind are given in Table 12-3, and their analysis and interpretation are given in Paragraph 12-3.2.

Blocked factorial designs have not been very widely used in experimentation in the physical sciences, and the presumption is that they are usually not the most suitable designs for the kinds of non-homogeneity that occur in these applications. (See Chapter 13 for other designs which make use of blocking.) For this reason, no numerical example is given in this Paragraph. This Paragraph is included for completeness, and serves to link the full factorials (Paragraph 12-2) and the fractional factorials (Paragraph 12-4).

TABLE 12-3. SOME BLOCKED FACTORIAL PLANS
(FOR USE WHEN FACTORIAL EXPERIMENT MUST BE SUB-DIVIDED INTO HOMOGENEOUS GROUPS)

Plans for Three Factors: $2^3 = 8$ Observations

(i) Four observations per block (ABC confounded with block effects).

Block 1   (1), ab, ac, bc

Block 2 a, b, c, abc

Plans for Four Factors: $2^4 = 16$ Observations

(i) Eight observations per block ($ABCD$ interaction confounded with block effects).

Block 1   (1), ab, ac, bc, ad, bd, cd, $abcd$

Block 2 a, b, c, abc, d, abd, acd, bcd

(ii) Four observations per block (AD, ABC, BCD, confounded with block effects).

Block 1   (1), bc, abd, acd

Block 2 a, abc, bd, cd

Block 3 b, c, ad, $abcd$

Block 4 d, bcd, ab, ac

Plans for Five Factors: $2^5 = 32$ Observations

(i) Sixteen observations per block ($ABCDE$ interaction confounded with block effects).

Block 1   (1), ab, ac, bc, ad, bd, cd, $abcd$, ae, be, ce, $abce$, de, $abde$, $acde$, $bcde$

Block 2 a, b, c, abc, d, abd, acd, bcd, e, abe, ace, bce, ade, bde, cde, $abcde$

(ii) Eight observations per block (BCE, ADE, $ABCD$, confounded with block effects).

Block 1   (1), ad, bc, $abcd$, abe, bde, ace, cde

Block 2 a, d, abc, bcd, be, $abde$, ce, $acde$

Block 3 b, abd, c, acd, ae, de, $abce$, $bcde$

Block 4 e, ade, bce, $abcde$, ab, bd, ac, cd

(iii) Four observations per block (AD, BE, ABC, BCD, CDE, ACE, $ABDE$, confounded with block effects).

Block 1   (1), bce, acd, $abde$

Block 2 a, $abce$, cd, bde

Block 3 b, ce, $abcd$, ade

Block 4 c, be, ad, $abcde$

Block 5 d, $bcde$, ac, abe

Block 6 e, bc, $acde$, abd

Block 7 ab, ace, bcd, de

Block 8 ae, abc, cde, bd

TABLE 12-3. SOME BLOCKED FACTORIAL PLANS (Continued)

Plans for Six Factors: $2^6 = 64$ Observations

(i) Thirty-two observations per block ($ABCDEF$ confounded with block effects).

Block 1   (1), *abcdef*, plus all treatment combinations represented by two letters (e.g., *ab, ac,* etc.) and by four letters (e.g., *abcd, bcde,* etc.)

Block 2   All treatment combinations represented by a single letter, by three letters, and by five letters.

(ii) Sixteen observations per block ($ABCD$, $BCEF$, $ADEF$, confounded with block effects).

Block 1   (1), *bc, ad, abcd, ef, bcef, adef, abcdef, bde, cde, abe, ace, bdf, cdf, abf, acf*

Block 2   *a, abc, d, bcd, aef, abcef, def, bcdef, abde, acde, be, ce, abdf, acdf, bf, cf*

Block 3   *b, c, abd, acd, bef, cef, abdef, acdef, de, bcde, ae, abce, df, bcdf, af, abcf*

Block 4   *e, bce, ade, abcde, f, bcf, adf, abcdf, bd, cd, ab, ac, bdef, cdef, abef, acef*

(iii) Eight observations per block (ADE, BCE, ACF, BDF, $ABCD$, $ABEF$, $CDEF$, confounded with block effects).

Block 1   (1), *ace, bde, abcd, adf, cdef, abef, bcf*

Block 2   *a, ce, abde, bcd, df, acdef, bef, abcf*

Block 3   *b, abce, de, acd, abdf, bcdef, aef, cf*

Block 4   *c, ae, bcde, abd, acdf, def, abcef, bf*

Block 5   *d, acde, be, abc, af, cef, abdef, bcdf*

Block 6   *e, ac, bd, abcde, adef, cdf, abf, bcef*

Block 7   *f, acef, bdef, abcdf, ad, cde, abe, bc*

Block 8   *ab, bce, ade, cd, bdf, abcdef, ef, acf*

(iv) Four observations per block (AD, BE, CF, ABC, BCD, CDE, DEF, ACE, AEF, ABF, BDF, $ABDE$, $BCEF$, $ACDF$, $ABCDEF$, confounded with block effects).

Block 1   (1), *bcef, acdf, abde*

Block 2   *a, abcef, cdf, bde*

Block 3   *b, cef, abcdf, ade*

Block 4   *c, bef, adf, abcde*

Block 5   *d, bcdef, acf, abe*

Block 6   *e, bcf, acdef, abd*

Block 7   *f, bce, acd, abdef*

Block 8   *ab, acef, bcdf, de*

Block 9   *ac, abef, df, bcde*

Block 10   *ad, abcdef, cf, be*

Block 11   *ae, abcf, cdef, bd*

Block 12   *af, abce, cd, bdef*

Block 13   *bc, ef, abdf, acde*

Block 14   *bf, ce, abcd, adef*

Block 15   *abc, aef, bdf, cde*

Block 16   *abf, ace, bcd, def*

TABLE 12-3.   SOME BLOCKED FACTORIAL PLANS (Continued)

Plans for Seven Factors: $2^7 = 128$ Observations

(i)   Sixty-four observations per block ($ABCDEFG$ confounded with block effects).

Block 1   (1), and all treatment combinations represented by two letters, four letters, or six letters (e.g., *ab*, *abcd*, etc.).

Block 2   All treatment combinations represented by a single letter, by three letters, and by five letters, plus *abcdefg*.

(ii) Thirty-two observations per block ($ABCD$, $ABEFG$, $CDEFG$, confounded with block effects).

Block 1   (1), *ab*, *abcd*, *ace*, *acf*, *acg*, *ade*, *adf*, *adg*, *bce*, *bcf*, *cdef*, *cdeg*, *cdfg*, *abcdef*, *abcdeg*, *abcdfg*, *abef*, *bcg*, *bde*, *bdf*, *bdg*, *abeg*, *abfg*, *cd*, *ef*, *eg*, *fg*, *acefg*, *adefg*, *bcefg*, *bdefg*

Block 2   *a*, *b*, *bcd*, *ce*, *cf*, *cg*, *de*, *df*, *dg*, *abce*, *abcf*, *acdef*, *acdeg*, *acdfg*, *bcdef*, *bcdeg*, *bcdfg*, *bef*, *abcg*, *abde*, *abdf*, *abdg*, *beg*, *bfg*, *acd*, *aef*, *aeg*, *afg*, *cefg*, *defg*, *abcefg*, *abdefg*

Block 3   *c*, *abc*, *abd*, *ae*, *af*, *ag*, *acde*, *acdf*, *acdg*, *be*, *bf*, *def*, *deg*, *dfg*, *abdef*, *abdeg*, *abdfg*, *abcef*, *bg*, *bcde*, *bcdf*, *bcdg*, *abceg*, *abcfg*, *d*, *cef*, *cfg*, *aefg*, *acdefg*, *befg*, *bcdefg*, *ceg*

Block 4   *e*, *abe*, *abcde*, *ac*, *acef*, *aceg*, *ad*, *adef*, *adeg*, *bc*, *bcef*, *cdf*, *cdg*, *cdefg*, *abcdf*, *abcdg*, *abcdfg*, *abf*, *bceg*, *bd*, *bdef*, *bdeg*, *abg*, *abefg*, *cde*, *f*, *g*, *efg*, *acfg*, *adfg*, *bcfg*, *bdfg*

(iii) Sixteen observations per block ($ABCD$, $BCEF$, $ADEF$, $ACFG$, $BDFG$, $ABEG$, $CDEG$, confounded with block effects).

Block 1   (1), *bde*, *adg*, *abeg*, *bcg*, *cdeg*, *abcd*, *ace*, *efg*, *bdfg*, *adef*, *abf*, *bcef*, *cdf*, *abcdefg*, *acfg*

Block 2   *a*, *abde*, *dg*, *beg*, *abcg*, *acdeg*, *bcd*, *ce*, *aefg*, *abdfg*, *def*, *bf*, *abcef*, *acdf*, *bcdefg*, *cfg*

Block 3   *b*, *de*, *abdg*, *aeg*, *cg*, *bcdeg*, *acd*, *abce*, *befg*, *dfg*, *abdef*, *af*, *cef*, *bcdf*, *acdefg*, *abcfg*

Block 4   *c*, *bcde*, *acdg*, *abceg*, *bg*, *deg*, *abd*, *ae*, *cefg*, *bcdfg*, *acdef*, *abcf*, *bef*, *df*, *abdefg*, *afg*

Block 5   *d*, *be*, *ag*, *abdeg*, *bcdg*, *ceg*, *abc*, *acde*, *defg*, *bfg*, *aef*, *abdf*, *bcdef*, *cf*, *abcefg*, *acdfg*

Block 6   *e*, *bd*, *adeg*, *abg*, *bceg*, *cdg*, *abcde*, *ac*, *fg*, *bdefg*, *adf*, *abef*, *bcf*, *cdef*, *abcdfg*, *acefg*

Block 7   *f*, *bdef*, *adfg*, *abefg*, *bcfg*, *cdefg*, *abcdf*, *acef*, *eg*, *bdg*, *ade*, *ab*, *bce*, *cd*, *abcdeg*, *acg*

Block 8   *g*, *bdeg*, *ad*, *abe*, *bc*, *cde*, *abcdg*, *aceg*, *ef*, *bdf*, *adefg*, *abfg*, *bcefg*, *cdfg*, *abcdef*, *acf*

(iv) Eight observations per block (ACF, ADE, BCE, BDF, CDG, ABG, EFG, $ABEF$, $CDEF$, $ABCD$, $BDEG$, $ACEG$, $ADFG$, $BCFG$, $ABCDEFG$, confounded with block effects).

Block 1   (1), *aceg*, *bdeg*, *abcd*, *adfg*, *cdef*, *abef*, *bcfg*

Block 2   *a*, *ceg*, *abdeg*, *bcd*, *dfg*, *acdef*, *bef*, *abcfg*

Block 3   *b*, *abceg*, *deg*, *acd*, *abdfg*, *bcdef*, *aef*, *cfg*

Block 4   *c*, *aeg*, *bcdeg*, *abd*, *acdfg*, *def*, *abcef*, *bfg*

Block 5   *d*, *acdeg*, *beg*, *abc*, *afg*, *cef*, *abdef*, *bcdfg*

Block 6   *e*, *acg*, *bdg*, *abcde*, *adefg*, *cdf*, *abf*, *bcefg*

Block 7   *f*, *acefg*, *bdefg*, *abcdf*, *adg*, *cde*, *abe*, *bcg*

Block 8   *g*, *ace*, *bde*, *abcdg*, *adf*, *cdefg*, *abefg*, *bcf*

Block 9   *ab*, *bceg*, *adeg*, *cd*, *bdfg*, *abcdef*, *ef*, *acfg*

Block 10 *ac*, *eg*, *abcdeg*, *bd*, *cdfg*, *adef*, *bcef*, *abfg*

Block 11 *ad*, *cdeg*, *abeg*, *bc*, *fg*, *acef*, *bdef*, *abcdfg*

Block 12 *ae*, *cg*, *abdg*, *bcde*, *defg*, *acdf*, *bf*, *abcefg*

Block 13 *af*, *cefg*, *abdefg*, *bcdf*, *dg*, *acde*, *be*, *abcg*

Block 14 *ag*, *ce*, *abde*, *bcdg*, *df*, *acdefg*, *befg*, *abcf*

Block 15 *bg*, *abce*, *de*, *acdg*, *abdf*, *bcdefg*, *aefg*, *cf*

Block 16 *abg*, *bce*, *ade*, *cdg*, *bdf*, *abcdefg*, *efg*, *acf*

12-3.2 ANALYSIS OF BLOCKED FACTORIAL EXPERIMENTS WHEN EACH FACTOR IS AT TWO LEVELS

12-3.2.1 Estimation of Main Effects and Interactions. The procedure of Paragraph 12-2.2.1 (Yates' method) should be used. Remember that certain of the interactions are confounded with block effects.

12-3.2.2 Testing for Significance of Main Effects and Interactions. Before using this procedure, read Paragraph 12-1.2, and perform the computations described in Paragraph 12-2.2.1.

Procedure

(1) Choose α, the level of significance.

(2) If there is no estimate of the variation due to experimental error available*, find the sum of squares of the g's corresponding to interactions of three or more factors in the Yates' Table (omitting those interactions that are confounded with blocks).

(3) To obtain s^2, divide the sum of squares obtained in Step 2 by $2^n\nu$, where ν is the number of interactions included. If an independent estimate of the variation due to experimental error *is* available, use this s^2.

(4) Look up $t_{1-\alpha/2}$ for ν degrees of freedom in Table A-4.
If higher order interactions are used to obtain s^2, ν is the number of interactions included.
If an independent estimate of s^2 is used, ν is the degrees of freedom associated with this estimate.

(5) Compute
$$w = (2^n)^{\frac{1}{2}} t_{1-\alpha/2}\, s$$

(6) For any main effect or interaction X, if $|g_X| > w$, conclude that X is different from zero, e.g., if $|g_A| > w$, conclude that the A effect is different from zero. Otherwise, there is no reason to believe that X is different from zero.

---

* See Paragraph 12-1.2.

12-4 FRACTIONAL FACTORIAL EXPERIMENTS (EACH FACTOR AT TWO LEVELS)

12-4.1 THE FRACTIONAL FACTORIAL DESIGNS

If there are many factors, a complete factorial experiment (Paragraph 12-2), requiring all possible combinations of levels of the factors, involves a large number of tests. This is true even when only two levels of each factor are being investigated. In such cases, the complete factorial experiment may overtax the available facilities. In other situations, it may not be practical to plan the entire experimental program in advance, and we may wish to conduct a few smaller experiments to serve as a guide to future work. It is possible that the complete set of experiments may furnish more information or precision than is needed for the purpose in hand.

In these cases, it is useful to have a plan that requires fewer tests than the complete factorial experiment. Recent developments in statistics have considered the problem of planning multifactor experiments that require measuring only a fraction of the total number of possible combinations. The *fraction* is a carefully prescribed subset of all possible combinations; its analysis is relatively straightforward; and the use of a fractional factorial does not preclude the possibility of later completion of the full factorial experiment.

In Figures 12-2, 12-3, and 12-4, let the letters A, B, C, D, E, F, and G, stand for seven factors to be investigated, and let the subscripts zero and one denote two alternative levels of each factor. The 128 $(= 2^7)$ possible experimental conditions are represented by the 128 cells of Figure 12-2. The shaded squares represent those experimental combinations to be investigated if the experimenter wishes to measure only half the 128 possible combinations. In the same way, the shaded cells in Figures 12-3 and 12-4 illustrate plans requiring only 32 and 16 measurements, respectively, instead of the full set of 128.

Fractional factorial experiments obviously cannot produce as much information as the full factorial. Economy is achieved at the expense of assuming that certain of the interactions between factors are negligible. Some of the larger fractions (e.g., the half-replicate shown in Figure 12-2) require only that third-order (and higher) interactions be assumed negligible, and this assumption is not uncommon. However, the plan calling for one-eighth of the possible combinations, as shown in Figure 12-4, can only be used for evaluating the main effects of each of the seven factors, and will not allow the evaluation of any two-factor interactions.

In a complete factorial experiment we have 2^n tests. In the analysis of a complete factorial, we have n main effects, $2^n - n - 1$ interaction effects, and an overall average effect. The 2^n tests can be used to give independent estimates of the 2^n effects. In a fractional factorial $\Big($ say the fraction $\dfrac{1}{2^b}\Big)$ there will be only 2^{n-b} tests and, therefore, 2^{n-b} independent estimates. In designing the fractional plans (i.e., in selecting an optimum subset of the 2^n total combinations), the goal is to keep each of the 2^{n-b} estimates as "clean" as possible — i.e., to keep the estimates of main effects and if possible second-order interactions free of confusion with each other.

If we plan to test whether or not certain of the effects are significant, we must have an estimate of the variation due to experimental error which is independent of our estimates of the effects. See Paragraph 12-1.2.

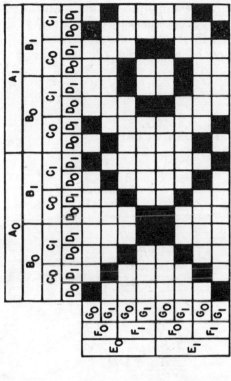

Figure 12-3. A one-quarter replicate of a 2^7 factorial.

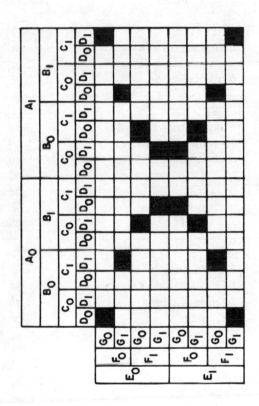

Figure 12-4. A one-eighth replicate of a 2^7 factorial.

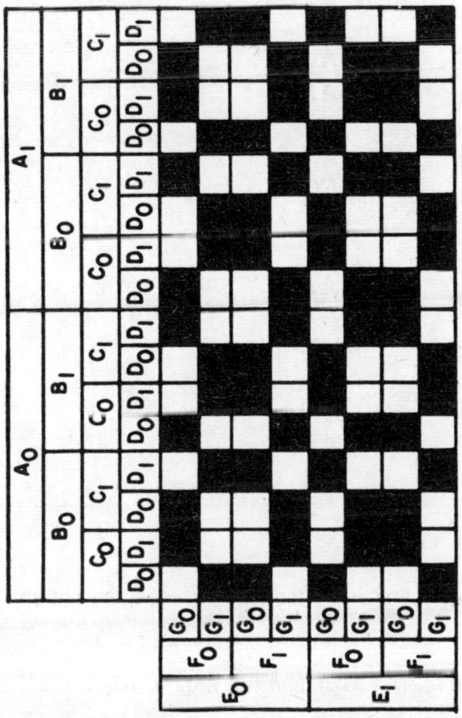

Figure 12-2. A one-half replicate of a 2^7 factorial.

Table 12-4 gives a number of useful two-level fractional factorial plans, together with the effects that can be estimated (assuming three-factor and higher-order interaction terms are negligible). The treatment combinations should be randomly allocated to the experimental material. More two-level plans may be found in reference [4], and fractional factorial plans for factors at three levels may be found in reference [5].

TABLE 12-4. SOME FRACTIONAL FACTORIAL PLANS

Plans	Treatment Combinations†	Estimated Effects‡
Plan 1:	(1)	T
Three factors ($n = 3$)	ac	$A - BC$
½ replication ($b = 1$)	bc	$B - AC$
4 observations	ab	$-C + AB$
Plan 2:	(1)	T
Four factors ($n = 4$)	ad	A
½ replication ($b = 1$)	bd	B
8 observations	ab	$AB + CD$
	cd	C
	ac	$AC + BD$
	bc	$BC + AD$
	$abcd$	D
Plan 3:	(1)	T
Five factors ($n = 5$)	ae	A
½ replication ($b = 1$)	be	B
16 observations	ab	AB
	ce	C
	ac	AC
	bc	BC
	$abce$	$-DE$
	de	D
	ad	AD
	bd	BD
	$abde$	$-CE$
	cd	CD
	$acde$	$-BE$
	$bcde$	$-AE$
	$abcd$	$-E$

† The order given is the order in which the data are to be listed in the first column of the Yates method of analysis (see Pars. 12-2.2.1 and 12-4.2.1).

‡ The order given is the order in which estimated effects come out in the last column of the Yates method of analysis. See Pars. 12-2.2.1 and 12-4.2.1.

TABLE 12-4. SOME FRACTIONAL FACTORIAL PLANS (Continued)

Plans	Treatment Combinations†	Estimated Effects‡
Plan 4:	(1)	T
Five factors ($n = 5$)	ad	$A - DE$
¼ replication ($b = 2$)	bde	$B - CE$
8 observations	abe	$AB + CD$
	cde	$C - BE$
	ace	$AC + BD$
	bc	$-E + BC + AD$
	$abcd$	$D - AE$
Plan 5:	(1)	T
Six factors ($n = 6$)	ae	A
¼ replication ($b = 2$)	bef	B
16 observations	abf	$AB + CE$
	cef	C
	acf	$AC + BE$
	bc	$BC + AE + DF$
	$abce$	E
	df	D
	$adef$	$AD + EF$
	bde	$BD + CF$
	abd	*
	cde	$CD + BF$
	acd	*
	$bcdf$	F
	$abcdef$	$AF + DE$
Plan 6:	(1)	T
Six factors ($n = 6$)	adf	$A - DE - CF$
⅛ replication ($b = 3$)	bde	$B - CE - DF$
8 observations	$abef$	$AB + CD + EF$
	$cdef$	$C - AF - BE$
	ace	$-F + AC + BD$
	bcf	$-E + AD + BC$
	$abcd$	$D - AE - BF$

† ‡ See footnote on page 12-16.

* To be used in our estimate of the variation due to experimental error.

TABLE 12-4.   SOME FRACTIONAL FACTORIAL PLANS (Continued)

Plans	Treatment Combinations†	Estimated Effects‡
Plan 7:	(1)	T
Seven factors ($n = 7$)	aeg	A
⅛ replication ($b = 3$)	$befg$	B
16 observations	abf	$AB + CE + DG$
	cef	C
	$acfg$	$AC + BE + FG$
	bcg	$BC + AE + DF$
	$abce$	E
	dfg	D
	$adef$	$AD + EF + BG$
	bde	$BD + CF + AG$
	$abdg$	G
	$cdeg$	$CD + BF + EG$
	acd	$*$
	$bcdf$	F
	$abcdefg$	$AF + DE + CG$
Plan 8:	(1)	T
Eight factors ($n = 8$)	$aegh$	A
1/16 replication ($b = 4$)	$befg$	B
16 observations	$abfh$	$AB + CE + DG + FH$
	$cefh$	C
	$acfg$	$AC + BE + FG + DH$
	$bcgh$	$BC + AE + DF + GH$
	$abce$	E
	$dfgh$	D
	$adef$	$AD + EF + BG + CH$
	$bdeh$	$BD + AG + CF + EH$
	$abdg$	G
	$cdeg$	$CD + AH + BF + EG$
	$acdh$	H
	$bcdf$	F
	$abcdefgh$	$AF + DE + CG + BH$

† ‡ * See footnotes, pages 12-16 and 12-17.

12-18

Data Sample 12-4 — Flame Tests of Fire-Retardant Treatments

Using Data Sample 12-2, we assume that a fractional factorial design had been used, instead of the full factorial. From Table 12-4, we use plan 2, a one-half replicate of four factors ($n = 4$, $b = 1$). The plan is reproduced as follows:

TREATMENT COMBINATIONS	ESTIMATED EFFECTS
(1)	T
ad	A
bd	B
ab	$AB + CD$
cd	C
ac	$AC + BD$
bc	$BC + AD$
$abcd$	D

The resulting data are shown in Table 12-5.

TABLE 12-5. RESULTS OF FLAME TESTS OF FIRE-RETARDANT TREATMENTS (FRACTIONAL FACTORIAL EXPERIMENT OF DATA SAMPLE 12-4)

		A_0				A_1			
		B_0		B_1		B_0		B_1	
C_0	D_0	4.2	(1)					2.9	ab
	D_1			5.0	bd	3.0	ad		
C_1	D_0			4.6	bc	2.8	ac		
	D_1	4.0	cd					2.3	$abcd$

12-4.2 ANALYSIS

12-4.2.1 Estimates of Main Effects and Interactions. We use the Yates procedure described in Paragraph 12-2.2.1, replacing n by n' where $n' = n - b$ for the particular fractional factorial used (see Table 12-4). In other words, make a table with $n' + 2$ columns. In column 1 of the Yates table, list the treatment combinations in the order given in the plan in Table 12-4. The last column of the Yates table (column $n' + 2$) will give the g's corresponding to the effects, in the order listed in the "estimated effects" column of Table 12-4. To obtain the estimates of main effects and interactions, divide each g by $2^{n'-1}$. In Table 12-6, we show the Yates method of analysis applied to a fractional factorial experiment, using the results of Data Sample 12-4.

For fractional factorial plans that are not given in Table 12-4, see Davies[3] for the Yates method of analysis.

TABLE 12-6. YATES' METHOD OF ANALYSIS USING DATA SAMPLE 12-4

1 Treatment Combination	2 Response (Yield)	3	4	5 g	Estimated Effect
(1)	4.2	7.2	15.1	28.8	T
ad	3.0	7.9	13.7	-6.8	A
bd	5.0	6.8	-3.3	0.8	B
ab	2.9	6.9	-3.5	-2.0	$AB + CD$
cd	4.0	-1.2	0.7	-1.4	C
ac	2.8	-2.1	0.1	-0.2	$AC + BD$
bc	4.6	-1.2	-0.9	-0.6	$BC + AD$
$abcd$	2.3	-2.3	-1.1	-0.2	D
Total	28.8				
Sum of Squares	110.34			882.72	

Checks: (see Steps 6, 7, and 8 of Paragraph 12-2.2.1).

The sum of column 2 should equal g_T, the first entry in column 5.

The sum of squares of entries in column 2 should equal the sum of squares of the g's divided by $2^{n'} = 2^3 = 8$. ($110.34 = 882.72/8 = 110.34$).

g_A = sum of all yields in which A is at its higher level minus sum of all yields in which A is at its lower level.

$g_A = 11.0 - 17.8 = -6.8$.

Similarly,

$g_B = 14.8 - 14.0 = 0.8$

$g_C = 13.7 - 15.1 = -1.4$.

12-4.2.2 Testing for Significance of Main Effects and Interactions. Before using this procedure, read Paragraph 12-1.2, and perform the computations specified in Paragraph 12-4.2.1.

Procedure	Example
(1) Choose α, the level of significance.	(1) Let $\alpha = .05$
(2) If no external estimate of the variation due to experimental error is available,* check the lines in the Yates table that correspond to estimated effects which are expected to be zero. Compute the sum of squares of the g's for the lines checked.	(2) See Step (3).
(3) To obtain s^2, divide the sum of squares obtained in Step (2) by $2^{n'}\nu$, where ν is the number of interactions included. If an independent estimate of the variation due to experimental error *is* available, use this s^2.	(3) In the analysis, we use an independent estimate of s^2, from 24 pairs of duplicate measurements obtained in another part of the larger program: $$s^2 = .0408$$ $$s = .202$$ $$\nu = 24$$
(4) Look up $t_{1-\alpha/2}$ for ν degrees of freedom in Table A-4.	(4) $t_{.975}$ for 24 d.f. $= 2.064$
(5) Compute $$w = (2^{n'})^{\frac{1}{2}} t_{1-\alpha/2}\, s$$	(5) $$w = \sqrt{8}\ (2.064)\ (0.202)$$ $$= (2.828)\ (0.417)$$ $$= 1.18$$
(6) For any main effect or interaction X, if the absolute value of g_X is greater than w, conclude that X is different from zero. For example, if $|g_A| > w$, conclude that the A effect is different from zero. Otherwise, there is no reason to believe that X is different from zero.	(6) See Table 12-6. $|g_A| = 6.8$, $|g_C| = 1.4$, and $|g_{AB+CD}| = 2.0$ are all greater than w; therefore, the main effect of A, the main effect of C, and the mixed interaction $AB + CD$ are believed to be significant.

---

* See Paragraph 12-1.2.

REFERENCES

1. F. Yates, *The Design and Analysis of Factorial Experiments*, Technical Communication No. 35, Imperial Bureau of Soil Science, Harpenden, England, 1937.

2. W. G. Cochran and G. M. Cox, *Experimental Designs* (2d. edition), John Wiley and Sons, Inc., New York, N.Y., 1957.

3. O. L. Davies (Ed.), *The Design and Analysis of Industrial Experiments*, Hafner Publishing Co., New York, N.Y., 1954.

4. National Bureau of Standards, *Fractional Factorial Experiment Designs For Factors at Two Levels*, Applied Mathematics Series, No. 48, U. S. Government Printing Office, Washington 25, D.C., 1957.

5. National Bureau of Standards, *Fractional Factorial Experiment Designs for Factors at Three Levels*, Applied Mathematics Series, No. 54, U. S. Government Printing Office, Washington 25, D.C., 1959.

CHAPTER 13

RANDOMIZED BLOCKS, LATIN SQUARES, AND OTHER SPECIAL-PURPOSE DESIGNS

13-1 INTRODUCTION

The experimental designs treated in this chapter (with a single exception) make use of the *planned grouping* discussed in Chapter 11. The exception is the completely-randomized design discussed in Paragraph 13-2, which is included here as a contrast to the *blocked designs* that follow. In Paragraph 13-3, we discuss the simplest type of blocked design, *randomized blocks*, where blocking is made with respect to one source of inhomogeneity and the block is large enough to accommodate all the treatments we wish to test. In Paragraph 13-4, *incomplete-block designs*, the blocking again is one-way, but the block size is not large enough for all treatments to be tested in every block. In one case, the designs are called *balanced incomplete-block* plans (Paragraph 13-4.2), because certain restrictions on the assignment of treatments to blocks lead to equal precision in the estimation of differences between treatments.

The *chain block* design, a special type of incomplete block design without this balance in the precision of the estimates, is discussed in Paragraph 13-4.3.

When the experimental plan is designed to eliminate two sources of inhomogeneity, two-way blocking is used. The Latin squares and Youden squares (Paragraphs 13-5 and 13-6) are examples of such designs.

13-2 COMPLETELY-RANDOMIZED PLANS

13-2.1 PLANNING

This plan is simple, and is the best choice when the experimental material is homogeneous and background conditions can be well controlled during the experiment. If there are a total of N available experimental units, and we wish to assign n_1, n_2, . . . , n_t experimental units respectively to each of the t treatments or products, then we proceed to assign the experimental units to the treatments at random. As an example, suppose we wish to test three types of ammunition of a given size and caliber, to see which type has the highest velocity. We have n_1, n_2, n_3 shells, respectively, of the three types. If the conditions under which the shells are fired are assumed to be the same for each shell, i.e., temperature, barrel conditions, etc., then the simplest plan is to choose the shells at random and fire them in that order. It is obvious that if we fired all the shells of one type first, and then fired all the shells of the next type, etc., we would have no insurance against influences on velocity such as the wearing of the gun barrel or changes in atmospheric conditions such as temperature. Randomization affords insurance against uncontrollable disturbances in the sense that such disturbances have the same chance of affecting each of the factors under study, and will be balanced out in the long run.

The results of a completely-randomized plan can be exhibited in a table such as Table 13-1.

TABLE 13-1. SCHEMATIC PRESENTATION OF RESULTS FOR COMPLETELY-RANDOMIZED PLANS

Observation	Treatment			
	1	2	...	t
1				
2				
3				
.				
.				
.				
Total				
Mean				

13-2.2 ANALYSIS

Follow the procedure of Chapter 3, Paragraph 3-4, which gives the method for comparing the averages of several products.

13-3 RANDOMIZED BLOCK PLANS

13-3.1 PLANNING

In comparing a number of treatments, it is clearly desirable that all other conditions be kept as nearly constant as possible.   Often the required number of tests is too large to be carried out under similar conditions.   In such cases, we may be able to divide the experiment into *blocks*, or planned homogeneous groups (see Chapter 11).   When each such group in the experiment contains exactly one observation on every treatment, the experimental plan is called a *randomized block plan*.

There are many situations where a randomized block plan can be profitably utilized.   For example, a testing scheme may take several days to complete.   If we expect some systematic differences between days, we might plan to observe each item on each day, or to conduct one test per day on each item.   A day would then represent a block.   In another situation, several persons may be conducting the tests or making the observations, and differences between operators are expected.   The tests or observations made by a given operator can be considered to represent a block.

The size of a block may be restricted by physical considerations.   Suppose we wished to test the wearing qualities of two different synthetic substances used as shoe soles.   The two feet of an individual constitute a logical block, since the kind and amount of wear usually is very nearly the same for each foot.

In general, a randomized block plan is one in which each of the treatments appears exactly once in every block.   The treatments are allocated to experimental units at random within a given block.

The results of a randomized block experiment can be exhibited in a two-way table such as Table 13-2, assuming we have b blocks and t treatments.

TABLE 13-2. SCHEMATIC PRESENTATION OF RESULTS FOR RANDOMIZED BLOCK PLANS

Block	Treatment				Total	Block Mean = B/t
	1	2	...	t		
1					B_1	
2					B_2	
.					.	
.					.	
.					.	
b					B_b	
Total	T_1	T_2	...	T_t	G	
Treatment Mean = T/b						

Since each treatment occurs exactly once in every block, the treatment totals or means are directly comparable without adjustment.

13-3.2 ANALYSIS

The analysis of a randomized block experiment depends on a number of assumptions. We assume that each of the observations is the sum of three components. If we let Y_{ij} be the observation on the ith treatment in the jth block, then

$$Y_{ij} = \varphi_i + \beta_j + e_{ij},$$

where β_j is a term peculiar to a given block. It is the amount by which the response of a given treatment in the jth block differs from the response of the same treatment averaged over all blocks, assuming no experimental error.

φ_i is a term peculiar to the ith treatment, and is constant for all blocks regardless of the block in which the treatment occurs. It may be regarded as the average value of the ith treatment averaged over all blocks in the experiment, assuming no experimental error.

e_{ij} is the experimental error associated with the measurement Y_{ij}.

In order to make interval estimates for, or to make tests on, the φ_i's or the β_j's, we generally assume that the experimental errors e_{ij}'s are independently and normally distributed. However, if the experiment was randomized properly, failure of this assumption will, in general, not cause serious difficulty.

Data Sample 13-3.2 — Conversion Gain of Resistors

The following data, tabulated as outlined in Table 13-2, represent conversion gain of four resistors measured in six test sets.   Conversion gain is defined as the ratio of available current-noise power to applied direct-current power expressed in decibel units, and is a measure of the efficiency with which a resistor converts direct-current power to available current-noise power.

We are interested in possible differences among treatments (test sets) and blocks (resistors).

Resistor (Blocks)	Test Set (Treatments)						Total	Mean
	1463	1506	1938	1946	1948	2140		
3	138.0	141.6	137.5	141.8	138.6	139.6	$B_1 = 837.1$	$b_1 = 139.52$
4	152.2	152.2	152.1	152.2	152.0	152.8	$B_2 = 913.5$	$b_2 = 152.25$
5	153.6	154.0	153.8	153.6	153.2	153.6	$B_3 = 921.8$	$b_3 = 153.63$
6	141.4	141.5	142.6	142.2	141.1	141.9	$B_4 = 850.7$	$b_4 = 141.78$
Total	$T_1 =$ 585.2	$T_2 =$ 589.3	$T_3 =$ 586.0	$T_4 =$ 589.8	$T_5 =$ 584.9	$T_6 =$ 587.9	$G =$ 3523.1	
Mean	$t_1 =$ 146.30	$t_2 =$ 147.32	$t_3 =$ 146.50	$t_4 =$ 147.45	$t_5 =$ 146.22	$t_6 =$ 146.98		

13-3.2.1 Estimation of the Treatment Effects.   A treatment effect φ_i is estimated by the mean of the observations on the ith treatment.   That is, the estimate of φ_i is $t_i = T_i/b$.

For example, see Data Sample 13-3.2.   The estimate of the effect of Test Set 1463 is $t_1 = T_1/4 = 585.2/4 = 146.30$.   Similarly, $t_2 = 147.32$, $t_3 = 146.50$, $t_4 = 147.45$, $t_5 = 146.22$, $t_6 = 146.98$.

13-3.2.2 Testing and Estimating Differences in Treatment Effects.

Procedure	Example
(1) Choose α, the significance level of the test.	(1) Let $\alpha = .05$

(2) Look up $q_{1-\alpha}(t, \nu)$ in Table A-10, where

$$\nu = (b-1)(t-1)$$

(2) From Data Sample 13-3.2,

$$q_{.95}(6, 15) = 4.59$$

(3) Compute

$$S_t = (T_1^2 + T_2^2 + \ldots + T_t^2)/b - G^2/tb$$

(3)

$$S_t = 517,181.998 - 517,176.400$$
$$= 5.598$$

(4) Compute

$$S_b = (B_1^2 + B_2^2 + \ldots + B_b^2)/t - G^2/tb$$

(4)

$$S_b = 518,104.065 - 517,176.400$$
$$= 927.665$$

(5) Compute

$$S = \sum_{i=1}^{t} \sum_{j=1}^{b} Y_{ij}^2 - G^2/tb,$$

i.e., compute the sum of the squares of all the observations, and subtract G^2/tb.

(5)

$$S = 518,123.13 - 517,176.40$$
$$= 946.73$$

(6) Compute

$$s^2 = (S - S_b - S_t)/(b-1)(t-1)$$

and

$$s$$

(6)

$$s^2 = 13.467/15$$
$$= 0.8978$$
$$s = 0.9475$$

(7) Compute

$$w = q_{1-\alpha} s/\sqrt{b}$$

(7)

$$w = (4.59)(0.9475)/\sqrt{4}$$
$$= 2.175$$

(8) If the absolute difference between any two estimated treatment effects exceeds w, decide that the treatment effects differ; otherwise, the experiment gives no reason to believe the treatment effects differ.

(8) Since there is no pair of treatment means whose difference exceeds 2.175, we have no reason to conclude that test sets differ.

Note: It should be noted that for all possible pairs of treatments i and j, we can make the statements

$$t_i - t_j - w \leq \varphi_i - \varphi_j \leq t_i - t_j + w$$

with $1 - \alpha$ confidence that all the statements are simultaneously true.

13-3.2.3 Estimation of Block Effects.

The block effect β_j is estimated by the mean of the observations in the jth block minus the grand mean. That is, the estimate of β_j, the jth block effect, is $b_j = B_j/t - G/bt$.

For example, using Data Sample 13-3.2, the grand average equals $G/bt = 3523.1/24 = 146.80$.

$$b_1 = 139.52 - 146.80 \qquad b_3 = 153.63 - 146.80$$
$$= -7.28 \qquad\qquad = 6.83$$

$$b_2 = 152.25 - 146.80 \qquad b_4 = 141.78 - 146.80$$
$$= 5.45 \qquad\qquad = -5.02$$

13-3.2.4 Testing and Estimating Differences in Block Effects.

Procedure	Example
(1) Choose α, the significance level of the test.	(1) Let $\alpha = .05$
(2) Look up $q_{1-\alpha}(b, \nu)$ in Table A-10, where $$\nu = (b - 1)(t - 1)$$	(2) From Data Sample 13-3.2: $$\nu = (4 - 1)(6 - 1)$$ $$= 15$$ $$q_{.95}(4, 15) = 4.08$$
(3)	(3) $S_t = 5.598$
(4) Same as Steps (3), (4), (5), and (6), in	(4) $S_b = 927.665$
(5) Paragraph 13-3.2.2	(5) $S = 946.73$
(6)	(6) $s^2 = 0.8978$ $s = 0.9475$
(7) Compute $$w' = q_{1-\alpha} s/\sqrt{t}$$	(7) $$w' = (4.08)(0.9475)/\sqrt{6}$$ $$= 1.578$$
(8) If the absolute difference between any two block effects exceeds w', conclude that the block effects differ; otherwise, the experiment gives no reason to believe that block effects differ.	(8) See Paragraph 13-3.2.3. The absolute difference between two block effects does exceed 1.578, and we conclude that resistors do differ.

Note: As in the case of treatment effects, we can make simultaneous statements about the difference between pairs of blocks i and j, with confidence $1 - \alpha$ that all the statements are simultaneously true. The statements are, for all i and j,

$$b_i - b_j - w' \leq \beta_i - \beta_j \leq b_i - b_j + w'.$$

13-4 INCOMPLETE BLOCK PLANS

13-4.1 GENERAL

Incomplete block plans are similar to the randomized block plans of Paragraph 13-3, in that they make use of planned grouping. The distinguishing feature of incomplete block plans is that the block size is not large enough to accommodate all treatments in one block. For example, suppose that a *block* is one day, but that the time required for each test is so long that all experimental treatments cannot be run in one day. The limitation may be due to lack of space; such is the case in spectrographic analysis where a block may be one photographic plate, and the number of specimens to be compared may exceed the capacity of the plate.

We discuss two kinds of randomized incomplete block plans — balanced incomplete block plans in Paragraph 13-4.2, and chain block plans in Paragraph 13-4.3. The former have the advantage of easy analysis and the important property that all differences between treatment effects are estimated with the same precision. The chain block plans have an advantage when we wish to keep the number of duplicate observations on treatments to a minimum, and are very useful when the difference in treatments considered worth detecting is large in comparison to the amount of experimental error. (Experimental error may be thought of as the difference between an observed treatment and the average of a large number of similar observations under similar conditions.)

Other incomplete block designs are available if these two classes do not meet the desires of the experimenter with regard to number of blocks, size of blocks, number of treatments, etc. An important and very large class of designs is the class called the "partially-balanced incomplete block designs" (see Bose, et al.[1]). Experiments using these plans, which are not discussed here, are slightly more complicated to analyze.

13-4.2 BALANCED INCOMPLETE BLOCK PLANS

13-4.2.1 Planning. We define r, b, t, k, λ, E, and N as follows:

r = number of replications (number of times each treatment appears in the plan);
b = number of blocks in the plan;
t = number of treatments;
k = number of treatments which appear in every block;
λ = number of blocks in which a given treatment-pair appears, $\lambda = \dfrac{r(k-1)}{t-1}$;

E = a constant used in the analysis, $E = t\lambda/rk$;
N = total number of observations, $N = tr = bk$.

Using this nomenclature, it is possible to enumerate the situations in which it is combinatorially possible to construct a balanced incomplete block design. Plans are listed in Table 13-3 for $4 \leq t \leq 10$, $r \leq 10$. For some other balanced incomplete block plans, see Cochran and Cox.[2]

If we wish to estimate and to make tests of block effects as well as treatment effects, we should consider the plans where $b = t$, i.e., the number of blocks equals the number of treatments. In such plans, called *symmetrical balanced incomplete block designs*, differences between block effects are estimated with equal precision for all pairs of blocks.

To use a given plan from Table 13-3, proceed as follows:

(1) Rearrange the blocks at random. (In a number of the plans in Table 13-3, the blocks are arranged in groups. In these plans, rearrange the blocks at random within their respective groups).

(2) Randomize the positions of the treatment numbers within each block.

(3) Assign the treatments at random to the treatment numbers in the plan.

TABLE 13-3. BALANCED INCOMPLETE BLOCK PLANS ($4 \leq t \leq 10$, $r \leq 10$)

Index

t	k	r	b	λ	E†	Plan No.††
4	2	3	6	1	2/3	1
	3	3	4	2	8/9	*
5	2	4	10	1	5/8	2
	3	6	10	3	5/6	*
	4	4	5	3	15/16	*
6	2	5	15	1	3/5	3
	3	5	10	2	4/5	4
	3	10	20	4	4/5	5
	4	10	15	6	9/10	6
	5	5	6	4	24/25	*
7	2	6	21	1	7/12	*
	3	3	7	1	7/9	7
	4	4	7	2	7/8	8
	6	6	7	5	35/36	*
8	2	7	28	1	4/7	9
	4	7	14	3	6/7	10
	7	7	8	6	48/49	*
9	2	8	36	1	9/16	*
	3	4	12	1	3/4	11
	4	8	18	3	27/32	12
	5	10	18	5	9/10	13
	6	8	12	5	15/16	14
	8	8	9	7	63/64	*
10	2	9	45	1	5/9	15
	3	9	30	2	20/27	16
	4	6	15	2	5/6	17
	5	9	18	4	8/9	18
	6	9	15	5	25/27	19
	9	9	10	8	80/81	*

† The constant $E = t\lambda/rk$ is used in the analysis.

†† The asterisk indicates plans that may be constructed by forming all possible combinations of the t treatments in blocks of size k.   The number of blocks b serves as a check that no block has been missed.

Plan 1: $t = 4$, $k = 2$, $r = 3$, $b = 6$, $\lambda = 1$, $E = 2/3$

Group I	Group II	Group III
(1) 1, 2	(3) 1, 3	(5) 1, 4
(2) 3, 4	(4) 2, 4	(6) 2, 3

Plan 2: $t = 5$, $k = 2$, $r = 4$, $b = 10$, $\lambda = 1$, $E = 5/8$

Group I	Group II
(1) 1, 2	(6) 1, 3
(2) 2, 5	(7) 2, 4
(3) 3, 4	(8) 3, 2
(4) 4, 1	(9) 4, 5
(5) 5, 3	(10) 5, 1

TABLE 13-3. BALANCED INCOMPLETE BLOCK PLANS* (Continued)
$(4 \leq t \leq 10, r \leq 10)$

Plan 3: $t = 6, k = 2, r = 5, b = 15, \lambda = 1, E = 3/5$

Group I	Group II	Group III	Group IV	Group V
(1) 1, 2	(4) 1, 3	(7) 1, 4	(10) 1, 5	(13) 1, 6
(2) 3, 4	(5) 2, 5	(8) 2, 6	(11) 2, 4	(14) 2, 3
(3) 5, 6	(6) 4, 6	(9) 3, 5	(12) 3, 6	(15) 4, 5

Plan 4: $t = 6, k = 3, r = 5, b = 10, \lambda = 2, E = 4/5$

(1) 1, 2, 5	(5) 1, 4, 5	(8) 2, 4, 6
(2) 1, 2, 6	(6) 2, 3, 4	(9) 3, 5, 6
(3) 1, 3, 4	(7) 2, 3, 5	(10) 4, 5, 6
(4) 1, 3, 6		

Plan 5: $t = 6, k = 3, r = 10, b = 20, \lambda = 4, E = 4/5$

Group I	Group II	Group III	Group IV
(1) 1, 2, 3	(3) 1, 2, 4	(5) 1, 2, 5	(7) 1, 2, 6
(2) 4, 5, 6	(4) 3, 5, 6	(6) 3, 4, 6	(8) 3, 4, 5

Group V	Group VI	Group VII	Group VIII
(9) 1, 3, 4	(11) 1, 3, 5	(13) 1, 3, 6	(15) 1, 4, 5
(10) 2, 5, 6	(12) 2, 4, 6	(14) 2, 4, 5	(16) 2, 3, 6

Group IX	Group X
(17) 1, 4, 6	(19) 1, 5, 6
(18) 2, 3, 5	(20) 2, 3, 4

Plan 6: $t = 6, k = 4, r = 10, b = 15, \lambda = 6, E = 9/10$

Group I	Group II	Group III
(1) 1, 2, 3, 4	(4) 1, 2, 3, 5	(7) 1, 2, 3, 6
(2) 1, 4, 5, 6	(5) 1, 2, 4, 6	(8) 1, 3, 4, 5
(3) 2, 3, 5, 6	(6) 3, 4, 5, 6	(9) 2, 4, 5, 6

Group IV	Group V
(10) 1, 2, 4, 5	(13) 1, 2, 5, 6
(11) 1, 3, 5, 6	(14) 1, 3, 4, 6
(12) 2, 3, 4, 6	(15) 2, 3, 4, 5

* In the Plans, block numbers are in parentheses followed by numbers which indicate treatments. In a number of the plans given, the blocks are arranged in groups. In setting up the experiment, make the groups as homogeneous as possible — i.e., if possible there should be more difference between blocks in different groups than between blocks in the same group.

TABLE 13-3.   BALANCED INCOMPLETE BLOCK PLANS* (Continued)
$(4 \leq t \leq 10, r \leq 10)$

Plan 7: $t = 7, k = 3, r = 3, b = 7, \lambda = 1, E = 7/9$

(1)	1, 2, 4	(3)	3, 4, 6	(5)	5, 6, 1	(7)	7, 1, 3
(2)	2, 3, 5	(4)	4, 5, 7	(6)	6, 7, 2		

Plan 8: $t = 7, k = 4, r = 4, b = 7, \lambda = 2, E = 7/8$

(1)	1, 2, 3, 6	(3)	3, 4, 5, 1	(5)	5, 6, 7, 3	(7)	7, 1, 2, 5
(2)	2, 3, 4, 7	(4)	4, 5, 6, 2	(6)	6, 7, 1, 4		

Plan 9: $t = 8, k = 2, r = 7, b = 28, \lambda = 1, E = 4/7$

Group I		Group II		Group III		Group IV	
(1)	1, 2	(5)	1, 3	(9)	1, 4	(13)	1, 5
(2)	3, 4	(6)	2, 8	(10)	2, 7	(14)	2, 3
(3)	5, 6	(7)	4, 5	(11)	3, 6	(15)	4, 7
(4)	7, 8	(8)	6, 7	(12)	5, 8	(16)	6, 8

Group V		Group VI		Group VII	
(17)	1, 6	(21)	1, 7	(25)	1, 8
(18)	2, 4	(22)	2, 6	(26)	2, 5
(19)	3, 8	(23)	3, 5	(27)	3, 7
(20)	5, 7	(24)	4, 8	(28)	4, 6

Plan 10: $t = 8, k = 4, r = 7, b = 14, \lambda = 3, E = 6/7$

Group I		Group II		Group III		Group IV	
(1)	1, 2, 3, 4	(3)	1, 2, 7, 8	(5)	1, 3, 6, 8	(7)	1, 4, 6, 7
(2)	5, 6, 7, 8	(4)	3, 4, 5, 6	(6)	2, 4, 5, 7	(8)	2, 3, 5, 8

Group V		Group VI		Group VII	
(9)	1, 2, 5, 6	(11)	1, 3, 5, 7	(13)	1, 4, 5, 8
(10)	3, 4, 7, 8	(12)	2, 4, 6, 8	(14)	2, 3, 6, 7

* See footnote on page 13-9.

TABLE 13-3. BALANCED INCOMPLETE BLOCK PLANS* (Continued)
$(4 \leq t \leq 10, r \leq 10)$

Plan 11: $t = 9, k = 3, r = 4, b = 12, \lambda = 1, E = 3/4$

Group I		Group II		Group III		Group IV	
(1)	1, 2, 3	(4)	1, 4, 7	(7)	1, 5, 9	(10)	1, 8, 6
(2)	4, 5, 6	(5)	2, 5, 8	(8)	7, 2, 6	(11)	4, 2, 9
(3)	7, 8, 9	(6)	3, 6, 9	(9)	4, 8, 3	(12)	7, 5, 3

Plan 12: $t = 9, k = 4, r = 8, b = 18, \lambda = 3, E = 27/32$

Group I		Group II	
(1)	1, 4, 6, 7	(10)	1, 2, 5, 7
(2)	2, 6, 8, 9	(11)	2, 3, 6, 5
(3)	3, 8, 9, 1	(12)	3, 4, 7, 9
(4)	4, 1, 3, 2	(13)	4, 9, 2, 1
(5)	5, 7, 1, 8	(14)	5, 1, 9, 6
(6)	6, 9, 4, 5	(15)	6, 8, 1, 3
(7)	7, 3, 2, 6	(16)	7, 6, 4, 8
(8)	8, 2, 5, 4	(17)	8, 5, 3, 4
(9)	9, 5, 7, 3	(18)	9, 7, 8, 2

Plan 13: $t = 9, k = 5, r = 10, b = 18, \lambda = 5, E = 9/10$

Group I		Group II	
(1)	1, 2, 3, 7, 8	(10)	1, 2, 3, 5, 9
(2)	2, 6, 8, 4, 1	(11)	2, 6, 5, 1, 8
(3)	3, 8, 5, 9, 2	(12)	3, 5, 1, 4, 6
(4)	4, 3, 9, 2, 6	(13)	4, 3, 2, 8, 7
(5)	5, 1, 7, 3, 4	(14)	5, 7, 9, 2, 4
(6)	6, 4, 2, 5, 7	(15)	6, 8, 7, 3, 5
(7)	7, 9, 1, 6, 3	(16)	7, 4, 8, 9, 1
(8)	8, 5, 4, 1, 9	(17)	8, 9, 4, 6, 3
(9)	9, 7, 6, 8, 5	(18)	9, 1, 6, 7, 2

Plan 14: $t = 9, k = 6, r = 8, b = 12, \lambda = 5, E = 15/16$

Group I		Group II	
(1)	1, 2, 4, 5, 7, 8	(4)	1, 2, 5, 6, 7, 9
(2)	2, 3, 5, 6, 8, 9	(5)	1, 3, 4, 5, 8, 9
(3)	1, 3, 4, 6, 7, 9	(6)	2, 3, 4, 6, 7, 8

Group III		Group IV	
(7)	1, 3, 5, 6, 7, 8	(10)	4, 5, 6, 7, 8, 9
(8)	1, 2, 4, 6, 8, 9	(11)	1, 2, 3, 4, 5, 6
(9)	2, 3, 4, 5, 7, 9	(12)	1, 2, 3, 7, 8, 9

* See footnote on page 13-9.

TABLE 13-3.   BALANCED INCOMPLETE BLOCK PLANS* (Continued)
$(4 \leq t \leq 10, r \leq 10)$

Plan 15: $t = 10, k = 2, r = 9, b = 45, \lambda = 1, E = 5/9$

Group I		Group II		Group III		Group IV		Group V	
(1)	1, 2	(6)	1, 3	(11)	1, 4	(16)	1, 5	(21)	1, 6
(2)	3, 4	(7)	2, 7	(12)	2, 10	(17)	2, 8	(22)	2, 9
(3)	5, 6	(8)	4, 8	(13)	3, 7	(18)	3, 10	(23)	3, 8
(4)	7, 8	(9)	5, 9	(14)	5, 8	(19)	4, 9	(24)	4, 10
(5)	9, 10	(10)	6, 10	(15)	6, 9	(20)	6, 7	(25)	5, 7

Group VI		Group VII		Group VIII		Group IX	
(26)	1, 7	(31)	1, 8	(36)	1, 9	(41)	1, 10
(27)	2, 6	(32)	2, 3	(37)	2, 4	(42)	2, 5
(28)	3, 9	(33)	4, 6	(38)	3, 5	(43)	3, 6
(29)	4, 5	(34)	5, 10	(39)	6, 8	(44)	4, 7
(30)	8, 10	(35)	7, 9	(40)	7, 10	(45)	8, 9

Plan 16: $t = 10, k = 3, r = 9, b = 30, \lambda = 2, E = 20/27$

(1)	1, 2, 3	(11)	1, 2, 4	(21)	1, 3, 5
(2)	2, 5, 8	(12)	2, 3, 6	(22)	2, 7, 6
(3)	3, 7, 4	(13)	3, 4, 8	(23)	3, 8, 9
(4)	4, 1, 6	(14)	4, 9, 5	(24)	4, 2, 10
(5)	5, 8, 7	(15)	5, 7, 1	(25)	5, 6, 3
(6)	6, 4, 9	(16)	6, 8, 9	(26)	6, 1, 8
(7)	7, 9, 1	(17)	7, 10, 3	(27)	7, 9, 2
(8)	8, 10, 2	(18)	8, 1, 10	(28)	8, 4, 7
(9)	9, 3, 10	(19)	9, 5, 2	(29)	9, 10, 1
(10)	10, 6, 5	(20)	10, 6, 7	(30)	10, 5, 4

Plan 17: $t = 10, k = 4, r = 6, b = 15, \lambda = 2, E = 5/6$

(1)	1, 2, 3, 4	(6)	1, 6, 8, 10	(11)	3, 5, 9, 10
(2)	1, 2, 5, 6	(7)	2, 3, 6, 9	(12)	3, 6, 7, 10
(3)	1, 3, 7, 8	(8)	2, 4, 7, 10	(13)	3, 4, 5, 8
(4)	1, 4, 9, 10	(9)	2, 5, 8, 10	(14)	4, 5, 6, 7
(5)	1, 5, 7, 9	(10)	2, 7, 8, 9	(15)	4, 6, 8, 9

* See footnote on page 13-9.

TABLE 13-3. BALANCED INCOMPLETE BLOCK PLANS* (Continued)
$(4 \leq t \leq 10, r \leq 10)$

Plan 18: $t = 10, k = 5, r = 9, b = 18, \lambda = 4, E = 8/9$

(1) 1, 2, 3, 4, 5	(7) 1, 4, 5, 6, 10	(13) 2, 5, 6, 8, 10
(2) 1, 2, 3, 6, 7	(8) 1, 4, 8, 9, 10	(14) 2, 6, 7, 9, 10
(3) 1, 2, 4, 6, 9	(9) 1, 5, 7, 9, 10	(15) 3, 4, 6, 7, 10
(4) 1, 2, 5, 7, 8	(10) 2, 3, 4, 8, 10	(16) 3, 4, 5, 7, 9
(5) 1, 3, 6, 8, 9	(11) 2, 3, 5, 9, 10	(17) 3, 5, 6, 8, 9
(6) 1, 3, 7, 8, 10	(12) 2, 4, 7, 8, 9	(18) 4, 5, 6, 7, 8

Plan 19: $t = 10, k = 6, r = 9, b = 15, \lambda = 5, E = 25/27$

(1) 1, 2, 4, 5, 8, 9	(6) 2, 3, 4, 6, 8, 10	(11) 1, 4, 5, 7, 8, 10
(2) 5, 6, 7, 8, 9, 10	(7) 1, 2, 6, 7, 9, 10	(12) 1, 2, 3, 5, 7, 10
(3) 2, 4, 5, 6, 9, 10	(8) 1, 3, 5, 6, 8, 9	(13) 2, 3, 5, 6, 7, 8
(4) 1, 2, 4, 6, 7, 8	(9) 1, 2, 3, 8, 9, 10	(14) 1, 3, 4, 5, 6, 10
(5) 3, 4, 7, 8, 9, 10	(10) 2, 3, 4, 5, 7, 9	(15) 1, 3, 4, 6, 7, 9

* See footnote on page 13-9.

For analysis, the results of a balanced incomplete block design may be exhibited in a table such as Table 13-4, which shows the arrangement for Plan 7 of Table 13-3.

TABLE 13-4. SCHEMATIC REPRESENTATION OF RESULTS FOR A BALANCED INCOMPLETE BLOCK PLAN

Plan 7 of Table 13-3 is used here for illustration.

Block	Treatment							Total
	A	B	C	D	E	F	G	
1	X	X		X				B_1
2		X	X		X			B_2
3			X	X		X		B_3
4				X	X		X	B_4
5	X				X	X		B_5
6		X				X	X	B_6
7	X		X				X	B_7
Total	T_A	T_B	T_C	T_D	T_E	T_F	T_G	G

13-4.2.2 Analysis. In the analysis of the balanced incomplete block plans the same model is used and the same assumptions are made as in the randomized block plans. The only difference is that, in the present case, the blocks do not each contain all of the treatments.

The analysis described here is sometimes called the intra-block analysis.

Data Sample 13-4.2.2 — Noise Measurement of Resistors

A certain film-type composition resistor used in electronic equipment is of the type which is mounted on a ceramic plate. An investigation was designed to determine the effects of four different geometrical shapes of resistors on the current-noise of these resistors. Since only three resistors could be mounted on one plate, an incomplete block design was used.   The plan required a total of 12 resistors (three of each of the four shapes).   In the plan, the ceramic plates are blocks ($b = 4$); the resistor shapes are treatments ($t = 4$) and the plan is summarized by the following parameters: $t = 4, b = 4, k = 3, r = 3, \lambda = 2, E = 8/9, N = 12$.   Note that this is a symmetrical balanced incomplete block design; i.e., the number of blocks equals the number of treatments.

The following entries are logarithms of the noise measurement.

Plates (Blocks)	Shapes (Treatments)				Total
	A	B	C	D	
1	1.11		.95	.82	$B_1 = 2.88$
2	1.70	1.22		.97	$B_2 = 3.89$
3	1.60	1.11	1.52		$B_3 = 4.23$
4		1.22	1.54	1.18	$B_4 = 3.94$
Total	$T_1 = 4.41$	$T_2 = 3.55$	$T_3 = 4.01$	$T_4 = 2.97$	$G = 14.94$

$t = 4, k = 3, b = 4, r = 3, \lambda = 2, E = \dfrac{8}{9}, N = 12.$

13-4.2.2.1 Estimating Treatment Effects.   We assume that the observations have been exhibited in a table such as Table 13-4.   The treatment effects cannot be estimated directly from the treatment averages, and must be adjusted for possible block effects.   The estimate of φ_i, the effect of the ith treatment, is

$$t_i = Q_i/Er + G/rt,$$

where

$$Q_i = T_i - [(\text{Sum of totals of all blocks containing treatment } i)/k].$$

For example, using Data Sample 13-4.2.2,

$$Q_1 = T_1 - \left(\frac{B_1 + B_2 + B_3}{3}\right)$$

$$= 4.41 - \frac{11.00}{3}$$

$$= 4.41 - 3.6667$$

$$= 0.7433$$

Similarly,

$$Q_2 = 3.55 - \frac{12.06}{3}$$

$$= 3.55 - 4.0200$$

$$= -0.4700$$

$$Q_3 = 4.01 - \frac{11.05}{3}$$

$$= 4.01 - 3.6833$$

$$= 0.3267$$

$$Q_4 = 2.97 - \frac{10.71}{3}$$

$$= 2.97 - 3.5700$$

$$= -0.6000$$

$$E = 8/9, \; r = 3, \; Er = 2.6667, \; t = 4, \; rt = 12,$$
$$G/rt = 14.94/12$$
$$= 1.2450$$

$$t_1 = \frac{Q_1}{Er} + \frac{G}{rt} \qquad\qquad t_3 = \frac{0.3267}{2.6667} + 1.2450$$

$$= \frac{0.7433}{2.6667} + 1.2450 \qquad\qquad = 1.3675$$

$$= 1.5237$$

$$t_2 = \frac{-0.4700}{2.6667} + 1.2450 \qquad\qquad t_4 = \frac{-0.6000}{2.6667} + 1.2450$$

$$= 1.0688 \qquad\qquad\qquad\qquad = 1.0200$$

13-4.2.2.2   Testing and Estimating Differences in Treatment Effects.

Procedure	Example

(1) Choose α, the significance level of the test.

(1) Let $\quad \alpha = .05$

(2) Look up $q_{1-\alpha}\,(t,\,\nu)$ in Table A-10, where

$$\nu = tr - t - b + 1$$

(2) From Data Sample 13-4.2.2:

$$t = 4$$
$$\nu = 5$$
$$q_{.95}\,(4,\,5) = 5.22$$

(3) Compute Q_i and t_i for each treatment. (The sum of the Q_i should equal zero.)

(3) See Paragraph 13-4.2.2.1

(4) Compute

$$S_t = \frac{Q_1^2 + Q_2^2 + \ldots + Q_t^2}{Er}$$

(4)

$$S_t = \frac{1.24012778}{2.6667}$$
$$= 0.46504$$

(5) Compute

$$S_b = \frac{B_1^2 + B_2^2 + \ldots + B_b^2}{k} - \frac{G^2}{rt}$$

(5)

$$S_b = \frac{56.8430}{3} - 18.60030$$
$$= 0.34737$$

(6) Compute

$$S = \Sigma Y_{ij}^2 - G^2/rt;$$

i.e., compute the sum of the squares of all the observations and subtract G^2/rt.

(6)

$$S = 19.4812 - 18.6003$$
$$= 0.88090$$

(7) Compute

$$s^2 = \frac{S - S_t - S_b}{tr - t - b + 1}$$

(7)

$$s^2 = \frac{0.06849}{5}$$
$$= 0.0137$$
$$s = 0.117$$

(8) Compute

$$w = q_{1-\alpha}\, s/\sqrt{Er}$$

(8)

$$w = \frac{(5.22)\,(0.117)}{1.63}$$
$$= \frac{0.611}{1.63}$$
$$= 0.375$$

(9) If the absolute difference between two estimated treatment effects exceeds w, conclude that the treatment effects differ; otherwise, conclude that the experiment gives no reason to believe that the treatment effects differ.

(9) Since there are differences between pairs of treatment effects that do exceed 0.375, we conclude that resistor shapes differ with regard to their effect on current noise.

Note: We can make simultaneous confidence interval statements about the differences between pairs of treatments i and j, with confidence $1 - \alpha$ that all statements are simultaneously true. The statements are, for all i and j,

$$t_i - t_j - w \leq \varphi_i - \varphi_j \leq t_i - t_j + w.$$

13-4.2.2.3 Estimating Block Effects. Like the treatment effects, block effects cannot be estimated directly from block averages, but must be adjusted according to which treatments occur in them. We discuss estimation of the block effects for symmetrical plans only, i.e., where $b = t$, the number of blocks equals the number of treatments. If it is required to estimate or test block effects in a balanced incomplete block plan which is not symmetric, a statistical text book such as Cochran and Cox[2] or Fisher and Yates[3] should be consulted.

For symmetric plans, the estimate of β_j, the jth block effect, is

$$b_j = Q'_j/Er$$

where

$$Q'_j = B_j - (\text{sum of totals of all treatments occurring in the } j\text{th block } /r).$$

For example, using Data Sample 13-4.2.2.

$$Q'_1 = B_1 - \left(\frac{T_1 + T_3 + T_4}{3}\right)$$

$$= 2.88 - \frac{11.39}{3}$$

$$= 2.88 - 3.7967$$

$$= -0.9167.$$

Similarly,

$$Q'_2 = 3.89 - \frac{10.93}{3}$$

$$= 3.89 - 3.6433$$

$$= 0.2467$$

$$Q'_3 = 4.23 - \frac{11.97}{3}$$

$$= 4.23 - 3.9900$$

$$= 0.2400$$

$$Q'_4 = 3.94 - \frac{10.53}{3}$$

$$= 3.94 - 3.5100$$

$$= 0.4300$$

$$Er = 2.6667$$
$$b_1 = -0.9167/2.6667$$
$$= -0.34376$$
$$b_2 = 0.2467/2.6667$$
$$= 0.09251$$
$$b_3 = 0.2400/2.6667$$
$$= 0.09000$$
$$b_4 = 0.4300/2.6667$$
$$= 0.16125$$

13-4.2.2.4 Testing and Estimating Differences in Block Effects. The procedure described applies to *symmetrical* balanced incomplete block plans only.

Procedure	Example
(1) Choose α, the significance level of the test.	(1) Let $\alpha = .05$

(2) Look up $q_{1-\alpha}(b, \nu)$ in Table A-10, where

$$\nu = tr - t - b + 1$$

(2) See Data Sample 13-4.2.2

$$t = 4$$
$$b = 4$$
$$r = 3$$
$$\nu = 5$$
$$q_{.95}(4, 5) = 5.22$$

(3) Compute Q'_i and b_i for each block. (The sum of the Q'_i should equal zero.)

(3) See Paragraph 13-4.2.2.3

(4) Compute

$$S'_b = (Q_1'^2 + Q_2'^2 + \ldots + Q_t'^2)/Er$$

(4)

$$Er = 2.6667$$
$$S'_b = 1.14369978/2.6667$$
$$= 0.42888$$

(5) Compute

$$S'_t = (T_1^2 + T_2^2 + \ldots + T_t^2)/r - G^2/rt$$

(5)

$$S'_t = 56.9516/3 - 18.60030$$
$$= 18.98387 - 18.60030$$
$$= 0.38357$$

(6) Compute

$$S = \Sigma Y_{ij}^2 - G^2/rt;$$

i.e., compute the sum of the squares of all individual observations and subtract G^2/rt.

(6)

$$S = 19.4812 - 18.60030$$
$$= 0.88090$$

(7) Compute

$$s^2 = (S - S'_t - S'_b)/(tr - t - b + 1)$$

and

$$s$$

(7)

$$s^2 = 0.06845/5$$
$$= 0.0137$$
$$s = 0.117$$

Note: $S'_t + S'_b$ (as computed in steps (4) and (5) above) should equal $S_t + S_b$ (as computed in Paragraph 13-4.2.2.2), and therefore the s^2 here should equal s^2 computed in Paragraph 13-4.2.2.2.

Note: $S'_t + S'_b = 0.81245$ from steps (4) and (5) above. $S_t + S_b = 0.81241$ from Paragraph 13-4.2.2.2. The discrepancy is due to rounding error, and would be larger if fewer decimal places were carried in the computation.

(8) Compute

$$w' = q_{1-\alpha}\, s/\sqrt{Er}$$

(8)

$$w' = (5.22)(0.117)/1.63$$
$$= 0.611/1.63$$
$$= 0.375$$

Procedure	Example
(9) If the absolute difference between any two estimated block effects exceed w', conclude that the block effects differ; otherwise, conclude that the experiment gives no reason to believe the block effects differ.	(9) Since there are differences between pairs of block effects that exceed 0.375, we conclude that blocks (plates) do differ.

Note: We can make simultaneous statements about the differences between pairs of blocks i and j, with confidence $1 - \alpha$ that all the statements are simultaneously true. The statements are, for all i and j,

$$b_i - b_j - w' \leq \beta_i - \beta_j \leq b_i - b_j + w'.$$

13-4.3 CHAIN BLOCK PLANS

13-4.3.1 Planning. The chain block plan is useful when observations are expensive and the experimental error is small. Such a plan can handle a large number of treatments relative to the total number of observations. We need make only a few more observations than we have treatments to compare. Before using a chain block plan, however, we should be confident that the important differences in treatment effects are substantially larger than experimental error.

In a chain block design, some treatments are observed once and some treatments are observed twice. Schematically, the plan can be represented as in Table 13-5.

TABLE 13-5. SCHEMATIC REPRESENTATION OF A CHAIN BLOCK PLAN

	Blocks				
	1	**2**	$\ldots$	$b - 1$	b
	A_1'	A_2'	$\ldots$	A_{b-1}'	A_b'
	A_2''	A_3''	$\ldots$	A_b''	A_1''
	x	x			x
	x	x			x
	$\cdot$	$\cdot$			$\cdot$
	$\cdot$	$\cdot$			$\cdot$
	$\cdot$	$\cdot$			$\cdot$
	x	x	$\ldots$		x
Total	B_1	B_2	$\ldots$	B_{b-1}	B_b	G
						(= Grand Total)

In Table 13-5, A_i' represents either a treatment or a group of treatments, and A_i'' represents the same treatment or group of treatments. The x's represent treatments for which we have only one observation, and we need not have the same number of such treatments in every block.

When the experimental conditions are appropriate for their use, chain blocks are a flexible and efficient design. They are easy to construct. After following through the example below, and with the help of Cochran and Cox,[2] the user should be able to produce a chain block plan suitable to his own needs. For a given number of blocks b and a given number of treatments t, various different plans may be constructed. The analysis is not too difficult, but is not as straightforward as the analysis of some simpler designs.

Two examples of chain block designs (Plan 1 and Plan 2) are given here. The numbers in each block represent treatments.

Plan 1:

4 Blocks $(b = 4)$

13 Treatments $(t = 13)$

Block

1	2	3	4
$\begin{Bmatrix}1\\2\end{Bmatrix}$	$\begin{Bmatrix}3\\4\end{Bmatrix}$	$\begin{Bmatrix}5\\6\end{Bmatrix}$	$\begin{Bmatrix}7\\8\end{Bmatrix}$
$\begin{Bmatrix}3\\4\end{Bmatrix}$	$\begin{Bmatrix}5\\6\end{Bmatrix}$	$\begin{Bmatrix}7\\8\end{Bmatrix}$	$\begin{Bmatrix}1\\2\end{Bmatrix}$
9	10	11	12
13			

Schematically, Plan 1 may be written:

Block

1	2	3	4
A_1'	A_2'	A_3'	A_4'
A_2''	A_3''	A_4''	A_1''
x	x	x	x
x			

In Plan 1, treatments 1 and 2 constitute the group A_1, which appears in block 1 and block 4; treatments 3 and 4 constitute the group A_2 (in block 1 and block 2); treatments 5 and 6 constitute the group A_3 (in block 2 and block 3); and treatments 7 and 8 constitute the group A_4 (in block 3 and block 4). The remaining treatments (9 through 13) are distributed among the blocks to make the number of treatments per block as equal as possible.

Treatments 1 through 8 appear twice each; treatments 9 through 13 appear once only. Treatment 1 never occurs without treatment 2, treatment 3 never occurs without treatment 4, etc. Thus, the treatments which are replicated twice fall into four groups (schematically A_1, A_2, A_3, A_4), and these groups are the links in the chain of blocks. Treatments 3 and 4 link blocks 1 and 2, treatments 5 and 6 link blocks 2 and 3, treatments 7 and 8 link blocks 3 and 4, and treatments 1 and 2 complete the chain by linking blocks 4 and 1.

Plan 2:

3 Blocks $(b = 3)$

11 Treatments $(t = 11)$

	Block	
1	2	3
$\begin{Bmatrix} 1 \\ 2 \\ 3 \end{Bmatrix}$	$\begin{Bmatrix} 4 \\ 5 \\ 6 \end{Bmatrix}$	$\begin{Bmatrix} 7 \\ 8 \\ 9 \end{Bmatrix}$
$\begin{Bmatrix} 4 \\ 5 \\ 6 \end{Bmatrix}$	$\begin{Bmatrix} 7 \\ 8 \\ 9 \end{Bmatrix}$	$\begin{Bmatrix} 1 \\ 2 \\ 3 \end{Bmatrix}$
10	11	

Schematically, Plan 2 may be written:

	Block	
1	2	3
A_1'	A_2'	A_3'
A_2''	A_3''	A_1''
x	x	

In Plan 2, the group of treatments 1, 2, and 3 are group A_1; treatments 4, 5, 6 constitute the group A_2; and treatments 7, 8, 9 constitute the group A_3. The remaining two treatments (10 and 11) are assigned to blocks 1 and 2. Treatments 1 through 9 appear twice each, and treatments 10 and 11 appear once each. Treatments 1, 2, and 3 always occur together as a group; treatments 4, 5, and 6 always occur together; and treatments 7, 8, and 9 always occur together. Thus, the treatments which are replicated twice fall into three groups (schematically A_1, A_2, A_3). Group A_2 links blocks 1 and 2, group A_3 links blocks 2 and 3, and group A_1 completes the chain by linking blocks 3 and 1.

To use a given chain block plan, the numbers should be allocated to the treatments at random.

13-4.3.2 Analysis. For purposes of analysis, the observations should be recorded in the form shown in Table 13-5.

The parameters of the plan are:

b = number of blocks in the plan;

k_i = number of observations in the ith block;

t = number of treatments;

m = number of treatments in each group A' and A'';

N = total number of observations.

Data Sample 13-4.3.2 — Spectrographic Determination of Nickel

The data are spectrographic determinations of nickel content of 42 rods prepared from the same ingot.   Only about 18 determinations could be made on the same photographic plate, and there were 42 "treatments" to be compared; therefore, a chain block plan was used.   In the experiment, there are three blocks (the photographic plates involved in the determinations) and 42 treatments (the rods).   The selected chain block plan is shown schematically in Table 13-6.   The parameters of this plan are: $b = 3$, $k = 18$, $t = 42$, $m = 4$, and $N = 54$.

The amounts of nickel were recorded as logarithms (base 10) of the ratio of the intensity of the nickel spectral line to the iron spectral line.   In Table 13-7, these determinations have been coded by multiplying by 10^3 and then subtracting 170.

The primary question to be answered is: Are there significant differences among rods (treatments)?

TABLE 13-6.   SCHEMATIC REPRESENTATION OF THE CHAIN BLOCK DESIGN DESCRIBED IN DATA SAMPLE 13-4.3.2

	Block		
	1	2	3
A_1' $\begin{cases} \\ \\ \\ \\ \end{cases}$	1 2 3 4	A_2' 5 6 7 8	A_3' 9 10 11 12
A_2'' $\begin{cases} \\ \\ \\ \\ \end{cases}$	5 6 7 8	A_3'' 9 10 11 12	A_1'' 1 2 3 4
	13	23	33
	14	24	34
	15	25	35
	16	26	36
	17	27	37
	18	28	38
	19	29	39
	20	30	40
	21	31	41
	22	32	42

The numbers in the blocks represent treatments.
The parameters of this plan are: $b = 3$, $k = 18$,
$t = 42$, $m = 4$, $N = 54$.

TABLE 13-7.   SPECTROGRAPHIC DETERMINATION OF NICKEL
(DATA SAMPLE 13-4.3.2)

	Plates (Blocks)		
	1	**2**	**3**
	A_1' $\begin{cases} 8 & t_1 \\ 7 & t_2 \\ 14 & t_3 \\ 9 & t_4 \end{cases}$	A_2' $\begin{cases} 4 & t_5 \\ 3 & t_6 \\ 10 & t_7 \\ 6 & t_8 \end{cases}$	A_3' $\begin{cases} -1 & t_9 \\ 0 & t_{10} \\ -3 & t_{11} \\ -8 & t_{12} \end{cases}$
	A_2'' $\begin{cases} 13 & t_5 \\ 15 & t_6 \\ 12 & t_7 \\ 9 & t_8 \end{cases}$	A_3'' $\begin{cases} 5 & t_9 \\ 7 & t_{10} \\ 2 & t_{11} \\ 6 & t_{12} \end{cases}$	A_1'' $\begin{cases} 1 & t_1 \\ 5 & t_2 \\ 2 & t_3 \\ 0 & t_4 \end{cases}$
	11	10	5
	5	9	−1
	17	6	−3
	14	7	−6
	12	6	2
	13	4	−2
	14	7	−2
	12	7	0
	8	9	1
	21	10	2
Total	$B_1 = 214$	$B_2 = 118$	$B_3 = -8$ $G = 324$

13-4.3.2.1　Estimating Treatment and Block Effects.　Since the method of estimating treatment effects requires calculation of the estimated block effects, we compute the block effects first.

Procedure

(1)　Compute the sum of the observations for each of the groups A_i', A_i''.　Call the totals X_i', X_i''.

(2)　Record the totals X_1', X_1'', etc., as shown:

X_1'	X_2'	$\ldots$	X_{b-1}'	X_b'	G'
X_1''	X_2''	$\ldots$	X_{b-1}''	X_b''	G''
D_1	D_2	$\ldots$	D_{b-1}	D_b	

Compute:

$$D_i = X_i' - X_i''$$
$$G' = X_1' + X_2' + \ldots + X_b'$$
$$G'' = X_1'' + X_2'' + \ldots + X_b''$$

$G''' =$ sum of all observations on treatments which occur once only.

$$G = G' + G'' + G'''$$

(3)　Compute

$$L_1 = (b - 1)(D_1 - D_2) + (b - 3)(D_b - D_3) + (b - 5)(D_{b-1} - D_4) + \ldots$$

where the sum is over $b/2$ terms if b is even, and $(b - 1)/2$ terms if b is odd.

(4)　Compute

$$H = (G'' - G')/mb$$

(5)　If there are m treatments in each group A_i' or A_i'', then we may estimate the first block effect as

$$b_1 = L_1/2mb.$$

(6)　Compute:

$$b_2 = b_1 + D_2/m + H$$
$$b_3 = b_2 + D_3/m + H$$

$$\cdot$$
$$\cdot$$
$$\cdot$$

$$b_b = b_{b-1} + D_1/m + H.$$

$b_1, b_2, \ldots, b_b$ are the estimated block effects.

Check:　The sum of the estimated block effects should equal zero.

(7)　The estimated treatment effects t_i are computed as follows:

If the treatment occurs twice, the estimated treatment effect is the average of the two observations minus the average of the estimated block effects for the two blocks in which the observations occur.

If the treatment occurs once, the estimated treatment effect is the observation on the treatment minus the estimate of block effect for the block in which the treatment occurs.

Check:　The sum of the estimated treatment effects should equal $G - \frac{1}{2}(G' + G'')$.

13-24

Example

(1) See Table 13-7.
     Sum of group A_1' = $\quad$ 38 $= X_1'$
     Sum of group A_1'' = $\quad$ 8 $= X_1''$

     Sum of group A_2' = $\quad$ 23 $= X_2'$
     Sum of group A_2'' = $\quad$ 49 $= X_2''$

     Sum of group A_3' = -12 $= X_3'$
     Sum of group A_3'' = $\quad$ 20 $= X_3''$

(2) X_1' = 38 $\qquad$ X_2' = $\quad$ 23 $\qquad$ X_3' = -12 $\qquad$ G' = 49
     X_1'' = 8 $\qquad$ X_2'' − $\quad$ 49 $\qquad$ X_3'' − $\quad$ 20 $\qquad$ G'' = 77
     _____
     D_1 = 30 $\qquad$ D_2 = -26 $\qquad$ D_3 = -32

     G' $\quad$ = 49
     G'' $\quad$ = 77
     G''' = 198 (from Table 13-7)
     G $\quad$ = 324 (from Table 13-7)

(3) In the example, $b = 3$ (odd), and there will be only one term.
     $L_1 = (3 - 1)(30 + 26)$
     $\quad = (2)(56)$
     $\quad = 112$

(4) $H = \dfrac{77 - 49}{4\,(3)}$

     $\quad = \dfrac{28}{12}$

     $\quad = 2.33$

(5) $b_1 = \dfrac{L_1}{2mb}$

     $\quad = \dfrac{112}{(2)\,(4)\,(3)}$

     $\quad = 4.67$

(6) $b_2 = 4.67 + \dfrac{-26}{4} + 2.33$

     $\quad = 0.50$

     $b_3 = 0.50 + \dfrac{-32}{4} + 2.33$

     $\quad = -5.17$

Check: $b_1 + b_2 + b_3 = 0$.

Example (cont)

(7) Treatments 1 through 12 occur twice.   In estimating these treatments, we need the following averages of block effects:

$$\frac{b_1 + b_3}{2} = \frac{-0.50}{2}$$
$$= -0.25$$

$$\frac{b_1 + b_2}{2} = \frac{5.17}{2}$$
$$= 2.58$$

$$\frac{b_2 + b_3}{2} = \frac{-4.67}{2}$$
$$= -2.33$$

Treatments 1 through 4 (occurring in Groups $A_1{}'$ and $A_1{}''$, in blocks 1 and 3) are estimated as follows:

$$t_1 = \frac{8 + 1}{2} + 0.25$$
$$= 4.75$$

$$t_2 = \frac{7 + 5}{2} + 0.25$$
$$= 6.25$$

$$t_3 = \frac{14 + 2}{2} + 0.25$$
$$= 8.25$$

$$t_4 = \frac{9 + 0}{2} + 0.25$$
$$= 4.75$$

Treatments 5 through 8 (occurring in Groups A_2' and A_2'', in blocks 1 and 2) are estimated as follows:

$$t_5 = \frac{4 + 13}{2} - 2.58$$
$$= 5.92$$

$$t_6 = \frac{3 + 15}{2} - 2.58$$
$$= 6.42$$

$$t_7 = \frac{10 + 12}{2} - 2.58$$
$$= 8.42$$

$$t_8 = \frac{6 + 9}{2} - 2.58$$
$$= 4.92$$

Example (cont)

Treatments 9 through 12 (occurring in Groups A_3' and A_3'', in blocks 2 and 3) are estimated as follows:

$$t_9 = \frac{-1+5}{2} + 2.33$$
$$= 4.33$$

$$t_{10} = \frac{0+7}{2} + 2.33$$
$$= 5.83$$

$$t_{11} = \frac{-3+2}{2} + 2.33$$
$$= 1.83$$

$$t_{12} = \frac{-8+6}{2} + 2.33$$
$$= 1.33$$

Treatments 13 through 42 occur only once, and are estimated as follows:

$11 - 4.67 =$	6.33	$10 - 0.50 =$	9.50	$5 - (-5.17) =$	10.17
$5 - 4.67 =$	0.33	$9 - 0.50 =$	8.50	$-1 - (-5.17) =$	4.17
$17 - \;'' \;=$	12.33	$6 - \;'' \;=$	5.50	$-3 - \;'' \;=$	2.17
$14 - \;'' \;=$	9.33	$7 - \;'' \;=$	6.50	$-6 - \;'' \;=$	-0.83
$12 - \;'' \;=$	7.33	$6 - \;'' \;=$	5.50	$2 - \;'' \;=$	7.17
$13 - \;'' \;=$	8.33	$4 - \;'' \;=$	3.50	$-2 - \;'' \;=$	3.17
$14 - \;'' \;=$	9.33	$7 - \;'' \;=$	6.50	$-2 - \;'' \;=$	3.17
$12 - \;'' \;=$	7.33	$7 - \;'' \;=$	6.50	$0 - \;'' \;=$	5.17
$8 - \;'' \;=$	3.33	$9 - \;'' \;=$	8.50	$1 - \;'' \;=$	6.17
$21 - \;'' \;=$	16.33	$10 - \;'' \;=$	9.50	$2 - \;'' \;=$	7.17

Check: $\sum\limits_{i=1}^{42} t_i = 261.00$; $G - \frac{1}{2}(G' + G'') = 324 - 63 = 261$.

13-4.3.2.2   Testing and Estimating Differences in Treatment Effects.   To test for differences in treatment effects, we proceed as follows:

Procedure

(1)   Choose α, the significance level of the test.

(2)   Look up $F_{1-\alpha}$ $(t - 1, N - b - t + 1)$, in Table A-5.

(3)   Compute $S_b = B_1^2/k_1 + B_2^2/k_2 + \ldots + B_b^2/k_b - G^2/N$.

(4)   Compute $S' = (G' - G'')^2/2bm$.

(5)   From each of the observations in A_1' subtract the observation on the same treatment in A_1''.

Call these differences $d_{11}, d_{12}, \ldots, d_{1m}$, and compute
$$S_1 = (d_{11}^2 + d_{12}^2 + \ldots + d_{1m}^2)/2 - D_1^2/2m.$$
Compute the comparable quantities $S_2, S_3, \ldots, S_b$.

(6)   Compute: $S_e = S' + S_1 + S_2 + \ldots + S_b$
and
$$s^2 = S_e/(N - b - t + 1).$$

(7)   Compute $S =$ (sum of squares of all the observations) $- G^2/N$.

(8)   Compute $S_t = S - S_b - S_e$.

(9)   Compute $F = (N - b - t + 1)S_t/(t - 1)S_e$.

(10)   If $F > F_{1-\alpha}$, conclude that the treatments differ; otherwise, conclude that the experiment gives no reason to believe that the treatments differ.

13-28

Example

(1) Let $\alpha = .01$

(2) $t = 42, b = 3, N = 54$ (see Table 13-6).
$t - 1 = 41, N - b - t + 1 = 10$
$F_{.99} (41, 10) = 4.17$

(3) See Table 13-7.

$$S_b = \frac{(214)^2}{18} + \frac{(118)^2}{18} + \frac{(-8)^2}{18} - \frac{(324)^2}{54}$$

$$= \frac{59784}{18} - \frac{104976}{54} = 3321.333 - 1944.0$$

$$= 1377.333$$

(4) $$S' = \frac{(49 - 77)^2}{(2)\,(3)\,(4)} = \frac{784}{24}$$

$$= 32.667$$

(5) $d_{11} = 7$ $d_{13} = 12$
$d_{12} = 2$ $d_{14} = 9$ $D_1 = 30$

$$S_1 = \frac{278}{2} - \frac{900}{8} = 139 - 112.5$$

$$= 26.5$$

$d_{21} = -9$ $d_{32} = -2$
$d_{22} = -12$ $d_{31} = -3$ $D_2 = -26$

$$S_2 = \frac{238}{2} - 84.5 = 119 - 84.5$$

$$= 34.5$$

$d_{31} = -6$ $d_{33} = -5$
$d_{32} = -7$ $d_{34} = -14$ $D_3 = -32$

$$S_3 = \frac{306}{2} - 128 = 153 - 128$$

$$= 25$$

(6) $S_c = 32.667 + 26.5 + 34.5 + 25$
$= 118.667$

$$s^2 = \frac{118.667}{10}$$

$$= 11.8667$$

(7) $$S = 3862 - \frac{(324)^2}{54} = 3862 - 1944$$

$$= 1918$$

(8) $S_t = 1918 - 1377.333 - 118.667$
$= 422$

(9) $$F = \frac{(10)\,(422)}{(41)\,(118.667)} = \frac{4220}{4865.347}$$

$$= 0.8674$$

(10) Since F is not greater than $F_{.99}$, we say there is not sufficient evidence to conclude that treatments (rods) differ.

13-5 LATIN SQUARE PLANS

13-5.1 PLANNING

A Latin square plan (or the Youden square plans in Paragraph 13-6) is useful when it is necessary or desirable to allow for two specific sources of non-homogeneity in the conditions affecting test results.   Such designs were originally applied in agricultural experimentation when the two directional sources of non-homogeneity were simply the two directions on the field, and the "square" was literally a square plot of ground.   Its usage has been extended to many other applications where there are two sources of non-homogeneity that may affect experimental results — for example, machines, positions, operators, runs, days.   A third variable, the experimental treatment, is then associated with the two source variables in a prescribed fashion.   The use of Latin squares is restricted by two conditions:

(1) the number of rows, columns, and treatments must all be the same;

(2) there must be no interactions between row and column factors (see Chapter 12, Paragraph 12-1.1, for definition of interaction).

Youden square plans (Paragraph 13-6) are less restrictive than Latin squares; the number of rows, columns, and treatments need not be the same, but only certain number combinations are possible.

As an example of a Latin square, suppose we wish to compare four materials with regard to their wearing qualities.   Suppose further that we have a wear-testing machine which can handle four samples simultaneously.   Two sources of inhomogeneity might be the variations from run to run, and the variation among the four positions on the wear machine.   In this situation, a 4×4 Latin square will enable us to allow for both sources of inhomogeneity if we can make four runs.   The Latin square plan is as follows: (The four materials are labelled A, B, C, D).

A 4×4 Latin Square

Run	Position Number			
	(1)	(2)	(3)	(4)
1	A	B	C	D
2	B	C	D	A
3	C	D	A	B
4	D	A	B	C

Examples of Latin squares from size 3×3 to 12×12 are given in Table 13-8.   In the case of the 4×4 Latin square, four are given; when a 4×4 Latin square is needed, one of the four should be selected at random.   The procedure to be followed in using a given Latin square is as follows:

(a) Permute the columns at random;

(b) Permute the rows at random;

(c) Assign letters randomly to the treatments.

TABLE 13-8. SELECTED LATIN SQUARES

3 × 3

```
A B C
B C A
C A B
```

4 × 4

1	2	3	4
A B C D	A B C D	A B C D	A B C D
B A D C	B C D A	B D A C	B A D C
C D B A	C D A B	C A D B	C D A B
D C A B	D A B C	D C B A	D C B A

5 × 5

```
A B C D E
B A E C D
C D A E B
D E B A C
E C D B A
```

6 × 6

```
A B C D E F
B F D C A E
C D E F B A
D A F E C B
E C A B F D
F E B A D C
```

7 × 7

```
A B C D E F G
B C D E F G A
C D E F G A B
D E F G A B C
E F G A B C D
F G A B C D E
G A B C D E F
```

8 × 8

```
A B C D E F G H
B C D E F G H A
C D E F G H A B
D E F G H A B C
E F G H A B C D
F G H A B C D E
G H A B C D E F
H A B C D E F G
```

9 × 9

```
A B C D E F G H I
B C D E F G H I A
C D E F G H I A B
D E F G H I A B C
E F G H I A B C D
F G H I A B C D E
G H I A B C D E F
H I A B C D E F G
I A B C D E F G H
```

10 × 10

```
A B C D E F G H I J
B C D E F G H I J A
C D E F G H I J A B
D E F G H I J A B C
E F G H I J A B C D
F G H I J A B C D E
G H I J A B C D E F
H I J A B C D E F G
I J A B C D E F G H
J A B C D E F G H I
```

11 × 11

```
A B C D E F G H I J K
B C D E F G H I J K A
C D E F G H I J K A B
D E F G H I J K A B C
E F G H I J K A B C D
F G H I J K A B C D E
G H I J K A B C D E F
H I J K A B C D E F G
I J K A B C D E F G H
J K A B C D E F G H I
K A B C D E F G H I J
```

12 × 12

```
A B C D E F G H I J K L
B C D E F G H I J K L A
C D E F G H I J K L A B
D E F G H I J K L A B C
E F G H I J K L A B C D
F G H I J K L A B C D E
G H I J K L A B C D E F
H I J K L A B C D E F G
I J K L A B C D E F G H
J K L A B C D E F G H I
K L A B C D E F G H I J
L A B C D E F G H I J K
```

(If squares of 5×5 and higher are used very frequently, then, strictly speaking, each time we use one we should choose a square at random from the set of all possible squares. Fisher and Yates[3] give complete representation of the squares from 4×4 to 6×6, and sample squares up to the 12×12.

The results of a Latin square experiment are recorded in a two-way table similar to the plan itself. The treatment totals and the row and column totals of the Latin square plan are each directly comparable without adjustment.

13-5.2 ANALYSIS

The analysis of Latin and Youden Squares (see Paragraph 13-6) is based on essentially the same assumptions as the analysis of randomized blocks. The essential difference is that in the case of randomized blocks we allow for one source of inhomogeneity (represented by blocks) while in the case of Latin and Youden squares we are simultaneously allowing for two kinds of inhomogeneity (represented by rows and columns). If we let Y_{ijm} be the observation on the ith treatment which occurs in the jth row and mth column, then we assume that Y_{ijm} is made up of four components; i.e.,

$$Y_{ijm} = \varphi_i + \rho_j + \kappa_m + e_{ijm},$$

where ρ_j is a term peculiar to the jth row, and is constant regardless of column or treatment effects.

κ_m is a term peculiar to the mth column, and is defined similarly to ρ_j.

φ_i is a term peculiar to the ith treatment, and is the same regardless of the row or column in which the treatment occurs. It may be regarded as the average value of the ith treatment for any given row (or column) averaged over all columns (or rows), assuming there is no experimental error.

e_{ijm} is the experimental error involved in the observation Y_{ijm}.

As in the case of randomized blocks, in order to make interval estimates, or to make tests, we generally assume that the experimental errors (e_{ijm}'s) are each independently and normally distributed. However, provided the experiment was randomized properly, failure of the latter assumption will in general not cause serious difficulty.

In the analysis, we assume the data are exhibited in a two-way table following the plan. We use the following notation for the various totals:

T_i = Sum of the observations on the ith treatment;

R_i = Sum of the observations in the ith row;

C_i = Sum of the observations in the ith column;

G = Sum of all the observations.

Data Sample 13-5.2 — Temperature Reference Cells

This is a study of chemical cells used as a means of setting up a reference temperature. For various reasons, only one thermometer could be applied to a cell at one time. The columns are the four thermometers and the rows are the four cells investigated. The letters refer to four runs, each run made on a separate day. The readings are converted to degrees Centigrade; only the third and fourth decimal places are recorded, because all the readings agreed up to the last two places.

Cells	Thermometers				Total	Mean
	I	II	III	IV		
1	A 36	B 38	C 36	D 30	$R_1 = 140$	35.0
2	C 17	D 18	A 26	B 17	$R_2 = 78$	19.5
3	B 30	C 39	D 41	A 34	$R_3 = 144$	36.0
4	D 30	A 45	B 38	C 33	$R_4 = 146$	36.5
Total	$C_1 = 113$	$C_2 = 140$	$C_3 = 141$	$C_4 = 114$	$G = 508$	
Mean	28.25	35.0	35.25	28.5		

13-5.2.1 Estimation of Treatment Effects. The estimate t_i of the ith treatment effect φ_i can be obtained directly by the treatment average T_i/r, where r is the number of times the treatment occurs (r also equals the number of treatments, the number of rows, and the number of columns).

For example, from Data Sample 13-5.2:

$$T_A = 141 \qquad T_C = 125$$

$$T_B = 123 \qquad T_D = 119$$

$r = 4$, and

$$t_A = 141/4 \qquad t_C = 125/4$$
$$= 35.25 \qquad\quad = 31.25$$

$$t_B = 123/4 \qquad t_D = 119/4$$
$$= 30.75 \qquad\quad = 29.75$$

13-5.2.2   Testing and Estimating Differences in Treatment Effects.

Procedure	Example

(1) Choose α, the significance level of the test.

(1) Let $\alpha = .05$

(2) Look up $q_{1-\alpha}\ (r,\ \nu)$ in Table A-10, where

$$\nu = (r-2)\ (r-1).$$

(2) From Data Sample 13-5.2:

$$r = 4,$$
$$\nu = 6$$
$$q_{.95}\ (4,\ 6) = 4.90$$

(3) Compute

$$S_t = \frac{T_1^2 + T_2^2 + \ldots + T_r^2}{r} - \frac{G^2}{r^2}$$

(3)

$$S_t = \frac{64796}{4} - \frac{258064}{16}$$
$$= 16199 - 16129$$
$$= 70$$

(4) Compute

$$S_r = \frac{R_1^2 + R_2^2 + \ldots + R_r^2}{r} - \frac{G^2}{r^2}$$

(4)

$$S_r = \frac{67736}{4} - 16129$$
$$= 805$$

(5) Compute

$$S_c = \frac{C_1^2 + C_2^2 + \ldots + C_r^2}{r} - \frac{G^2}{r^2}$$

(5)

$$S_c = \frac{65246}{4} - 16129$$
$$= 182.5$$

(6) Compute

$$S = \text{(sum of squares of all the observations)} - G^2/r^2$$

(6)

$$S = 17230 - 16129$$
$$= 1101$$

(7) Compute:

$$s^2 = \frac{S - S_t - S_r - S_c}{(r-2)\ (r-1)}$$

and

$$s$$

(7)

$$s^2 = \frac{43.5}{6}$$
$$= 7.25$$
$$s = 2.693$$

(8) Compute

$$w = q_{1-\alpha}\ s/\sqrt{r}$$

(8)

$$w = (4.90)\ (2.693)/\sqrt{4}$$
$$= 6.60$$

(9) If the absolute difference between any two estimated treatment effects exceeds w, decide that the treatment effects differ; otherwise, decide that the experiment gives no reason to believe the treatment effects differ.

(9) The largest difference between pairs of treatment effects is 5.50, which does not exceed 6.60. We conclude that treatments (runs) do not differ.

Note: We can make simultaneous statements about the differences between pairs of treatments i and j, with confidence $1 - \alpha$ that all the statements are true simultaneously. The statements are, for all i and j,

$$t_i - t_j - w \leq \varphi_i - \varphi_j \leq t_i - t_j + w.$$

13-5.2.3 Estimation of Row (or Column) Effects. The row (or column) effects can be estimated directly by subtracting G/r^2 from the row (or column) averages. That is, we estimate ρ_i by $r_i = R_i/r - G/r^2$, and κ_i by $c_i = C_i/r - G/r^2$.

For example, from Data Sample 13-5.2:

$$G/r^2 = 508/16$$
$$= 31.75$$

$$r_1 = \frac{140}{4} - 31.75 \qquad\qquad c_1 = \frac{113}{4} - 31.75$$
$$= 3.25 \qquad\qquad\qquad\quad = -3.50$$

$$r_2 = \frac{78}{4} - 31.75 \qquad\qquad c_2 = \frac{140}{4} - 31.75$$
$$= -12.25 \qquad\qquad\qquad = 3.25$$

$$r_3 = \frac{144}{4} - 31.75 \qquad\qquad c_3 = \frac{141}{4} - 31.75$$
$$= 4.25 \qquad\qquad\qquad\quad = 3.50$$

$$r_4 = \frac{146}{4} - 31.75 \qquad\qquad c_4 = \frac{114}{4} - 31.75$$
$$= 4.75 \qquad\qquad\qquad\quad = -3.25$$

13-5.2.4 Testing and Estimating Differences in Row (or Column) Effects.

Procedure	**Example**
(1) through (7) Same as in Paragraph 13-5.2.2	Using Data Sample 13-5.2: $s = 2.693$, and ordinarily would have already been computed for the test of Paragraph 13-5.2.2.

(8) Compute

$$w = qs/\sqrt{r}$$

(9) If the absolute difference between any two estimated row effects r_i exceeds w, conclude that the row effects differ; otherwise, there is no reason to believe that row effects differ.

If the absolute difference between any two estimated column effects c_i exceeds w, conclude that the column effects differ; otherwise there is no reason to believe that column effects differ.

(8)

$$w = 6.60$$

(9) See Paragraph 13-5.2.3.
There is at least one pair of row effects that differ by more than 6.60. We therefore conclude that rows (cells) do differ.

There is at least one pair of column effects that differ by more than 6.60. We therefore conclude that columns (thermometers) do differ.

Note: We can make simultaneous statements about the differences between pairs of rows i and j with confidence $1 - \alpha$ that all the statements are simultaneously true. The statements are, for all i and j,

$$r_i - r_j - w \leq \rho_i - \rho_j \leq r_i - r_j + w.$$

(For a similar set of statements about the columns, replace

$$r_i, r_j, \rho_i, \rho_j, \text{ by } c_i, c_j, \kappa_i, \kappa_j).$$

13-6   YOUDEN SQUARE PLANS

13-6.1   PLANNING

The Youden square, like the Latin square, is used when we wish to allow for two kinds of inhomogeneity.   The conditions for the use of a Youden square, however, are less restrictive than for the Latin square.   The use of Latin square plans is restricted by the fact that the number of rows, columns, and treatments must all be the same.   Youden squares have the same number of rows and treatments, but a fairly wide choice in the number of columns is possible.   We use the following notation:

t = number of treatments to be compared;

b = number of levels of one source of inhomogeneity (rows);

k = number of levels of the other source of inhomogeneity (columns);

r = number of replications of each treatment.

In a Youden square, $t = b$ and $k = r$.

In Paragraph 13-5 (Latin Square plans), an example was shown in which we wished to test four materials with regard to their wearing qualities.   There were two sources of inhomogeneity; these were the variation among the four positions on the machine, and the variations from run to run. In order to use the Latin square plan, we had to make 4 runs.   A Youden square arrangement for this case would require only 3 runs.   In all the plans given in Table 13-9, the analysis is essentially the same; and for each of the designs, all differences between treatment effects are estimated with the same precision.

The procedure to be followed in using a given Youden square is as follows:

(a)   Permute the rows at random;

(b)   Permute the columns at random;

(c)   Assign letters at random to the treatments.

The results of an experiment using a Youden square plan are recorded in a two-way table which looks like the plan itself.   See the plans shown in Table 13-9.

In some instances where there are two sources of inhomogeneity, a suitable Latin or Youden square may not exist.   For a number of sets of values of t, b, and k, other plans or arrangements do exist which enable the experimenter to allow for the two sources of heterogeneity, in a fairly simple manner.   Because the analysis and interpretation is more complicated than for the plans given in this Chapter, a statistician should be consulted.

TABLE 13-9. YOUDEN SQUARE ARRANGEMENTS ($r \leq 10$)

Index

Plan Number	$t = b$	$r = k$	λ	$E = t\lambda/rk$	Remarks
1	3	2	1	3/4	*
2	4	3	2	8/9	*
3	5	4	3	15/16	*
4	6	5	4	24/25	*
5	7	3	1	7/9	
6	7	4	2	7/8	†Complement of Plan 5
7	7	6	5	35/36	*
8	8	7	6	48/49	*
9	9	8	7	63/64	*
10	10	9	8	80/81	*
11	11	5	2	22/25	
12	11	6	3	11/12	Complement of Plan 11
13	11	10	9	99/100	*
14	13	4	1	13/16	
15	13	9	6	26/27	Complement of Plan 14
16	15	7	3	45/49	
17	15	8	4	15/16	Complement of Plan 16
18	16	6	2	8/9	
19	16	10	6	24/25	
20	19	9	4	76/81	
21	19	10	5	19/20	Complement of Plan 20
22	21	5	1	21/25	
23	25	9	3	25/27	
24	31	6	1	31/36	
25	31	10	3	93/100	
26	37	9	2	74/81	See Cochran and Cox[2] pp. 529-535.
27	57	8	1	57/64	
28	73	9	1	73/81	
29	91	10	1	91/100	

* Blocks in these Plans are columns of Latin squares with one row deleted.

† The "complement" of a plan is developed as follows: Construct the first block (column) by writing all treatments that did not appear in the first block of the original plan. With these letters as starting points, complete each row by writing in alphabetical order all remaining treatment letters followed by A, B, C, . . . until every treatment letter appears once in each row. For example, Plan 6 is developed from Plan 5 as follows: The first block of Plan 5 is ABD; its complement and therefore the first block of Plan 6 is CEFG. The complete layout for Plan 6 is:

Row	Block 1	2	3	4	5	6	7
1	C	D	E	F	G	A	B
2	E	F	G	A	B	C	D
3	F	G	A	B	C	D	E
4	G	A	B	C	D	E	F

Note: The detailed plans given are only those which are not easily derivable from other designs — see Index at beginning of this Table.

Plan 5: $t = b = 7, r = k = 3$

Row	Block 1	2	3	4	5	6	7
1	A	B	C	D	E	F	G
2	B	C	D	E	F	G	A
3	D	E	F	G	A	B	C

TABLE 13-9. YOUDEN SQUARE ARRANGEMENTS ($r \leq 10$) (Continued)

Plan 11: $t = b = 11, r = k = 5$

Row	Block										
	1	2	3	4	5	6	7	8	9	10	11
1	A	B	C	D	E	F	G	H	I	J	K
2	E	F	G	H	I	J	K	A	B	C	D
3	F	G	H	I	J	K	A	B	C	D	E
4	G	H	I	J	K	A	B	C	D	E	F
5	I	J	K	A	B	C	D	E	F	G	H

Plan 14: $t = b = 13, r = k = 4$

Row	Block												
	1	2	3	4	5	6	7	8	9	10	11	12	13
1	A	B	C	D	E	F	G	H	I	J	K	L	M
2	B	C	D	E	F	G	H	I	J	K	L	M	A
3	D	E	F	G	H	I	J	K	L	M	A	B	C
4	J	K	L	M	A	B	C	D	E	F	G	H	I

Plan 16: $t = b = 15, r = k = 7$

Row	Block														
	1	2	3	4	5	6	7	8	9	10	11	12	13	14	15
1	A	B	C	D	E	F	G	H	I	J	K	L	M	N	O
2	B	C	D	E	F	G	H	I	J	K	L	M	N	O	A
3	C	D	E	F	G	H	I	J	K	L	M	N	O	A	B
4	E	F	G	H	I	J	K	L	M	N	O	A	B	C	D
5	F	G	H	I	J	K	L	M	N	O	A	B	C	D	E
6	I	J	K	L	M	N	O	A	B	C	D	E	F	G	H
7	K	L	M	N	O	A	B	C	D	E	F	G	H	I	J

Plan 18: $t = b = 16, r = k = 6$

Row	Block															
	1	2	3	4	5	6	7	8	9	10	11	12	13	14	15	16
1	A	B	C	D	E	F	G	H	I	J	K	L	M	N	O	P
2	B	C	D	A	F	G	H	E	J	K	L	I	N	O	P	M
3	C	D	A	B	G	H	E	F	K	L	I	J	O	P	M	N
4	E	F	G	H	I	J	K	L	M	N	O	P	A	B	C	D
5	L	I	J	K	P	M	N	O	D	A	B	C	H	E	F	G
6	M	N	O	P	A	B	C	D	E	F	G	H	I	J	K	L

TABLE 13-9. YOUDEN SQUARE ARRANGEMENTS ($r \leq 10$) (Continued)

Plan 19: $t = b = 16$, $r = k = 10$

Row	Block															
	1	2	3	4	5	6	7	8	9	10	11	12	13	14	15	16
1	A	B	C	D	E	F	G	H	I	J	K	L	M	N	O	P
2	C	A	B	E	F	D	J	I	H	G	M	K	L	P	N	O
3	D	C	A	K	M	G	H	E	L	I	J	B	P	O	F	N
4	N	E	P	A	H	B	D	C	F	K	O	G	I	J	L	M
5	M	N	O	P	B	A	F	D	E	C	G	I	J	H	K	L
6	B	J	H	G	A	I	L	O	M	N	D	C	E	F	P	K
7	L	K	I	B	O	P	N	A	D	F	C	H	G	E	M	J
8	J	H	F	L	G	M	A	P	K	O	B	N	C	D	E	I
9	I	P	L	O	N	K	C	M	J	A	H	E	F	B	D	G
10	O	M	K	J	L	N	P	G	A	E	F	D	B	I	C	H

Plan 20: $t = b = 19$, $r = k = 10$

Row	Block																		
	1	2	3	4	5	6	7	8	9	10	11	12	13	14	15	16	17	18	19
1	A	B	C	D	E	F	G	H	I	J	K	L	M	N	O	P	Q	R	S
2	C	D	E	F	G	H	I	J	K	L	M	N	O	P	Q	R	S	A	B
3	E	F	G	H	I	J	K	L	M	N	O	P	Q	R	S	A	B	C	D
4	F	G	H	I	J	K	L	M	N	O	P	Q	R	S	A	B	C	D	E
5	G	H	I	J	K	L	M	N	O	P	Q	R	S	A	B	C	D	E	F
6	H	I	J	K	L	M	N	O	P	Q	R	S	A	B	C	D	E	F	G
7	K	L	M	N	O	P	Q	R	S	A	B	C	D	E	F	G	H	I	J
8	N	O	P	Q	R	S	A	B	C	D	E	F	G	H	I	J	K	L	M
9	O	P	Q	R	S	A	B	C	D	E	F	G	H	I	J	K	L	M	N

Plan 22: $t = b = 21$, $r = k = 5$

Row	Block																				
	1	2	3	4	5	6	7	8	9	10	11	12	13	14	15	16	17	18	19	20	21
1	A	B	C	D	E	F	G	H	I	J	K	L	M	N	O	P	Q	R	S	T	U
2	B	C	D	E	F	G	H	I	J	K	L	M	N	O	P	Q	R	S	T	U	A
3	E	F	G	H	I	J	K	L	M	N	O	P	Q	R	S	T	U	A	B	C	D
4	O	P	Q	R	S	T	U	A	B	C	D	E	F	G	H	I	J	K	L	M	N
5	Q	R	S	T	U	A	B	C	D	E	F	G	H	I	J	K	L	M	N	O	P

13-6.2 ANALYSIS

The same model is used, and the same assumptions are made, as in the Latin square analysis in Paragraph 13-5.2.   The analysis presented here is sometimes called the intrablock analysis.

In the analysis we assume that the data are exhibited in a two-way table following the plan. (See the plans given in Table 13-9).   We label the various totals as follows:

T_i = sum of the observations on the ith treatment;

R_i = sum of the observations in the ith row;

C_i = sum of the observations in the ith column;

G = sum of all observations.

Data Sample 13-6.2 — Intercomparison of Thermometers*

The example involves an intercomparison of thermometers.   Seven thermometers, designated by the letters A, B, C, D, E, F, G, were set up in a bath.   The bath temperature could not be kept exactly constant, and the experiment was designed so that valid comparisons could be made among the thermometers, despite the variations in bath temperature.

The seven thermometers were read in sets of three, as follows:

	Order of Reading Within a Set		
Set	1	2	3
1	A	B	D
2	E	F	A
3	B	C	E
4	F	G	B
5	C	D	F
6	G	A	C
7	D	E	G

The two sources of inhomogeneity here are the order of reading within a set, and the set-to-set variation.

Number of treatments (thermometers)......... $t = 7$
Number of rows (sets)...................... $b = 7$
Number of columns (order).................. $k = 3$
Number of replications of each treatment...... $r = 3$

* Adapted with permission from *Statistical Methods for Chemists* (pp. 102-105) by W. J. Youden, copyright, 1951, John Wiley and Sons, Inc.

Data Sample 13-6.2 — Intercomparison of Thermometers (cont)

The thermometers had scale divisions of one-tenth of a degree, and were read to the third place with optical aid. The readings were made just above 30°C; for convenience, only the last two places are entered in the following tabulation, i.e., the entry 56 represents a reading of 30.056°C.

Set	Order of Reading Within a Set 1	2	3	Total
1	A 56	B 31	D 35	$R_1 = 122$
2	E 16	F 41	A 58	$R_2 = 115$
3	B 41	C 53	E 24	$R_3 = 118$
4	F 46	G 32	B 46	$R_1 = 124$
5	C 54	D 43	F 50	$R_5 = 147$
6	G 34	A 68	C 60	$R_6 - 162$
7	D 50	E 32	G 38	$R_i = 120$
Total	$C_1 = 297$	$C_2 = 300$	$C_3 = 311$	$G = 908$

13-6.2.1 Estimation of Treatment Effects. The estimate t_i, of the ith treatment effect φ_i is

$$t_i = Q_i/Er + G/bk,$$

where

$$Q_i = T_i - (n_{i1} R_1 + n_{i2} R_2 + \ldots + n_{ib} R_b)/r$$

T_i = total for the ith treatment

R = total for the row

n_{ij} = the number of times the ith treatment occurs in the jth row.

13-41

13-6.2.1 (cont)

For example, using Data Sample 13-6.2,

where $E = 7/9$, $k = r = 3$, $b = 7$, $Er = 21/9$

$$T_A = 182 \qquad\qquad T_E = 72$$
$$T_B = 118 \qquad\qquad T_F = 137$$
$$T_C = 167 \qquad\qquad T_G = 104$$
$$T_D = 128$$

$$Q_A = 182 - \frac{122 + 115 + 162}{3}$$
$$= 182 - 133$$
$$= 49$$

$$Q_E = 72 - \frac{115 + 118 + 120}{3}$$
$$= 72 - 117.66667$$
$$= -45.66667$$

$$Q_B = 118 - \frac{122 + 118 + 124}{3}$$
$$= 118 - 121.33333$$
$$= -3.33333$$

$$Q_F = 137 - \frac{115 + 124 + 147}{3}$$
$$= 137 - 128.66667$$
$$= 8.33333$$

$$Q_C = 167 - \frac{118 + 147 + 162}{3}$$
$$= 167 - 142.33333$$
$$= 24.66667$$

$$Q_G = 104 - \frac{124 + 162 + 120}{3}$$
$$= 104 - 135.33333$$
$$= -31.33333$$

$$Q_D = 128 - \frac{122 + 147 + 120}{3}$$
$$= 128 - 129.66667$$
$$= -1.66667$$

$$Er = \frac{21}{9}, \ bk = 21, \ \frac{G}{bk} = \frac{908}{21} = 43.238095$$

$$t_A = \frac{9\,(49)}{21} + 43.238095$$
$$= 21 + 43.238095$$
$$= 64.238095$$

$$t_E = \frac{9\,(-45.66667)}{21} + 43.238095$$
$$= -19.571430 + 43.238095$$
$$= 23.666665$$

$$t_B = \frac{9\,(-3.33333)}{21} + 43.238095$$
$$= -1.428570 + 43.238095$$
$$= 41.809525$$

$$t_F = \frac{9\,(8.33333)}{21} + 43.238095$$
$$= 3.571427 + 43.238095$$
$$= 46.809522$$

$$t_C = \frac{9\,(24.66667)}{21} + 43.238095$$
$$= 10.571430 + 43.238095$$
$$= 53.809525$$

$$t_G = \frac{9\,(-31.33333)}{21} + 43.238095$$
$$= -13.428570 + 43.238095$$
$$= 29.809525$$

$$t_D = \frac{9\,(-1.66667)}{21} + 43.238095$$
$$= -0.714287 + 43.238095$$
$$= 42.523808$$

13-6.2.2 Testing and Estimating Differences in Treatment Effects.

Procedure	Example

(1) Choose α, the significance level of the test.

(1) Let $\alpha = .05$

(2) Look up $q_{1-\alpha}(t, \nu)$ in Table A-10, where

$$\nu = (b-1)(r-2)$$

(2) Using Data Sample 13-6.2,

$$\nu = 6(1) = 6$$
$$q_{.95}(7, 6) = 5.90$$

(3) Compute

$$S_t = \frac{Q_1^2 + Q_2^2 + \ldots + Q_i^2}{Er}$$

(3)

$$S_t = \frac{9}{21}(6160.00019)$$
$$= 2640.000$$

(4) Compute

$$S_r = \frac{R_1^2 + R_2^2 + \ldots + R_b^2}{k} - \frac{G^2}{bk}$$

(4)

$$S_r = \frac{119002}{3} - \frac{824464}{21}$$
$$= 627.143$$

(5) Compute

$$S_c = \frac{C_1^2 + C_2^2 + \ldots + C_r^2}{b} - \frac{G^2}{bk}$$

(5)

$$S_c = \frac{274930}{7} - 39260.190$$
$$= 15.524$$

(6) Compute

$$S = (\text{sum of squares of all observations}) - G^2/bk$$

(6)

$$S = 42558 - 39260.190$$
$$= 3297.810$$

(7) Compute:

$$s^2 = \frac{S - S_t - S_r - S_c}{(b-1)(r-2)}$$

and

$$s$$

(7)

$$s^2 = 15.143/6$$
$$= 2.524$$
$$s = 1.589$$

(8) Compute

$$w = q_{1-\alpha} s/\sqrt{Er}$$

(8)

$$w = \frac{5.90(1.589)}{1.528}$$
$$= 6.136$$

(9) If the absolute difference between any two estimated treatment effects exceeds w, decide that the treatment effects differ; otherwise, decide that the experiment gives no reason to believe the treatment effects differ.

(9) See the estimated treatment effects in Paragraph 13-6.2.1. Taken in pairs, there are differences which exceed 6.136, and we conclude that thermometers do differ.

Note: We can make simultaneous statements about the differences between pairs of treatments i and j, with confidence $1 - \alpha$ that all the statements are simultaneously true. The statements are, for all i and j,

$$t_i - t_j - w \leq \varphi_i - \varphi_j \leq t_i - t_j + w.$$

13-6.2.3 Estimation of Column Effects. The column effects can be estimated directly from the column means; i.e., the estimate of the ith column effect is

$$c_i = C_i/b - G/bk.$$

For example, using Data Sample 13-6.2,

$$C_1 = \frac{297}{7} - \frac{908}{21}$$

$$= 42.43 - 43.24$$

$$= -0.81$$

$$C_2 = \frac{300}{7} - 43.24$$

$$= 42.86 - 43.24$$

$$= -0.38$$

$$C_3 = \frac{311}{7} - 43.24$$

$$= 44.43 - 43.24$$

$$= 1.19$$

13-6.2.4 Testing and Estimating Differences in Column Effects.

Procedure	Example
(1) Choose α, the significance level of the test.	(1) Let $\alpha = .05$
(2) Look up $q_{1-\alpha}(k, \nu)$ in Table A-10, where $\nu = (b-1)(r-2)$.	(2) $\nu = 6(1) = 6$ $q_{.95}(3, 6) = 4.34$
(3) through (7) $\begin{cases}$ Same as Steps (3) through (7) of Paragraph 13-6.2.2.	(3) through (7) $\begin{cases}$ See Paragraph 13-6.2.2. $s = 1.589$
(8) Compute $w_c = q_{1-\alpha}\, s/\sqrt{b}$	(8) $w_c = \dfrac{4.34\,(1.589)}{2.646}$ $= 2.61$
(9) If the absolute difference between any two estimated column effects exceeds w_c, decide that the column effects differ; otherwise, decide that the experiment gives no reason to believe the column effects differ.	(9) There are no differences between pairs of column effects that exceed 2.61. We conclude that the column effects (order of reading within set) do not differ.

Note: As in the case of treatment effects, we can make a set of simultaneous statements about the difference between pairs of columns i and j. The statements are, for all i and j,

$$c_i - c_j - w_c \leq \kappa_i - \kappa_j \leq c_i - c_j + w_c.$$

13-6.2.5 Estimation of Row Effects. The estimate of the jth row effect ρ_j is $r_j = Q_j' \, 'Er$, where

$$Q_j' = R_j - (n_{1j} T_1 + n_{2j} T_2 + \ldots + n_{bj} T_b)/r$$

and, as before, n_{ij} is the number of times the ith treatment occurs in the jth row.

For example, using Data Sample 13-6.2:

$$Q_1' = 122 - \frac{182 + 118 + 128}{3}$$
$$= 122 - 142.67$$
$$= -20.67$$

$$Q_2' = 115 - \frac{72 + 137 + 182}{3}$$
$$= 115 - 130.33$$
$$= -15.33$$

$$Q_3' = 118 - \frac{118 + 167 + 72}{3}$$
$$= 118 - 119.00$$
$$= -1.00$$

$$Q_4' = 124 - \frac{137 + 104 + 118}{3}$$
$$= 124 - 119.67$$
$$= 4.33$$

$$Q_5' = 147 - \frac{167 + 128 + 137}{3}$$
$$= 147 - 144.00$$
$$= 3.00$$

$$Q_6' = 162 - \frac{104 + 182 + 167}{3}$$
$$= 162 - 151.00$$
$$= 11.00$$

$$Q_7' = 120 - \frac{128 + 72 + 104}{3}$$
$$= 120 - 101.33$$
$$= 18.67$$

$$Er = \frac{21}{9}, \ \frac{1}{Er} = \frac{9}{21}$$

$$r_1 = \frac{9\,(-20.67)}{21}$$
$$= -8.86$$

$$r_2 = \frac{9\,(-15.33)}{21}$$
$$= -6.57$$

$$r_3 = \frac{9\,(-1.00)}{21}$$
$$= -0.43$$

$$r_1 = \frac{9\,(4.33)}{21}$$
$$= 1.86$$

$$r_5 = \frac{9\,(3.00)}{21}$$
$$= 1.29$$

$$r_6 = \frac{9\,(11.00)}{21}$$
$$= 4.71$$

$$r_7 = \frac{9\,(18.67)}{21}$$
$$= 8.00$$

13-6.2.6   Testing and Estimating Differences in Row Effects.

Procedure	Example
(1) Choose α, the significance level of the test.	(1) Let $\alpha = .05$
(2) Look up $q_{1-\alpha}(b, \nu)$ in Table A-10, where $$\nu = (b - 1)(r - 2).$$	(2) From Data Sample 13-6.2: $$(b - 1)(r - 2) = 6(1)$$ $$= 6$$ $$q_{.95}(7, 6) = 5.90$$
(3) through (7) $\left\{\begin{array}{l}\text{Same as Steps (3) through (7) of}\\ \text{Paragraph 13-6.2.2.}\end{array}\right.$	(3) through (7) $\left\{\begin{array}{l}\text{See Paragraph 13-6.2.2.}\\ s = 1.589\end{array}\right.$
(8) Compute $$w_r = q_{1-\alpha}\, s / \sqrt{k}$$	(8) $$w_r = \frac{5.90\,(1.589)}{1.732}$$ $$= 5.41$$
(9) If the absolute difference between any two estimated row effects exceeds w_r, decide that the row effects differ; otherwise, decide that the experiment gives no reason to believe that row effects differ.	(9) There are differences between pairs of row effects that exceed 5.41. Therefore, we conclude that rows (sets) do differ.

Note: As in the case of the treatment and column effects, we can make a set of simultaneous statements about the differences between pairs of columns i and j. The statements are, for all i and j,

$$r_i - r_j - w_r \le \rho_i - \rho_j \le r_i - r_j + w_r.$$

REFERENCES

1. R. C. Bose, W. H. Clatworthy, and S. S. Shrikhande, "Tables of Partially Balanced Designs with Two Associate Classes," *Technical Bulletin No. 107*, North Carolina Agricultural Experiment Station, 1954. (Reprinted by Institute of Statistics, Raleigh, N. C., Reprint Series No. 50).

2. W. G. Cochran and G. M. Cox, *Experimental Designs* (2d edition), John Wiley & Sons, Inc., New York, N. Y., 1957.

3. R. A. Fisher and F. Yates, *Statistical Tables for Biological, Agricultural and Medical Research* (5th edition), Oliver and Boyd, Ltd., Edinburgh, and Hafner Publishing Co., New York, N. Y., 1957.

CHAPTER 14

EXPERIMENTS TO DETERMINE OPTIMUM CONDITIONS OR LEVELS

14-1 INTRODUCTION

In many industrial-type processes, there is a measurable end-property whose value is of primary interest and which we would like to have attain some optimum value. This end-property is called *yield* or *response* in the language of experimental design. For example, the end-property might be:

(a) the *actual yield* of the process, which we would like to maximize;

(b) a strength property, which we would like to maximize;

(c) cost, which we would like to minimize; or,

(d) some chemical or physical characteristic that would be most desirable at a maximum or at a minimum, as specified.

The value of this primary end-property will depend on the values or settings of a number of factors in the process which affect the end-property. In such cases, the goal of experimentation is to find the settings of the factors which result in an optimum response. Often, we are interested in knowing not only the values of the variables that result in optimum response, but also how much change in response results from small deviations from the optimum settings — i.e., we would like to know the nature of the response function in the vicinity of this optimum.

14-2 THE RESPONSE FUNCTION

In a factorial experiment where the levels of all factors are quantitative (e.g., time, temperature, pressure, amount of catalyst, purity of ingredients, etc.), we can think of the response y as a function of the levels of the experimental factors. For an n-factor experiment, we could write:

True yield

$$y = \Phi(x_1, x_2, \ldots, x_n)$$

where

$$x_1 = \text{level of factor 1}$$
$$x_2 = \text{level of factor 2}$$
etc.

For observed values of y, we can write:

$$Y_u = \Phi(x_{1u}, x_{2u}, \ldots, x_{nu}) + e_u$$

where

Y_u = the uth observation of y, where $u = 1, 2, \ldots, N$ represent the N observations in the factorial experiment;

x_{1u} = level of factor 1 for the uth observation;

x_{2u} = level of factor 2 for the uth observation; etc.;

and

e_u = the experimental error of the uth observation.

The function Φ can be called the response function. If we could determine the function Φ, we could describe the results of the experiment completely, and could even predict y for values of the factors that were not included in the experiment (but the function *should not* be used for prediction outside the range of experiment). Ordinarily, the mathematical form of the function is completely unknown, but often it can be satisfactorily approximated within a limited region by a polynomial in x_{iu}. Just as the relation $y = \Phi(x)$ can be represented by a curve, the relation between y and two factors x_1 and x_2, i.e., $y = \Phi(x_1, x_2)$, can be represented by a surface called the response surface, as shown in Figure 14-1; or, alternatively, by a contour diagram which traces contours of equal response as shown in Figure 14-2.

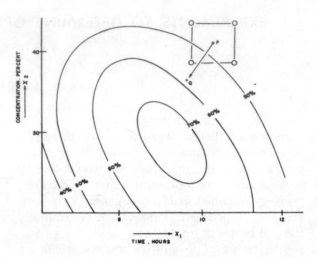

Figure 14-2. Yield contours for the surface of Figure 14-1 with 2^2 factorial design.

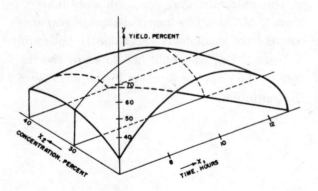

Figure 14-1. A response surface.

The study of response surfaces is a very complex topic. A general notion of possible applications is given here, but no details are provided. An extensive bibliography is given at the end of this Chapter. Since this is a relatively new field, the bibliography is fairly complete at the time of preparation.

14-3 EXPERIMENTAL DESIGNS

Experimental designs and methods of analysis have been developed for fitting polynomials of the first and second degree; these designs are called first and second order designs, respectively. One will hear these designs described as, for example, "a first order design in 2 dimensions" or "a second order design in 4 dimensions" — in general, a kth order design in n dimensions. The dimension n refers to the number of independent variables (x_i) in the response function, and the order k refers to the degree of the fitted polynomial function.

A design in which only one variable is controlled is a one-dimensional design, and we observe y as a function of the single variable x, i.e., $y = \Phi(x)$. The first approach in describing such a relationship may be that of fitting a first order equation, i.e., a straight line $y = \beta_0 + \beta_1 x$, as detailed in ORDP 20-110, Chapter 5. If it has been determined that the relationship cannot be adequately represented by a straight line, a second-degree (or higher degree) polynomial may be fitted as detailed in ORDP 20-110, Chapter 6. A one-dimensional design, however, is not usual in this kind of experimentation and, ordinarily, more variables will be involved.

If we are interested in studying response y as a function of two variables (x_1 and x_2), we represent the function as

$$y = \Phi(x_1, x_2).$$

Again, as a first step, we could fit a first order model (now the equation of a plane)

$$y = \beta_0 + \beta_1 x_1 + \beta_2 x_2.$$

Where three or more variables are controlled, we have a function of the type

$$y = \Phi(x_1, x_2, \ldots, x_n).$$

A general aim in selecting and constructing experimental designs when observing a function of several quantitative variables, is that the selected design should permit relatively simple and straightforward estimation of the coefficients of the fitted equation. Two-level factorial designs are important designs for fitting first order models — particularly in the two-dimensional case. New designs, with special advantageous properties, have been developed by G.E.P. Box and followers. Most first order designs will provide information about the adequacy of the first order model, and second order designs are available when first order models are inadequate.

14-4 FINDING THE OPTIMUM

In general, experimentation proceeds sequentially. Initial levels of the variables are chosen so that the levels are either near present operating conditions or are believed to be near optimum response. A design is chosen, and experimental observations are made at values of the variables which are specified by the design. In general, first order designs will provide information on the adequacy of the first order model, will indicate whether the response is near the optimum, and will indicate the direction to move to approach closer to the optimum. Another first order design may then be run at a new position, or a second order design may be run at the original position. The methods are extremely flexible and useful. A complete description of the methods cannot be included here, and the reader is advised to consult the references described in Paragraph 14-5.

14-5   RECOMMENDED SOURCES FOR FURTHER STUDY

The bibliography contains references which have been classified into three groups:

     I. Elementary and Introductory Reading
    II. Advanced Reading
   III. Applications.

Group I contains those articles that will be most helpful to the novice. For the reader who is completely unacquainted with the techniques, the following reading program is suggested. First, read the series of articles by Bradley[1] and Hunter[2] which appeared in *Industrial Quality Control*. Follow this by reading the appropriate chapter in Cochran and Cox[3] or Davies[4], or by reading the Hunter article[5]. Another introductory article, which requires a higher level of mathematical background, is by Box and Hunter[6]. From these introductory readings, proceed to the articles in Group II or III which are of particular interest.

The classification into the three groups had to be somewhat arbitrary. In particular, the reader will notice some anomalies in Group II where some articles are not highly mathematical, but have been included for historical reasons. The level of mathematics required for the Group II references varies a great deal, but one can ordinarily predict the level by knowledge of the journal in which the article appears.

Group III contains articles that deal primarily with applications.

REFERENCES

1. R. A. Bradley, "Determination of Optimum Operating Conditions by Experimental Methods — Part I, Mathematics and Statistics Fundamental to the Fitting of Response Surfaces," *Industrial Quality Control*, Vol. 15, No. 1, pp. 16-20, July 1958.

2. J. S. Hunter, "Determination of Optimum Operating Conditions by Experimental Methods — Part II, Models and Methods," *Industrial Quality Control*, Vol. 15, No. 6, pp. 16-24, December 1958; No. 7, pp. 7-15, January 1959; No. 8, pp. 6-14, February 1959.

3. W. G. Cochran and G. M. Cox, *Experimental Designs* (2d edition), Ch. 8A, John Wiley & Sons, Inc., New York, N. Y., 1957.

4. O. L. Davies (Ed.), *The Design and Analysis of Industrial Experiments*, Ch. 11, Oliver and Boyd, Ltd., Edinburgh, and Hafner Publishing Co., New York, N. Y., 1954.

5. J. S. Hunter, "Statistical Methods for Determining Optimum Conditions," *Transactions 10th Annual Convention*, p. 415, American Society for Quality Control, Milwaukee, Wis., 1956.

6. G. E. P. Box and J. S. Hunter, "Experimental Designs for Exploring Response Surfaces," *Proceedings, Symposium on Design of Industrial Experiments*, November 1956, North Carolina State College, Raleigh, N. C., 1957. ASTIA Document AD 148008. Also published in V. Chew (Ed.), *Experimental Designs in Industry*, pp. 138-190, John Wiley & Sons, Inc., New York, N. Y., 1958

SELECTED BIBLIOGRAPHY

I. *Elementary and Introductory Reading*

S. L. Andersen, "Use of Mathematical Models in Design and Analysis of Experiments," *Proceedings, Rutgers Quality Control Conference*, American Society for Quality Control, September 1956.

R. A. Bradley, "Mathematics and Statistics Fundamental to the Fitting of Response Surfaces," *Proceedings, Rutgers Quality Control Conference*, American Society for Quality Control, September 1955.

R. A. Bradley, "Determination of Optimum Operating Conditions by Experimental Methods — Part 1, Mathematics and Statistics Fundamental to the Fitting of Response Surfaces," *Industrial Quality Control*, Vol. XV, No. 1, pp. 16-20, July 1958.

W. G. Cochran and G. M. Cox, *Experimental Designs* (2d edition), John Wiley & Sons, Inc., New York, N. Y., 1957.

O. L. Davies (Ed.), *The Design and Analysis of Industrial Experiments*, Ch. 11, Oliver and Boyd, Ltd., Edinburgh, and Hafner Publishing Co., New York, N. Y., 1954.

J. S. Hunter, "Statistical Methods for Determining Optimum Conditions," *Transactions 10th Annual Convention*, p. 415, American Society for Quality Control, Milwaukee, Wis., 1956.

J. S. Hunter, "A Discussion on Rotatable Designs," *Transactions 12th Annual Convention*, p. 531, American Society for Quality Control, Milwaukee, Wis., 1958.

J. S. Hunter, "Determination of Optimum Operating Conditions by Experimental Methods — Part II, Models and Methods," *Industrial Quality Control*, Vol. 15, No. 6, pp. 16-24, December 1958; No. 7, pp. 7-15, January 1959; and No. 8, pp. 6-14, February 1959.

II. *Advanced Reading*

R. L. Anderson, "Recent Advances in Finding Best Operating Conditions," *Journal of the American Statistical Association*, Vol. 48, p. 789, 1953.

R. C. Bose and R. L. Carter, "Complex Representation in the Construction of Rotatable Designs," *Annals of Mathematical Statistics*, Vol. 30, p. 771, 1959.

R. C. Bose and N. R. Draper, "Second Order Rotatable Designs in Three Dimensions," *Annals of Mathematical Statistics*, Vol. 30, p. 1097, 1959.

G. E. P. Box, "Statistical Design in Study of Analytical Methods," *Analyst*, Vol. 77, p. 879, 1952.

G. E. P. Box, "Multi-Factor Designs of First Order," *Biometrika*, Vol. 39, p. 49, 1952.

G. E. P. Box, "The Exploration and Exploitation of Response Surfaces: Some General Considerations and Examples," *Biometrics*, Vol. 10, p. 16, 1954.

G. E. P. Box, "Integration of Techniques in Process Development," *Transactions 11th Annual Convention*, p. 687, American Society for Quality Control, Milwaukee, Wis., 1957.

G. E. P. Box, "Some General Considerations in Process Optimization," *Transactions American Society of Mechanical Engineers, Vol. 82, Series D-J. of Basic Engineering*, p. 113, March 1960.

G. E. P. Box and D. W. Behnken, "Some New Three-Level Designs for the Study of Quantitative Variables," *Technometrics*, Vol. 2, p. 455, 1960.

II. *Advanced Reading (Cont)*

G. E. P. Box and D. W. Behnken, "Simplex-sum Designs: A Class of Second Order Rotatable Designs Derivable from Those of First Order," *Annals of Mathematical Statistics*, Vol. 31, p. 838, 1960.

G. E. P. Box and N. R. Draper, "A Basis for the Selection of a Response Surface Design," *Journal of the American Statistical Association*, Vol. 54, p. 622, 1959.

G. E. P. Box, R. J. Hader, and J. S. Hunter, "The Effect of Inadequate Models in Surface Fitting," *Mimeo Series No. 91*, Institute of Statistics, Raleigh, N. C., 1954.

G. E. P. Box and J. S. Hunter, "Multi-Factor Experimental Designs," *Mimeo Series No. 92*, Institute of Statistics, Raleigh, N. C., 1954.

G. E. P. Box and J. S. Hunter, "A Confidence Region for the Solution of a Set of Simultaneous Equations with an Application to Experimental Design," *Biometrika*, Vol. 41, p. 190, 1954.

G. E. P. Box and J. S. Hunter, "Multi-Factor Experimental Designs for Exploring Response Surfaces," *Annals of Mathematical Statistics*, Vol. 28, p. 195, 1957.

G. E. P. Box and J. S. Hunter, "Experimental Designs for Exploring Response Surfaces," *Proceedings, Symposium on Design of Industrial Experiments*, November 1956, North Carolina State College, Raleigh, N. C., 1957. Also published in V. Chew (Ed.), *Experimental Designs in Industry*, John Wiley & Sons, Inc., New York, N. Y., 1958.

G. E. P. Box and K. B. Wilson, "On the Experimental Attainment of Optimum Conditions," *Journal of the Royal Statistical Society, Series B*, Vol. 13, p. 1, 1951.

G. E. P. Box and P. V. Youle, "The Exploration and Exploitation of Response Surfaces; An Example of the Link Between the Fitted Surface and the Basic Mechanism of the System," *Biometrics*, Vol. 11, p. 287, 1955.

S. Brooks, "Comparison of Methods for Estimating the Optimal Factor Combination," *Sc. D. thesis*, Johns Hopkins University, Baltimore, Md., 1955.

S. H. Brooks and M. R. Mickey, "Optimum Estimation of Gradient Direction in Steepest Ascent Experiments," *Proceedings, Symposium on Optimization Techniques in Chemical Engineering*, May 18, 1960, p. 79, Office of Special Services to Business and Industry, New York University, New York, N. Y.

R. L. Carter, "New Designs for the Exploration of Response Surfaces," *Mimeo Series No. 172*, Institute of Statistics, Raleigh, N. C., 1957.

R. M. DeBaun, "Block Effects in the Determination of Optimum Conditions," *Biometrics*, Vol. 12, p. 20, 1956.

R. M. DeBaun, "An Experimental Design for Three Factors at Three Levels," *Nature*, Vol. 181, p. 209, 1956.

R. M. DeBaun, "Response Surface Designs for Three Factors at Three Levels," *Technometrics*, Vol. 1, p. 1, 1959.

N. R. Draper, "Second Order Rotatable Designs in Four or More Dimensions," *Annals of Mathematical Statistics*, Vol. 31, p. 23, 1960.

N. R. Draper, "Third Order Rotatable Designs in Three Dimensions," *Annals of Mathematical Statistics*, Vol. 31, p. 865, 1960.

N. R. Draper, "A Third Order Rotatable Design in Four Dimensions," *Annals of Mathematical Statistics*, Vol. 31, p. 875, 1960.

O. Dykstra, "Partial Duplication of Response Surface Designs," *Technometrics*, Vol. 2, p. 185, 1960.

M. Friedman and L. J. Savage, "Planning Experiments Seeking Maxima," Ch. 13 of *Techniques of Statistical Analysis*, (edited by C. Eisenhart, M. W. Hastay, and W. A. Wallis), McGraw-Hill Book Co., New York, N. Y., 1947.

D. A. Gardiner, A. H. E. Grandage, and R. J. Hader, "Some Third Order Rotatable Designs," *Mimeo Series No. 149*, Institute of Statistics, Raleigh, N. C., 1956.

D. A. Gardiner, A. H. E. Grandage, and R. J. Hader, "Third Order Rotatable Designs for Exploring Response Surfaces," *Annals of Mathematical Statistics*, Vol. 30, p. 1082, 1959.

R. J. Hader, "Variances of Regression Coefficients for Split Plot Multi-Factor Experiments," *Technical Report No. 8*, Institute of Statistics, Raleigh, N. C., 1954.

II. *Advanced Reading (Cont)*

H. O. Hartley, "Smallest Composite Designs for Quadratic Response Surfaces," *Biometrics*, Vol. 15, p. 611, 1959.

H. Hotelling, "Experimental Determination of the Maximum of a Function," *Annals of Mathematical Statistics*, Vol. 12, p. 20, 1941.

J. S. Hunter, "Multi-Factor Experimental Designs," *Ph. D. thesis*, North Carolina State College, Raleigh, N. C., 1954.

J. S. Hunter, "Searching for Optimum Conditions," *Transactions New York Academy of Science, Ser. 11*, Vol. 17, 1954.

K. B. Madhava, "Sequential Approach in Factorial Designs," *Review International Statistical Institute*, Vol. 24, p. 64, 1956.

D. R. Read, "The Design of Chemical Experiments," *Biometrics*, Vol. 10, p. 1, 1954.

A. W. Umland and W. N. Smith, "The Use of Lagrange Multipliers With Response Surfaces," *Technometrics*, Vol. 1, p. 289, 1959.

III. *Applications*

D. S. Brown, W. R. Turner, and A. C. Smith, Jr., "Sealing Strength of Waxpolyethylene Blends," *Tappi*, Vol. 41, p. 295, 1958.

N. L. Carr, "Kinetics of Catalytic Isomerization of n-Pentane," *Industrial and Engineering Chemistry*, Vol. 52, p. 391, 1960.

D. J. Cestoni, R. E. Ringelman, and L. R. Olson, "Process Engineering of a Petrochemical Plant," *Chemical Engineering Progress*, Vol. 56, p. 73, 1960.

C. D. Chang, O. K. Kononenko, and R. E. Franklin, Jr., "Maximum Data Through a Statistical Design," *Industrial and Engineering Chemistry*, Vol. 52, p. 939, 1960.

W. O. Cochran, "Procedures for Selection of Optimum Conditions," *Proceedings Symposium on Optimization Techniques in Chemical Engineering*, p. 91, May 1960, Office of Special Services to Business and Industry, New York University, New York, N. Y.

R. M. DeBaun and A. M. Schneider, "Experiences with Response Surface Designs," *Proceedings Symposium on Design of Industrial Experiments, November 1956*, North Carolina State College, Raleigh, N. C., 1957. Also published in V. Chew (Ed.), *Experimental Designs in Industry*, pp. 235-246, John Wiley & Sons, Inc., New York, N. Y., 1958.

D. A. Deckman and M. Van Winkle, "Perforated Plate Column Studies by the Box Method of Experimentation," *Industrial and Engineering Chemistry*, Vol. 51, p. 1015, 1959.

J. L. Folks, "Optimal Design Considerations in Response Surface Exploration," *Transactions 3rd Annual Technical Conference*, p. 143, Chemical Division, American Society for Quality Control, Milwaukee, Wis., September 1959.

R. H. Glaser, "An Application of the Box Technique to the Evaluation of Electrical Components," *Proceedings 4th National Symposium on Reliability and Quality Control in Electronics*, p. 161, Institute of Radio Engineers, New York, N. Y., January 1958.

H. Grohskopf, "Statistics in the Chemical Process Industries — Present and Future," *Industrial and Engineering Chemistry*, Vol. 52, p. 497, 1960.

W. C. Hackler, W. W. Kriegel, and R. J. Hader, "Effect of Raw Material Ratios on Absorption of Whiteware Compositions," *Journal American Ceramic Society*, Vol. 39, p. 20, 1956.

R. J. Hader, et al., "An Investigation of Some of the Relationships Between Copper, Iron, and Molybdenum in the Growth and Nutrition of Lettuce," *Proceedings American Soil Sciences Society*, Vol. 21, p. 59, 1957.

III. *Applications (Cont)*

E. O. Heady, J. T. Pesek, and W. G. Brown, "Crop Response Surfaces and Economic Optima in Fertilizer Use," *Iowa State College Agricultural Experiment Station Research Bulletin*, Vol. 424, p. 292, 1955.

A. E. Hoerl, "Optimum Solution of Many Variables Equations," *Chemical and Engineering Progress*, Vol. 55, p. 69, 1959.

A. E. Hoerl, "Statistical Analysis of an Industrial Production Problem," *Industrial and Engineering Chemistry*, Vol. 52, p. 513, 1960.

D. Q. Kern and O. O. Kenworthy, "Formulation and Compounding Optimization — a Farewell to the Cookbook," *Industrial and Engineering Chemistry*, Vol. 52, p. 42A, 1960.

E. E. Lind, J. Goldin, and J. B. Hickman, "Fitting Yield and Cost Response Surfaces," *Chemical Engineering Progress*, Vol. 56, p. 62, 1960.

R. W. Mooney, et al., "Precipitation of Calcium Hydrogen Orthophosphate," *Industrial and Engineering Chemistry*, Vol. 52, p. 427, 1960.

F. P. Pike, et al., "Application of Statistical Procedures to a Study of the Flooding Capacity of a Pulse Column," *North Carolina State College, Chemical Engineering Technical Report*, 1954.

P. B. Roth and G. Switlyk, "The Determination of Response Surfaces for Textile Resin Finishes," *Statistical Methods in the Chemical Industry*, p. 113, American Society for Quality Control, Milwaukee, Wis., January 12, 1957.

B. S. Sanderson, "The Use of Box-Wilson Techniques in the Study of a Titania Pigment Process," *Statistical Methods in the Chemical Industry*, p. 51, American Society for Quality Control, Milwaukee, Wis., January 12, 1957.

C. T. Shewell, "Paper Studies in Catalytic Cracking," *Transactions 10th Annual Convention*, p. 1, American Society for Quality Control, Milwaukee, Wis., 1956.

R. F. Sweeney, et al., "Mathematics, Computers, Operations Research, and Statistics," *Industrial and Engineering Chemistry*, Vol. 53, p. 329, 1961.

P. W. Tidwell, "Chemical Process Improvement by Response Surface Methods," *Industrial and Engineering Chemistry*, Vol. 52, p. 510, 1960.

R. Vaswani, "Sequential Decisioning Technique for Optimization of Complex Systems," *Journal of Industrial Engineering*, Vol. 7, p. 174, 1956.

P. Whidden, "Design of Experiment in Metals Processing," *Transactions 10th Annual Convention*, p. 677, American Society for Quality Control, Milwaukee, Wis., 1956.

SECTION 4

SPECIAL TOPICS

DISCUSSION OF TECHNIQUES IN CHAPTERS 15 THROUGH 23

In this Section, a number of important but as yet non-standard techniques are presented for answering questions similar to those considered in ORDP 20-110, Section 1. In addition, various special topics, such as transformation of data to simplify the statistical analysis, treatment of outlying observations, expression of uncertainties of final results, use of control charts in experimental work, etc., are discussed in sufficient detail to serve as an introduction for the reader who wishes to pursue these topics further in the published literature.

All A-Tables referenced in these Chapters are contained in ORDP 20-114, Section 5.

CHAPTER 15

SOME SHORTCUT TESTS FOR SMALL SAMPLES
FROM NORMAL POPULATIONS

15-1 GENERAL

Shortcut tests are characterized by their simplicity. The calculations are simple, and often may be done on a slide rule. Further, they are easily learned. An additional advantage in their use is that their simplicity implies fewer errors, and this may be important where time spent in checking is costly.

The main disadvantage of the shortcut tests as compared to the tests given in ORDP 20-110, Chapters 3 and 4, is that with the same values of α and n, the shortcut test will, in general, have a larger β, — i.e., it will result in a higher proportion of *errors of the second kind*. For the tests given in this chapter, this increase in error will usually be rather small if the sample sizes involved are each of the order of 10 or less.

Unlike the *nonparametric* tests of Chapter 16, these tests require the assumption of *normality* of the underlying populations. Small departures from normality, however, will usually have a negligible effect on the test — i.e., the values of α and β, in general, will differ from their intended values by only a slight amount.

No descriptions of the operating characteristics of the tests or of methods of determining sample size are given in this chapter.

15-2 COMPARING THE AVERAGE OF A NEW PRODUCT WITH THAT OF A STANDARD

15-2.1 DOES THE AVERAGE OF THE NEW PRODUCT DIFFER FROM THE STANDARD?

Data Sample 15-2.1 — Depth of Penetration

Ten rounds of a new type of shell are fired into a target, and the depth of penetration is measured for each round. The depths of penetration are:

$$10.0, 9.8, 10.2, 10.5, 11.4, 10.8, 9.8, 12.2, 11.6, 9.9 \text{ cms.}$$

The average penetration depth, m_0, of the standard comparable shell is 10.0 cm.

The question to be answered is: Does the new type differ from the standard type with respect to average penetration depth (either a decrease, or an increase, being of interest)?

Procedure	**Example**
(1) Choose α, the significance level of the test.	(1) Let $\alpha = .01$
(2) Look up $\varphi_{1-\alpha/2}$ in Table A-12 for the appropriate n.	(2) $n = 10$ $\varphi_{.995} = 0.333$
(3) Compute $\bar{X}$, the mean of the n observations.	(3) $\bar{X} = 10.62$
(4) Compute w, the difference between the largest and smallest of the n observations.	(4) $w = 2.4$
(5) Compute $\varphi = (\bar{X} - m_0)/w$	(5) $\varphi = \dfrac{10.62 - 10.00}{2.4}$ $= 0.258$
(6) If $|\varphi| > \varphi_{1-\alpha/2}$, conclude that the average performance of the new product differs from that of the standard; otherwise, there is no reason to believe that they differ.	(6) Since 0.258 is not larger than 0.333, there is no reason to believe that the new type shell differs from the standard.

15-2.2 DOES THE AVERAGE OF THE NEW PRODUCT EXCEED THE STANDARD?

In terms of Data Sample 15-2.1, let us suppose that — in advance of looking at the data — the important question is: Does the average of the new type exceed that of the standard?

Procedure	**Example**
(1) Choose α, the significance level of the test.	(1) Let $\alpha = .01$
(2) Look up $\varphi_{1-\alpha}$ in Table A-12, for the appropriate n.	(2) $n = 10$ $\varphi_{.99} = 0.288$
(3) Compute $\bar{X}$, the mean of the n observations.	(3) $\bar{X} = 10.62$
(4) Compute w, the difference between the largest and smallest of the n observations.	(4) $w = 2.4$
(5) Compute $\varphi = (\bar{X} - m_0)/w$	(5) $\varphi = \dfrac{10.62 - 10.00}{2.4}$ $= 0.258$
(6) If $\varphi > \varphi_{1-\alpha}$, conclude that the average of the new product exceeds that of the standard; otherwise, there is no reason to believe that the average of the new product exceeds the standard.	(6) Since 0.258 is not larger than 0.288, there is no reason to believe that the average of the new type exceeds that of the standard.

15-2.3 IS THE AVERAGE OF THE NEW PRODUCT LESS THAN THE STANDARD?

In terms of Data Sample 15-2.1, let us suppose that — in advance of looking at the data — the important question is: Is the average of the new type *less than* that of the standard?

Procedure	Example
(1) Choose α, the significance level of the test.	(1) Let $\alpha = .01$
(2) Look up $\varphi_{1-\alpha}$ in Table A-12, for the appropriate n.	(2) $n = 10$ $\varphi_{.99} = 0.288$
(3) Compute $\bar{X}$, the mean of the n observations.	(3) $\bar{X} = 10.62$
(4) Compute w, the difference between the largest and smallest of the n observations.	(4) $w = 2.4$
(5) Compute $\varphi = (m_0 - \bar{X})/w$	(5) $\varphi = \dfrac{10.00 - 10.62}{2.4}$ $= -0.258$
(6) If $\varphi > \varphi_{1-\alpha}$, conclude that the average of the new product is less than that of the standard; otherwise, there is no reason to believe that the average of the new product is less than that of the standard.	(6) Since -0.258 is not larger than 0.288, there is no reason to believe that the average of the new type is less than that of the standard.

15-3   COMPARING THE AVERAGES OF TWO PRODUCTS

15-3.1   DO THE PRODUCTS A AND B DIFFER IN AVERAGE PERFORMANCE?

Data Sample 15-3.1 — Capacity of Batteries

Form: A set of n measurements is available from each of two materials or products. The procedure* given requires that both sets contain the same number of measurements (i.e., $n_1 = n_B = n$).

Example: There are available two independent sets of measurements of battery capacity.

Set A	Set B
138	140
143	141
136	139
141	143
140	138
142	140
142	142
146	139
137	141
135	138

Procedure	Example
(1) Choose α, the significance level of the test.	(1) Let $\alpha = .01$
(2) Look up $\varphi'_{1-\alpha/2}$ in Table A-13, for the appropriate n.	(2) $n = 10$ $\varphi'_{.995} = 0.419$
(3) Compute $\bar{X}_A$, $\bar{X}_B$, the means of the two samples.	(3) $\bar{X}_A = 140.0$ $\bar{X}_B = 140.1$
(4) Compute w_A, w_B, the ranges (or difference between the largest and smallest values) for each sample.	(4) $w_A = 146 - 135$ $= 11$ $w_B = 143 - 138$ $= 5$
(5) Compute $$\varphi' = \frac{\bar{X}_A - \bar{X}_B}{\frac{1}{2}(w_A + w_B)}$$	(5) $\varphi' = \dfrac{140.0 - 140.1}{8}$ $= -0.0125$
(6) If $|\varphi'| > \varphi'_{1-\alpha/2}$, conclude that the averages of the two products differ; otherwise, there is no reason to believe that the averages of A and B differ.	(6) Since 0.0125 is not larger than 0.419, there is no reason to believe that the average of A differs from the average of B.

---

* This procedure is not appropriate when the observations are "paired", i.e., when each measurement from A is associated with a corresponding measurement from B (see Paragraph 3-3.1.4). In the paired observation case, the question may be answered by the following procedure: compute $\bar{X}_d$ as shown in Paragraph 3-3.1.4 and follow the procedure of Paragraph 15-2.1, using $\bar{X} = \bar{X}_d$ and $m_0 = 0$.

15-3.2 DOES THE AVERAGE OF PRODUCT A EXCEED THE AVERAGE OF PRODUCT B?

In terms of Data Sample 15-3.1, let us suppose that — in advance of looking at the data — the important question is: Does the average of A exceed the average of B?

Again, as in Paragraph 15-3.1, the procedure is appropriate when two independent sets of measurements are available, each containing the same number of observations ($n_A = n_B = n$), but is not appropriate when the observations are paired (see Paragraph 3-3.1.4). In the paired observation case, the question may be answered by the following procedure: compute $\bar{X}_d$ as shown in Paragraph 3-3.2.4, and follow the procedure of Paragraph 15-2.2, using $\bar{X} = \bar{X}_d$ and $m_0 = 0$.

Procedure	Example
(1) Choose α, the significance level of the test.	(1) Let $\alpha = .05$
(2) Look up $\varphi'_{1-\alpha}$ in Table A-13, for the appropriate n.	(2) $\quad n = 10$ $\quad \varphi'_{.95} = .250$
(3) Compute $\bar{X}_A$, $\bar{X}_B$, the means of the two samples.	(3) $\quad \bar{X}_A = 140.0$ $\quad \bar{X}_B = 140.1$
(4) Compute w_A, w_B, the ranges (or difference between the largest and smallest values) for each sample.	(4) $\quad w_A = 11$ $\quad w_B = 5$
(5) Compute $$\varphi' = \frac{\bar{X}_A - \bar{X}_B}{\frac{1}{2}(w_A + w_B)}$$	(5) $$\varphi' = \frac{140.0 - 140.1}{8}$$ $$= -0.0125$$
(6) If $\varphi' > \varphi'_{1-\alpha}$, conclude that the average of A exceeds that of B; otherwise, there is no reason to believe that the average of A exceeds that of B.	(6) Since -0.0125 is not larger than 0.250, there is no reason to believe that the average of A exceeds the average of B.

15-4 COMPARING THE AVERAGES OF SEVERAL PRODUCTS
DO THE AVERAGES OF t PRODUCTS DIFFER?

Data Sample 15-4 — Breaking-Strength of Cement Briquettes

The following data relate to breaking-strength of cement briquettes (in pounds per square inch).

	Group				
	1	2	3	4	5
	518	508	554	555	536
	560	574	598	567	492
	538	528	579	550	528
	510	534	538	535	572
	544	538	544	540	506
ΣX_i	2670	2682	2813	2747	2634
n_i	5	5	5	5	5
$\bar{X}_i$	534.0	536.4	562.6	549.4	526.8

Excerpted with permission from *Statistical Exercises*, "Part II, Analysis of Variance and Associated Techniques," by N. L. Johnson, Copyright, 1957, Department of Statistics, University College, London.

The question to be answered is: Does the average breaking-strength differ for the different groups?

Procedure	Example
(1) Choose α, the significance level of the test.	(1) Let $\alpha = .01$
(2) Look up L_α in Table A-15, corresponding to t and n. $n = n_1 = n_2 = \ldots = n_t$, the number of observations on each product.	(2) $t = 5$ $n = 5$ $L_\alpha = 1.02$
(3) Compute $w_1, w_2, \ldots, w_t$, the ranges of the n observations from each product.	(3) $w_1 = 50$ $w_2 = 66$ $w_3 = 60$ $w_4 = 32$ $w_5 = 80$
(4) Compute $\bar{X}_1, \bar{X}_2, \ldots, \bar{X}_t$, the means of the observations from each product.	(4) $\bar{X}_1 = 534.0$ $\bar{X}_2 = 536.4$ $\bar{X}_3 = 562.6$ $\bar{X}_4 = 549.4$ $\bar{X}_5 = 526.8$
(5) Compute $w' = w_1 + w_2 + \ldots + w_t$. Compute w'', the difference between the largest and the smallest of the means $\bar{X}_i$.	(5) $w' = 288$ $w'' = 562.6 - 526.8$ $\quad = 35.8$

Procedure (Cont)	Example (Cont)
(6) Compute $L = nw''/w'$	(6) $L = 179/288$ $= 0.62$
(7) If $L > L_\alpha$, conclude that the averages of the t products differ; otherwise, there is no reason to believe that the averages differ.	(7) Since L is less than L_α, there is no reason to believe that the group averages differ.

15-5 COMPARING TWO PRODUCTS WITH RESPECT TO VARIABILITY OF PERFORMANCE

15-5.1 DOES THE VARIABILITY OF PRODUCT A DIFFER FROM THAT OF PRODUCT B?

The data of Data Sample 15-3.1 are used to illustrate the procedure.
The question to be answered is: Does the variability of A differ from the variability of B?

Procedure	Example
(1) Choose α, the significance level of the test.	(1) Let $\alpha = .01$
(2) Look up $F'_{\alpha/2}(n_A, n_B)$ and $F'_{1-\alpha/2}(n_A, n_B)$ in Table A-11*.	(2) $n_A = 10$ $n_B = 10$ $F'_{.005}(10, 10) = .37$ $F'_{.995}(10, 10) = 2.7$
(3) Compute w_A, w_B, the ranges (or difference between the largest and smallest observations) for A and B, respectively.	(3) $w_A = 11$ $w_B = 5$
(4) Compute $F'' = w_A/w_B$	(4) $F' = 11/5$ $= 2.2$
(5) If $F' < F'_{\alpha/2}(n_A, n_B)$ or $F' > F'_{1-\alpha/2}(n_A, n_B)$, conclude that the variability in performance differs; otherwise, there is no reason to believe that the variability differs.	(5) Since F' is not less than .37 and is not greater than 2.7, there is no reason to believe that the variability differs.

* When using Table A-11, sample sizes need not be equal, but cannot be larger than 10.

15-5.2 DOES THE VARIABILITY OF PRODUCT A EXCEED THAT OF PRODUCT B?

In terms of Data Sample 15-3.1, the question to be answered is: Does the variability of A exceed the variability of B?

Procedure	Example

(1) Choose α, the significance level of the test.

(1) Let $\alpha = .01$

(2) Look up $F'_{1-\alpha}(n_A, n_B)$ in Table A-11*.

(2) $n_A = 10$
$n_B = 10$
$F'_{.99}(10, 10) = 2.4$

(3) Compute w_A, w_B, the ranges (or difference between the largest and smallest observations) for A and B, respectively.

(3) $w_A = 11$
$w_B = 5$

(4) Compute $F' = w_A/w_B$

(4) $F' = 11/5$
$= 2.2$

(5) If $F' > F'_{1-\alpha}(n_A, n_B)$, conclude that the variability in performance of A exceeds the variability in performance of B; otherwise, there is no reason to believe that the variability in performance of A exceeds that of B.

(5) Since F' is not larger than $F'_{.99}$, there is no reason to believe that the variability of set A exceeds that of set B.

---

* When using Table A-11, sample sizes need not be equal, but cannot be larger than 10.

CHAPTER 16

SOME TESTS WHICH ARE INDEPENDENT OF THE FORM OF THE DISTRIBUTION

16-1 GENERAL

This chapter outlines a number of test procedures in which very little is assumed about the nature of the population distributions. In particular, the population distributions are not assumed to be "normal". These tests are often called "nonparametric" tests. The assumptions made here are that the individual observations are independent* and that all observations on a given material (product, or process) have the same underlying distribution. The procedures are strictly correct only if the underlying distribution is continuous, and suitable warnings in this regard are given in each test procedure.

In this chapter, the same wording is used for the problems as was used in ORDP 20-110, Chapter 3 (e.g., "Does the average differ from a standard?"), because the general import of the questions is the same. The specific tests employed, however, are fundamentally different.

If the underlying populations are indeed normal, these tests are poorer than the ones given in Chapter 3, in the sense that β, the probability of the second kind of error, is always larger for given α and n. For some other distributions, however, the nonparametric tests actually may have a smaller error of the second kind. The increase in the second kind of error, when nonparametric tests are applied to normal data, is surprisingly small and is an indication that these tests should receive more use.

Operating characteristic curves and methods of obtaining sample sizes are not given for these tests. Roughly speaking, most of the tests of this chapter require a sample size about 1.1 times that required by the tests given in Chapter 3 (see Paragraphs 3-2 and 3-3 for appropriate normal sample size formulas). For the sign test (Paragraphs 16-2.1, 16-3.1, 16-4.1, 16-5.1, and 16-6.1), a factor of 1.2 is more appropriate.

For the problem of comparing with a standard (Paragraphs 16-2, 16-3, and 16-4), two methods of solution are given and the choice may be made by the user. The sign test (Paragraphs 16-2.1, 16-3.1, and 16-4.1) is a very simple test which is useful under very general conditions. The Wilcoxon signed-ranks test (Paragraphs 16-2.2, 16-3.2, and 16-4.2) requires the assumption that the underlying distribution is symmetrical. When the assumption of symmetry can be made, the signed-ranks test is a more powerful test than the sign test, and is not very burdensome for fairly small samples.

For the problem of comparing two products (Paragraphs 16-5 and 16-6), two methods of solution are also given, but each applies to a specific situation with regard to the source of the data.

The procedures of this chapter assume that the pertinent question has been chosen before taking the observations.

---

* Except for certain techniques which are given for "paired observations"; in that case, the *pairs* are assumed to be *independent*.

16-2   DOES THE AVERAGE OF A NEW PRODUCT DIFFER FROM A STANDARD?

Data Sample 16-2 — Reverse-Bias Collector Current of Ten Transistors

The data are measurements of I_{CBO} for ten transistors of the same type, where I_{CBO} is the reverse-bias collector current recorded in microamperes.

The standard value m_0 is 0.28μa.

Transistor	I_{CBO}
1	0.28
2	.18
3	.24
4	.30
5	.40
6	.36
7	.15
8	.42
9	.23
10	.48

16-2.1   DOES THE AVERAGE OF A NEW PRODUCT DIFFER FROM A STANDARD?   THE SIGN TEST

Procedure

(1) Choose α, the significance level of the test. Table A-33 provides for values of $\alpha = .25$, .10, .05, and .01 for this two-sided test.

(2) Discard observations which happen to be equal to m_0, and let n be the number of observations actually used. (If more than 20% of the observations need to be discarded, this procedure should not be used).

(3) For each observation X_i, record the sign of the difference $X_i - m_0$.
Count the number of occurrences of the less frequent sign. Call this number r.

(4) Look up $r(\alpha, n)$, in Table A-33.

(5) If r is less than, or is equal to, $r(\alpha, n)$, conclude that the average of the new product differs from the standard; otherwise, there is no reason to believe that the averages differ.

Example

(1) Let $\alpha = .05$

(2) In Data Sample 16-2, $m_0 = .28$. Discard the first observation.

$$n = 9$$

(3) The less frequent sign is $-$.

Since there are 4 minus signs,
$$r = 4$$

(4) $r(.05, 9) = 1$

(5) Since r is not less than $r(.05, 9)$, there is no reason to believe that the average current differs from $m_0 = .28\mu$a.

16-2.2 DOES THE AVERAGE OF A NEW PRODUCT DIFFER FROM A STANDARD? THE WILCOXON SIGNED-RANKS TEST

Procedure	Example

(1) Choose α, the significance level of the test. Table A-34 provides for values of $\alpha = .05$, .02, and .01 for this two-sided test. Discard any observations which happen to be equal to m_0, and let n be the number of observations actually used.

(1) Let $\alpha = .05$
In Data Sample 16-2, $m_0 = .28$. Discard the first observation.

$$n = 9$$

(2) Look up $T_\alpha(n)$, in Table A-34.

(2) $T_{.05}(9) = 6$

(3) For each observation X_i, compute

$$X_i' = X_i - m_0$$

(3)   (4)

$X_i - m_0$	Signed rank
$-.10$	-5
$-.04$	-2
$+.02$	$+1$
$+.12$	$+6$
$+.08$	$+4$
$-.13$	-7
$+.14$	$+8$
$-.05$	-3
$+.20$	$+9$

(4) Disregarding signs, rank the X_i' according to their numerical value, i.e., assign the rank of 1 to the X_i' which is numerically smallest, the rank of 2 to the X_i' which is next smallest, etc. In case of ties, assign the average of the ranks which would have been assigned had the X_i''s differed only slightly. (If more than 20% of the observations are involved in ties, this procedure should not be used.)
To the assigned ranks 1, 2, 3, etc., prefix a + or a − sign, according to whether the corresponding X_i' is positive or negative.

(5) Sum the ranks prefixed by a + sign, and the ranks prefixed by a − sign. Let T be the smaller (disregarding sign) of the two sums.

(5) Sum + = 28
Sum − = 17
   $T = 17$

(6) If $T \leq T_\alpha(n)$, conclude that the average performance of the new type differs from that of the standard; otherwise, there is no reason to believe that the averages differ.

(6) Since T is not less than $T_{.05}(9)$, there is no reason to believe that the average current differs from $m_0 = .28\mu a$.

16-3　DOES THE AVERAGE OF A NEW PRODUCT EXCEED
THAT OF A STANDARD?

Data Sample 16-3 — Reverse-Bias Collector Current of Twenty Transistors

The data are a set of measurements I_{CBO} for 20 transistors, where I_{CBO} is the reverse-bias collector current recorded in microamperes.

The standard value m_0 is $0.28\mu a$.

Transistor	I_{CBO}
1	$0.20\mu a$
2	.16
3	.20
4	.48
5	.92
6	.33
7	.20
8	.53
9	.42
10	.50
11	.19
12	.22
13	.18
14	.17
15	1.20
16	.14
17	.09
18	.13
19	.26
20	.66

16-3.1　DOES THE AVERAGE OF A NEW PRODUCT EXCEED THAT OF A STANDARD?　THE SIGN TEST

Procedure

(1) Choose α, the significance level of the test. Table A-33 provides for values of $\alpha = .125$, .05, .025, and .005 for this one-sided test.

(2) Discard observations which happen to be equal to m_0, and let n be the number of observations actually used.　(If more than 20% of the observations need to be discarded, this procedure should not be used.)

(3) For each observation X_i, record the sign of the difference $X_i - m_0$.
Count the number of minus signs.
Call this number r.

(4) Look up $r(\alpha, n)$, in Table A-33.

Example

(1) Let　　$\alpha = .025$

(2) In Data Sample 16-3, $m_0 = .28$.　Since no observations are equal to m_0,
$$\dot{n} = 20$$

(3)
$$r = 12$$

(4)　$r(.025, 20) = 5$

Procedure (Cont)	Example (Cont)

(5) If r is less than, or is equal to, $r\,(\alpha,\,n)$, conclude that the average of the new product exceeds the standard; otherwise, there is no reason to believe that the average of the new product exceeds that of the standard.

(5) Since r is not less than $r\,(.025,\,20)$, there is no reason to believe that the average current exceeds $m_0 = .28\mu a$.

16-3.2 DOES THE AVERAGE OF A NEW PRODUCT EXCEED THAT OF A STANDARD? THE WILCOXON SIGNED-RANKS TEST

Procedure	Example

(1) Choose α, the significance level of the test. Table A-34 provides for values of $\alpha = .025$, .01, and .005 for this one-sided test. Discard any observations which happen to be equal to m_0, and let n be the number of observations actually used.

(1) Let $\alpha = .025$
In Data Sample 16-3, $m_0 = .28\mu a$.   Since no observations are equal to m_0,

$$n = 20$$

(2) Look up $T_\alpha\,(n)$, in Table A-34.

(2) $T_{.025}\,(20) = 52$

(3) For each observation X_i, compute

$$X'_i = X_i - m_0.$$

(4) Disregarding signs, rank the X'_i according to their numerical value, i.e., assign the rank of 1 to the X'_i which is numerically smallest, the rank of 2 to the X'_i which is next smallest, etc.   In case of ties, assign the average of the ranks which would have been assigned had the X'_i's differed only slightly.   (If more than 20% of the observations are involved in ties, this procedure should not be used.)
To the assigned ranks 1, 2, 3, etc., prefix a $+$ or a $-$ sign according to whether the X'_i is positive or negative.

(3)   (4)

$X_i - m_0$	Signed Rank
-0.08	$-\ 5$
-0.12	-10
-0.08	$-\ 5$
0.20	$+15$
0.64	$+19$
0.05	$+\ 2$
-0.08	$-\ 5$
0.25	$+17$
0.14	$+11.5$
0.22	$+16$
-0.09	$-\ 7$
-0.06	$-\ 3$
-0.10	$-\ 8$
-0.11	$-\ 9$
0.92	$+20$
-0.14	-11.5
-0.19	-14
-0.15	-13
-0.02	$-\ 1$
0.38	$+18$

(5) Let T be the absolute value of the sum of the ranks preceded by a negative sign.

(5) $T = 91.5$

(6) If $T \leq T_\alpha\,(n)$, conclude that the average performance of the new product exceeds that of the standard; otherwise, there is no reason to believe that the average of the new product exceeds that of the standard.

(6) Since T is not smaller than $T_{.025}\,(20)$, there is no reason to believe that the average current exceeds $m_0 = .28\mu a$.

16-4 IS THE AVERAGE OF A NEW PRODUCT LESS THAN THAT OF A STANDARD?

Data Sample 16-4 — Tensile Strength of Aluminum Alloy

The data are measurements of ultimate tensile strength (psi) for twenty test specimens of aluminum alloy.   The standard value for tensile strength is $m_0 = 27,000$ psi.

Specimen	Ultimate Tensile Strength (psi)
1	24,200
2	25,900
3	26,000
4	26,000
5	26,300
6	26,450
7	27,250
8	27,450
9	27,550
10	28,550
11	29,150
12	29,900
13	30,000
14	30,400
15	30,450
16	30,450
17	31,450
18	31,600
19	32,400
20	33,750

16-4.1 IS THE AVERAGE OF A NEW PRODUCT LESS THAN THAT OF A STANDARD?   THE SIGN TEST

Procedure

(1) Choose α, the significance level of the test. Table A-33 provides for values of $\alpha = .125$, .05, .025, and .005 for this one-sided test.

(2) Discard observations which happen to be equal to m_0, and let n be the number of observations actually used.   (If more than 20% of the observations need to be discarded, this procedure should not be used.)

(3) For each observation X_i, record the sign of the difference $X_i - m_0$.
Count the number of plus signs.   Call this number r.

(4) Look up $r(\alpha, n)$, in Table A-33.

Example

(1) Let $\alpha = .025$

(2) In Data Sample 16-4, $m_0 = 27,000$.   Since no observations are equal to m_0,

$$n = 20$$

(3)

There are 14 plus signs.
$$r = 14$$

(4) $r(.025, 20) = 5$

Procedure (Cont)	Example (Cont)

(5) If r is less than, or is equal to, $r(\alpha, n)$, conclude that the average of the new product is less than the standard; otherwise, there is no reason to believe that the average of the new product is less than the standard.

(5) Since r is not less than $r(.025, 20)$, there is no reason to believe that the average tensile strength is less than $m_0 = 27,000$ psi.

16-4.2 IS THE AVERAGE OF A NEW PRODUCT LESS THAN THAT OF A STANDARD? THE WILCOXON SIGNED-RANKS TEST

Procedure

(1) Choose α, the significance level of the test. Table A-34 provides for values of $\alpha = .025$, .01, and .005 for this one-sided test. Discard any observations which happen to be equal to m_0, and let n be the number of observations actually used.

(2) Look up $T_\alpha(n)$, in Table A-34.

(3) For each observation X_i, compute

$$X_i' = X_i - m_0.$$

(4) Disregarding signs, rank the X_i' according to their numerical value, i.e., assign the rank of 1 to the X_i' which is numerically smallest, the rank of 2 to the X_i' which is next smallest, etc. In case of ties, assign the average of the ranks which would have been assigned had the X_i''s differed only slightly. (If more than 20% of the observations are involved in ties, this procedure should not be used.)
To the assigned ranks 1, 2, 3, etc., prefix a $+$ or a $-$ sign according to whether the corresponding X_i' is positive or negative.

(5) Let T be the sum of the ranks preceded by a $+$ sign.

(6) If $T \leq T_\alpha(n)$, conclude that the average of the new product is less than that of the standard; otherwise, there is no reason to believe that the average of the new product is less than that of the standard.

Example

(1) Let $\alpha = .025$
In Data Sample 16-4,

$$m_0 = 27,000.$$

Since no observations are equal to m_0,

$$n = 20$$

(2) $T_{.025}(20) = 52$

(3)   (4)

$X_i - m_0$	Signed Rank
-2800	-11
-1100	-8
-1000	-6.5
-1000	-6.5
-700	-5
-550	-3.5
250	$+1$
450	$+2$
550	$+3.5$
1550	$+9$
2150	$+10$
2900	$+12$
3000	$+13$
3400	$+14$
3450	$+15.5$
3450	$+15.5$
4450	$+17$
4600	$+18$
5400	$+19$
6750	$+20$

(5) $T = 169.5$

(6) Since T is not less than $T_{.025}(20)$, there is no reason to believe that the average tensile strength is less than $m_0 = 27,000$ psi.

16-5   DO PRODUCTS A AND B DIFFER IN AVERAGE PERFORMANCE?

Two procedures are given to answer this question.   Each of the procedures is applicable to a different situation, depending upon how the data have been taken.

Situation 1 (for which the sign test of Paragraph 16-5.1 is applicable) is the case where observations on the two things being compared have been obtained in pairs.   Each of the two observations on a pair has been obtained under similar conditions, but the different pairs need not have been obtained under similar conditions.   Specifically, the sign test procedure tests whether the *median* difference between A and B can be considered equal to zero.

Situation 2 (for which we use the Wilcoxon-Mann-Whitney test of Paragraph 16-5.2) is the case where two independent samples have been drawn — one from population A and one from population B.   This test answers the following kind of questions — if the two distributions are of the same form, are they displaced with respect to each other?   Or, if the distributions are quite different in form, do the observations on A systematically tend to exceed the observations on B?

16-5.1   DO PRODUCTS A AND B DIFFER IN AVERAGE PERFORMANCE?   THE SIGN TEST FOR PAIRED OBSERVATIONS

Data Sample 16-5.1 — Reverse-Bias Collector Currents of Two Types of Transistors

Ten pairs of measurements of I_{CBO} on two types of transistors are available, as follows:

Type A	Type B
.19	.21
.22	.27
.18	.15
.17	.18
1.20	.40
.14	.08
.09	.14
.13	.28
.26	.30
.66	.68

Procedure	Example
(1) Choose α, the significance level of the test. Table A-33 provides for values of $\alpha = .25$, .10, .05, and .01 for this two-sided test.	(1) Let $\alpha = .10$
(2) For each pair, record the sign of the difference $X_A - X_B$. Discard any difference which happens to equal zero. Let n be the number of differences remaining. (If more than 20% of the observations need to be discarded, this procedure should not be used.)	(2) In Data Sample 16-5.1, $n = 10$
(3) Count the number of occurrences of the less frequent sign. Call this r.	(3) There are 3 plus signs. $r = 3$
(4) Look up $r(\alpha, n)$, in Table A-33.	(4) $r(.10, 10) = 1$
(5) If r is less than, or is equal to, $r(\alpha, n)$, conclude that the averages differ; otherwise, there is no reason to believe that the averages differ.	(5) Since r is not less than $r(.10, 10)$, there is no reason to believe that the two types differ in average current.

Note: The Wilcoxon Signed-Ranks Test also may be used to compare the averages of two products in the paired-sample situation; follow the procedure of Paragraph 16-2.2, substituting $X'_i = X_1 - X_B$ for $X'_i = X_i - m_0$ in step (3) of that procedure.

16-5.2 DO PRODUCTS A AND B DIFFER IN AVERAGE PERFORMANCE? THE WILCOXON-MANN-WHITNEY TEST FOR TWO INDEPENDENT SAMPLES

Data Sample 16-5.2 — Forward Current Transfer Ratio of Two Types of Transistors

The data are measurements of h_{fe} for two independent groups of transistors, where h_{fe} is the small-signal short-circuit forward current transfer ratio.

Group A	Group B
50.5 (9)*	57.0 (17)
37.5 (1)	52.0 (11)
49.8 (7)	51.0 (10)
56.0 (15.5)	44.2 (3)
42.0 (2)	55.0 (14)
56.0 (15.5)	62.0 (19)
50.0 (8)	59.0 (18)
54.0 (13)	45.2 (5)
48.0 (6)	53.5 (12)
	44.4 (4)

* The numbers shown in parentheses are the ranks, from lowest to highest, for all observations combined, as required in Step (2) of the following Procedure and Example.

Procedure	**Example**
(1) Choose α, the significance level of the test. Table A-35 provides for values of $\alpha = .01$, .05, .10, and .20 for this two-sided test when n_A, $n_B \leq 20$.	(1) Let $\alpha = .10$
(2) Combine the observations from the two samples, and rank them in order of increasing size from smallest to largest. Assign the rank of 1 to the lowest, a rank of 2 to the next lowest, etc. (Use algebraic size, i.e., the lowest rank is assigned to the largest negative number, if there are negative numbers). In case of ties, assign to each the average of the ranks which would have been assigned had the tied observations differed only slightly. (If more than 20% of the observations are involved in ties, this procedure should not be used.)	(2) In Data Sample 16-5.2, the ranks of the nineteen individual observations, from lowest to highest, are shown in parentheses beside the respective observations. Note that the two tied observations (56.0) are each given the rank 15.5 (instead of ranks 15 and 16), and that the next larger observation is given the rank 17.
(3) Let: n_1 = smaller sample n_2 = larger sample $n = n_1 + n_2$	(3) $n_1 = 9$ $n_2 = 10$ $n = 19$
(4) Compute R, the sum of the ranks for the smaller sample. (If the two samples are equal in size, use the sum of the ranks for either sample.) Compute $R' = n_1 (n + 1) - R$	(4) $R = 77$ $R' = 9 (20) - 77$ $= 103$
(5) Look up $R_\alpha (n_1, n_2)$, in Table A-35.	(5) $R_{.10} (9, 10) = 69$
(6) If either R or R' is smaller than, or is equal to, $R_\alpha (n_1, n_2)$, conclude that the averages of the two products differ; otherwise, there is no reason to believe that the averages of the two products differ.	(6) Since neither R nor R' is smaller than $R_{.10} (9, 10)$, there is no reason to believe that the averages of the two groups differ.

16-6 DOES THE AVERAGE OF PRODUCT A EXCEED THAT OF PRODUCT B?

Two procedures are given to answer this question. In order to choose the procedure that is appropriate to a particular situation, read the discussion in Paragraph 16-5.

16-6.1 DOES THE AVERAGE OF PRODUCT A EXCEED THAT OF PRODUCT B? THE SIGN TEST FOR PAIRED OBSERVATIONS

In terms of Data Sample 16-5.1, assume that we had asked in advance (not after looking at the data) whether the average I_{CBO} was larger for Type A than for Type B.

Procedure	Example
(1) Choose α, the significance level of the test. Table A-33 provides for values of $\alpha = .125$, .05, .025, and .005 for this one-sided test.	(1) Let $\alpha = .025$
(2) For each pair, record the sign of the difference $X_{A} - X_{B}$. Discard any difference which happens to equal zero. Let n be the number of differences remaining. (If more than 20% of the observations need to be discarded, this procedure should not be used.)	(2) In Data Sample 16-5.1, $n = 10$
(3) Count the number of minus signs. Call this number r.	(3) There are 7 minus signs. $r = 7$
(4) Look up $r(\alpha, n)$, in Table A-33.	(4) $r(.025, 10) = 1$
(5) If r is less than, or is equal to, $r(\alpha, n)$, conclude that the average of product A exceeds the average of product B; otherwise, there is no reason to believe that the average of product A exceeds that of product B.	(5) Since r is not less than $r(.025, 10)$, there is no reason to believe that the average of Type A exceeds the average of Type B.

Note: The Wilcoxon Signed-Ranks Test also may be used to compare the averages of two products in the paired-sample situations; follow the procedure of Paragraph 16-3.2, substituting $X'_i = X_A - X_B$ for $X'_i = X_i - m_0$ in Step (3) of that Procedure.

16-6.2 DOES THE AVERAGE OF PRODUCT A EXCEED THAT OF PRODUCT B? THE WILCOXON-MANN-WHITNEY TEST FOR TWO INDEPENDENT SAMPLES

Data Sample 16-6.2 — Output Admittance of Two Types of Transistors

The data are observations of h_{ob} for two types of transistors, where h_{ob} = small-signal open-circuit output admittance.

Type A	Type B
.291 (5)*	.246 (1)
.390 (10)	.252 (2)
.305 (7)	.300 (6)
.331 (9)	.289 (4)
.316 (8)	.258 (3)

* The numbers shown in parentheses are the ranks, from lowest to highest, for all observations combined, as required in Step (2) of the following Procedure and Example.

Does the average h_{ob} for Type A exceed that for Type B?

Procedure	**Example**

(1) Choose α, the significance level of the test. Table A-35 provides for values of $\alpha = .005$, $.025$, $.05$, and $.10$ for this one-sided test, when n_A, $n_B \leq 20$.

(1) Let $\quad \alpha = .05$

(2) Combine the observations from the two populations, and rank them in order of increasing size from smallest to largest. Assign the rank of 1 to the lowest, a rank of 2 to the next lowest, etc. (Use algebraic size, i.e., the lowest rank is assigned to the largest negative number if there are negative numbers). In case of ties, assign to each the average of the ranks which would have been assigned had the tied observations differed only slightly. (If more than 20% of the observations are involved in ties, this procedure should not be used.)

(2) In Data Sample 16-6.2, the ranks of the ten individual observations, from lowest to highest, are shown beside the respective observations.

(3) Let: n_1 = smaller sample
$\qquad n_2$ = larger sample
$\qquad n = n_1 + n_2$

(3) $\qquad n_1 = 5$
$\qquad n_2 = 5$
$\qquad n = 10$

(4) Look up $R_\alpha (n_1, n_2)$, in Table A-35.

(4) $R_{.05} (5, 5) = 19$

(5a) If the two samples are equal in size, or if n_B is the smaller, compute R_B the sum of the ranks for sample B. If R_B is less than, or is equal to, $R_\alpha (n_1, n_2)$, conclude that the average for product A exceeds that for product B; otherwise, there is no reason to believe that the average for product A exceeds that for product B.

(5a) $\qquad R_B = 16$
Since R_B is less than $R_{.05} (5, 5)$, conclude that the average for Type A exceeds that for Type B.

(5b) If n_A is smaller than n_B, compute R_A the sum of the ranks for sample A, and compute $R'_A = n_A (n + 1) - R_A$.
If R'_A is less than, or is equal to, $R_\alpha (n_1, n_2)$, conclude that the average for product A exceeds that for product B; otherwise, there is no reason to believe that the two products differ.

16-7 COMPARING THE AVERAGES OF SEVERAL PRODUCTS
DO THE AVERAGES OF t PRODUCTS DIFFER?

Data Sample 16-7 — Life Tests of Three Types of Stopwatches

Samples from each of three types of stopwatches were tested. The following data are thousands of cycles (on-off-restart) survived until some part of the mechanism failed.

Type 1	Type 2	Type 3
1.7 (1)*	13.6 (6)	13.4 (5)
1.9 (2)	19.8 (8)	20.9 (9)
6.1 (3)	25.2 (12)	25.1 (10.5)
12.5 (4)	46.2 (16.5)	29.7 (13)
16.5 (7)	46.2 (16.5)	46.0 (18)
25.1 (10.5)	61.1 (19)	
30.5 (14)		
42.1 (15)		
82.5 (20)		

* The numbers shown in parentheses are the ranks, from lowest to highest, for all observations combined, as required in Step (3) of the following Procedure and Example.

TABLE 16-1. WORK TABLE FOR DATA SAMPLE 16-7

	Ranks Type 1	Ranks Type 2	Ranks Type 3
	1	6	5
	2	8	9
	3	12	10.5
	4	16.5	13
	7	16.5	18
	10.5	19	
	14		
	15		
	20		
R_i	$R_1 = 76.5$	$R_2 = 78.0$	$R_3 = 55.5$
n_i	9	6	5
R_i^2/n_i	650.25	1014.00	616.05

Does the average length of "life" differ for the three types?

Procedure	**Example**
(1) Choose α, the significance level of the test.	(1) Let $\alpha = .10$
(2) Look up $\chi^2_{1-\alpha}$ for $t - 1$ degrees of freedom, in Table A-3, where t is the number of products to be compared.	(2) $t = 3$ $\chi^2_{.90}$ for 2 d.f. $= 4.61$
(3) We have n_1, n_2, . . . , n_t observations on each of the products 1, 2, . . . , t.	(3) In Data Sample 16-7,

$$N = n_1 + n_2 + \ldots + n_t.$$

$$N = 9 + 6 + 5 = 20.$$

Assign ranks to each observation according to its size in relation to all N observations. That is, assign rank 1 to the smallest, 2 to the next larger, etc., and N to the largest. In case of ties, assign to each of the tied observations the average of the ranks which would have been assigned had the observations differed slightly. (If more than 20% of the observations are involved in ties, this procedure should not be used.)	The assigned ranks are shown in Data Sample 16-7 and in Table 16-1.
(4) Compute R_i, the sum of the ranks of the observations on the ith product, for each of the products.	(4) $R_1 = 76.5$ $R_2 = 78.0$ $R_3 = 55.5$
(5) Compute	(5)

$$H = \frac{12}{N(N+1)} \sum_{i=1}^{t} \frac{R_i^2}{n_i} - 3(N+1)$$

$$H = \frac{12}{420}(2280.30) - 63$$
$$= 2.15$$

(6) If $H > \chi^2_{1-\alpha}$, conclude that the averages of the t products differ; otherwise, there is no reason to believe that the averages differ.	(6) Since H is not larger than $\chi^2_{.90}$, there is no reason to believe that the averages for the three types differ.

Note: When using this Procedure, each of the n_i should be at least 5. If any n_i are less than 5, the level of significance α may be considerably different from the intended value.

CHAPTER 17

THE TREATMENT OF OUTLIERS

17-1 THE PROBLEM OF REJECTING OBSERVATIONS

Every experimenter, at some time, has obtained a set of observations, purportedly taken under the same conditions, in which one observation was widely different, or an outlier from the rest.

The problem that confronts the experimenter is whether he should keep the suspect observation in computation, or whether he should discard it as being a faulty measurement. The word reject will mean *reject in computation*, since every observation should be recorded. A careful experimenter will want to make a record of his "rejected" observations and, where possible, detect and carefully analyze their cause(s).

It should be emphasized that we are not discussing the case where we *know* that the observation differs because of an assignable cause, i.e., a dirty test-tube, or a change in operating conditions. We are dealing with the situation where, as far as we are able to ascertain, all the observations are on approximately the same footing. One observation is suspect however, in that it seems to be set apart from the others. We wonder whether it is not so far from the others that we can reject it as being caused by some assignable but thus far unascertained cause.

When a measurement is far-removed from the great majority of a set of measurements of a quantity, and thus possibly reflects a gross error, the question of whether that measurement should have a full vote, a diminished vote, or no vote in the final average — and in the determination of precision — is a very difficult question to answer completely in general terms. If on investigation, a trustworthy explanation of the discrepancy is found, common sense dictates that the value concerned should be excluded from the final average and from the estimate of precision, since these presumably are intended to apply to the unadulterated system. If, on the other hand, no explanation for the apparent anomalousness is found, then common sense would seem to indicate that it should be included in computing the final average and the estimate of precision. Experienced investigators differ in this matter. Some, e.g., J. W. Bessel, would always include it. Others would be inclined to exclude it, on the grounds that it is better to exclude a possibly "good" measurement than to include a possibly "bad" one. The argument for exclusion is that *when a "good" measurement is excluded* we simply lose some of the relevant information, with consequent decrease in precision and the introduction of some bias (both being theoretically computable); whereas, *when a truly anomalous measurement is included* it vitiates our results, biasing both the final average and the estimate of precision by unknown, and generally unknowable, amounts.

There have been many criteria proposed for guiding the rejection of observations. For an excellent summary and critical review of the classical rejection procedures, and some more modern ones, see P. R. Rider[1]. One of the more famous classical rejection rules is "Chauvenet's criterion," which is not recommended. This criterion is based on the normal distribution and advises rejection of an extreme observation if the probability of occurrence of such deviation from the mean of the n measurements is less than $1/2n$. Obviously, for small n, such a criterion rejects too easily.

A review of the history of rejection criteria, and the fact that new criteria are still being proposed, leads us to realize that no completely satisfactory rule can be devised for any and all situations. We cannot devise a criterion that will not reject a predictable amount from endless arrays of perfectly good data; the amount of data rejected of course depends on the rule used. This is the price we pay for using any rule for rejection of data. No available criteria are superior to the judgment of an experienced investigator who is thoroughly familiar with his measurement process. For an excellent discussion of this point, see E. B. Wilson, Jr.[2]. Statistical rules are given primarily for the benefit of inexperienced investigators, those working with a new process, or those who simply want justification for what they would have done anyway.

Whatever rule is used, it must bear some resemblance to the experimenter's feelings about the nature and possible frequency of errors. For an extreme example — if the experimenter feels that about one outlier in twenty reflects an actual blunder, and he uses a rejection rule that throws out the two extremes in every sample, then his reported data obviously will be "clean" with respect to extreme blunders — but the effects of "little" blunders may still be present. The *one and only* sure way to avoid publishing any "bad" results is to throw away all results.

With the foregoing reservations, Paragraphs 17-2 and 17-3 give some suggested procedures for judging outliers. In general, the rules to be applied to a single experiment (see Paragraph 17-3) reject only what would be rejected by an experienced investigator anyway.

17-2 REJECTION OF OBSERVATIONS IN ROUTINE EXPERIMENTAL WORK

The best tools for detection of *errors* (e.g., systematic errors, gross errors) in routine work are the control charts for the mean and range. These charts are described in Chapter 18, which also contains a table of factors to facilitate their application, Table 18-2.

17-3 REJECTION OF OBSERVATIONS IN A SINGLE EXPERIMENT

We assume that our experimental observations (except for the truly discordant ones) come from a single normal population with mean m and standard deviation σ. In a particular experiment, we have obtained n observations and have arranged them in order from lowest to highest $(X_1 \leq X_2 \leq \ldots \leq X_n)$. We consider procedures applicable to two situations: when observations which are either too large or too small would be considered faulty and rejectable, see Paragraph 17-3.1; when we consider rejectable those observations that are extreme in one direction only (e.g., when we want to reject observations that are too large but never those that are too small, or vice versa), see Paragraph 17-3.2. The proper choice between the situations must be made on *a priori* grounds, and not on the basis of the data to be analyzed.

For each situation, procedures are given for four possible cases with regard to our knowledge of m and σ.

17-3.1 WHEN EXTREME OBSERVATIONS IN EITHER DIRECTION ARE CONSIDERED REJECTABLE

17-3.1.1 Population Mean and Standard Deviation Unknown — Sample in Hand is the Only Source of Information.

[The Dixon Criterion]

Procedure

(1) Choose α, the probability or risk we are willing to take of rejecting an observation that really belongs in the group.

(2) If:

$3 \leq n \leq 7$	Compute r_{10}
$8 \leq n \leq 10$	Compute r_{11}
$11 \leq n \leq 13$	Compute r_{21}
$14 \leq n \leq 25$	Compute r_{22},

where r_{ij} is computed as follows:

r_{ij}	If X_n is Suspect	If X_1 is Suspect
r_{10}	$(X_n - X_{n-1})/(X_n - X_1)$	$(X_2 - X_1)/(X_n - X_1)$
r_{11}	$(X_n - X_{n-1})/(X_n - X_2)$	$(X_2 - X_1)/(X_{n-1} - X_1)$
r_{21}	$(X_n - X_{n-2})/(X_n - X_2)$	$(X_3 - X_1)/(X_{n-1} - X_1)$
r_{22}	$(X_n - X_{n-2})/(X_n - X_3)$	$(X_3 - X_1)/(X_{n-2} - X_1)$

(3) Look up $r_{1-\alpha/2}$ for the r_{ij} from Step (2), in Table A-14.

(4) If $r_{ij} > r_{1-\alpha/2}$, reject the suspect observation; otherwise, retain it.

17-3.1.2 Population Mean and Standard Deviation Unknown — Independent External Estimate of Standard Deviation is Available.

[The Studentized Range]

Procedure

(1) Choose α, the probability or risk we are willing to take of rejecting an observation that really belongs in the group.

(2) Look up $q_{1-\alpha}(n, \nu)$ in Table A-10. n is the number of observations in the sample, and ν is the number of degrees of freedom for s, the independent external estimate of the standard deviation obtained from concurrent or past data — *not* from the sample in hand.

(3) Compute $w = q_{1-\alpha}s$.

(4) If $X_n - X_1 > w$, reject the observation that is suspect; otherwise, retain it.

17-3.1.3 Population Mean Unknown — Value for Standard Deviation Assumed.

Procedure

(1) Choose α, the probability or risk we are willing to take of rejecting an observation that really belongs in the group.

(2) Look up $q_{1-\alpha}(n, \infty)$ in Table A-10.

(3) Compute $w = q_{1-\alpha}\sigma$.

(4) If $X_n - X_1 > w$, reject the observation that is suspect; otherwise, retain it.

17-3.1.4 Population Mean and Standard Deviation Known.

Procedure	Example
(1) Choose α, the probability or risk we are willing to take of rejecting an observation when all n really belong in the same group.	(1) Let $\alpha = .10$, for example.

(2) Compute $\alpha' = 1 - (1 - \alpha)^{1/n}$ (We can compute this value using logarithms, or by reference to a table of fractional powers.)

(2) If $n = 20$, for example,
$$\alpha' = 1 - (1 - .10)^{1/20}$$
$$= 1 - (.90)^{1/20}$$
$$= 1 - .9947$$
$$= .0053$$

(3) Look up $z_{1-\alpha'/2}$ in Table A-2. (Interpolation in Table A-2 may be required. The recommended method is graphical interpolation, using probability paper.)

(3) $1 - \alpha'/2 = 1 - (.0053/2)$
$$= .9974$$
$$z_{.9974} = 2.80$$

(4) Compute:
$$a = m - \sigma z_{1-\alpha'/2}$$
$$b = m + \sigma z_{1-\alpha'/2}$$

(4)
$$a = m - 2.80\,\sigma$$
$$b = m + 2.80\,\sigma$$

(5) Reject any observation that does not lie in the interval from a to b.

(5) Reject any observation that does not lie in the interval from
$$m - 2.80\,\sigma \quad \text{to}$$
$$m + 2.80\,\sigma.$$

17-3.2 WHEN EXTREME OBSERVATIONS IN ONLY ONE DIRECTION ARE CONSIDERED REJECTABLE

17-3.2.1 Population Mean and Standard Deviation Unknown — Sample in Hand is the Only Source of Information.

[The Dixon Criterion]

Procedure

(1) Choose α, the probability or risk we are willing to take of rejecting an observation that really belongs in the group.

(2) If:

$3 \leq n \leq 7$	Compute r_{10}
$8 \leq n \leq 10$	Compute r_{11}
$11 \leq n \leq 13$	Compute r_{21}
$14 \leq n \leq 25$	Compute r_{22},

where r_{ij} is computed as follows:

r_{ij}	If Only Large Values are Suspect	If Only Small Values are Suspect
r_{10}	$(X_n - X_{n-1})/(X_n - X_1)$	$(X_2 - X_1)/(X_n - X_1)$
r_{11}	$(X_n - X_{n-1})/(X_n - X_2)$	$(X_2 - X_1)/(X_{n-1} - X_1)$
r_{21}	$(X_n - X_{n-2})/(X_n - X_2)$	$(X_3 - X_1)/(X_{n-1} - X_1)$
r_{22}	$(X_n - X_{n-2})/(X_n - X_3)$	$(X_3 - X_1)/(X_{n-2} - X_1)$

(3) Look up $r_{1-\alpha}$ for the r_{ij} from Step (2), in Table A-14.

(4) If $r_{ij} > r_{1-\alpha}$, reject the suspect observation; otherwise, retain it.

17-3.2.2 Population Mean and Standard Deviation Unknown — Independent External Estimate of Standard Deviation is Available.

[Extreme Studentized Deviate From Sample Mean; The Nair Criterion]

Procedure

(1) Choose α, the probability or risk we are willing to take of rejecting an observation that really belongs in the group.

(2) Look up $t_\alpha (n, \nu)$ in Table A-16. n is the number of observations in the sample, and ν is the number of degrees of freedom for s_ν the independent external estimate of the standard deviation obtained from concurrent or past data — *not* from the sample in hand.

(3) If only observations that are too large are considered rejectable, compute

$$t_n = (X_n - \bar{X})/s_\nu.$$

Or, if only observations that are too small are considered rejectable, compute

$$t_1 = (\bar{X} - X_1)/s_\nu.$$

(4) If t_n (or t_1, as appropriate) is larger than $t_\alpha (n, \nu)$, reject the observation that is suspect; otherwise, retain it.

17-3.2.3 Population Mean Unknown — Value for Standard Deviation Assumed.

[Extreme Standardized Deviate From Sample Mean]

Procedure

(1) Choose α, the probability or risk we are willing to take of rejecting an observation that really belongs in the group.

(2) Look up $t_\alpha (n, \infty)$ in Table A-16.

(3) If observations that are too large are considered rejectable, compute

$$t_n = (X_n - \bar{X})/\sigma.$$

Or, if observations that are too small are considered rejectable, compute

$$t_1 = (\bar{X} - X_1)/\sigma.$$

(4) If t_n (or t_1, as appropriate) is larger than $t_\alpha (n, \infty)$, reject the observation that is suspect; otherwise, retain it.

17-3.2.4 Population Mean and Standard Deviation Known.

Procedure	Example
(1) Choose α, the probability or risk we are willing to take of rejecting an observation when all n really belong in the same group.	(1) Let $\alpha = .10$, for example.
(2) Compute $\alpha'2 = 1 - (1 - \alpha)^{1/n}$. (We can compute this value using logarithms, or by reference to a table of fractional powers.)	(2) If $n = 20$, for example, $$\alpha'2 = 1 - (1 - .10)^{1/20}$$ $$= 1 - (.90)^{1/20}$$ $$= 1 - .9947$$ $$= .0053$$
(3) Look up $z_{1-\alpha'2}$ in Table A-2. (Interpolation in Table A-2 may be required. The recommended method is graphical interpolation using probability paper.)	(3) $1 - \alpha'2 = 1 - .0053$ $$= .9947$$ $$z_{.9947} = 2.55$$
(4) Compute: $$a = m - \sigma z_{1-\alpha'/2}$$ $$b = m + \sigma z_{1-\alpha'2}$$	(4) $$a = m - 2.55\,\sigma$$ $$b = m + 2.55\,\sigma$$
(5) Reject any observation that does not lie in the interval from a to b.	(5) Reject any observation that does not lie in the interval from $$m - 2.55\,\sigma \qquad \text{to}$$ $$m + 2.55\,\sigma.$$

REFERENCES

1. P. R. Rider, "Criteria for Rejection of Observations," *Washington University Studies — New Series, Science and Technology*, No. 8, October 1933.

2. E. B. Wilson, Jr., *An Introduction to Scientific Research*, pp. 256-258, McGraw-Hill Book Co., Inc., New York, N. Y., 1952.

ADDITIONAL READING

W. J. Dixon, "Processing Data for Outliers," *Biometrics*, Vol. 9, No. 1, pp. 74-89, March 1953.

F. E. Grubbs, "Sample Criteria for Testing Outlying Observations," *Annals of Mathematical Statistics*, Vol. 21, No. 1, pp. 27-58, March 1950.

A. Hald, *Statistical Theory with Engineering Applications*, pp. 333-336, John Wiley & Sons, Inc., New York, N. Y., 1952.

F. Proschan, "Testing Suspected Observations," *Industrial Quality Control*, Vol. XIII, No. 7, pp. 14-19, January 1957.

CHAPTER 18

THE PLACE OF CONTROL CHARTS IN EXPERIMENTAL WORK

18-1 PRIMARY OBJECTIVE OF CONTROL CHARTS

Control charts have very important functions in experimental work, although their use in laboratory situations has been discussed only briefly by most textbooks. Control charts can be used as a form of statistical test in which the primary objective is to test whether or not the process is in *statistical control*. The process is in *statistical control* when repeated samples from the process behave as random samples from a stable probability distribution; thus, the underlying conditions of a process *in control* are such that it is possible to make predictions in the probability sense.

The control limits are usually computed by using formulas which utilize the information from the samples themselves. The computed limits are placed as lines on the specific chart, and the decision is made that the process was *in control* if all points fall within the control limits. If all points are not within the limits, then the decision is made that the process is *not in control*.

The basic assumption underlying most statistical techniques is that the data are a random sample from a stable probability distribution, which is another way of saying that the process is in *statistical control*. It is the validity of this basic assumption which the control chart is designed to test. The control chart is used to demonstrate the existence of statistical control, and to monitor a controlled process. As a monitor, a given control chart indicates a particular type of departure from control.

18-2 INFORMATION PROVIDED BY CONTROL CHARTS

Control charts provide a running graphical record of small subgroups of data taken from a repetitive process. Control charts may be kept on any of various characteristics of each small subgroup — e.g., on the average, standard deviation, range, or proportion defective. The chart for each particular characteristic is designed to detect certain specified departures in the process from the assumed conditions. The process may be a measurement process as well as a production process. The order of groups is usually with respect to time, but not necessarily so. The grouping is such that the members of the same group are more likely to be alike than are members of different groups.

Primarily, control charts can be used to demonstrate whether or not the process is in statistical control. When the charts show lack of control, they indicate where or when the trouble occurred. Often they indicate the nature of the trouble, e.g., trends or runs, sudden shifts in the mean, increased variability, etc.

In addition to serving as a method of testing for control, control charts also provide additional and useful information in the form of estimates of the characteristics of a controlled process. This information is altogether too-frequently overlooked. For example, one very important piece of information which can be obtained from a control chart for the range or standard deviation is an estimate of the variability σ of a routine measurement or production process. It should be remembered that many of the techniques of Section 1, Chapter 3, are given in parallel for known σ and unknown σ. Most experimental scientists have very good knowledge of the variability of their measurements, but hesitate to assume *known* σ without additional justification. Control charts can be used to provide the justification.

Finally, as was pointed out in Chapter 17, Paragraph 17-2, a control chart is the most satisfactory criterion for rejection of observations in a *routine* laboratory operation. An excellent discussion of the use of control charts to detect particular kinds of trouble is given by Olmstead[1]. The three most important types of control charts in this connection are the charts for the average $\bar{X}$, range R, and standard deviation σ. The order of usefulness of each type of chart in particular situations is shown in Table 18-1, where a "1" means most useful, "2" is the next best, and dots denote "not appropriate".

As can be seen from Table 18-1, the $\bar{X}$ and R charts are the most useful of the three types. The R chart is preferred to the σ chart because of its simplicity and versatility; and, unless there are compelling reasons to use the σ chart, the R chart is the method of choice.

TABLE 18-1. TESTS FOR LOCATING AND IDENTIFYING SPECIFIC TYPES OF ASSIGNABLE CAUSES

Type of Assignable Cause	Control Charts*		
	$\bar{X}$	R	σ
Gross Error (Blunder)	1	2	..
Shift in Average	1	..	..
Shift in Variability	..	1	2
Slow Fluctuation (Trend)	1	..	..
Fast Fluctuation (Cycle)	..	1	2
Combination:			
(a) Production	1	2	..
(b) Research	..	..	..
Covariation	1	..	..

* The numeral 1 denotes the most useful type of chart; 2 denotes the next best; and, .. denote charts which are not appropriate for the particular cause.

Adapted with permission from *Industrial Quality Control*, Vol. IX, No. 3, (November, 1952) and No. 4, (January, 1953) from article entitled "How to Detect the Type of an Assignable Cause" by P. S. Olmstead.

18-3 APPLICATIONS OF CONTROL CHARTS

Table 18-2 is a summary table of factors for control charts for $\bar{X}$, R, and σ, when equal size samples are involved. Note carefully the footnote to Table 18-2, beginning "When using $s = \sqrt{\dfrac{\Sigma(X_i - \bar{X})^2}{n-1}} \ldots$", because s is so defined in *this* Handbook. The last column of Table 18-2 gives values of $\sqrt{\dfrac{n-1}{n}}$ for convenience in using the Table factors with values of s.

The most explicit details of application to a variety of possible situations, e.g., to samples of unequal size, are given in the ASTM Manual[2]; in using that Manual, however, the reader again must be wary of the difference between the definition of σ given therein, and the definition of s given in this Handbook.

Actual examples of laboratory applications in the chemical field can be found in a series of comprehensive bibliographies published in *Analytical Chemistry*[3,4,5,6]. These four articles are excellent reviews that successively bring up-to-date the recent developments in statistical theory and statistical applications that are of interest in chemistry. Further, these bibliographies are divided by subject matter, and thus provide means for locating articles on control charts in the laboratory. They are not limited to control chart applications, however.

Industrial Quality Control[7], the monthly journal of the American Society for Quality Control, is the most comprehensive publication in this field.

For a special technique with ordnance examples, see Grubbs[8].

TABLE 18-2. FACTORS FOR COMPUTING 3-SIGMA CONTROL LIMITS

Number of Observations in Sample, n	Chart for Averages			Chart for Standard Deviations						Chart for Ranges							$\sqrt{\dfrac{n-1}{n}}$
	Factors for Control Limits			Factors for Central Line		Factors for Control Limits				Factors for Central Line		Factors for Control Limits					
	A	A_1	A_2	c_2	$1/c_2$	B_1	B_2	B_3	B_4	d_2	$1/d_2$	d_3	D_1	D_2	D_3	D_4	
2	2.121	3.760	1.880	0.5642	1.7725	0	1.843	0	3.267	1.128	0.8865	0.853	0	3.686	0	3.267	.70711
3	1.732	2.394	1.023	0.7236	1.3820	0	1.858	0	2.568	1.693	0.5907	0.888	0	4.358	0	2.575	.81650
4	1.500	1.880	0.729	0.7979	1.2533	0	1.808	0	2.266	2.059	0.4857	0.880	0	4.698	0	2.282	.86603
5	1.342	1.596	0.577	0.8407	1.1894	0	1.756	0	2.089	2.326	0.4299	0.864	0	4.918	0	2.115	.89443
6	1.225	1.410	0.483	0.8686	1.1512	0.026	1.711	0.030	1.970	2.534	0.3946	0.848	0	5.078	0	2.004	.91287
7	1.134	1.277	0.419	0.8882	1.1259	0.105	1.672	0.118	1.882	2.704	0.3698	0.833	0.205	5.203	0.076	1.924	.92582
8	1.061	1.175	0.373	0.9027	1.1078	0.167	1.638	0.185	1.815	2.847	0.3512	0.820	0.387	5.307	0.136	1.864	.93541
9	1.000	1.094	0.337	0.9139	1.0942	0.219	1.609	0.239	1.761	2.970	0.3367	0.808	0.546	5.394	0.184	1.816	.94281
10	0.949	1.028	0.308	0.9227	1.0837	0.262	1.584	0.284	1.716	3.078	0.3249	0.797	0.687	5.469	0.223	1.777	.94868
11	0.905	0.973	0.285	0.9300	1.0753	0.299	1.561	0.321	1.679	3.173	0.3152	0.787	0.812	5.534	0.256	1.744	.95346
12	0.866	0.925	0.266	0.9359	1.0684	0.331	1.541	0.354	1.646	3.258	0.3069	0.778	0.924	5.592	0.284	1.716	.95743
13	0.832	0.884	0.249	0.9410	1.0627	0.359	1.523	0.382	1.618	3.336	0.2998	0.770	1.026	5.646	0.308	1.692	.96077
14	0.802	0.848	0.235	0.9453	1.0579	0.384	1.507	0.406	1.594	3.407	0.2935	0.762	1.121	5.693	0.329	1.671	.96362
15	0.775	0.816	0.223	0.9490	1.0537	0.406	1.492	0.428	1.572	3.472	0.2880	0.755	1.207	5.737	0.348	1.652	.96609
16	0.750	0.788	0.212	0.9523	1.0501	0.427	1.478	0.448	1.552	3.532	0.2831	0.749	1.285	5.779	0.364	1.636	.96825
17	0.728	0.762	0.203	0.9551	1.0470	0.445	1.465	0.466	1.534	3.588	0.2787	0.743	1.359	5.817	0.379	1.621	.97014
18	0.707	0.738	0.194	0.9576	1.0442	0.461	1.454	0.482	1.518	3.640	0.2747	0.738	1.426	5.854	0.392	1.608	.97183
19	0.688	0.717	0.187	0.9599	1.0418	0.477	1.443	0.497	1.503	3.689	0.2711	0.733	1.490	5.888	0.404	1.596	.97333
20	0.671	0.697	0.180	0.9619	1.0396	0.491	1.433	0.510	1.490	3.735	0.2677	0.729	1.548	5.922	0.414	1.586	.97468
21	0.655	0.679	0.173	0.9638	1.0376	0.504	1.424	0.523	1.477	3.778	0.2647	0.724	1.606	5.950	0.425	1.575	.97590
22	0.640	0.662	0.167	0.9655	1.0358	0.516	1.415	0.534	1.466	3.819	0.2618	0.720	1.659	5.979	0.434	1.566	.97701
23	0.626	0.647	0.162	0.9670	1.0342	0.527	1.407	0.545	1.455	3.858	0.2592	0.716	1.710	6.006	0.443	1.557	.97802
24	0.612	0.632	0.157	0.9684	1.0327	0.538	1.399	0.555	1.445	3.895	0.2567	0.712	1.759	6.031	0.452	1.548	.97895
25	0.600	0.619	0.153	0.9696	1.0313	0.548	1.392	0.565	1.435	3.931	0.2544	0.709	1.804	6.058	0.459	1.541	.97980

Adapted with permission from *ASTM Manual on Quality Control of Materials*, p. 115, copyright, 1951, American Society for Testing Materials.

FORMULAS*

Purpose of Chart	Chart for	Central Line	3-Sigma Control Limits
For analyzing past data for control ($\bar{\bar{X}}$, $\bar{\sigma}$, $\bar{R}$ are average values for the data being analyzed)	Averages	$\bar{\bar{X}}$	$\bar{\bar{X}} \pm A_1\bar{\sigma}$, or $\bar{\bar{X}} \pm A_2\bar{R}$
	Standard deviations	$\bar{\sigma}$	$B_3\bar{\sigma}$ and $B_4\bar{\sigma}$
	Ranges	$\bar{R}$	$D_3\bar{R}$ and $D_4\bar{R}$
For controlling performance to standard values ($\bar{X}'$, σ', R_n' are selected standard values; $R_n' = d_2\sigma'$ for samples of size n)	Averages	$\bar{X}'$	$\bar{X}' \pm A\sigma'$, or $\bar{X}' \pm A_2R_n'$
	Standard deviations	$c_2\sigma'$	$B_1\sigma'$ and $B_2\sigma'$
	Ranges	$d_2\sigma'$, or R_n'	$D_1\sigma'$ and $D_2\sigma'$, or D_3R_n' and D_4R_n'

* When using $s = \sqrt{\dfrac{\Sigma(X_i - \bar{X})^2}{n-1}}$ for the standard deviation of a sample instead of $\sigma = \sqrt{\dfrac{\Sigma(X_i - \bar{X})^2}{n}}$, one must make the following changes in the formulas for the central line and for the 3-sigma limits:

(1) Replace A_1 by $\sqrt{\dfrac{n-1}{n}} A_1$; replace $\bar{\sigma}$ by $\bar{s}$; make no change in B_3 and B_4;

(2) Replace c_2, B_1, B_2 by $\sqrt{\dfrac{n}{n-1}} c_2$, $\sqrt{\dfrac{n}{n-1}} B_1$ and $\sqrt{\dfrac{n}{n-1}} B_2$, respectively.

REFERENCES

1. P. S. Olmstead, "How to Detect the Type of an Assignable Cause," Parts I and II, *Industrial Quality Control*, Vol. IX, Nos. 3, pp. 32-38 (November 1952) and 4, pp. 22-32 (January 1953).

2. *ASTM Manual on Quality Control of Materials*, American Society for Testing Materials, 1916 Race St., Philadelphia 3, Pa., 1951.

3. G. Wernimont, "Statistics Applied to Analysis", *Analytical Chemistry*, Vol. 21, p. 115, 1949.

4. R. J. Hader and W. J. Youden, "Experimental Statistics", *Analytical Chemistry*, Vol. 24, p. 120, 1952.

5. J. Mandel and F. J. Linnig, "Statistical Methods in Chemistry", *Analytical Chemistry*, Vol. 28, p. 770, 1956.

6. Ibid., Vol. 30, p. 739, 1958.

7. *Industrial Quality Control*, Monthly Journal, The American Society for Quality Control, 161 W. Wisconsin Ave., Milwaukee 3, Wis.

8. F. E. Grubbs, "The Difference Control Chart with Example of Its Use", *Industrial Quality Control*, Vol. III, No. 1, pp. 22-25, July 1946.

SOME RECOMMENDED GENERAL TEXTS

American Standard Z 1.3-1958, *Control Chart Method of Controlling Quality During Production*, available from American Standards Association, Inc., 10 East Fortieth St., New York 16, N. Y.

D. J. Cowden, *Statistical Methods in Quality Control*, Prentice-Hall, Inc., Englewood Cliffs, N. J., 1957.

A. J. Duncan, *Quality Control and Industrial Statistics*, Richard D. Irwin, Inc., Chicago, Ill., 1952.

E. L. Grant, *Statistical Quality Control*, (2d edition), McGraw-Hill Book Co., New York, N. Y., 1952.

W. A. Shewhart, *Economic Control of Quality of Manufactured Product*, Van Nostrand Inc., New York, N. Y., 1931. (The first and still a very significant book in the field).

CHAPTER 19

STATISTICAL TECHNIQUES FOR ANALYZING EXTREME-VALUE DATA*

19-1 EXTREME-VALUE DISTRIBUTIONS

Classical applications of statistical methods, which frequently concern average values and other quantities following the symmetrical normal distribution, are inadequate when the quantity of interest is the largest or the smallest in a set of magnitudes. Applications of the techniques described in this Chapter already have been made in a number of fields. Meteorological phenomena that involve extreme pressures, temperatures, rainfalls, wind velocities, etc., have been treated by extreme-value techniques. The techniques are also applicable in the study of floods and droughts.

Other examples of extreme-value problems occur in the fracturing of metals, textiles, and other materials under applied force, and in fatigue phenomena. In these instances, the observed strength of a specimen often differs from the calculated strength, and depends, among other things, upon the length and volume. An explanation is to be found in the existence of weakening flaws assumed to be distributed at random in the body and assumed not to influence one another in any way. The observed strength is determined by the strength of the weakest region — just as no chain is stronger than its weakest link. Thus, it is apparent that whenever extreme observations are encountered it will pay to consider the use of extreme-value techniques.

19-2 USE OF EXTREME-VALUE TECHNIQUES

19-2.1 LARGEST VALUES

A simplified account is given here. Primary sources for the detailed theory and methods are References 1, 2, 3, which also contain extensive bibliographies. References 4 through 10, also given at the end of this Chapter, provide additional information and examples of applications.

Figure 19-1 illustrates the frequency form of a typical curve for the distribution of largest observations.

The curve in Figure 19-1 is the derivative of the function

$$\Phi(y) = \exp\left[-\exp\left(-y\right)\right].$$

Unlike the normal distribution, this curve is skewed, with its maximum to the left of the mean and the longer of its tails extending to the right. The outstanding feature of such a distribution is that very large values are much more likely to occur than are very small values. This agrees with common experience. Very low maximum values are most unusual, while very high ones do occur occasionally. Theoretical considerations lead to a curve of this nature, called the *distribution of largest values* or the *extreme-value distribution*.

In using the extreme-value method, all the observed maxima, such as the largest wind velocity observed in each year during a fifty-

* Adapted with permission from *The American Statistician*, Vol. 8, No. 5, December 1954, from article entitled "Some Applications of Extreme-Value Methods" by E. J. Gumbel and J. Lieblein; and, from *National Bureau of Standards Technical News Bulletin 38*, No. 2, pp. 29-31, February 1954, from article entitled "Extreme-Value Methods for Engineering Problems".

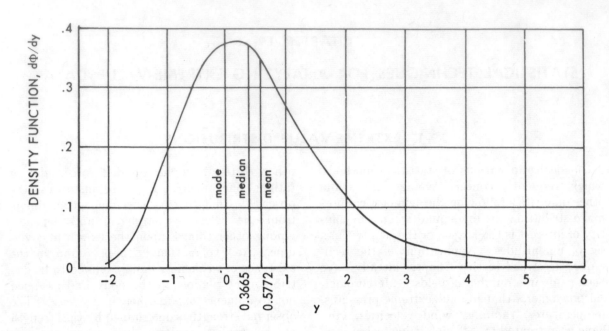

Figure 19-1.   Theoretical distribution of largest values.

Adapted with permission from *The American Statistician*, Vol. 8, No. 5, December 1954, from article entitled "Some Applications of Extreme-Value Methods" by E. J. Gumbel and J. Lieblein.

year period, are first ranked in order of size from the smallest to the largest,

$$X_1 \leq X_2 \leq \ldots \leq X_i \leq \ldots \leq X_n.$$

A plotting position (X_i, P_i) is obtained for each observation by associating with X_i the probability coordinate $P_i = i/(n + 1)$, where i is the rank of the observation, counting from the smallest. The data are plotted on a special graph paper, called extreme-value probability paper*, designed so that the "ideal" extreme-value distribution will plot exactly as a straight line. Consequently, the closeness of the plotted points to a straight line is an indication of how well the data fit the theory.

---

* Extreme-value probability paper may be obtained from three sources: (a) U. S. Department of Commerce, Weather Bureau; (b) Environmental Protection Section, Research and Development Branch, Military Planning Division, Office of the Quartermaster General; (c) Technical and Engineering Aids for Management, 104 Belrose Ave., Lowell, Mass.

Extreme-value probability paper has a uniform scale along one axis, usually the vertical, which is used for the observed values as shown in Figure 19-2. The horizontal axis then serves as the probability scale, and is marked according to the doubly-exponential formula. Thus, in Figure 19-2, the space between 0.01 and 0.5 is much less than the space between 0.5 and 0.99. The limiting values zero and one are never reached, as is true of any probability paper designed for an unlimited variate.

An extreme-value plot (Figure 19-2) of the maximum atmospheric pressures in Bergen, Norway, for the period between 1857 and 1926, showed by inspection that the observed data satisfactorily fitted the theory. Fitting the line by eye may be sufficient. Details of fitting a computed line are given in Gumbel.[1] From the fitted straight line, it is possible to predict, for example, that a pressure of 793 mm corresponds to a probability of 0.994; that is, pres-

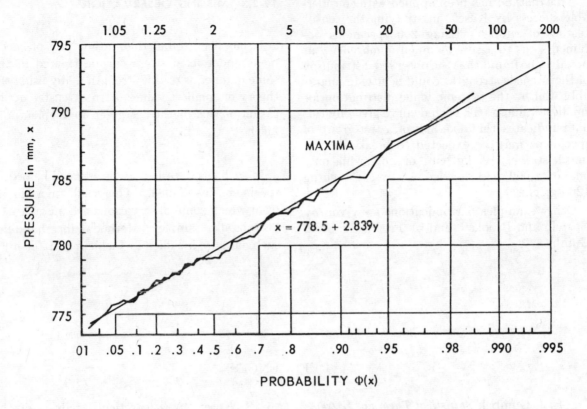

Figure 19-2. Annual maxima of atmospheric pressure, Bergen, Norway, 1857-1926.

Adapted with permission from *The American Statistician*, Vol. 8, No. 5, December 1954, from article entitled "Some Applications of Extreme-Value Methods" by E. J. Gumbel and J. Lieblein.

sures of this magnitude have less than one chance in 100 of being exceeded in any particular year.

In studies of the normal acceleration increments experienced by an airplane flying through gusty air, see Gumbel and Carlson,[4] page 394, an instrument was employed that indicated only the maximum shocks. Thus, only one maximum value was obtained from a single flight. A plot representing 26 flights of the same aircraft indicated that the probability that the largest recorded gust will not be exceeded in any other flight was 0.96; i.e., a chance of four in 100 of encountering a gust more severe than any recorded. A more recent study, Lieblein,[5] presents refinements especially adapted to very small samples of extreme data, and also to larger samples where it is necessary to obtain the greatest amount of information from a limited set of costly data.

19-2.2 SMALLEST VALUES

Extreme-value theory can also be used to study the smallest observations, since the corresponding limiting distribution is simply related to the distribution of largest values. The steps in applying the "smallest value" theory are very similar to those for the largest-value case. For example, engineers have long been interested in the problem of predicting the tensile strength of a bar or specimen of homogeneous material. One approach is to regard the specimen as being composed of a large number of pieces of very short length. The tensile strength of the entire specimen is limited by the strength of the weakest of these small pieces. Thus, the tensile strength at which the entire specimen will fail is a smallest-value phenomenon. The smallest-value approach can be used even though the number and individual strengths of the "small pieces" are unknown.

This method has been applied with considerable success by Kase[6] in studying the tensile testing of rubber. Using 200 specimens obtained so as to assure as much homogeneity as possible, he found that the observed distribution of their tensile strengths could be fitted remarkably well by the extreme-value distribution for smallest values. The fitted curve given by this data indicates that one-half of a test group of specimens may be expected to break under a tensile stress of 105 kg./cm.^{2} or more, while only one in 1,000 will survive a stress exceeding 126 kg./cm.^{2}.

Other examples of applications are given by Epstein and Brooks[7] and by Freudenthal and Gumbel[8][9].

19-2.3 MISSING OBSERVATIONS

It has been found that fatigue life of specimens under fixed stress can be treated in the same manner as tensile strength — by using the theory of smallest values. An extensive application of this method is given in Lieblein and Zelen[10].

In such cases, tests may be stopped before all specimens have failed. This results in a sample from which some observations are missing — a "censored" sample. Methods for handling such data are included in Lieblein and Zelen[10].

REFERENCES

1. E. J. Gumbel, *Statistical Theory of Extreme Values and Some Practical Applications*, National Bureau of Standards Applied Mathematics Series No. 33, U. S. Government Printing Office, Washington, D. C., 1954.

2. National Bureau of Standards, *Probability Tables for the Analysis of Extreme-Value Data*, Applied Mathematics Series No. 22, U. S. Government Printing Office, Washington, D. C., 1953.

3. E. J. Gumbel, *Statistics of Extremes*, Columbia University Press, New York, N. Y., 1958.

4. E. J. Gumbel and P. G. Carlson, "Extreme Values in Aeronautics", *Journal of the Aeronautical Sciences*, Vol. 21, No. 6, pp. 389-398, June 1954.

5. J. Lieblein, "A New Method for Analyzing Extreme-Value Data", *NACA Technical Note 3053*, National Advisory Committee for Aeronautics, January 1954.

6. S. Kase, "A Theoretical Analysis of the Distribution of Tensile Strength of Vulcanized Rubber," *Journal of Polymer Science*, Vol. 11, No. 5, pp. 425-431, November 1953.

7. B. Epstein and H. Brooks, "The Theory of Extreme Values and Its Implications in the Study of the Dielectric Strength of Paper Capacitors", *Journal of Applied Physics*, Vol. 19, pp. 544-550, 1948.

8. A. M. Freudenthal and E. J. Gumbel, "On the Statistical Interpretation of Fatigue Tests", *Proceedings of the Royal Society A*, Vol. 216, pp. 309-332, 1953.

9. A. M. Freudenthal and E. J. Gumbel, "Minimum Life in Fatigue", *Journal of the American Statistical Association*, Vol. 49, pp. 575-597, September 1954.

10. J. Lieblein and M. Zelen, "Statistical Investigation of the Fatigue Life of Deep-Groove Ball Bearings", *Journal of Research of the National Bureau of Standards*, Vol. 57, No. 5, pp. 273-316, November 1956.

CHAPTER 20

THE USE OF TRANSFORMATIONS

20-1 GENERAL REMARKS ON THE NEED FOR TRANSFORMATIONS

The scale on which a property is usually measured (that is, the units in which it is ordinarily expressed) may not be the most suitable for statistical analysis and interpretation. Statistical techniques are always based on assumptions. The validity of results obtained through their use in practice always depends, sometimes critically, on the assumed conditions being met, at least to a sufficient degree of approximation. Essentially all of the standard techniques for the statistical analysis and interpretation of measurement data (e.g., those given in ORDP 20-110, Section 1, Chapters 1 through 6) are based upon assumed *normality* of the underlying distribution involved; and many (e.g., the majority of those considered in Chapters 5 and 6) also require (at least approximate) *equality of variances* from group to group. Furthermore, the analysis-of-variance tests considered in ORDP 20-112, Section 3, depend not only on normality and equality of variances among subgroups, but also on *additivity* of the "effects" that characterize real differences of interest among the materials, processes, or products under consideration; see Eisenhart.[1]

Real-life data do not always conform to the conditions required for the strict, or even approximate, validity of otherwise appropriate techniques of statistical analysis. When this is the case, a transformation (change of scale) applied to the raw data may put the data in such form that the appropriate conventional analysis can be performed validly. Bartlett[2] provides a good general survey of the practical aspects of transformations, together with a fairly complete bibliography of the subject to 1947.

20-2 NORMALITY AND NORMALIZING TRANSFORMATIONS

20-2.1 IMPORTANCE OF NORMALITY

The dependence of many standard statistical techniques on normality of the underlying distribution is twofold. First, standard statistical techniques are in the main based on the sample mean $\bar{X}$, and the sample estimate s of the population standard deviation. A normal distribution is completely determined by its mean m and its standard deviation σ; and in sampling from a normal distribution, $\bar{X}$ and s together summarize all of the information available in the sample about the parent distribution. This 100% efficiency of $\bar{X}$ and s in samples from a normal distribution does not carry over to non-normal distributions. Consequently, if the population distribution of a characteristic of interest is markedly non-normal, confidence intervals for the population mean m and standard deviation σ based on $\bar{X}$ and s will tend to be wider, and tests of hypotheses regarding m or σ will have less power, than those based on the particular functions of the sample values that are the efficient estimators of the location and dispersion parameters of the non-normal distribution concerned. In other words, use of $\bar{X}$ and s as sample measures of the location and dispersion characteristics of a population distribution may result in an intrinsic loss of efficiency in the case of markedly non-normal distributions, even if the correct sampling distributions of x^2, t, F, etc., appropriate to the non-normal distribution concerned are employed.

Second, the customary tables of percentage points of χ^2, t, F, and of factors for confidence intervals, tolerance limits, and so forth, are based on the assumption of sampling from a normal distribution. These percentage points, tolerance-limit factors, and so forth, are not strictly valid when sampling from non-normal distributions. The distribution of s^2, which is identically that of $\chi^2\sigma^2/\nu$ for ν degrees of freedom in the case of sampling from a normal distribution, is especially sensitive to departures from normality. Consequently, the actual significance levels, confidence coefficients, etc., associated with the procedures of Chapter 4 may differ somewhat from their nominal values when sampling from only moderately non-normal material is involved. Fortunately, the percentage points of t- and F-tests of hypotheses about means are not so sensitive to departures from normality, so that the standard tests of hypotheses about, and confidence intervals for, population means will be valid to a good approximation for moderately non-normal populations — but there may be some loss of efficiency, as noted above.

20-2.2 NORMALIZATION BY AVERAGING

Many physical measurement processes produce approximately normally-distributed data; some do not. Even when measurement errors are approximately normally distributed, sampling of a material, product, or process may be involved, and the distribution of the characteristic of interest in the sampled population may be definitely non-normal — or, at least, it may be considered risky to assume normality. In such cases, especially when the basic measurements are plentiful or easy to obtain in large numbers, an effective *normalization* almost always can be achieved — except for extremely non-normal distributions — if the questions of interest with respect to the population concerned can be rephrased in terms of the parameters of the corresponding sampling distribution of the arithmetic means of random samples of size four or more. This normalizational trick is of extremely wide applicability; but results, of course, in a substantial reduction in the number of observations available for statistical analysis. Consequently, it should not be applied when the basic measurements themselves are few in number and costly to obtain. In such cases, if assumption of normality of the population distribution of the basic observations is considered risky, or definitely is known to be false, then we may take recourse in available distribution-free techniques; see Chapter 16.

20-2.3 NORMALIZING TRANSFORMATIONS

If we know from theoretical considerations or previous experience that some simple transformation will approximately normalize the particular kind of data in hand, then, both for convenience and in the interest of efficiency, we may prefer to use normal-based standard techniques on the transformed data, rather than use distribution-free techniques on the data in their original form. For example, certain kinds of data are quite definitely known to be approximately normal in logs, and the use of a log transformation in these cases may become routine. Indeed, this transformation is the subject of an entire book which is devoted to its theoretical and empirical bases, and its uses and usefulness in a wide variety of situations; see Aitchison and Brown.[3]

Table 20-1 gives a selection of transformations that are capable of normalizing a wide variety of non-normal types. They are arranged in groups according as the range of variation of the original variable X is from 0 to ∞, from 0 to 1, or from -1 to $+1$. Their "normalizing power" is exemplified in Figure 20-1. For the theoretical bases of these and other normalizing transformations, the advanced reader is referred to the papers of Curtiss[4] and Johnson.[5]

Original Distributions　　　　　　**Transformed Distributions**

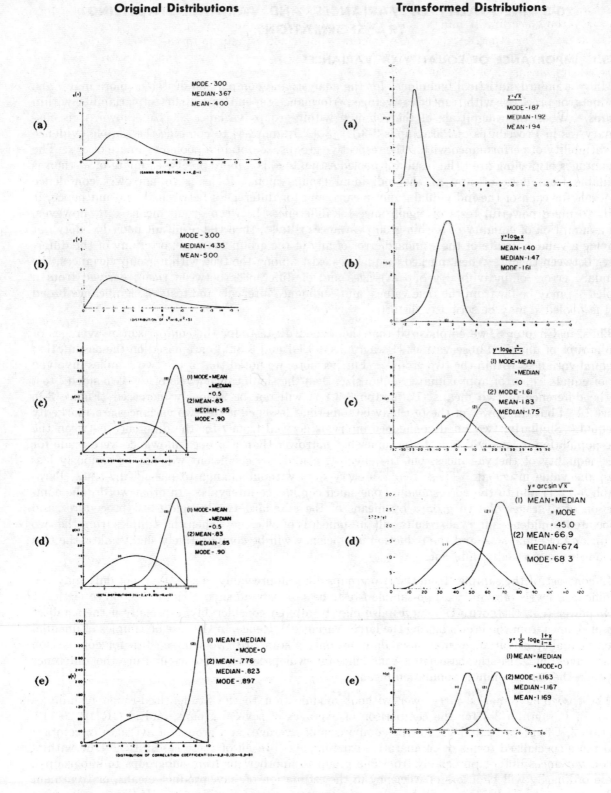

Figure 20 1.　Normalizing effect of some frequently used transformations.

20-3 INEQUALITY OF VARIANCES, AND VARIANCE-STABILIZING TRANSFORMATIONS

20-3.1 IMPORTANCE OF EQUALITY OF VARIANCES

Many standard statistical techniques for the analysis and comparison of two or more materials, products, or processes with respect to average performance depend on equality of variability within groups. When the magnitude of the common within-groups variance σ^2 is unknown, it is customary (as in Procedures of Paragraphs 3-3.1.1, 3-3.2.1, and 3-4) to combine the sample evidence on variability of performance within the respective groups, to obtain a pooled estimate of σ^2. The advantages of pooling are: the resultant pooled estimate s^2 is a more precise estimate of σ^2 than is available from data of any of the individual groups alone; it leads to narrower confidence intervals for each of the individual group means, and for differences between them; and hence, it leads to more powerful tests of significance for differences between group means. If, however, the assumption of equality of within-group variances is false, then the resultant pooled s^2 does not provide a valid estimate of the standard error of any of the group averages, or of any of the differences between them. When marked inequalities exist among the true within-group variances, the standard errors of individual group averages and of differences between them, derived from a pooled s^2, may be far from the true values; and confidence intervals and tests of significance based on the pooled s^2 may be seriously distorted.

Thus, in Chapter 3, we emphasized that the standard t-tests for the comparison of averages of two groups of unpaired observations (Paragraphs 3-3.1.1 and 3-3.2.1) are based on the assumption of equal variances within the two groups. Furthermore, we noted that if the two samples involved are of equal size, or of approximately equal size, then the significance levels of the two sided t-test of the difference of two means (Paragraph 3-3.1.1) will not be seriously increased (Figure 3-9, curve (A)); but the power of the test may be somewhat lessened if the two variances are markedly unequal. Similarly, two-sided confidence intervals derived from t for the difference between the two population means will tend to be somewhat narrower than if proper allowance were made for the inequality of the variances, but the effective confidence coefficient will not be seriously less than the value intended. These remarks carry over without change to one-sided t-tests (Paragraph 3-3.2.1) and to the corresponding one-sided confidence intervals. In other words, the comparison of averages of two groups by means of the standard two sample t-test procedures and associated confidence intervals results only in some loss of efficiency when the samples from the two groups are of equal size, and the reduction in efficiency will be comparatively slight unless the two variances are markedly different.

In contrast, if the samples from the two groups differ appreciably in size, then not only may the significance levels of standard two-sample t-tests be seriously affected (Figure 3-9, curve (B)) but their power (i.e., the entire OC curve) also may be altered considerably, especially if the smallest sample comes from the group having the larger variance. Hence, in the case of samples of unequal size, inequality of variances may invalidate not only a standard two-sample t-test for comparison of averages, but also the associated confidence-interval procedures for estimating the difference between the corresponding population means.

The foregoing remarks carry over without modification to the Studentized-range techniques given in Paragraph 3-4 for the comparison of averages of several groups, and in ORDP 20-112, Section 3, Chapters 12 and 13, for the comparison of averages and groups of averages in complex and more specialized forms of comparative experiments. In all of these cases, if the true within-group variances differ appreciably from one group to another (or from subgroups to subgroups), there ordinarily will be a loss of efficiency in the estimation of, say, product means, or treatment differences. Similarly, there will be a loss of power in tests of significance. If the samples from the respective groups are of unequal sizes and the true within-group variances are markedly unequal, these losses may be substantial. Some of the estimates of group means and differences between group means may have much smaller or much larger standard errors than others, so that pair-wise t-tests, or Studentized-range tests, derived from a pooled standard-deviation estimate s may correspond to significance levels far from those intended; and the actual effective confidence coefficients associated with the corresponding confidence intervals may differ substantially from one another, and from their nominal values.

20-3.2 TYPES OF VARIANCE INHOMOGENEITY

The situations in which variance inhomogeneity may present a problem can be divided into two types:

(a) Situations in which there is a functional dependence of the variance of an observation on the mean of the group to which it belongs. Functional dependence of the variance of an observation on its mean or expected value is an intrinsic characteristic of many non-normal distributions. The second column of Table 20-1 gives some specific examples. Or, it may be a basic property of the phenomena under investigation quite apart from the form of the underlying distribution involved. Thus, in studies of various types of "growth" phenomena, the amount of variation present at any given stage of the "growth," as measured by the standard deviation of observations at that stage, is apt to be proportional to the average size characteristic of that stage.

TABLE 20-1. SOME FREQUENTLY USED TRANSFORMATIONS

Transformation $Y = f(X)$	Appropriate Situation		Approximate Variance on Transformed Scale $\sigma_Y^2 \simeq [f'(m)]^2 \sigma_X^2$	Examples of Appropriate Distributions	
	Range of Variable	Characteristics of Distribution		Distribution and Its Parameters	Approximate Variance on Transformed Scale
$\sqrt{X}$	$0 \leq X \leq \infty$	Variance proportional to the mean $\text{Var} = \lambda^2 \cdot \text{mean}$	$\lambda^2/4$	*Continuous* Gamma distributions Mean $= p\beta$ Var $= p\beta^2$	$1/4p$
				Discrete Poisson distribution* $X = 0, 1, 2, \ldots$ Mean $= m$ Var $= m$	$1/4$
$\log_e X$ or $\log_{10} X$	$0 \leq X \leq \infty$	Standard deviation proportional to mean $\text{Var} = \lambda^2 (\text{mean})^2$	For $\log_e$, λ^2 For $\log_{10}$, $0.183 \lambda^2$	Distributions of s^2 in samples of size n for normal distribution Mean $= \sigma^2$ Var $= \dfrac{2\sigma^4}{n-1} = \left(\dfrac{2}{n-1}\right)(\text{mean})^2$	For $\log_e$, $\dfrac{2}{n-1}$ For $\log_{10}$, $\dfrac{0.377}{n-1}$
$\log_e \dfrac{X}{1-X} = 2\tanh^{-1}(2X-1)$ or $\log_{10} \dfrac{X}{1-X}$	$0 \leq X \leq 1$	*Type A* Mean $= m$ Var $= \lambda^2 m(1-m)$	For $\log_e$, $\dfrac{\lambda^2}{m(1-m)}$ For $\log_{10}$, $\dfrac{0.189 \lambda^2}{m(1-m)}$	Beta distributions Mean $= \dfrac{p}{p+q}$ Var $= \dfrac{pq}{(p+q)^2(p+q+1)}$	
		Type B Mean $= m$ Var $= \lambda^2 m^2 (1-m)^2$	For $\log_e$, λ^2 For $\log_{10}$, $0.189 \lambda^2$	Empirical	
$\arcsin \sqrt{X}$ (radians) or $\arcsin \sqrt{X}$ (degrees)	$0 \leq X \leq 1$	Mean $= m$ Var $= \lambda^2 m(1-m)$	For radians, $\lambda^2/4$ For degrees, $821 \lambda^2$	*Continuous* Beta distributions	For radians, $\dfrac{1}{4(p+q+1)}$ For degrees, $\dfrac{821}{p+q+1}$
				Discrete Binomial distributions‡ $X = 0, 1/n, 2/n, \ldots, n/n$ Mean $= p$ Var $= p(1-p)/n$	For radians, $1/4n$ For degrees, $821n$
$\frac{1}{2}\log_e \dfrac{1+X}{1-X} = \tanh^{-1} X$ or $\log_{10} \dfrac{1+X}{1-X}$	$-1 \leq X \leq +1$	$\text{Var} = \lambda^2 [1 - (\text{mean})^2]^2$	For $\frac{1}{2}\log_e$, λ^2 For $\log_{10}$, $0.754 \lambda^2$	Distribution of correlation coefficient r in samples from a normal distribution Mean $= \rho\left[1 - \dfrac{1-\rho^2}{2n} + \ldots\right]$ Var $= (1-\rho^2)^2\left[\dfrac{1}{n} + \dfrac{11\rho^2}{2n^2} - \ldots\right]$	For $\frac{1}{2}\log_e$, $\dfrac{1}{n-3}$ For $\log_{10}$, $\dfrac{0.754}{n-3}$
Probit	Sensitivity Testing			See ORDP 20-111, Chapter 10	

* For $1 < m < 10$, use the Freeman-Tukey[19] modification $Y = \frac{1}{2}(\sqrt{X} + \sqrt{X+1})$.
† Use $\log_e (X+1)$ or $\log_{10} (X+1)$ to avoid difficulties with zeros in the data.
‡ For greater accuracy, use Bartlett's[2] modification,
for $X = 0$, $Y = \arcsin \sqrt{1/4n}$
and $X = 1$, $Y = \arcsin \sqrt{(4n-1)/4n}$.

(b) Situations in which there is present incidental desultory heterogeneity of variance, arising from inadequate control of conditions or procedure; from differences or shortcomings of equipment or personnel; from use of inhomogeneous material or inadequate sampling methods; or from other disturbing features (e.g., partial failure of one or more of the products or treatments) that tend to produce less, or greater, variability among observations in some groups than in others in an irregular manner.

Situations of the first type, in which the variance inhomogeneity present is simply the consequence of a functional dependence of the variance of an observation on its mean or expected value, are most easily handled statistically by employing an appropriate variance-stabilizing transformation. Details are given in Paragraph 20-3.3. Statistical analyses of data arising from the second irregular type of variance heterogeneity should be left to experts. Variance-stabilizing transformations are of little or no help in such situations. Helpful advice, illustrated by worked examples, can be found in two papers by Cochran.[6, 7] Recourse usually must be made to subdividing the experimental observations into approximately homogenous subgroups; or to omission of parts of the experiment that have yielded data very different from the rest. An overall analysis may be impossible. Combination of the pertinent evidence from the respective subdivisions of the data may involve complex weighting and laborious arithmetic. Various procedures for the combination of evidence from different experiments, or from separately analyzed parts of a single experiment, have been examined and evaluated in a later paper by Cochran.[8] Irregular heterogeneity of variance should be avoided whenever possible, by adequate design of experiments and careful attention to the control of conditions, procedures, etc.

20-3.3 VARIANCE-STABILIZING TRANSFORMATIONS

When experimentally determined values $X_1, X_2, \ldots,$ are such that their variances $\sigma^2_{X_i}$ are functionally *dependent* on their mean values m_{X_i} in accordance with a common functional relationship, say

$$\sigma^2_{X_i} = g(m_{X_i}), \ (i = 1, 2, \ldots), \tag{20-1}$$

then we may gain the advantages of variance homogeneity in the statistical analysis of such data by replacing the original values $X_1, X_2, \ldots,$ by transformed values $Y_1 = f(X_1), Y_2 = f(X_2), \ldots,$ whose variances $\sigma^2_{Y_i}$ are (at least, to a good approximation) functionally *independent* of their mean values m_{Y_i}. Five such variance-stabilizing transformations $Y = f(X)$ are given in the first column of Table 20-1; the "situations" (i.e., the range of X and the form of the function $g(m)$ in equation (20-1)) for which each is appropriate* are indicated in the second column; and the third column shows the approximate variances of the corresponding transformed values Y, as given by the approximate formula

$$\sigma^2_Y \simeq [f'(m)] \sigma^2_X, \tag{20-2}$$

where $f'(m)$ denotes the derivative of the function $y = f(X)$ evaluated at $X = m$, the mean value of the original variable X.

Figure 20-2 presents comparisons of the actual values of the variances σ^2_Y of the transformed values Y and the corresponding approximate values given by formula (20-2), for four of the transformations listed in Table 20-1.

---

* The third transformation in the first column of Table 20-1, $\log \dfrac{X}{1 - X}$, is variance-stabilizing only for "situations" of type B.

Panel (1)

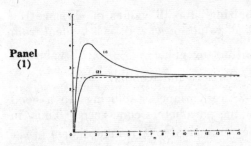

Dependence of the variances of two functions of a sample value X from a Poisson distribution on the Poisson parameter, m. (1) Variance of $\sqrt{X}$; (2) Variance of $\frac{1}{2}\left\{\sqrt{X} + \sqrt{X+1}\right\}$.

Panel (2)

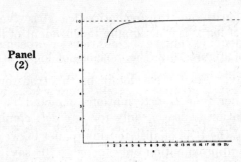

The ratio of the variance of $\log_e s^2$ to its approximate value $2/(n-1)$ in samples of size n from a normal distribution.

Panel (3)

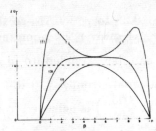

Dependence of the variances of three functions of a sample proportion X/n on the population proportion p when the *sample size is 10*. (1) 40 Var (X/n); (2) 40 Var $(\sin^{-1}\sqrt{X/n})$; (3) 40 Var (φ_β), where

$$\varphi_\beta = \begin{cases} \sin^{-1}\sqrt{1/4\,n} & \text{for } X = 0 \\ \sin^{-1}\sqrt{X/n} & \text{for } X = 1, 2, \ldots, n-1 \\ \sin^{-1}\sqrt{(4\,n-1)/4\,n} & \text{for } X = n \end{cases}$$

Panel (4)

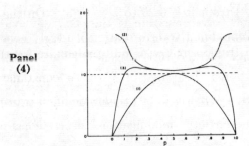

Dependence of the variances of three functions of a sample proportion X/n on the population proportion p when the *sample size is 20*. (1) 80 Var (X/n); (2) 80 Var $(\sin^{-1}\sqrt{X/n})$; (3) 80 Var (φ_β), where

$$\varphi_\beta = \begin{cases} \sin^{-1}\sqrt{1/4\,n} & \text{for } X = 0 \\ \sin^{-1}\sqrt{X/n} & \text{for } X = 1, 2, \ldots, n-1 \\ \sin^{-1}\sqrt{(4\,n-1)/4\,n} & \text{for } X = n \end{cases}$$

Panel (5)

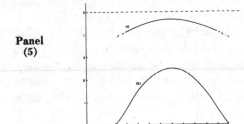

Dependence of the variance of the sample correlation coefficient r and of the variance of the transformation $z' = \frac{1}{2}\log\left(\frac{1+r}{1-r}\right)$ on the true correlation coefficient ρ for *sample size n = 5*. (1) Variance of z'; (2) Variance of r.

Panel (6)

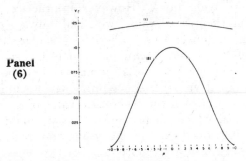

Dependence of the variance of the sample correlation coefficient r and of the variance of the transformation $z' = \frac{1}{2}\log\left(\frac{1+r}{1-r}\right)$ on the true correlation coefficient ρ for *sample size n = 11*. (1) Variance of z'; (2) Variance of r.

Figure 20-2. Variance-stabilizing effect of some frequently used transformations.

The logarithmic transformation $\log s^2$ is "variance-stabilizing" for all values of n, since the variance of $\log s^2$ is functionally independent of its mean for all values of n; and, as is evident from panel 2 of Figure 20-2, the variance of $\log s^2$ is close to its limiting value $\frac{2}{n-1}$ for all values of $n \geq 5$, say. For further details on this transformation, see Bartlett and Kendall.[9]

The other four transformations depicted in Figure 20-2 are variance-stabilizing (to a good approximation at least), only for *favorable* combinations of the parameters concerned. Thus, in the case of the Poisson distribution (panel 1), we see that the variance of $\sqrt{X}$ is independent of m_X to a good approximation only for $m \geq 10$, say; but the variance of the more sophisticated transformation $\frac{1}{2}(\sqrt{X} + \sqrt{X+1})$, devised by Freeman and Tukey[10], is nearly constant for $n \geq 3$, say. A table to facilitate the use of this transformation has been published by Mosteller *et al*[11, 12]. Similarly, for the binomial distribution: from panel 3 we see that when $n = 10$, the variance of $\arcsin\sqrt{X/n}$ is no more stable as p ranges from 0 to 1, than is the variance of X/n itself; but *with Bartlett's modifications*[13, 14] *for $X = 0$ and $X = 1$*, the variance is essentially constant $\left(\text{at } \frac{1.13}{4n}\right)$ from $p = 0.25$ to $p = 0.75$. On the other hand, when $n = 20$ (panel 4), the variance of the unmodified transformation is nearly constant from $p = 0.25$ to $p = 0.75$, so that the unmodified transformation is quite adequate for this range of p. However, by adopting Bartlett's modifications, the range of variance constancy $\left(\text{at } \frac{1.06}{4n}\right)$ can be extended to $p = 0.12$ and $p = 0.88$. When $n = 30$, the unmodified transformation is adequate from $p = 0.18$ to $p = 0.82$, and with Bartlett's modifications, nearly constant variance $\left(\text{at } \frac{1.035}{4n}\right)$ is achieved from $p = 0.08$ to $p = 0.92$. Finally, panels 5 and 6 show the variance-stabilizing power of the $\log\frac{1+r}{1-r}$ transformation of the correlation coefficient r, due to Fisher,[15] for $n = 5$ and $n = 10$.

Figure 20-2 and the foregoing discussion serve to bring out a very important feature of variance-stabilizing transformations: over any range of *favorable circumstances* for which a particular variance-stabilizing transformation Y has an essentially constant and known variance σ_Y^2, we also have, in addition to the advantages of variance constancy, all of the attendant advantages of "σ-known" techniques. However, in practice, before proceeding on the assumption that σ_Y^2 has a particular theoretical value, we should always evaluate an estimate of σ_Y^2, say s_Y^2, from the data on hand, and check to see whether s_Y^2 is consistent with the presumed theoretical value of σ_Y^2. If it is, then "σ-known" techniques should be used in the interest of greater efficiency. On the other hand, if the magnitude of s_Y^2 indicates that the effective value of σ_Y^2 is substantially greater than its theoretical value, then "σ-unknown" techniques, based on s_Y, must be used. In such cases, the excess of s_Y^2 over the theoretical value of σ_Y^2 indicates the amount of additional variation present in the data, which, in principle at least, could be eliminated in future experiments of the same kind by improved experiment design and measurement-error control.

20-4 LINEARITY, ADDITIVITY, AND ASSOCIATED TRANSFORMATIONS

20-4.1 DEFINITION AND IMPORTANCE OF LINEARITY AND ADDITIVITY

Experimental data are much easier to interpret when the effects of the variables concerned are *linear* and *additive*.

When only a single independent variable x is involved, then *linearity* of the phenomena under investigation means that the response y corresponding to input x can be expressed in the form

$$y = \beta_0 + \beta_1 x \tag{20-3}$$

when x and y are expressed on appropriate scales. Equation (20-3) is the equation of a straight line in the x, y-plane. The analysis and interpretation of such linear relationships derived from experimental data are considered in detail in Chapter 5.

In the case of two independent or input variables, say x and z, if the dependence of the response y on these two variables is of the form

$$\begin{aligned} y &= \beta_0 + \beta_1 x + \beta_2 z + \beta_3 xz \\ &= (\beta_0 + \beta_2 z) + (\beta_1 + \beta_3 z)x \\ &= (\beta_0 + \beta_1 x) + (\beta_2 + \beta_3 x)z \end{aligned} \tag{20-4}$$

then clearly the response y depends linearly on x for fixed values of z, and linearly on z for fixed values of x; but the effect of changes in x and z will be additive if and only if the cross product term is missing (i.e., $\beta_3 \equiv 0$). Only in this case will a given change in x, say δx, produce the same change in y regardless of the value of z, and a given change in z, say δz, produce the same change in y regardless of the value of x; and hence together produce the same total change in y, irrespective of the "starting values" of x and z. In other words, for *linearity and additivity* in the case of two independent variables, the response surface must be of the form

$$y = \beta_0 + \beta_1 x + \beta_2 z \tag{20-5}$$

which is the equation of a plane in the three-dimensional x, z, y-space.

Similar remarks extend to the case of three or more independent variables, in which case for *linearity and additivity* the response surface must be of the form

$$y = \beta_0 + \beta_1 x + \beta_2 z + \beta_3 u + \beta_4 v + \beta_5 w + \ldots \tag{20-6}$$

which is the equation of a hyperplane in the $(x, z, u, v, w, \ldots, y)$-space.

When, as in equation (20-4), the cross-product term $\beta_3 xz$ is present, the effect of a given change in x, say δx, will depend upon the corresponding value of z; the effect of a given change in z, say δz, will depend upon the corresponding value of x; and the joint effect of δx *and* δz will depend on the "starting values" of x and z. In such cases, we say that there is an *interaction* between the factors x and z with respect to their effect on the response y. Hence, in the contrary case, when the changes in y resulting from changes in the two variables x and z *are additive*, it is customary to say that there is *no interaction* between x and z with respect to their effect on the response y.

Many of the standard techniques of statistical analysis, especially analysis-of-variance techniques, depend explicitly on linearity and additivity of the phenomenon under investigation. Thus, the usual analysis of randomized-block experiments (Paragraph 13-3.2) is based on the assumption that the response y_{ij} of the ith treatment in the jth block can be expressed in the form

$$y_{ij} = \varphi_i + \beta_j, \tag{20-7}$$

where φ_i serves to characterize the expected response of the ith treatment, and may be regarded as the average response of the ith treatment over all of the blocks of the experiment; and β_j characterizes the effect of the jth block, and is the amount by which the response in the jth block of *any one* of the treatments may be expected to differ from its average response over all blocks. Similarly, in the analysis of Latin-square experiments (Paragraph 13-5.2.1), it usually is assumed that y_{ijm}, the response of the ith treatment under conditions corresponding to the jth row and the mth column, can be represented in the form

$$y_{ijm} = \varphi_i + \rho_j + \kappa_m,   \text{(20-8)}$$

where, as before, φ_i serves to characterize the ith treatment, and may be regarded as the expected response for the ith treatment averaged over all combinations of conditions (corresponding to the rows and columns) included in the experiment; ρ_j serves to characterize the jth row, and may be regarded as the amount by which the response of *any one* of the treatments may be expected to differ under the conditions of the jth row from *its* response averaged over all of the experiment; and κ_m serves to characterize the mth column, and may be regarded as the amount by which the response of *any* treatment may be expected to differ under the conditions of the mth column from *its* response averaged over the entire experiment.

In the case of factorial-type experiments involving many factors (Chapter 12), complete additivity as defined by equation (20-6) is rarely realistic. However, if *internal estimates* of experimental error are to be obtainable from the experimental data in hand (Paragraph 12-1.2.1), then at least some of the higher-order interaction terms, involving, say, three or more factors (e.g., terms in xzw, xzu, . . . ; $xzwu$, . . . ; $xzwuv$, . . .) must either be absent or at least of negligible magnitude in comparison to σ, the actual standard deviation of the measurements involved.

Thus the importance of additivity in the analysis and interpretation of randomized-block, Latin-square, and other multi-factor experiments is seen to be twofold: first, only when the effects of treatments and blocks, or treatments and rows and columns, etc., are strictly additive can we use a single number φ_i to represent the effect of the ith treatment under the range of conditions included in the experiment; and second, only when strict additivity prevails will the residual deviations of the observed responses Y from response surfaces of the form of equation (20-5), (20-6), (20-7), or (20-8), provide unbiased estimates s^2 of the actual experimental-error variance σ^2 associated with the experimental setup concerned. In the absence of strict additivity, for example, when "interaction" cross-product terms $(\varphi\beta)_{ij}$ need to be added to equation (20-7), the actual effect of the ith treatment will depend upon the conditions corresponding to the particular block concerned, being $\varphi_i + (\varphi\beta)_{i1}$ for the first block, $\varphi_i + (\varphi\beta)_{i2}$ for the second block, etc. Furthermore, if the experimental data are analyzed on the supposition that equation (20-7) holds, whereas the cross-product terms actually are necessary to describe the situation accurately, then the resulting residual sum of squares will contain a component due to the sum of the squares of the interaction terms $(\varphi\beta)_{ij}$. Consequently, the resulting variance estimates s^2 will tend to exceed the true experimental-error variance σ^2, to reduce the apparent "significance" of experimental estimates of the actual treatment effects φ_i, and to yield unnecessarily wide confidence interval estimates for the φ_i, and for differences between them. Worse, the customary distribution theory will no longer be strictly applicable, so that the resulting tests for significance and confidence interval estimates will, at best, be only approximately valid.

Therefore, it is highly desirable that the effects of treatments and other factors involved in a complex experiment, if not additive, at least have negligible interactions, in the sense that the corresponding terms needed to depict the situation accurately be individually and collectively negligible in comparison with the corresponding main effects (φ_i, β_j, etc.) and also with respect to the true experimental-error variance σ^2.

20-4.2 TRANSFORMATION OF DATA TO ACHIEVE LINEARITY AND ADDITIVITY

It should be noted that in connection with the linear relationship in equation (20-3) we added a qualifying phrase "when x and y are expressed on appropriate scales." This qualification was added because, if a response y depends *non-linearly* on the corresponding input x and the form of this non-linear relationship is known, then sometimes it is possible to make a transformation of one or both of the variables so that the relationship between the transformed variables y' and x' is of the form of equation (20-3) with y' in place of y and x' in place of x. A number of such linearizing transformations are considered in Paragraph 5-4.4, and are summarized in Table 5-4.

The art of transformation of data to achieve additivity is far less well developed than are the arts of transformation to achieve normality, constancy of variance, and linearity. The only situation that comes to mind for which the exact transformation needed to achieve additivity is obvious, is the case where, say, treatment, row, and column effects are multiplicative in the original units, so that instead of equation (20-8) we have

$$y_{ijm} = \varphi_i \rho_j \kappa_m. \tag{20-9}$$

On taking logarithms this becomes

$$\log y_{ijm} = \log \varphi_i + \log \rho_j + \log \kappa_m, \tag{20-10}$$

which clearly is of the form given in equation (20-8) in terms of the variables

$$y'_{ijm} = \log y_{ijm}, \quad \varphi'_i = \log \varphi_i, \quad \rho'_j = \log \rho_j, \quad \text{and} \quad \kappa'_m = \log \kappa_m.$$

Fortunately, it often happens that a transformation chosen for the purpose of achieving constancy of variance also improves the situation to some extent with respect to linearity and additivity. But, this will not always be the case. In some situations, if we can find a transformation that improves linearity or additivity we may choose to forego the advantages of constancy of variance. Such is the case, for example, when we adopt the *probit transformation* (Chapter 10) in order to achieve linearity, with the consequent necessity of performing weighted analyses of the transformed data to allow for non-constancy of variance. In other cases, variance constancy may be so advantageous that we are willing to proceed on the assumption that additivity also is achieved by the transformation to stabilize variance — a situation explored by Cochran[16] for the cases of binomial or Poisson-distributed data.

20-5 CONCLUDING REMARKS

One important characteristic of all of the transformations given in Table 20-1 is that they all are *order preserving:* the relative rank order (with respect to magnitude) of the original *individual measurements* $X_1, X_2, \ldots$ is strictly preserved in their transforms $Y_1 = f(X_1), Y_2 = f(X_2) \ldots$. Consequently, the relative rank order of subgroup means $\bar{X}_{(1)}, \bar{X}_{(2)}, \ldots$ of the original measurements will usually — but not necessarily* — be preserved in the corresponding subgroup means $\bar{Y}_{(1)}, \bar{Y}_{(2)}, \ldots$ evaluated from the transformed data. When these subgroup means on the Y-scale are transformed back to the X-scale by the inverse transformation $X = g(Y)$, their transforms $\bar{X}'_{(1)} = g(\bar{Y}_{(1)}), \bar{X}'_{(2)} = g(\bar{Y}_{(2)}), \ldots$ will always be in the same relative rank order as the subgroup

---

* For example, let the original data consist of the following two groups of two observations each: 1, 10 and 5, 5. Then, $\bar{X}_1 = 5.5$, $\bar{X}_2 = 5$, and $\bar{X}_1 > \bar{X}_2$. If now we change to $Y = \log_{10} X$, the data become 0, 1 and 0.699, 0.699 so that $\bar{Y}_1 = 0.5$, $\bar{Y}_2 = 0.699$, and $\bar{Y}_1 < \bar{Y}_2$.

means $\bar{Y}_{(1)}$, $\bar{Y}_{(2)}$, ... on the Y-scale; and hence, usually — but not always — in the same relative rank order as the original subgroup means $\bar{X}_{(1)}$, $\bar{X}_{(2)}$, ... on the X-scale. In other words, by using one of these transformations, we ordinarily will not seriously distort the relative magnitudes of treatment effects, of block effects, etc.

The "transformed-back" subgroup means $\bar{X}'_{(1)}$, $\bar{X}'_{(2)}$, ... , will, of course, not have the same meaning as the "straight-forward" subgroup means $\bar{X}_{(1)}$, $\bar{X}_{(2)}$, ... Thus, in the case of the logarithmic transformation $y = \log X$, if the subgroup means $\bar{Y}_{(1)}$, $\bar{Y}_{(2)}$, ... on the transformed scale (Y) are *arithmetic means* of the corresponding Y values, then the "transformed-back" subgroup means $\bar{X}'_{(1)} = $ anti-log $\bar{Y}_{(1)}$, $\bar{X}'_{(2)} = $ anti-log $\bar{Y}_{(2)}$, ... , are estimates, *not* of the corresponding population arithmetic means $\mu_{(1)}$, $\mu_{(2)}$, ... , *but rather* of the corresponding population *geometric means* $\gamma_{(1)}$, $\gamma_{(2)}$, ... On the other hand, if instead of considering subgroup means, we were to consider subgroup medians $\tilde{X}_{(1)}$, $\tilde{X}_{(2)}$, ... , then the corresponding subgroup medians $\tilde{Y}_{(1)}$, $\tilde{Y}_{(2)}$, ... , on the Y-scale will always be in the same relative rank order as the original subgroup medians on the X-scale; and the "transformed-back" subgroup medians $\tilde{X}'_{(1)} = g(\tilde{Y}_{(1)})$, $\tilde{X}'_{(2)} = g(\tilde{Y}_{(2)})$, ... , will be *identically equal to* the original subgroup medians $\tilde{X}_{(1)}$, $\tilde{X}_{(2)}$, ... Consequently, if there is some danger of distortion through the use of a transformation to achieve normality, constancy of variance, linearity, or additivity, then consideration should be given to:

(a) whether, for the technical purposes at issue, discussion might not be equally or perhaps even more conveniently conducted in terms of the transformed values Y, thus obviating the necessity of transforming back to the original X-scale; or,

(b) whether, for purposes of discussion, population medians rather than population means might well be equally or perhaps more meaningful.

In this connection, it must be pointed out that confidence limits for means, differences between means (medians, differences between medians) etc., evaluated in terms of the transformed values Y can be "transformed back" directly into confidence limits for the corresponding magnitudes* on the original X-scale. On the other hand, estimated standard errors of means (medians), differences between means (differences between medians), etc., evaluated on the transformed scale Y cannot be "transformed-back" directly into standard errors of the corresponding "transformed-back" magnitudes on the original scale X. Hence, if standard errors of *final results* are to be given as a way of indicating their respective imprecisions, such standard errors must be evaluated for, and stated as being applicable only to, *final results* expressed on the transformed scale Y.

As so eloquently remarked by Acton[17, pp 221-222]:

"These three reasons for transforming . . . [i.e., to achieve normality, constancy of variance, or additivity] have no obvious mathematical compulsion to be compatible; a transformation to introduce additivity might well throw out normality and mess up the constancy of variance beyond all recognition. Usually, the pleasant cloak of obscurity hides knowledge of all but one property from us — and so we cheerfully transform to vouchsafe unto ourselves this one desirable property while carefully refraining from other considerations about which query is futile. But there is a brighter side to this picture. The gods who favor statisticians have frequently ordained that the world be well behaved, and so we often find that a transformation to obtain one of these *desiderata* in fact achieves them all (well, *almost* achieves them!)."

Nevertheless, the following sobering advice from Tippett[18, pp 344-345] should not go unheeded: —

"If a transformed variate [y], having convenient statistical properties, can be substituted for x in the technical arguments from the results and in their applications, there is everything to be said for making the transformation. But otherwise the situation can become obscure. Suppose, for example, that there is an interaction between treatments and looms when the measure is warp breakage rate and that the interaction disappears for the logarithm of the warp breakage rate. It requires some clear thinking to decide what this signifies technically; and the situation becomes somewhat obscure when, as so often happens, the effects are not overwhelmingly significant, and it is remembered that a verdict 'no significant interaction' is not equivalent to 'no interaction.' If the technical interpretation has to be in terms of the untransformed variate x, and after the statistical analysis has been performed on [y], means and so on have to be converted back to x, statistical difficulties arise and the waters deepen. Readers are advised not to make transformations on statistical grounds alone unless they are good swimmers and have experience of the currents."

---

* E.g., for *geometric means* on the X-scale, if the transformation involved is $Y = \log X$ and *arithmetic means* are employed on the Y-scale.

REFERENCES

1. C. Eisenhart, "The Assumptions Underlying the Analysis of Variance," *Biometrics*, Vol. 3, No. 1, pp. 1-21, March 1947.

2. M. S. Bartlett, "The Use of Transformations," *Biometrics*, Vol. 3, No. 1, pp. 39-52, March 1947.

3. J. Aitchison and J. A. C. Brown, *The Lognormal Distribution*, Cambridge University Press, Cambridge, England, 1957.

4. J. H. Curtiss, "On Transformations Used in the Analysis of Variance," *Annals of Mathematical Statistics*, Vol. 14, No. 2, pp. 107-122, June 1943.

5. N. L. Johnson, "Systems of Frequency Curves Generated by Methods of Translation," *Biometrika*, Vol. 36, Pts. 1 and 2, pp. 149-176, June 1949.

6. W. G. Cochran, "Some Difficulties in the Statistical Analysis of Replicated Experiments," *Empire Journal of Experimental Agriculture*, Vol. VI, No. 22, pp. 157-175, April 1938.

7. W. G. Cochran, "Some Consequences When the Assumptions for the Analysis of Variance Are Not Satisfied," *Biometrics*, Vol. 3, No. 1, pp. 22-38, March 1947.

8. W. G. Cochran, "The Combination of Estimates from Different Experiments," *Biometrics*, Vol. 10, No. 1, pp. 101-129, March 1954.

9. M. S. Bartlett and D. G. Kendall, "The Statistical Analysis of Variance — Heterogeneity and the Logarithmic Transformation," *Journal of the Royal Statistical Society, Supplement* Vol. VIII, No. 1, pp. 128-138, 1946.

10. M. F. Freeman and J. W. Tukey, "Transformations Related to the Angular and the Square Root," *Annals of Mathematical Statistics*, Vol. 21, No. 4, pp. 607-611, December 1950.

11. F. Mosteller and R. R. Bush, "Selected Quantitative Techniques," Ch. 8 of *Handbook of Social Psychology* (Edited by G. Lindzey), Addison-Wesley Publishing Co., Inc., Reading, Mass., 1954.

12. F. Mosteller and C. Youtz, "Tables of the Freeman-Tukey Transformations for the Binomial and Poisson Distributions," *Biometrika*, Vol. 48, Pts. 3 and 4, pp. 433-440, December 1961.

13. M. S. Bartlett, "Some Examples of Statistical Methods of Research in Agriculture and Applied Biology," *Journal of the Royal Statistical Society, Supplement* Vol. IV, No. 2, pp. 137-170, 1937; especially second footnote on p. 168.

14. C. Eisenhart, "Inverse Sine Transformation of Proportions," Ch. 16 of *Selected Techniques of Statistical Analysis* (Edited by C. Eisenhart, M. W. Hastay, and W. A. Wallis), McGraw-Hill Book Co., Inc., New York, N. Y., 1947.

15. R. A. Fisher, "On the 'Probable Error' of a Coefficient of Correlation Deduced from a Small Sample," *Metron*, Vol. 1, No. 4, pp. 1-32, 1921.

16. W. G. Cochran, "The Analysis of Variance When Experimental Errors Follow the Poisson or Binomial Laws," *Annals of Mathematical Statistics*, Vol. 11, No. 3, pp. 335-347, September 1940.

17. F. S. Acton, *Analysis of Straight-Line Data*, John Wiley and Sons, Inc., New York, N. Y., 1959.

18. L. H. C. Tippett, *The Methods of Statistics* (4th edition), John Wiley and Sons, Inc., New York, N. Y., 1952.

CHAPTER 21

THE RELATION BETWEEN CONFIDENCE INTERVALS
AND TESTS OF SIGNIFICANCE*

21-1 INTRODUCTION

Several chapters in this Handbook are concerned with statistical tests of significance — see, for example, ORDP 20-110, Chapters 3 and 4. In Paragraph 3-2.1.1, the problem is that of deciding whether the average of a new product differs from the known or specified average m_0 of the standard product. The test procedure involves computing a quantity u and comparing u with the difference between the observed average $\bar{X}$ and the standard average m_0. This comparison is the test of significance. A further step in the procedure, however, notes that the interval $\bar{X} \pm u$ is in fact a confidence interval estimate of the true mean of the new product.

In ORDP 20-111, Chapter 8, the problem of comparing an observed proportion with a standard proportion is done directly in terms of the confidence interval for the observed proportion, completely omitting the test-of-significance step given in Chapter 3 for comparisons involving quantitative data. Tables and charts that give confidence intervals for an observed proportion are used, and we "test" whether the observed proportion differs from the standard by noting whether or not the standard proportion is included in the appropriate interval.

Many statistical consultants, when analyzing an experiment for the purpose of testing a statistical hypothesis, e.g., when comparing means of normal populations, find that they prefer to present results in terms of the appropriate confidence interval.

It must be noted of course that not every statistical test can be put in the form of a confidence interval. In general, tests that are direct tests of the value of a parameter of the parent population can be expressed in terms of confidence intervals.

When the results of a statistical test can alternatively be stated in terms of a confidence interval for a parameter, why would we prefer the confidence interval statement? Some authorities have stressed the point that experimenters are not typically engaged in disproving things, but are looking for evidence for affirmative conclusions; after rejecting the null hypothesis, the experimenter will look for a reasonable hypothesis to accept. The relation between confidence intervals and tests of significance is mentioned only briefly in most textbooks, and ordinarily no insight is given as to which conclusion might be more appropriate. (A notable exception is Wallis and Roberts[1].)

* Adapted with permission from *The American Statistician*, Vol. 14, No. 1, 1960, from article entitled "The Relation Between Confidence Intervals and Tests of Significance — A Teaching Aid" by Mary G. Natrella.

21-2   A PROBLEM IN COMPARING AVERAGES

In this Chapter, we review both procedures with reference to a numerical example, which was given in Paragraph 3-2.1.1.

For a certain type of shell, specifications state that the amount of powder should average 0.735 lb. In order to determine whether the average for the present stock meets the specification, twenty shells are taken at random and the weight of powder is determined. The sample average $\bar{X}$ is 0.710 lb. The estimated standard deviation s is 0.0504 lb. The question to be answered is whether or not the average of present stock differs from the specification value. In order to use a two-sided test of significance at the $(1 - \alpha)$ probability level, we compute a critical value, to be called u. Let

$$u = \frac{t^* s}{\sqrt{n}}$$

where t^* is the positive number exceeded by $100 \left(\dfrac{\alpha}{2} \right) \%$ of the t-distribution with $n - 1$ degrees of freedom. (See Table A-4.)

In the above example with $\alpha = .05$, t^* equals 2.09 and u equals 0.0236 lb. The test of significance says that if $|\bar{X} - 0.735| > u$, we decide that the average for present stock differs from the specified average. Since

$$|0.710 - 0.735| > 0.0236,$$

we decide that there *is* a difference.

From the same data, we also can compute a 95% confidence interval for the average of present stock. This confidence interval is $\bar{X} \pm u = 0.710 \pm 0.0236$, or the interval from 0.686 to 0.734 lb. The confidence interval can be used for a test of significance; since it *does NOT include* the standard value 0.735, we conclude that the average for the present stock *DOES differ* from the standard.

Comparisons of two materials (see Paragraph 3-3.1.1 for the case of both means unknown and equal variances) may be made similarly. In computing a test of significance, we compare the difference between sample means, $|\bar{X}_A - \bar{X}_B|$, with a computed critical quantity, again called u. If $|\bar{X}_A - \bar{X}_B|$ is larger than u, we declare that the means differ significantly at the chosen level. We also note that the interval

$$(\bar{X}_A - \bar{X}_B) \pm u$$

is a confidence interval for the difference between the true means $(m_A - m_B)$; if the computed interval does not include zero, we conclude from the experiment that the two materials differ in mean value.

21-3   TWO WAYS OF PRESENTING THE RESULTS

Here then are two ways to answer the original question. We may present the result of a test of significance, or we may present a confidence interval. The significance test is a go no-go decision. We compute a critical value u, and we compare it with an observed difference. If the observed difference exceeds u, we announce a significant difference; if it does not, we announce that there is *NO difference*. If we had no OC curve for the test, our decision would be a yes-no proposition with no shadowland of indifference. The significance test may have said *NO*, but only the OC curve can qualify this by showing that this particular experiment had only a ghost of a chance of saying *YES* to this particular question. For example, see Figure 21-1. If the true value of $d = \left| \dfrac{m - m_0}{\sigma} \right|$ were equal to 0.5, a sample of 10 is not likely to detect a difference, but a sample of 100 is almost certain to detect such a difference.

Using a rejection criterion alone is not the proper way to think of a significance test; we should always think of the associated OC curve as part and parcel of the test. Unfortunately, this has not always been the case. As a matter of fact, many experimenters who use significance tests are using them as though there were no such thing as an OC curve.

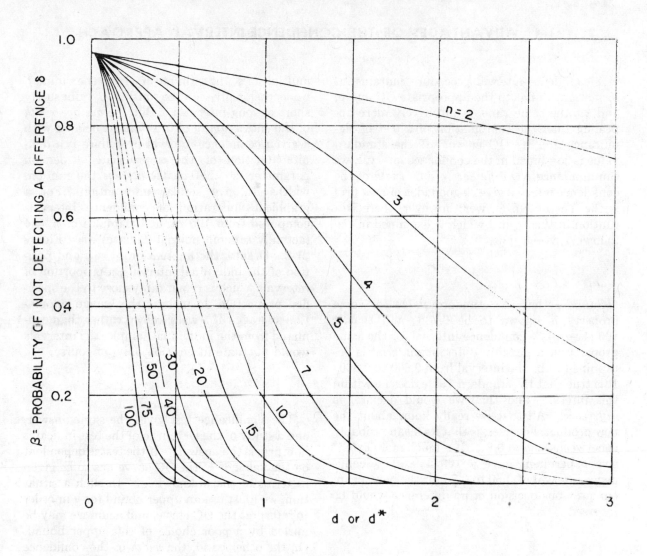

Figure 21-1.   Reprint of Figure 3-1.   OC curves for the two-sided t-test ($\alpha = .05$).

Adapted with permission from *Annals of Mathematical Statistics*, Vol. 17, No. 2, June 1946, pp. 178-197, from article entitled "Operating Characteristics for the Common Statistical Tests of Significance" by C. D. Ferris, F. E. Grubbs, and C. L. Weaver.

21-4 ADVANTAGES OF THE CONFIDENCE-INTERVAL APPROACH

A confidence-interval procedure contains information similar to the appropriate OC curve, and, at the same time, is intuitively more appealing than the combination of a test of significance and its OC curve. If the standard value is contained in the confidence interval, we can announce *NO difference*. The *width* of the confidence interval gives a good idea of how firm is the Yes or No answer; however, there is a caution in this regard which is explained in the following paragraphs.

Suppose that the standard value for some property is known to be 0.735, and that a $100(1-\alpha)\%$ confidence interval for the same property of a possibly different material is determined to be the interval from 0.600 to 0.800. It is true that the standard value does lie within this interval, and that we would declare *no difference*. All that we really know about the new product, however, is that its mean probably is between 0.6 and 0.8. If a much more extensive experiment gave a $100(1-\alpha)\%$ confidence interval of 0.60 to 0.70 for the new mean, our previous decision of no difference would be reversed.

On the other hand, if the computed confidence interval for the same confidence coefficient had been 0.710 to 0.750, our answer would still have been *no difference*, but we would have said *NO* more loudly and firmly. The confidence interval not only gives a Yes or No answer, but, by its width, also gives an indication of whether the answer should be whispered or shouted.

This is certainly true when the width of the interval for a given confidence coefficient is a function only of n and the appropriate dispersion parameter (e.g., known σ). When the width itself is a random variable (e.g., is a fixed multiple of s, the estimate of σ from the sample), we occasionally can be misled by unusually short or long intervals. But the *average width* of the entire *family* of intervals associated with a given confidence-interval procedure is a definite function of the appropriate dispersion parameter, so that *on the average* the random widths do give similar information. For a graphical illustration of confidence intervals computed from 100 random samples of $n = 4$ (actually random normal deviates), see Figure 21-2. Despite the fluctuation in size and position of the individual intervals, a proportion of intervals which is remarkably close to the specified proportion do include the known population average. If σ were known rather than estimated from the individual sample, the intervals would fluctuate in position only, of course.

The significance test gives the same answer, and a study of the OC curve of the test indicates how firm is the answer. If the test is dependent on the value of σ, the OC curve has to be given in terms of the unknown σ. In such a situation, we must use an upper bound for σ in order to interpret the OC curve, and again we may be misled by a poor choice of this upper bound. On the other hand, the *width* of the confidence interval is part and parcel of the information provided by that method. No *a priori* estimates need be made of σ as would be necessary to interpret the OC curve. Furthermore, a great advantage of confidence intervals is that the width of the interval is in the same units as the parameter itself. The experimenter finds this information easy to grasp, and easy to compare with other information he may have.

The most striking illustration of information provided by confidence intervals is shown in the charts of confidence limits for a binomial parameter. In this case, the limits depend only on n and the parameter itself, and we cannot be misled in an individual sample.

Suppose that a new item is being tested for comparison with a standard. We observe two defectives in a sample of 10, and we estimate the proportion defective for the new item as 0.20. The 95% confidence interval given in Table A-22, corresponding to an observed proportion of 0.20 ($n = 10$), is 0.04 to 0.60. Assume that the known proportion defective for the standard P_0 is 0.10. Our experiment with a sample of 10 gives a confidence interval which includes P_0; and, therefore, we announce *no difference* be-

tween the new item and the standard in this' regard. Intuitively, however, we feel that the interval 0.04 to 0.60 is so wide that our experiment was not very indicative. Suppose that we test 100 new items and observe 20 defectives. The observed proportion defective again is 0.20. The confidence interval from Table A-24 is 0.13 to 0.29, and does *not* include $P_0 = 0.10$. This time, we are forced to announce that the new item *is different* from the standard; and the narrower width of the confidence interval (0.13 to 0.29) gives us some confidence in doing so.

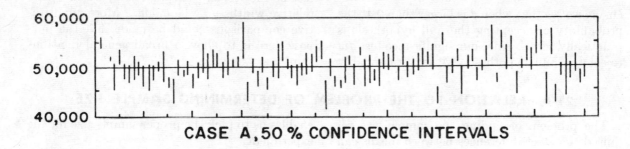

CASE A, 50% CONFIDENCE INTERVALS

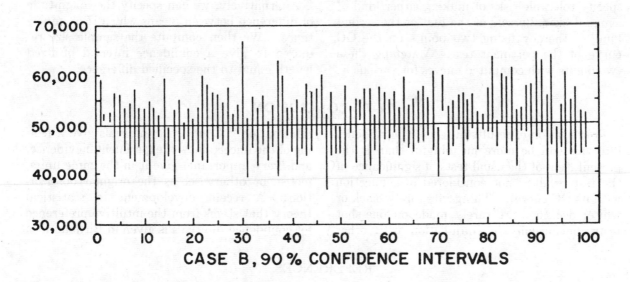

CASE B, 90% CONFIDENCE INTERVALS

Figure 21-2. Reprint of Figure 1-8. Computed confidence intervals for 100 samples of size 4 drawn at random from a normal population with $m = 50,000$ psi, $\sigma = 5,000$ psi. Case A shows 50% confidence intervals; Case B shows 90% confidence intervals.

21-5 DEDUCTIONS FROM THE OPERATING CHARACTERISTIC (OC) CURVE

The foregoing paragraphs have shown that it is possible to have some notion of the discriminatory power of the test from the size of confidence intervals. Is it also possible, in reverse, to deduce from the OC curve what kind of confidence interval we would get for the new mean? Although we cannot deduce the exact width of the confidence interval, we can infer the order of magnitude. Suppose that: we have measured 100 items; we have performed a two-sided t-test (does the average m differ from m_0?); and we have obtained a significant result. Look at the curve for $n = 100$ in Figure 21-1, which plots the probability of accepting H_0 (the null hypothesis) against $d = \left| \dfrac{m - m_0}{\sigma} \right|$. From the curve, we see that when d is larger than 0.4, the probability of accepting the null hypothesis is practically zero. Since our significance test *did* reject the null hypothesis, we may reasonably

assume that our $d = \left| \dfrac{m - m_0}{\sigma} \right|$ is larger than 0.4, and may perhaps infer a bound for the true value of $|m - m_0|$ — in other words, some "confidence interval" for m.

On the other hand, suppose that only 10 items were tested and a significant result was obtained. If we look at the curve for $n = 10$, we see that the value of d which is practically certain to be picked up on a significance test is $d = 1.5$ or larger. As expected, a significant result from an experiment which tested only 10 items corresponds to a wider confidence interval for m than the interval inferred from the test of 100 items. A rough comparison of the relative widths may be made. More quantitative comparisons could be made, but the purpose here is to show a broad general relationship.

21-6 RELATION TO THE PROBLEM OF DETERMINING SAMPLE SIZE

The problem of finding the sample size required to detect differences between means can be approached in two ways also. We can specify tolerable risks of making either kind of *wrong* decision (errors of the first or the second kind) — thereby fixing two points on the OC curve of the pertinent test. Matching these two points with computed curves for various n,

enables us to pick the proper sample size for the experiment.

Alternatively, we can specify the magnitude of difference between means which is of importance. We then compute the sample size required to give a confidence interval of fixed length equal to the specified difference.

21-7 CONCLUSION

Presentation of results in terms of confidence intervals can be more meaningful than is the presentation of the usual tests of significance (if the test result is not considered in connection with its OC curve). Things are rarely black or white; decisions are rarely made on one-shot tests, but usually in conjunction with other

information. Confidence intervals give a feeling of the uncertainty of experimental evidence, and (very important) give it in the same units, metric or otherwise, as the original observations. A recent development in statistical theory that stems from the intuitive preference for confidence intervals is given in Birnbaum[2].

REFERENCES

1. W. A. Wallis and H. V. Roberts, *Statistics, A New Approach*, pp. 461-463, The Free Press, Glencoe, Ill., 1956.

2. A. Birnbaum, "Confidence Curves: An Omnibus Technique for Estimation and Testing Statistical Hypotheses," *Journal of the American Statistical Association*, Vol. 56, No. 294, pp. 246-249, June 1961.

CHAPTER 22

NOTES ON STATISTICAL COMPUTATIONS

22-1 CODING IN STATISTICAL COMPUTATIONS

Coding is the term used when arithmetical operations are applied to the original data in order to make the numbers easier to handle in computation. The possible coding operations are:

(a) Multiplication (or its inverse, division) to change the order of magnitude of the recorded numbers for computing purposes.

(b) Addition (or its inverse, subtraction) of a constant — applied to recorded numbers which are nearly equal, to reduce the number of figures which need be carried in computation.

When the recorded results contain non-significant zeros, (e.g., numbers like .000121 or like 11,100), coding is clearly desirable. There obviously is no point in copying these zeros a large number of times, or in adding additional useless zeros when squaring, etc. Of course, these results could have been given as 121×10^{-4} or 11.1×10^3, in which case coding for order of magnitude would not be necessary.

The purpose of coding is to save labor in computation. On the other hand, the process of coding and decoding the results introduces more opportunities for error in computation. The decision of whether to code or not must be considered carefully, weighing the advantage of saved labor against the disadvantage of more likely mistakes. With this in mind, the following five rules are given for coding and decoding.

1. The whole set of observed results must be treated alike.

2. The possible coding operations are the two general types of arithmetic operations:

    (a) addition (or subtraction); and,

    (b) multiplication (or division). Either (a) or (b), or both together, may be used as necessary to make the original numbers more tractable.

3. Careful note must be kept of how the data have been coded.

4. The desired computation is performed on the coded data.

5. The process of decoding a computed result depends on the computation that has been performed, and is indicated separately for several common computations, in the following Paragraphs (a) through (d).

(a) *The mean* is affected by every coding operation. Therefore, we must apply the inverse operation and reverse the order of operations used in coding, to put the coded mean back into original units. For example, if the data have been coded by first multiplying by 10,000 and then subtracting 120, decode the mean by adding 120 and then dividing by 10,000.

Observed Results	Coded Results
.0121	1
.0130	10
.0125	5
Mean .0125	Coded mean 5

$$\text{Decoding: Mean} = \frac{\text{Coded mean} + 120}{10,000}$$

$$= \frac{125}{10,000}$$

$$= .0125$$

(b) *A standard deviation* computed on coded data is affected by multiplication or division only. The standard deviation is a measure of dispersion, like the range, and is not affected by adding or subtracting a constant to the whole set of data. Therefore, if the data have been coded by addition or subtraction only, no adjustment is needed in the computed standard deviation. If the coding has involved multiplication (or division), the inverse operation must be applied to the computed standard deviation to bring it back to original units.

(c) *A variance* computed on coded data must be: multiplied by the square of the coding factor, if division has been used in coding; or divided by the square of the coding factor, if multiplication was used in coding.

(d) *Coding which involves loss of significant figures:* The kind of coding thus far discussed has involved no loss in significant figures. There is another method of handling data, however, that involves both *coding* and *rounding*, and is also called "coding". This operation is sometimes used when the original data are considered to be too finely-recorded for the purpose.

For example, suppose that the data consist of weights (in pounds) of shipments of some bulk material. If average weight is the characteristic of interest, and if the range of the data is large, we might decide to work with weights coded to the nearest hundred pounds, as follows:

Observed Weights Units: lbs.	Coded Data Units: 100 lbs.
7,123	71
10,056	101
100,310	1003
5,097	51
543	5
.	.
.	.
.	.
etc.	etc.

Whether or not the resulting average of the coded data gives us sufficient information will depend on the range of the data and the intended use of the result. It should be noted that this "coding" requires a higher order of judgment than the strictly arithmetical coding discussed in previous examples, because some loss of information does occur. The decision to "code" in this way should be made by someone who understands the source of the data and the intended use of the computations. The grouping of data in a frequency distribution is coding of this kind.

22-2 ROUNDING IN STATISTICAL COMPUTATIONS

22-2.1 ROUNDING OF NUMBERS

Rounded numbers are inherent in the process of reading and recording data. The readings of an experimenter are rounded numbers to start with, because all measuring equipment is of limited accuracy. Often he records results to even less accuracy than is attainable with the available equipment, simply because such results are completely adequate for his immediate purpose. Computers often are required to round numbers — either to simplify the arithmetic calculations, or because it cannot be avoided, as when 3.1416 is used for π or 1.414 is used for $\sqrt{2}$.

When a number is to be rounded to a specific number of significant figures, the rounding procedure should be carried out in accordance with the following three rules.

1. When the figure next beyond the last place to be retained is less than 5, the figure in the last place retained should be kept unchanged.

For example, .044 is rounded to .04.

2. When the figure next beyond the last figure or place to be retained is greater than 5, the figure in the last place retained should be increased by 1.

For example, .046 is rounded to .05.

3. When the figure next beyond the last figure to be retained is 5, and,

(a) there are no figures or are only zeros beyond this 5, an odd figure in the last place to be retained should be increased by 1, an even figure should be kept unchanged.

For example, .045 or .0450 is rounded to .04; .055 or .0550 is rounded to .06.

(b) if the 5 is followed by any figures other than zero, the figure in the last place to be retained should be increased by 1, whether odd or even.

For example, in rounding to two decimals, .0451 is rounded to .05.

A number should always be rounded off in one step to the number of figures that are to be recorded, and should not be rounded in two or more steps of successive roundings.

22-2.2 ROUNDING THE RESULTS OF SINGLE ARITHMETIC OPERATIONS

Nearly all numerical calculations arising in the problems of everyday life are in some way approximate. The aim of the computer should be to obtain results consistent with the data, with a minimum of labor. We can be guided in the various arithmetical operations by some basic rules regarding significant figures and the rounding of data:

1. *Addition.* When several approximate numbers are to be added, the sum should be rounded to the number of decimal places (not significant figures) no greater than in the addend which has the smallest number of decimal places.

Although the result is determined by the least accurate of the numbers entering the operation, one more decimal place in the more-accurate numbers should be retained, thus eliminating inherent errors in the numbers.

For example:

$$
\begin{array}{r}
4.01 \\
.002 \\
.623 \\
\hline
4.635
\end{array}
$$

The sum should be rounded to and recorded as 4.64.

2. *Subtraction.* When one approximate number is to be subtracted from another, they must both be rounded off to the same place before subtracting.

Errors arising from the subtraction of nearly-equal approximate numbers are frequent and troublesome, often making the computation practically worthless. Such errors can be avoided when the two nearly-equal numbers can be approximated to more significant digits.

3. *Multiplication.* If the less-accurate of two approximate numbers contains n significant digits, their product can be relied upon for n digits at most, and should not be written with more.

As a practical working plan, carry intermediate computations out in full, and round off the final result in accordance with this rule.

4. *Division.* If the less-accurate of either the dividend or the divisor contains n significant digits, their quotient can be relied upon for n digits at most, and should not be written with more.

Carry intermediate computations out in full, and round off the final result in accordance with this rule.

5. *Powers and Roots.* If an approximate number contains n significant digits, its power can be relied upon for n digits at most; its root can be relied upon for at least n digits.

6. *Logarithms.* If the mantissa of the logarithm in an n-place log table is not in error by more than two units in the last significant figure, the antilog is correct to $n - 1$ significant figures.

The foregoing statements are working rules only. More complete explanations of the rules, together with procedures for determining explicit bounds to the accuracy of particular computations, are given in Scarborough[1], and the effects of rounding on statistical analyses of large numbers of observations are discussed in Eisenhart[2].

22-2.3 ROUNDING THE RESULTS OF A SERIES OF ARITHMETIC OPERATIONS

Most engineers and physical scientists are well acquainted with the rules for reporting a result to the proper number of significant figures. From a computational point of view, they know these rules too well. It is perfectly true, for example, that a product of two numbers should be reported to the same number of significant figures as the least-accurate of the two numbers. It is not so true that the two numbers should be rounded to the same number of significant figures before multiplication. A better rule is to round the more-accurate number to one more figure than the less-accurate number, and then to round the product to the same number of figures as the less-accurate one. The great emphasis against reporting more figures than are reliable has led to a prejudice against carrying enough figures in computation.

Assuming that the reader is familiar with the rules of the preceding Paragraph 22-2.2, regarding significant figures in a single arithmetical operation, the following paragraphs will stress the less well-known difficulties which arise in a computation consisting of a long series of different arithmetic operations. In such a computation, strict adherence to the rules at each stage can wipe out all meaning from the final results.

For example, in computing the slope of a straight line fitted to observations containing three significant figures, we would not report the slope to seven significant figures; but, if we round to three significant figures after each necessary step in the computation, we might end up with no significant figures in the value of the slope.

It is easily demonstrated by carrying out a few computations of this nature that there is real danger of losing all significance by too-

strict adherence to rules devised for use at the final stage. The greatest trouble of this kind comes where we must subtract two nearly-equal numbers, and many statistical computations involve such subtractions.

The rules generally given for rounding-off, were given in a period when the average was the only property of interest in a set of data. Reasonable rounding does little damage to the average. Now, however, we almost always calculate the standard deviation, and this statistic does suffer from too-strict rounding. Suppose we have a set of numbers:

$$
\begin{array}{r}
3.1 \\
3.2 \\
3.3 \\
\hline
\text{Avg. } = 3.2
\end{array}
$$

If the three numbers are rounded off to one significant figure, they are all identical. The average of the rounded figures is the same as the rounded average of the original figures, but all information about the variation in the original numbers is lost by such rounding.

The generally recommended procedure is to carry two or three extra figures throughout the computation, and then to round off the final reported answer (e.g., standard deviation, slope of a line, etc.) to a number of significant figures consistent with the original data. However, in some special computations such as the fitting of equations by least squares methods given in ORDP 20-110, Chapters 5 and 6, one should carry extra decimals in the intermediate steps — decimals sufficiently in excess of the number considered significant to insure that the computational errors in the final solutions are negligible in relation to their statistical imprecision as measured by their standard errors. For example, on a hand-operated computing machine, use its total capacity and trim the figures off as required in the final results. (See Chapter 23.)

REFERENCES

1. J. B. Scarborough, *Numerical Mathematical Analysis*, Chapter 1, (3d edition), The Johns Hopkins Press, Baltimore, Md., 1955.
2. C. Eisenhart, *Techniques of Statistical Analysis*, Chapter 4, McGraw-Hill Book Co., New York, N. Y., 1947.

CHAPTER 23

EXPRESSION OF THE UNCERTAINTIES OF FINAL RESULTS

23-1 INTRODUCTION

Measurement of some property of a thing in practice always takes the form of a sequence of steps or operations that yield as an end result a number that serves to represent the amount or quantity of some particular property of a thing — a number that indicates how much of this property the thing has, for someone to use for a specific purpose. The end result may be the outcome of a single reading of an instrument, with or without corrections for departures from prescribed conditions. More often, it is some kind of average; e.g., the arithmetic mean of a number of independent determinations of the same magnitude, or the final result of a least squares "reduction" of measurements of a number of different magnitudes that bear known relations with each other in accordance with a definite experimental plan. In general, the purpose for which the answer is needed determines the precision or accuracy of measurement required, and ordinarily also determines the method of measurement employed.

Although the accuracy required of a reported value depends primarily on the use, or uses, for which it is intended, we should not ignore the requirements of other uses to which the reported value is likely to be put. A certified or reported value whose accuracy is entirely unknown is worthless.

Strictly speaking, the actual *error* of a reported value, that is, the magnitude and sign of its deviation from the truth, is usually unknowable. Limits to this error, however, can usually be inferred — with some risk of being incorrect — from the *precision* of the measurement process by which the reported value was obtained, and from reasonable limits to the possible *bias* of the measurement process. The *bias*, or *systematic error*, of a measurement process is the magnitude and direction of its tendency to measure something other than what was intended; its *precision* refers to the typical *closeness together* of successive independent measurements of a single magnitude generated by repeated applications of the process under specified conditions; and, its *accuracy* is determined by the *closeness to the true value* characteristic of such measurements.

Precision and *accuracy* are inherent characteristics of the measurement process employed, and not of the particular end result obtained. From experience with a particular measurement process and knowledge of its sensitivity to uncontrolled factors, we can often place reasonable bounds on its likely systematic error (bias). It also is necessary to know how well the particular value in hand is likely to agree with other values that the same measurement process might have provided in this instance, or might yield on remeasurement of the same magnitude on another occasion. Such information is provided by the *standard error* of the reported value, which measures the characteristic disagreement of repeated determinations of the same quantity by the same method, and thus serves to indicate the precision (strictly, the *imprecision*) of the reported value.

The uncertainty of a reported value is indicated by giving credible limits to its likely inaccuracy. No single form of expression for these limits is universally satisfactory. In fact, different forms of expression are recommended, the choice of which will depend on the relative magnitudes of the imprecision and likely bias; and on their relative importance in relation to the intended use of the reported value, as well as to other possible uses to which it may be put.

Four distinct cases need to be recognized:

1. *Both systematic error and imprecision negligible* in relation to the requirements of the intended and likely uses of the result.

2. *Systematic error not negligible*, but *imprecision negligible*, in relation to the requirements.

3. *Neither systematic error nor imprecision negligible* in relation to the requirements.

4. *Systematic error negligible*, but *imprecision not negligible* in relation to the requirements.

Specific recommendations are made below with respect to each of these four cases, supplemented by further discussion of each case in Paragraphs 23-2 through 23-5. These recommendations may be summarized as follows:

(a) Two numerics, respectively expressing the imprecision and bounds to the systematic error of the result, should be used whenever: (1) the margin is narrow between ability to measure and the accuracy or precision require-ments of the situation; or, (2) the imprecision and the bounds to the systematic error are nearly equal in indicating possible differences from the *true value*. Such instances come under Case 3.

(b) A quasi-absolute type of statement with one numeric, placing bounds on the inaccuracy of the result, should be used whenever: (1) a wide or adequate margin exists between ability to measure and the accuracy requirements of the situation (Case 1); (2) the imprecision is negligibly small in comparison with the bounds placed on the systematic error (Case 2); or, (3) the control is so satisfactory that the extent of error is known.

(c) A single numeric expressing the imprecision of the result should be used whenever the systematic error is either zero by definition or negligibly small in comparison with the imprecision (Case 4).

(d) Expressions of uncertainty should be given in sentence form whenever feasible.

(e) The form "$a \pm b$" should be avoided as much as possible; and never used without explicit explanation of its connotation.

23-2 SYSTEMATIC ERROR AND IMPRECISION BOTH NEGLIGIBLE
(CASE 1)

In this case, the certified or reported result should be given correct to the number of significant figures consistent with the accuracy requirements of the situation, together with an explicit statement of its accuracy or correctness.

For example:
... the wavelengths of the principal visible lines of mercury 198 have been measured relative to the 6057.802106 A (Angstrom units) line of krypton 98, and their values in vacuum are certified to be

5792.2685 A
5771.1984 A
5462.2706 A
4359.5625 A
4047.7146 A

correct to eight significant figures.

It must be emphasized that when no statement of accuracy or precision accompanies a certified or reported number, then, in accordance with the usual conventions governing rounding, this number will be interpreted as being accurate within $\pm \frac{1}{2}$ unit in the last significant figure given; i.e., it will be understood that its inaccuracy before rounding was less than ± 5 units in the next place.

23-3 SYSTEMATIC ERROR NOT NEGLIGIBLE, IMPRECISION NEGLIGIBLE
(CASE 2)

In such cases:

(a) Qualification of a certified or reported result should be limited to a single quasi-absolute type of statement that places bounds on its inaccuracy;

(b) These bounds should be stated to no more than two significant figures;

(c) The certified or reported result itself should be given (i.e., rounded) to the last place affected by the stated bounds, unless it is desired to indicate and preserve such relative accuracy or precision of a higher order that the result may possess for certain particular uses;

(d) Accuracy statements should be given in sentence form in all cases, except when a number of results of different accuracies are presented, e.g., in tabular arrangement. If it is necessary or desirable to indicate the respective accuracies of a number of results, the results should be given in the form $a \pm b$ (or $a \begin{smallmatrix} +b \\ -c \end{smallmatrix}$, if necessary) with an appropriate explanatory remark (as a footnote to the table, or incorporated in the accompanying text) to the effect that the $\pm b$, or $\begin{smallmatrix} +b \\ -c \end{smallmatrix}$, signify bounds to the errors to which the a's may be subject.

The particular form of the quasi-absolute type of statement employed in a given instance ordinarily will depend upon personal taste, experience, current and past practice in the field of activity concerned, and so forth. Some examples of good practice are:

... is (are) not in error by more than 1 part in (x).

... is (are) accurate within $\pm$ (x units) (or $\pm$ (x)%).

... is (are) believed accurate within (........).

Positive wording, as in the first two of these quasi-absolute statements, is appropriate only when the stated bounds to the possible inaccuracy of the certified or reported value are themselves reliably established. On the other hand, when the indicated bounds are somewhat conjectural, it is desirable to signify this fact (and thus put the reader on guard) by inclusion of some modifying expression such as "believed", "considered", "estimated to be", "thought to be", and so forth, as exemplified by the third of the foregoing examples.

Results should never be presented in the form "$a \pm b$", without explanation. If no explanation is given, many persons will automatically take $\pm b$ to signify bounds to the inaccuracy of a. Others may assume that b is the *standard error* or the *probable error* of a, and hence that the uncertainty of a is at least $\pm 3b$, or $\pm 4b$, respectively. Still others may take b to be an indication merely of the imprecision of the individual measurements; that is, to be the *standard deviation*, the *average deviation*, or the *probable error of a SINGLE observation*. Each of these interpretations reflects a practice of which instances can be found in current scientific literature. As a step in the direction of reducing this current confusion, we urge that the use of "$a \pm b$" in presenting results in official documents be limited to that sanctioned under (d) above.

The term *uncertainty*, with the quantitative connotation of limits to the likely departure from the truth, and not simply connoting vague lack of certainty, may sometimes be used effectively to achieve a conciseness of expression otherwise difficult or impossible to attain. Thus, we might make a statement such as:

The uncertainties in the above values are not more than ± 0.5 degree in the range $0°$ to $1100°C$, and then increase to ± 2 degrees at $1450°C$.;

or,

The uncertainty in this value does not exceed .... excluding (or, including) the uncertainty of .... in the value .... adopted for the reference standard involved.

Finally, the following forms of quasi-absolute statements are considered poor practice, and should be avoided:

The accuracy of ...... is 5 percent.
The accuracy of ...... is ±2 percent.

These statements are presumably intended to mean that the result concerned is not inaccurate, i.e., not in error, by more than 5 percent or 2 percent, respectively; but they explicitly state the opposite.

23-4 NEITHER SYSTEMATIC ERROR NOR IMPRECISION NEGLIGIBLE (CASE 3)

In such cases:

(a) A certified or reported result should be qualified by: (1) a quasi-absolute type of statement that places bounds on its systematic error; and, (2) a separate statement of its standard error or its probable error, explicitly identified, as a measure of its imprecision;

(b) The bounds to its systematic error and the measure of its imprecision should be stated to no more than two significant figures;

(c) The certified or reported result itself should be stated, at most, to the last place affected by the finer of the two qualifying statements, unless it is desired to indicate and preserve such relative accuracy or precision of a higher order that the result may possess for certain particular uses;

(d) The qualification of a certified or reported result, with respect to its imprecision and systematic error, should be given in sentence form, except when results of different precision or with different bounds to their systematic errors are presented in tabular arrangement. If it is necessary or desirable to indicate their respective imprecisions or bounds to their respective systematic errors, such information may be given in a parallel column or columns, with appropriate identification.

Here, and in Paragraph 23-5, the term *standard error* is to be understood as signifying *the standard deviation of the reported value itself*, not as signifying *the standard deviation of a single determination* (unless, of course, the reported value is the result of a single determination only).

The above recommendations should not be construed to exclude the presentation of a quasi-absolute type of statement placing bounds on the inaccuracy, i.e., on the overall uncertainty, of a certified or reported value, provided that separate statements of its imprecision and its possible systematic error are included also. Bounds indicating the overall uncertainty of a reported value should not be numerically less than the corresponding bounds placed on the systematic error outwardly increased by at least two times the standard error. The fourth of the following examples of good practice is an instance at point:

The standard errors of these values do not exceed 0.000004 inch, and their systematic errors are not in excess of 0.00002 inch.

The standard errors of these values are less than (x units), and their systematic errors are thought to be less than $\pm$ (y units).

. . . with a standard error of (x units), and a systematic error of not more than $\pm$ (y units).

. . . with an overall uncertainty of ±3 percent based on a standard error of 0.5 percent and an allowance of ±1.5 percent for systematic error.

When a reliably established value for the relevant standard error is available, based on considerable recent experience with the measurement process or processes involved, and the dispersion of the present measurements is in keeping with this experience, then this established value of the standard error should be used. When experience indicates that the relevant standard error is subject to fluctuations greater than the intrinsic variation of such a measure, then an appropriate upper bound should be given, e.g., as in the first two of the above examples, or by changing "a standard error . . ." in the third and fourth examples to "an upper bound to the standard error . . .".

When there is insufficient recent experience with the measurement processes involved, an estimate of the standard error must of necessity be computed, by recognized statistical procedures, from the same measurements as the certified or reported value itself. It is essential that such computations be carried out according to an agreed-upon standard procedure, and that the results thereof be presented in sufficient detail to enable the reader to form his own judgment and make his own allowances for their inherent uncertainties. To avoid possible misunderstanding in such cases:

(a) the term *computed standard error* should be used;

(b) the estimate of the standard error employed should be that obtained from the relation

estimate of standard error

$$= \sqrt{\frac{\text{sum of squared residuals}}{n\nu}},$$

where n is the (effective) number of completely independent determinations of which a is the arithmetic mean (or, other appropriate least squares adjusted value) and ν is the number of degrees of freedom involved in the sum of squared residuals (i.e., the number of residuals minus the number of fitted constants and/or other independent constraints); and,

(c) the number of degrees of freedom ν should be explicitly stated.

If the reported value a is the arithmetic mean, then:

estimate of standard error $= \sqrt{\dfrac{s^2}{n}}$

where s^2 is computed as shown in ORDP 20-110, Chapter 2, Paragraph 2-2.2, and n is the number of completely independent determinations of which a is the arithmetic mean.

For example:

The computed probable error (or, standard error) of these values is (x units), based on (ν) degrees of freedom, and the systematic error is estimated to be less than $\pm$ (y units).

. . . which is the arithmetic mean of (n) independent determinations and has a computed standard error of . . . .

. . . with an overall uncertainty of ± 5.2 km/sec based on a standard error of 1.5 km/sec and bounds of ± 0.7 km/sec on the systematic error. (The figure 5.2 equals 0.7 plus 3 times 1.5).

Or, if based on a computed standard error:

. . . with an overall uncertainty of ± 7 km/sec derived from bounds of ± 0.7 km/sec on the systematic error and a computed standard error of 1.5 km/sec based on 9 degrees of freedom. (The figure 7 is approximately equal to $0.7 + 4.3(1.5)$, where 4.3 is the two-tail 0.002 probability value of Student's t for 9 degrees of freedom. As $\nu \to \infty$, $t_{.002}(\nu) \to 3.090$.)

23-5 SYSTEMATIC ERROR NEGLIGIBLE, IMPRECISION NOT NEGLIGIBLE (CASE 4)

In such cases:

(a) Qualification of a certified or reported value should be limited to a statement of its standard error or of an upper bound thereto, whenever a reliable determination of such value or bound is available. Otherwise, a computed value of the standard error so designated should be given, together with a statement of the number of degrees of freedom on which it is based;

(b) The standard error or upper bound thereto, should be stated to not more than two significant figures;

(c) The certified or reported result itself should be stated, at most, to the last place affected by the stated value or bound to its imprecision, unless it is desired to indicate and preserve such relative precision of a higher order that the result may possess for certain particular uses;

(d) The qualification of a certified or reported result with respect to its imprecision should be given in sentence form, except when results of different precision are presented in tabular arrangement and it is necessary or desirable to indicate their respective imprecisions, in which event such information may be given in a parallel column or columns, with appropriate identification.

The above recommendations should not be construed to exclude the presentation of a quasi-absolute type of statement placing bounds on its possible inaccuracy, provided that a separate statement of its imprecision is included also. Such bounds to its inaccuracy should be numerically equal to at least two times the stated standard error. The fourth of the following

examples of good practice is an instance at point:

> The standard errors of these values are less than (x units).
> . . . with a standard error of (x units).
> . . . .

> . . . with a computed standard error of (x units) based on (ν) degrees of freedom.
> . . . with an overall uncertainty of ± 4.5 km/sec derived from a standard error of 1.5 km/sec. (The figure 4.5 equals 3 times 1.5).

Or, if based on a computed standard error:

> . . . with an overall uncertainty of ± 6.5 km/sec derived from a computed standard error of 1.5 km/sec (based on 9 degrees of freedom). (The figure 6.5 equals 4.3 times 1.5, where 4.3 is the two-tail 0.002 probability value of Student's t for 9 degrees of freedom. As $\nu \to \infty$, $t_{.002}(\nu) \to 3.090$.

The remarks with regard to a computed standard error in Paragraph 23-4 apply with equal force to the last two of the above examples.

SECTION 5

TABLES

LIST OF TABLES

Table No.	Title	Page
A-1	Cumulative normal distribution—values of P	T-2
A-2	Cumulative normal distribution—values of z_P	T-3
A-3	Percentiles of the χ^2 distribution	T-4
A-4	Percentiles of the t distribution	T-5
A-5	Percentiles of the F distribution	T-6
A-6	Factors for two-sided tolerance limits for normal distributions	T-10
A-7	Factors for one-sided tolerance limits for normal distributions	T-14
A-8	Sample sizes required to detect prescribed differences between averages when the sign of the difference is not important	T-16
A-9	Sample sizes required to detect prescribed differences between averages when the sign of the difference is important	T-17
A-10	Percentiles of the studentized range, q	T-18
A-11	Percentiles of $F' = \dfrac{w_A}{w_B}$	T-24
A-12	Percentiles for $\phi = \dfrac{\bar{X} - m_O}{w}$	T-26
A-13	Percentiles for $\phi' = \dfrac{\bar{X}_A - \bar{X}_B}{\frac{1}{2}(w_A + w_B)}$	T-26
A-14	Criteria for rejection of outlying observations	T-27
A-15	Critical values of L for Link-Wallace Test	T-28
A-16	Percentage points of the extreme studentized deviate from sample mean	T-30
A-17	Confidence belts for the correlation coefficient	T-31
A-18	Weighting coefficients for probit analysis	T-32
A-19	Maximum and minimum working probits and range	T-33
A-20	Factors for computing two-sided confidence limits for σ	T-34
A-21	Factors for computing one-sided confidence limits for σ	T-36
A-22	Confidence limits for a proportion (two-sided)	T-37
A-23	Confidence limits for a proportion (one-sided)	T-41
A-24	Confidence belts for proportions for $n > 30$	T-45
A-25	Sample size required for comparing a proportion with a standard proportion when the sign of the difference is not important	T-48
A-26	Sample size required for comparing a proportion with a standard proportion when the sign of the difference is important	T-51
A-27	Table of arc sine transformation for proportions	T-54
A-28	Minimum contrasts required for significance in 2×2 tables with equal samples	T-55

LIST OF TABLES (CONT)

Table No.	Title	Page
A-29	Tables for testing significance in 2×2 tables with unequal samples	T-59
A-30	Tables for distribution-free tolerance limits (two-sided)	T-75
A-31	Tables for distribution-free tolerance limits (one-sided)	T-76
A-32	Confidence associated with a tolerance limit statement	T-77
A-33	Critical values of r for the sign test	T-78
A-34	Critical values of $T_\alpha(n)$ for the Wilcoxon signed-ranks test	T-79
A-35	Critical values of smaller rank sum for the Wilcoxon-Mann-Whitney Test	T-80
A-36	Short table of random numbers	T-82
A-37	Short table of random normal deviates	T-86

SECTION 5

TABLES

This section contains all the mathematical tables referenced throughout Sections 1 through 4 of this handbook, and needed in the application of the given procedures. The tables have been informally arranged in groups as follows: Tables A-1 through A-5 are needed for the "standard" tests of significance; Tables A-6 through A-21 are further tables concerning the analysis of samples from normal distributions; Tables A-22 through A-27 are concerned with analysis of samples from binomial distributions; Tables A-30 through A-35 are for distribution-free techniques; and Tables A-36 and A-37 are sample pages of tables of random numbers and random normal deviates.

THE GREEK ALPHABET

A	α	alpha	N	ν	nu
B	β	beta	Ξ	ξ	xi
Γ	γ	gamma	O	o	omicron
Δ	δ	delta	Π	π	pi
E	ϵ	epsilon	P	ρ	rho
Z	ζ	zeta	Σ	σ	sigma
H	η	eta	T	τ	tau
Θ	θ	theta	Υ	υ	upsilon
I	ι	iota	Φ	ϕ	phi
K	κ	kappa	X	χ	chi
Λ	λ	lambda	Ψ	ψ	psi
M	μ	mu	Ω	ω	omega

TABLE A-1. CUMULATIVE NORMAL DISTRIBUTION — VALUES OF P

Values of P corresponding to z_P for the normal curve.

z is the standard normal variable.   The value of P for $-z_P$ equals one minus the value of P for $+z_P$,
e.g., the P for -1.62 equals $1 - .9474 = .0526$.

z_P	.00	.01	.02	.03	.04	.05	.06	.07	.08	.09
.0	.5000	.5040	.5080	.5120	.5160	.5199	.5239	.5279	.5319	.5359
.1	.5398	.5438	.5478	.5517	.5557	.5596	.5636	.5675	.5714	.5753
.2	.5793	.5832	.5871	.5910	.5948	.5987	.6026	.6064	.6103	.6141
.3	.6179	.6217	.6255	.6293	.6331	.6368	.6406	.6443	.6480	.6517
.4	.6554	.6591	.6628	.6664	.6700	.6736	.6772	.6808	.6844	.6879
.5	.6915	.6950	.6985	.7019	.7054	.7088	.7123	.7157	.7190	.7224
.6	.7257	.7291	.7324	.7357	.7389	.7422	.7454	.7486	.7517	.7549
.7	.7580	.7611	.7642	.7673	.7704	.7734	.7764	.7794	.7823	.7852
.8	.7881	.7910	.7939	.7967	.7995	.8023	.8051	.8078	.8106	.8133
.9	.8159	.8186	.8212	.8238	.8264	.8289	.8315	.8340	.8365	.8389
1.0	.8413	.8438	.8461	.8485	.8508	.8531	.8554	.8577	.8599	.8621
1.1	.8643	.8665	.8686	.8708	.8729	.8749	.8770	.8790	.8810	.8830
1.2	.8849	.8869	.8888	.8907	.8925	.8944	.8962	.8980	.8997	.9015
1.3	.9032	.9049	.9066	.9082	.9099	.9115	.9131	.9147	.9162	.9177
1.4	.9192	.9207	.9222	.9236	.9251	.9265	.9279	.9292	.9306	.9319
1.5	.9332	.9345	.9357	.9370	.9382	.9394	.9406	.9418	.9429	.9441
1.6	.9452	.9463	.9474	.9484	.9495	.9505	.9515	.9525	.9535	.9545
1.7	.9554	.9564	.9573	.9582	.9591	.9599	.9608	.9616	.9625	.9633
1.8	.9641	.9649	.9656	.9664	.9671	.9678	.9686	.9693	.9699	.9706
1.9	.9713	.9719	.9726	.9732	.9738	.9744	.9750	.9756	.9761	.9767
2.0	.9772	.9778	.9783	.9788	.9793	.9798	.9803	.9808	.9812	.9817
2.1	.9821	.9826	.9830	.9834	.9838	.9842	.9846	.9850	.9854	.9857
2.2	.9861	.9864	.9868	.9871	.9875	.9878	.9881	.9884	.9887	.9890
2.3	.9893	.9896	.9898	.9901	.9904	.9906	.9909	.9911	.9913	.9916
2.4	.9918	.9920	.9922	.9925	.9927	.9929	.9931	.9932	.9934	.9936
2.5	.9938	.9940	.9941	.9943	.9945	.9946	.9948	.9949	.9951	.9952
2.6	.9953	.9955	.9956	.9957	.9959	.9960	.9961	.9962	.9963	.9964
2.7	.9965	.9966	.9967	.9968	.9969	.9970	.9971	.9972	.9973	.9974
2.8	.9974	.9975	.9976	.9977	.9977	.9978	.9979	.9979	.9980	.9981
2.9	.9981	.9982	.9982	.9983	.9984	.9984	.9985	.9985	.9986	.9986
3.0	.9987	.9987	.9987	.9988	.9988	.9989	.9989	.9989	.9990	.9990
3.1	.9990	.9991	.9991	.9991	.9992	.9992	.9992	.9992	.9993	.9993
3.2	.9993	.9993	.9994	.9994	.9994	.9994	.9994	.9995	.9995	.9995
3.3	.9995	.9995	.9995	.9996	.9996	.9996	.9996	.9996	.9996	.9997
3.4	.9997	.9997	.9997	.9997	.9997	.9997	.9997	.9997	.9997	.9998

TABLE A-2. CUMULATIVE NORMAL DISTRIBUTION — VALUES OF z_P

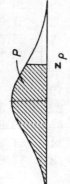

Values of z_P corresponding to P for the normal curve.
z is the standard normal variable

P	.00	.01	.02	.03	.04	.05	.06	.07	.08	.09
.00	—	−2.33	−2.05	−1.88	−1.75	−1.64	−1.55	−1.48	−1.41	−1.34
.10	−1.28	−1.23	−1.18	−1.13	−1.08	−1.04	−0.99	−0.95	−0.92	−0.88
.20	−0.84	−0.81	−0.77	−0.74	−0.71	−0.67	−0.64	−0.61	−0.58	−0.55
.30	−0.52	−0.50	−0.47	−0.44	−0.41	−0.39	−0.36	−0.33	−0.31	−0.28
.40	−0.25	−0.23	−0.20	−0.18	−0.15	−0.13	−0.10	−0.08	−0.05	−0.03
.50	0.00	0.03	0.05	0.08	0.10	0.13	0.15	0.18	0.20	0.23
.60	0.25	0.28	0.31	0.33	0.36	0.39	0.41	0.44	0.47	0.50
.70	0.52	0.55	0.58	0.61	0.64	0.67	0.71	0.74	0.77	0.81
.80	0.84	0.88	0.92	0.95	0.99	1.04	1.08	1.13	1.18	1.23
.90	1.28	1.34	1.41	1.48	1.55	1.64	1.75	1.88	2.05	2.33

Special Values

P	.001	.005	.010	.025	.050	.100
z_P	−3.090	−2.576	−2.326	−1.960	−1.645	−1.282

P	.999	.995	.990	.975	.950	.900
z_P	3.090	2.576	2.326	1.960	1.645	1.282

TABLE A-3. PERCENTILES OF THE χ^2 DISTRIBUTION

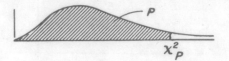

Values of χ_P^2 corresponding to P

df	$\chi^2_{.005}$	$\chi^2_{.01}$	$\chi^2_{.025}$	$\chi^2_{.05}$	$\chi^2_{.10}$	$\chi^2_{.90}$	$\chi^2_{.95}$	$\chi^2_{.975}$	$\chi^2_{.99}$	$\chi^2_{.995}$
1	.000039	.00016	.00098	.0039	.0158	2.71	3.84	5.02	6.63	7.88
2	.0100	.0201	.0506	.1026	.2107	4.61	5.99	7.38	9.21	10.60
3	.0717	.115	.216	.352	.584	6.25	7.81	9.35	11.34	12.84
4	.207	.297	.484	.711	1.064	7.78	9.49	11.14	13.28	14.86
5	.412	.554	.831	1.15	1.61	9.24	11.07	12.83	15.09	16.75
6	.676	.872	1.24	1.64	2.20	10.64	12.59	14.45	16.81	18.55
7	.989	1.24	1.69	2.17	2.83	12.02	14.07	16.01	18.48	20.28
8	1.34	1.65	2.18	2.73	3.49	13.36	15.51	17.53	20.09	21.96
9	1.73	2.09	2.70	3.33	4.17	14.68	16.92	19.02	21.67	23.59
10	2.16	2.56	3.25	3.94	4.87	15.99	18.31	20.48	23.21	25.19
11	2.60	3.05	3.82	4.57	5.58	17.28	19.68	21.92	24.73	26.76
12	3.07	3.57	4.40	5.23	6.30	18.55	21.03	23.34	26.22	28.30
13	3.57	4.11	5.01	5.89	7.04	19.81	22.36	24.74	27.69	29.82
14	4.07	4.66	5.63	6.57	7.79	21.06	23.68	26.12	29.14	31.32
15	4.60	5.23	6.26	7.26	8.55	22.31	25.00	27.49	30.58	32.80
16	5.14	5.81	6.91	7.96	9.31	23.54	26.30	28.85	32.00	34.27
18	6.26	7.01	8.23	9.39	10.86	25.99	28.87	31.53	34.81	37.16
20	7.43	8.26	9.59	10.85	12.44	28.41	31.41	34.17	37.57	40.00
24	9.89	10.86	12.40	13.85	15.66	33.20	36.42	39.36	42.98	45.56
30	13.79	14.95	16.79	18.49	20.60	40.26	43.77	46.98	50.89	53.67
40	20.71	22.16	24.43	26.51	29.05	51.81	55.76	59.34	63.69	66.77
60	35.53	37.48	40.48	43.19	46.46	74.40	79.08	83.30	88.38	91.95
120	83.85	86.92	91.58	95.70	100.62	140.23	146.57	152.21	158.95	163.64

For large degrees of freedom,

$$\chi_P^2 = \tfrac{1}{2}(z_P + \sqrt{2\nu - 1})^2 \text{ approximately,}$$

where ν = degrees of freedom and z_P is given in Table A-2.

Adapted with permission from *Introduction to Statistical Analysis* (2d ed.) by W. J. Dixon and F. J. Massey, Jr., Copyright, 1957, McGraw-Hill Book Company, Inc.

TABLE A-4. PERCENTILES OF THE *t* DISTRIBUTION

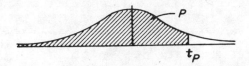

df	$t_{.60}$	$t_{.70}$	$t_{.80}$	$t_{.90}$	$t_{.95}$	$t_{.975}$	$t_{.99}$	$t_{.995}$
1	.325	.727	1.376	3.078	6.314	12.706	31.821	63.657
2	.289	.617	1.061	1.886	2.920	4.303	6.965	9.925
3	.277	.584	.978	1.638	2.353	3.182	4.541	5.841
4	.271	.569	.941	1.533	2.132	2.776	3.747	4.604
5	.267	.559	.920	1.476	2.015	2.571	3.365	4.032
6	.265	.553	.906	1.440	1.943	2.447	3.143	3.707
7	.263	.549	.896	1.415	1.895	2.365	2.998	3.499
8	.262	.546	.889	1.397	1.860	2.306	2.896	3.355
9	.261	.543	.883	1.383	1.833	2.262	2.821	3.250
10	.260	.542	.879	1.372	1.812	2.228	2.764	3.169
11	.260	.540	.876	1.363	1.796	2.201	2.718	3.106
12	.259	.539	.873	1.356	1.782	2.179	2.681	3.055
13	.259	.538	.870	1.350	1.771	2.160	2.650	3.012
14	.258	.537	.868	1.345	1.761	2.145	2.624	2.977
15	.258	.536	.866	1.341	1.753	2.131	2.602	2.947
16	.258	.535	.865	1.337	1.746	2.120	2.583	2.921
17	.257	.534	.863	1.333	1.740	2.110	2.567	2.898
18	.257	.534	.862	1.330	1.734	2.101	2.552	2.878
19	.257	.533	.861	1.328	1.729	2.093	2.539	2.861
20	.257	.533	.860	1.325	1.725	2.086	2.528	2.845
21	.257	.532	.859	1.323	1.721	2.080	2.518	2.831
22	.256	.532	.858	1.321	1.717	2.074	2.508	2.819
23	.256	.532	.858	1.319	1.714	2.069	2.500	2.807
24	.256	.531	.857	1.318	1.711	2.064	2.492	2.797
25	.256	.531	.856	1.316	1.708	2.060	2.485	2.787
26	.256	.531	.856	1.315	1.706	2.056	2.479	2.779
27	.256	.531	.855	1.314	1.703	2.052	2.473	2.771
28	.256	.530	.855	1.313	1.701	2.048	2.467	2.763
29	.256	.530	.854	1.311	1.699	2.045	2.462	2.756
30	.256	.530	.854	1.310	1.697	2.042	2.457	2.750
40	.255	.529	.851	1.303	1.684	2.021	2.423	2.704
60	.254	.527	.848	1.296	1.671	2.000	2.390	2.660
120	.254	.526	.845	1.289	1.658	1.980	2.358	2.617
∞	.253	.524	.842	1.282	1.645	1.960	2.326	2.576

Adapted by permission from *Introduction to Statistical Analysis* (2d ed.) by W. J. Dixon and F. J. Massey, Jr., Copyright, 1957, McGraw-Hill Book Company, Inc. Entries originally from Table III of *Statistical Tables* by R. A. Fisher and F. Yates, 1938, Oliver and Boyd, Ltd., London.

TABLE A-5. PERCENTILES OF THE F DISTRIBUTION

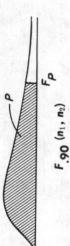

$F_{.90}(n_1, n_2)$

n_1 = degrees of freedom for numerator

n_2 \ n_1	1	2	3	4	5	6	7	8	9	10	12	15	20	24	30	40	60	120	∞
1	39.86	49.50	53.59	55.83	57.24	58.20	58.91	59.44	59.86	60.19	60.71	61.22	61.74	62.00	62.26	62.53	62.79	63.06	63.33
2	8.53	9.00	9.16	9.24	9.29	9.33	9.35	9.37	9.38	9.39	9.41	9.42	9.44	9.45	9.46	9.47	9.47	9.48	9.49
3	5.54	5.46	5.39	5.34	5.31	5.28	5.27	5.25	5.24	5.23	5.22	5.20	5.18	5.18	5.17	5.16	5.15	5.14	5.13
4	4.54	4.32	4.19	4.11	4.05	4.01	3.98	3.95	3.94	3.92	3.90	3.87	3.84	3.83	3.82	3.80	3.79	3.78	3.76
5	4.06	3.78	3.62	3.52	3.45	3.40	3.37	3.34	3.32	3.30	3.27	3.24	3.21	3.19	3.17	3.16	3.14	3.12	3.10
6	3.78	3.46	3.29	3.18	3.11	3.05	3.01	2.98	2.96	2.94	2.90	2.87	2.84	2.82	2.80	2.78	2.76	2.74	2.72
7	3.59	3.26	3.07	2.96	2.88	2.83	2.78	2.75	2.72	2.70	2.67	2.63	2.59	2.58	2.56	2.54	2.51	2.49	2.47
8	3.46	3.11	2.92	2.81	2.73	2.67	2.62	2.59	2.56	2.54	2.50	2.46	2.42	2.40	2.38	2.36	2.34	2.32	2.29
9	3.36	3.01	2.81	2.69	2.61	2.55	2.51	2.47	2.44	2.42	2.38	2.34	2.30	2.28	2.25	2.23	2.21	2.18	2.16
10	3.29	2.92	2.73	2.61	2.52	2.46	2.41	2.38	2.35	2.32	2.28	2.24	2.20	2.18	2.16	2.13	2.11	2.08	2.06
11	3.23	2.86	2.66	2.54	2.45	2.39	2.34	2.30	2.27	2.25	2.21	2.17	2.12	2.10	2.08	2.05	2.03	2.00	1.97
12	3.18	2.81	2.61	2.48	2.39	2.33	2.28	2.24	2.21	2.19	2.15	2.10	2.06	2.04	2.01	1.99	1.96	1.93	1.90
13	3.14	2.76	2.56	2.43	2.35	2.28	2.23	2.20	2.16	2.14	2.10	2.05	2.01	1.98	1.96	1.93	1.90	1.88	1.85
14	3.10	2.73	2.52	2.39	2.31	2.24	2.19	2.15	2.12	2.10	2.05	2.01	1.96	1.94	1.91	1.89	1.86	1.83	1.80
15	3.07	2.70	2.49	2.36	2.27	2.21	2.16	2.12	2.09	2.06	2.02	1.97	1.92	1.90	1.87	1.85	1.82	1.79	1.76
16	3.05	2.67	2.46	2.33	2.24	2.18	2.13	2.09	2.06	2.03	1.99	1.94	1.89	1.87	1.84	1.81	1.78	1.75	1.72
17	3.03	2.64	2.44	2.31	2.22	2.15	2.10	2.06	2.03	2.00	1.96	1.91	1.86	1.84	1.81	1.78	1.75	1.72	1.69
18	3.01	2.62	2.42	2.29	2.20	2.13	2.08	2.04	2.00	1.98	1.93	1.89	1.84	1.81	1.78	1.75	1.72	1.69	1.66
19	2.99	2.61	2.40	2.27	2.18	2.11	2.06	2.02	1.98	1.96	1.91	1.86	1.81	1.79	1.76	1.73	1.70	1.67	1.63
20	2.97	2.59	2.38	2.25	2.16	2.09	2.04	2.00	1.96	1.94	1.89	1.84	1.79	1.77	1.74	1.71	1.68	1.64	1.61
21	2.96	2.57	2.36	2.23	2.14	2.08	2.02	1.98	1.95	1.92	1.87	1.83	1.78	1.75	1.72	1.69	1.66	1.62	1.59
22	2.95	2.56	2.35	2.22	2.13	2.06	2.01	1.97	1.93	1.90	1.86	1.81	1.76	1.73	1.70	1.67	1.64	1.60	1.57
23	2.94	2.55	2.34	2.21	2.11	2.05	1.99	1.95	1.92	1.89	1.84	1.80	1.74	1.72	1.69	1.66	1.62	1.59	1.55
24	2.93	2.54	2.33	2.19	2.10	2.04	1.98	1.94	1.91	1.88	1.83	1.78	1.73	1.70	1.67	1.64	1.61	1.57	1.53
25	2.92	2.53	2.32	2.18	2.09	2.02	1.97	1.93	1.89	1.87	1.82	1.77	1.72	1.69	1.66	1.63	1.59	1.56	1.52
26	2.91	2.52	2.31	2.17	2.08	2.01	1.96	1.92	1.88	1.86	1.81	1.76	1.71	1.68	1.65	1.61	1.58	1.54	1.50
27	2.90	2.51	2.30	2.17	2.07	2.00	1.95	1.91	1.87	1.85	1.80	1.75	1.70	1.67	1.64	1.60	1.57	1.53	1.49
28	2.89	2.50	2.29	2.16	2.06	2.00	1.94	1.90	1.87	1.84	1.79	1.74	1.69	1.66	1.63	1.59	1.56	1.52	1.48
29	2.89	2.50	2.28	2.15	2.06	1.99	1.93	1.89	1.86	1.83	1.78	1.73	1.68	1.65	1.62	1.58	1.55	1.51	1.47
30	2.88	2.49	2.28	2.14	2.05	1.98	1.93	1.88	1.85	1.82	1.77	1.72	1.67	1.64	1.61	1.57	1.54	1.50	1.46
40	2.84	2.44	2.23	2.09	2.00	1.93	1.87	1.83	1.79	1.76	1.71	1.66	1.61	1.57	1.54	1.51	1.47	1.42	1.38
60	2.79	2.39	2.18	2.04	1.95	1.87	1.82	1.77	1.74	1.71	1.66	1.60	1.54	1.51	1.48	1.44	1.40	1.35	1.29
120	2.75	2.35	2.13	1.99	1.90	1.82	1.77	1.72	1.68	1.65	1.60	1.55	1.48	1.45	1.41	1.37	1.32	1.26	1.19
∞	2.71	2.30	2.08	1.94	1.85	1.77	1.72	1.67	1.63	1.60	1.55	1.49	1.42	1.38	1.34	1.30	1.24	1.17	1.00

n_2 = degrees of freedom for denominator

TABLE A-5 (Continued). PERCENTILES OF THE F DISTRIBUTION

$F_{.95}(n_1, n_2)$

n_1 = degrees of freedom for numerator

n_2 \ n_1	1	2	3	4	5	6	7	8	9	10	12	15	20	24	30	40	60	120	∞
1	161.4	199.5	215.7	224.6	230.2	234.0	236.8	238.9	240.5	241.9	243.9	245.9	248.0	249.1	250.1	251.1	252.2	253.3	254.3
2	18.51	19.00	19.16	19.25	19.30	19.33	19.35	19.37	19.38	19.40	19.41	19.43	19.45	19.45	19.46	19.47	19.48	19.49	19.50
3	10.13	9.55	9.28	9.12	9.01	8.94	8.89	8.85	8.81	8.79	8.74	8.70	8.66	8.64	8.62	8.59	8.57	8.55	8.53
4	7.71	6.94	6.59	6.39	6.26	6.16	6.09	6.04	6.00	5.96	5.91	5.86	5.80	5.77	5.75	5.72	5.69	5.66	5.63
5	6.61	5.79	5.41	5.19	5.05	4.95	4.88	4.82	4.77	4.74	4.68	4.62	4.56	4.53	4.50	4.46	4.43	4.40	4.36
6	5.99	5.14	4.76	4.53	4.39	4.28	4.21	4.15	4.10	4.06	4.00	3.94	3.87	3.84	3.81	3.77	3.74	3.70	3.67
7	5.59	4.74	4.35	4.12	3.97	3.87	3.79	3.73	3.68	3.64	3.57	3.51	3.44	3.41	3.38	3.34	3.30	3.27	3.23
8	5.32	4.46	4.07	3.84	3.69	3.58	3.50	3.44	3.39	3.35	3.28	3.22	3.15	3.12	3.08	3.04	3.01	2.97	2.93
9	5.12	4.26	3.86	3.63	3.48	3.37	3.29	3.23	3.18	3.14	3.07	3.01	2.94	2.90	2.86	2.83	2.79	2.75	2.71
10	4.96	4.10	3.71	3.48	3.33	3.22	3.14	3.07	3.02	2.98	2.91	2.85	2.77	2.74	2.70	2.66	2.62	2.58	2.54
11	4.84	3.98	3.59	3.36	3.20	3.09	3.01	2.95	2.90	2.85	2.79	2.72	2.65	2.61	2.57	2.53	2.49	2.45	2.40
12	4.75	3.89	3.49	3.26	3.11	3.00	2.91	2.85	2.80	2.75	2.69	2.62	2.54	2.51	2.47	2.43	2.38	2.34	2.30
13	4.67	3.81	3.41	3.18	3.03	2.92	2.83	2.77	2.71	2.67	2.60	2.53	2.46	2.42	2.38	2.34	2.30	2.25	2.21
14	4.60	3.74	3.34	3.11	2.96	2.85	2.76	2.70	2.65	2.60	2.53	2.46	2.39	2.35	2.31	2.27	2.22	2.18	2.13
15	4.54	3.68	3.29	3.06	2.90	2.79	2.71	2.64	2.59	2.54	2.48	2.40	2.33	2.29	2.25	2.20	2.16	2.11	2.07
16	4.49	3.63	3.24	3.01	2.85	2.74	2.66	2.59	2.54	2.49	2.42	2.35	2.28	2.24	2.19	2.15	2.11	2.06	2.01
17	4.45	3.59	3.20	2.96	2.81	2.70	2.61	2.55	2.49	2.45	2.38	2.31	2.23	2.19	2.15	2.10	2.06	2.01	1.96
18	4.41	3.55	3.16	2.93	2.77	2.66	2.58	2.51	2.46	2.41	2.34	2.27	2.19	2.15	2.11	2.06	2.02	1.97	1.92
19	4.38	3.52	3.13	2.90	2.74	2.63	2.54	2.48	2.42	2.38	2.31	2.23	2.16	2.11	2.07	2.03	1.98	1.93	1.88
20	4.35	3.49	3.10	2.87	2.71	2.60	2.51	2.45	2.39	2.35	2.28	2.20	2.12	2.08	2.04	1.99	1.95	1.90	1.84
21	4.32	3.47	3.07	2.84	2.68	2.57	2.49	2.42	2.37	2.32	2.25	2.18	2.10	2.05	2.01	1.96	1.92	1.87	1.81
22	4.30	3.44	3.05	2.82	2.66	2.55	2.46	2.40	2.34	2.30	2.23	2.15	2.07	2.03	1.98	1.94	1.89	1.84	1.78
23	4.28	3.42	3.03	2.80	2.64	2.53	2.44	2.37	2.32	2.27	2.20	2.13	2.05	2.01	1.96	1.91	1.86	1.81	1.76
24	4.26	3.40	3.01	2.78	2.62	2.51	2.42	2.36	2.30	2.25	2.18	2.11	2.03	1.98	1.94	1.89	1.84	1.79	1.73
25	4.24	3.39	2.99	2.76	2.60	2.49	2.40	2.34	2.28	2.24	2.16	2.09	2.01	1.96	1.92	1.87	1.82	1.77	1.71
26	4.23	3.37	2.98	2.74	2.59	2.47	2.39	2.32	2.27	2.22	2.15	2.07	1.99	1.95	1.90	1.85	1.80	1.75	1.69
27	4.21	3.35	2.96	2.73	2.57	2.46	2.37	2.31	2.25	2.20	2.13	2.06	1.97	1.93	1.88	1.84	1.79	1.73	1.67
28	4.20	3.34	2.95	2.71	2.56	2.45	2.36	2.29	2.24	2.19	2.12	2.04	1.96	1.91	1.87	1.82	1.77	1.71	1.65
29	4.18	3.33	2.93	2.70	2.55	2.43	2.35	2.28	2.22	2.18	2.10	2.03	1.94	1.90	1.85	1.81	1.75	1.70	1.64
30	4.17	3.32	2.92	2.69	2.53	2.42	2.33	2.27	2.21	2.16	2.09	2.01	1.93	1.89	1.84	1.79	1.74	1.68	1.62
40	4.08	3.23	2.84	2.61	2.45	2.34	2.25	2.18	2.12	2.08	2.00	1.92	1.84	1.79	1.74	1.69	1.64	1.58	1.51
60	4.00	3.15	2.76	2.53	2.37	2.25	2.17	2.10	2.04	1.99	1.92	1.84	1.75	1.70	1.65	1.59	1.53	1.47	1.39
120	3.92	3.07	2.68	2.45	2.29	2.17	2.09	2.02	1.96	1.91	1.83	1.75	1.66	1.61	1.55	1.50	1.43	1.35	1.25
∞	3.84	3.00	2.60	2.37	2.21	2.10	2.01	1.94	1.88	1.83	1.75	1.67	1.57	1.52	1.46	1.39	1.32	1.22	1.00

n_2 = degrees of freedom for denominator

Adapted with permission from *Biometrika Tables for Statisticians*, Vol. I (2d ed.), edited by E. S. Pearson and H. O. Hartley, Copyright 1958, Cambridge University Press.

TABLE A-5 (Continued). PERCENTILES OF THE F DISTRIBUTION

$F_{.975}(n_1, n_2)$

n_1 = degrees of freedom for numerator

n_2＼n_1	1	2	3	4	5	6	7	8	9	10	12	15	20	24	30	40	60	120	∞
1	647.8	799.5	864.2	899.6	921.8	937.1	948.2	956.7	963.3	968.6	976.7	984.9	993.1	997.2	1001	1006	1010	1014	1018
2	38.51	39.00	39.17	39.25	39.30	39.33	39.36	39.37	39.39	39.40	39.41	39.43	39.45	39.46	39.46	39.47	39.48	39.49	39.50
3	17.44	16.04	15.44	15.10	14.88	14.73	14.62	14.54	14.47	14.42	14.34	14.25	14.17	14.12	14.08	14.04	13.99	13.95	13.90
4	12.22	10.65	9.98	9.60	9.36	9.20	9.07	8.98	8.90	8.84	8.75	8.66	8.56	8.51	8.46	8.41	8.36	8.31	8.26
5	10.01	8.43	7.76	7.39	7.15	6.98	6.85	6.76	6.68	6.62	6.52	6.43	6.33	6.28	6.23	6.18	6.12	6.07	6.02
6	8.81	7.26	6.60	6.23	5.99	5.82	5.70	5.60	5.52	5.46	5.37	5.27	5.17	5.12	5.07	5.01	4.96	4.90	4.85
7	8.07	6.54	5.89	5.52	5.29	5.12	4.99	4.90	4.82	4.76	4.67	4.57	4.47	4.42	4.36	4.31	4.25	4.20	4.14
8	7.57	6.06	5.42	5.05	4.82	4.65	4.53	4.43	4.36	4.30	4.20	4.10	4.00	3.95	3.89	3.84	3.78	3.73	3.67
9	7.21	5.71	5.08	4.72	4.48	4.32	4.20	4.10	4.03	3.96	3.87	3.77	3.67	3.61	3.56	3.51	3.45	3.39	3.33
10	6.94	5.46	4.83	4.47	4.24	4.07	3.95	3.85	3.78	3.72	3.62	3.52	3.42	3.37	3.31	3.26	3.20	3.14	3.08
11	6.72	5.26	4.63	4.28	4.04	3.88	3.76	3.66	3.59	3.53	3.43	3.33	3.23	3.17	3.12	3.06	3.00	2.94	2.88
12	6.55	5.10	4.47	4.12	3.89	3.73	3.61	3.51	3.44	3.37	3.28	3.18	3.07	3.02	2.96	2.91	2.85	2.79	2.72
13	6.41	4.97	4.35	4.00	3.77	3.60	3.48	3.39	3.31	3.25	3.15	3.05	2.95	2.89	2.84	2.78	2.72	2.66	2.60
14	6.30	4.86	4.24	3.89	3.66	3.50	3.38	3.29	3.21	3.15	3.05	2.95	2.84	2.79	2.73	2.67	2.61	2.55	2.49
15	6.20	4.77	4.15	3.80	3.58	3.41	3.29	3.20	3.12	3.06	2.96	2.86	2.76	2.70	2.64	2.59	2.52	2.46	2.40
16	6.12	4.69	4.08	3.73	3.50	3.34	3.22	3.12	3.05	2.99	2.89	2.79	2.68	2.63	2.57	2.51	2.45	2.38	2.32
17	6.04	4.62	4.01	3.66	3.44	3.28	3.16	3.06	2.98	2.92	2.82	2.72	2.62	2.56	2.50	2.44	2.38	2.32	2.25
18	5.98	4.56	3.95	3.61	3.38	3.22	3.10	3.01	2.93	2.87	2.77	2.67	2.56	2.50	2.44	2.38	2.32	2.26	2.19
19	5.92	4.51	3.90	3.56	3.33	3.17	3.05	2.96	2.88	2.82	2.72	2.62	2.51	2.45	2.39	2.33	2.27	2.20	2.13
20	5.87	4.46	3.86	3.51	3.29	3.13	3.01	2.91	2.84	2.77	2.68	2.57	2.46	2.41	2.35	2.29	2.22	2.16	2.09
21	5.83	4.42	3.82	3.48	3.25	3.09	2.97	2.87	2.80	2.73	2.64	2.53	2.42	2.37	2.31	2.25	2.18	2.11	2.04
22	5.79	4.38	3.78	3.44	3.22	3.05	2.93	2.84	2.76	2.70	2.60	2.50	2.39	2.33	2.27	2.21	2.14	2.08	2.00
23	5.75	4.35	3.75	3.41	3.18	3.02	2.90	2.81	2.73	2.67	2.57	2.47	2.36	2.30	2.24	2.18	2.11	2.04	1.97
24	5.72	4.32	3.72	3.38	3.15	2.99	2.87	2.78	2.70	2.64	2.54	2.44	2.33	2.27	2.21	2.15	2.08	2.01	1.94
25	5.69	4.29	3.69	3.35	3.13	2.97	2.85	2.75	2.68	2.61	2.51	2.41	2.30	2.24	2.18	2.12	2.05	1.98	1.91
26	5.66	4.27	3.67	3.33	3.10	2.94	2.82	2.73	2.65	2.59	2.49	2.39	2.28	2.22	2.16	2.09	2.03	1.95	1.88
27	5.63	4.24	3.65	3.31	3.08	2.92	2.80	2.71	2.63	2.57	2.47	2.36	2.25	2.19	2.13	2.07	2.00	1.93	1.85
28	5.61	4.22	3.63	3.29	3.06	2.90	2.78	2.69	2.61	2.55	2.45	2.34	2.23	2.17	2.11	2.05	1.98	1.91	1.83
29	5.59	4.20	3.61	3.27	3.04	2.88	2.76	2.67	2.59	2.53	2.43	2.32	2.21	2.15	2.09	2.03	1.96	1.89	1.81
30	5.57	4.18	3.59	3.25	3.03	2.87	2.75	2.65	2.57	2.51	2.41	2.31	2.20	2.14	2.07	2.01	1.94	1.87	1.79
40	5.42	4.05	3.46	3.13	2.90	2.74	2.62	2.53	2.45	2.39	2.29	2.18	2.07	2.01	1.94	1.88	1.80	1.72	1.64
60	5.29	3.93	3.34	3.01	2.79	2.63	2.51	2.41	2.33	2.27	2.17	2.06	1.94	1.88	1.82	1.74	1.67	1.58	1.48
120	5.15	3.80	3.23	2.89	2.67	2.52	2.39	2.30	2.22	2.16	2.05	1.94	1.82	1.76	1.69	1.61	1.53	1.43	1.31
∞	5.02	3.69	3.12	2.79	2.57	2.41	2.29	2.19	2.11	2.05	1.94	1.83	1.71	1.64	1.57	1.48	1.39	1.27	1.00

n_2 = degrees of freedom for denominator

TABLE A-5 (Continued). PERCENTILES OF THE F DISTRIBUTION

$F_{.99}$ (n_1, n_2)

n_1 = degrees of freedom for numerator

n_2 = degrees of freedom for denominator

n_2 \ n_1	1	2	3	4	5	6	7	8	9	10	12	15	20	24	30	40	60	120	∞
1	4052	4999.5	5403	5625	5764	5859	5928	5982	6022	6056	6106	6157	6209	6235	6261	6287	6313	6339	6366
2	98.50	99.00	99.17	99.25	99.30	99.33	99.36	99.37	99.39	99.40	99.42	99.43	99.45	99.46	99.47	99.47	99.48	99.49	99.50
3	34.12	30.82	29.46	28.71	28.24	27.91	27.67	27.49	27.35	27.23	27.05	26.87	26.69	26.60	26.50	26.41	26.32	26.22	26.13
4	21.20	18.00	16.69	15.98	15.52	15.21	14.98	14.80	14.66	14.55	14.37	14.20	14.02	13.93	13.84	13.75	13.65	13.56	13.46
5	16.26	13.27	12.06	11.39	10.97	10.67	10.46	10.29	10.16	10.05	9.89	9.72	9.55	9.47	9.38	9.29	9.20	9.11	9.02
6	13.75	10.92	9.78	9.15	8.75	8.47	8.26	8.10	7.98	7.87	7.72	7.56	7.40	7.31	7.23	7.14	7.06	6.97	6.88
7	12.25	9.55	8.45	7.85	7.46	7.19	6.99	6.84	6.72	6.62	6.47	6.31	6.16	6.07	5.99	5.91	5.82	5.74	5.65
8	11.26	8.65	7.59	7.01	6.63	6.37	6.18	6.03	5.91	5.81	5.67	5.52	5.36	5.28	5.20	5.12	5.03	4.95	4.86
9	10.56	8.02	6.99	6.42	6.06	5.80	5.61	5.47	5.35	5.26	5.11	4.96	4.81	4.73	4.65	4.57	4.48	4.40	4.31
10	10.04	7.56	6.55	5.99	5.64	5.39	5.20	5.06	4.94	4.85	4.71	4.56	4.41	4.33	4.25	4.17	4.08	4.00	3.91
11	9.65	7.21	6.22	5.67	5.32	5.07	4.89	4.74	4.63	4.54	4.40	4.25	4.10	4.02	3.94	3.86	3.78	3.69	3.60
12	9.33	6.93	5.95	5.41	5.06	4.82	4.64	4.50	4.39	4.30	4.16	4.01	3.86	3.78	3.70	3.62	3.54	3.45	3.36
13	9.07	6.70	5.74	5.21	4.86	4.62	4.44	4.30	4.19	4.10	3.96	3.82	3.66	3.59	3.51	3.43	3.34	3.25	3.17
14	8.86	6.51	5.56	5.04	4.69	4.46	4.28	4.14	4.03	3.94	3.80	3.66	3.51	3.43	3.35	3.27	3.18	3.09	3.00
15	8.68	6.36	5.42	4.89	4.56	4.32	4.14	4.00	3.89	3.80	3.67	3.52	3.37	3.29	3.21	3.13	3.05	2.96	2.87
16	8.53	6.23	5.29	4.77	4.44	4.20	4.03	3.89	3.78	3.69	3.55	3.41	3.26	3.18	3.10	3.02	2.93	2.84	2.75
17	8.40	6.11	5.18	4.67	4.34	4.10	3.93	3.79	3.68	3.59	3.46	3.31	3.16	3.08	3.00	2.92	2.83	2.75	2.65
18	8.29	6.01	5.09	4.58	4.25	4.01	3.84	3.71	3.60	3.51	3.37	3.23	3.08	3.00	2.92	2.84	2.75	2.66	2.57
19	8.18	5.93	5.01	4.50	4.17	3.94	3.77	3.63	3.52	3.43	3.30	3.15	3.00	2.92	2.84	2.76	2.67	2.58	2.49
20	8.10	5.85	4.94	4.43	4.10	3.87	3.70	3.56	3.46	3.37	3.23	3.09	2.94	2.86	2.78	2.69	2.61	2.52	2.42
21	8.02	5.78	4.87	4.37	4.04	3.81	3.64	3.51	3.40	3.31	3.17	3.03	2.88	2.80	2.72	2.64	2.55	2.46	2.36
22	7.95	5.72	4.82	4.31	3.99	3.76	3.59	3.45	3.35	3.26	3.12	2.98	2.83	2.75	2.67	2.58	2.50	2.40	2.31
23	7.88	5.66	4.76	4.26	3.94	3.71	3.54	3.41	3.30	3.21	3.07	2.93	2.78	2.70	2.62	2.54	2.45	2.35	2.26
24	7.82	5.61	4.72	4.22	3.90	3.67	3.50	3.36	3.26	3.17	3.03	2.89	2.74	2.66	2.58	2.49	2.40	2.31	2.21
25	7.77	5.57	4.68	4.18	3.85	3.63	3.46	3.32	3.22	3.13	2.99	2.85	2.70	2.62	2.54	2.45	2.36	2.27	2.17
26	7.72	5.53	4.64	4.14	3.82	3.59	3.42	3.29	3.18	3.09	2.96	2.81	2.66	2.58	2.50	2.42	2.33	2.23	2.13
27	7.68	5.49	4.60	4.11	3.78	3.56	3.39	3.26	3.15	3.06	2.93	2.78	2.63	2.55	2.47	2.38	2.29	2.20	2.10
28	7.64	5.45	4.57	4.07	3.75	3.53	3.36	3.23	3.12	3.03	2.90	2.75	2.60	2.52	2.44	2.35	2.26	2.17	2.06
29	7.60	5.42	4.54	4.04	3.73	3.50	3.33	3.20	3.09	3.00	2.87	2.73	2.57	2.49	2.41	2.33	2.23	2.14	2.03
30	7.56	5.39	4.51	4.02	3.70	3.47	3.30	3.17	3.07	2.98	2.84	2.70	2.55	2.47	2.39	2.30	2.21	2.11	2.01
40	7.31	5.18	4.31	3.83	3.51	3.29	3.12	2.99	2.89	2.80	2.66	2.52	2.37	2.29	2.20	2.11	2.02	1.92	1.80
60	7.08	4.98	4.13	3.65	3.34	3.12	2.95	2.82	2.72	2.63	2.50	2.35	2.20	2.12	2.03	1.94	1.84	1.73	1.60
120	6.85	4.79	3.95	3.48	3.17	2.96	2.79	2.66	2.56	2.47	2.34	2.19	2.03	1.95	1.86	1.76	1.66	1.53	1.38
∞	6.63	4.61	3.78	3.32	3.02	2.80	2.64	2.51	2.41	2.32	2.18	2.04	1.88	1.79	1.70	1.59	1.47	1.32	1.00

TABLE A-6. FACTORS FOR TWO-SIDED TOLERANCE LIMITS FOR NORMAL DISTRIBUTIONS

Factors K such that the probability is γ that at least a proportion P of the distribution will be included between $\overline{X} \pm Ks$, where $\overline{X}$ and s are estimates of the mean and the standard deviation computed from a sample size of n.

P〳n	$\gamma = 0.75$					$\gamma = 0.90$				
	0.75	0.90	0.95	0.99	0.999	0.75	0.90	0.95	0.99	0.999
2	4.498	6.301	7.414	9.531	11.920	11.407	15.978	18.800	24.167	30.227
3	2.501	3.538	4.187	5.431	6.844	4.132	5.847	6.919	8.974	11.309
4	2.035	2.892	3.431	4.471	5.657	2.932	4.166	4.943	6.440	8.149
5	1.825	2.599	3.088	4.033	5.117	2.454	3.494	4.152	5.423	6.879
6	1.704	2.429	2.889	3.779	4.802	2.196	3.131	3.723	4.870	6.188
7	1.624	2.318	2.757	3.611	4.593	2.034	2.902	3.452	4.521	5.750
8	1.568	2.238	2.663	3.491	4.444	1.921	2.743	3.264	4.278	5.446
9	1.525	2.178	2.593	3.400	4.330	1.839	2.626	3.125	4.098	5.220
10	1.492	2.131	2.537	3.328	4.241	1.775	2.535	3.018	3.959	5.046
11	1.465	2.093	2.493	3.271	4.169	1.724	2.463	2.933	3.849	4.906
12	1.443	2.062	2.456	3.223	4.110	1.683	2.404	2.863	3.758	4.792
13	1.425	2.036	2.424	3.183	4.059	1.648	2.355	2.805	3.682	4.697
14	1.409	2.013	2.398	3.148	4.016	1.619	2.314	2.756	3.618	4.615
15	1.395	1.994	2.375	3.118	3.979	1.594	2.278	2.713	3.562	4.545
16	1.383	1.977	2.355	3.092	3.946	1.572	2.246	2.676	3.514	4.484
17	1.372	1.962	2.337	3.069	3.917	1.552	2.219	2.643	3.471	4.430
18	1.363	1.948	2.321	3.048	3.891	1.535	2.194	2.614	3.433	4.382
19	1.355	1.936	2.307	3.030	3.867	1.520	2.172	2.588	3.399	4.339
20	1.347	1.925	2.294	3.013	3.846	1.506	2.152	2.564	3.368	4.300
21	1.340	1.915	2.282	2.998	3.827	1.493	2.135	2.543	3.340	4.264
22	1.334	1.906	2.271	2.984	3.809	1.482	2.118	2.524	3.315	4.232
23	1.328	1.898	2.261	2.971	3.793	1.471	2.103	2.506	3.292	4.203
24	1.322	1.891	2.252	2.959	3.778	1.462	2.089	2.489	3.270	4.176
25	1.317	1.883	2.244	2.948	3.764	1.453	2.077	2.474	3.251	4.151
26	1.313	1.877	2.236	2.938	3.751	1.444	2.065	2.460	3.232	4.127
27	1.309	1.871	2.229	2.929	3.740	1.437	2.054	2.447	3.215	4.106

TABLE A-6 (Continued). FACTORS FOR TWO-SIDED TOLERANCE LIMITS FOR NORMAL DISTRIBUTIONS

	γ = 0.95					γ = 0.99				
P n	0.75	0.90	0.95	0.99	0.999	0.75	0.90	0.95	0.99	0.999
2	22.858	32.019	37.674	48.430	60.573	114.363	160.193	188.491	242.300	303.054
3	5.922	8.380	9.916	12.861	16.208	13.378	18.930	22.401	29.055	36.616
4	3.779	5.369	6.370	8.299	10.502	6.614	9.398	11.150	14.527	18.383
5	3.002	4.275	5.079	6.634	8.415	4.643	6.612	7.855	10.260	13.015
6	2.604	3.712	4.414	5.775	7.337	3.743	5.337	6.345	8.301	10.548
7	2.361	3.369	4.007	5.248	6.676	3.233	4.613	5.488	7.187	9.142
8	2.197	3.136	3.732	4.891	6.226	2.905	4.147	4.936	6.468	8.234
9	2.078	2.967	3.532	4.631	5.899	2.677	3.822	4.550	5.966	7.600
10	1.987	2.839	3.379	4.433	5.649	2.508	3.582	4.265	5.594	7.129
11	1.916	2.737	3.259	4.277	5.452	2.378	3.397	4.045	5.308	6.766
12	1.858	2.655	3.162	4.150	5.291	2.274	3.250	3.870	5.079	6.477
13	1.810	2.587	3.081	4.044	5.158	2.190	3.130	3.727	4.893	6.240
14	1.770	2.529	3.012	3.955	5.045	2.120	3.029	3.608	4.737	6.043
15	1.735	2.480	2.954	3.878	4.949	2.060	2.945	3.507	4.605	5.876
16	1.705	2.437	2.903	3.812	4.865	2.009	2.872	3.421	4.492	5.732
17	1.679	2.400	2.858	3.754	4.791	1.965	2.808	3.345	4.393	5.607
18	1.655	2.366	2.819	3.702	4.725	1.926	2.753	3.279	4.307	5.497
19	1.635	2.337	2.784	3.656	4.667	1.891	2.703	3.221	4.230	5.399
20	1.616	2.310	2.752	3.615	4.614	1.860	2.659	3.168	4.161	5.312
21	1.599	2.286	2.723	3.577	4.567	1.833	2.620	3.121	4.100	5.234
22	1.584	2.264	2.697	3.543	4.523	1.808	2.584	3.078	4.044	5.163
23	1.570	2.244	2.673	3.512	4.484	1.785	2.551	3.040	3.993	5.098
24	1.557	2.225	2.651	3.483	4.447	1.764	2.522	3.004	3.947	5.039
25	1.545	2.208	2.631	3.457	4.413	1.745	2.494	2.972	3.904	4.985
26	1.534	2.193	2.612	3.432	4.382	1.727	2.469	2.941	3.865	4.935
27	1.523	2.178	2.595	3.409	4.353	1.711	2.446	2.914	3.828	4.888

TABLE A-6 (Continued). FACTORS FOR TWO-SIDED TOLERANCE LIMITS FOR NORMAL DISTRIBUTIONS

P \ n	γ = 0.75					γ = 0.90				
	0.75	0.90	0.95	0.99	0.999	0.75	0.90	0.95	0.99	0.999
30	1.297	1.855	2.210	2.904	3.708	1.417	2.025	2.413	3.170	4.049
35	1.283	1.834	2.185	2.871	3.667	1.390	1.988	2.368	3.112	3.974
40	1.271	1.818	2.166	2.846	3.635	1.370	1.959	2.334	3.066	3.917
45	1.262	1.805	2.150	2.826	3.609	1.354	1.935	2.306	3.030	3.871
50	1.255	1.794	2.138	2.809	3.588	1.340	1.916	2.284	3.001	3.833
55	1.249	1.785	2.127	2.795	3.571	1.329	1.901	2.265	2.976	3.801
60	1.243	1.778	2.118	2.784	3.556	1.320	1.887	2.248	2.955	3.774
65	1.239	1.771	2.110	2.773	3.543	1.312	1.875	2.235	2.937	3.751
70	1.235	1.765	2.104	2.764	3.531	1.304	1.865	2.222	2.920	3.730
75	1.231	1.760	2.098	2.757	3.521	1.298	1.856	2.211	2.906	3.712
80	1.228	1.756	2.092	2.749	3.512	1.292	1.848	2.202	2.894	3.696
85	1.225	1.752	2.087	2.743	3.504	1.287	1.841	2.193	2.882	3.682
90	1.223	1.748	2.083	2.737	3.497	1.283	1.834	2.185	2.872	3.669
95	1.220	1.745	2.079	2.732	3.490	1.278	1.828	2.178	2.863	3.657
100	1.218	1.742	2.075	2.727	3.484	1.275	1.822	2.172	2.854	3.646
110	1.214	1.736	2.069	2.719	3.473	1.268	1.813	2.160	2.839	3.626
120	1.211	1.732	2.063	2.712	3.464	1.262	1.804	2.150	2.826	3.610
130	1.208	1.728	2.059	2.705	3.456	1.257	1.797	2.141	2.814	3.595
140	1.206	1.724	2.054	2.700	3.449	1.252	1.791	2.134	2.804	3.582
150	1.204	1.721	2.051	2.695	3.443	1.248	1.785	2.127	2.795	3.571
160	1.202	1.718	2.047	2.691	3.437	1.245	1.780	2.121	2.787	3.561
170	1.200	1.716	2.044	2.687	3.432	1.242	1.775	2.116	2.780	3.552
180	1.198	1.713	2.042	2.683	3.427	1.239	1.771	2.111	2.774	3.543
190	1.197	1.711	2.039	2.680	3.423	1.236	1.767	2.106	2.768	3.536
200	1.195	1.709	2.037	2.677	3.419	1.234	1.764	2.102	2.762	3.529
250	1.190	1.702	2.028	2.665	3.404	1.224	1.750	2.085	2.740	3.501
300	1.186	1.696	2.021	2.656	3.393	1.217	1.740	2.073	2.725	3.481
400	1.181	1.688	2.012	2.644	3.378	1.207	1.726	2.057	2.703	3.453
500	1.177	1.683	2.006	2.636	3.368	1.201	1.717	2.046	2.689	3.434
600	1.175	1.680	2.002	2.631	3.360	1.196	1.710	2.038	2.678	3.421
700	1.173	1.677	1.998	2.626	3.355	1.192	1.705	2.032	2.670	3.411
800	1.171	1.675	1.996	2.623	3.350	1.189	1.701	2.027	2.663	3.402
900	1.170	1.673	1.993	2.620	3.347	1.187	1.697	2.023	2.658	3.396
1000	1.169	1.671	1.992	2.617	3.344	1.185	1.695	2.019	2.654	3.390
∞	1.150	1.645	1.960	2.576	3.291	1.150	1.645	1.960	2.576	3.291

TABLE A-6 (Continued). FACTORS FOR TWO-SIDED TOLERANCE LIMITS FOR NORMAL DISTRIBUTIONS

| | γ = 0.95 | | | | | γ = 0.99 | | | | |
n \ P	0.75	0.90	0.95	0.99	0.999	0.75	0.90	0.95	0.99	0.999
30	1.497	2.140	2.549	3.350	4.278	1.668	2.385	2.841	3.733	4.768
35	1.462	2.090	2.490	3.272	4.179	1.613	2.306	2.748	3.611	4.611
40	1.435	2.052	2.445	3.213	4.104	1.571	2.247	2.677	3.518	4.493
45	1.414	2.021	2.408	3.165	4.042	1.539	2.200	2.621	3.444	4.399
50	1.396	1.996	2.379	3.126	3.993	1.512	2.162	2.576	3.385	4.323
55	1.382	1.976	2.354	3.094	3.951	1.490	2.130	2.538	3.335	4.260
60	1.369	1.958	2.333	3.066	3.916	1.471	2.103	2.506	3.293	4.206
65	1.359	1.943	2.315	3.042	3.886	1.455	2.080	2.478	3.257	4.160
70	1.349	1.929	2.299	3.021	3.859	1.440	2.060	2.454	3.225	4.120
75	1.341	1.917	2.285	3.002	3.835	1.428	2.042	2.433	3.197	4.084
80	1.334	1.907	2.272	2.986	3.814	1.417	2.026	2.414	3.173	4.053
85	1.327	1.897	2.261	2.971	3.795	1.407	2.012	2.397	3.150	4.024
90	1.321	1.889	2.251	2.958	3.778	1.398	1.999	2.382	3.130	3.999
95	1.315	1.881	2.241	2.945	3.763	1.390	1.987	2.368	3.112	3.976
100	1.311	1.874	2.233	2.934	3.748	1.383	1.977	2.355	3.096	3.954
110	1.302	1.861	2.218	2.915	3.723	1.369	1.958	2.333	3.066	3.917
120	1.294	1.850	2.205	2.898	3.702	1.358	1.942	2.314	3.041	3.885
130	1.288	1.841	2.194	2.883	3.683	1.349	1.928	2.298	3.019	3.857
140	1.282	1.833	2.184	2.870	3.666	1.340	1.916	2.283	3.000	3.833
150	1.277	1.825	2.175	2.859	3.652	1.332	1.905	2.270	2.983	3.811
160	1.272	1.819	2.167	2.848	3.638	1.326	1.896	2.259	2.968	3.792
170	1.268	1.813	2.160	2.839	3.527	1.320	1.887	2.248	2.955	3.774
180	1.264	1.808	2.154	2.831	3.616	1.314	1.879	2.239	2.942	3.759
190	1.261	1.803	2.148	2.823	3.606	1.309	1.872	2.230	2.931	3.744
200	1.258	1.798	2.143	2.816	3.597	1.304	1.865	2.222	2.921	3.731
250	1.245	1.780	2.121	2.788	3.561	1.286	1.839	2.191	2.880	3.678
300	1.236	1.767	2.106	2.767	3.535	1.273	1.820	2.169	2.850	3.641
400	1.223	1.749	2.084	2.739	3.499	1.255	1.794	2.138	2.809	3.589
500	1.215	1.737	2.070	2.721	3.475	1.243	1.777	2.117	2.783	3.555
600	1.209	1.729	2.060	2.707	3.458	1.234	1.764	2.102	2.763	3.530
700	1.204	1.722	2.052	2.697	3.445	1.227	1.755	2.091	2.748	3.511
800	1.201	1.717	2.046	2.688	3.434	1.222	1.747	2.082	2.736	3.495
900	1.198	1.712	2.040	2.682	3.426	1.218	1.741	2.075	2.726	3.483
1000	1.195	1.709	2.036	2.676	3.418	1.214	1.736	2.068	2.718	3.472
∞	1.150	1.645	1.960	2.576	3.291	1.150	1.645	1.960	2.576	3.291

TABLE A-7. FACTORS FOR ONE-SIDED TOLERANCE LIMITS FOR NORMAL DISTRIBUTIONS

Factors K such that the probability is γ that at least a proportion P of the distribution will be less than $\overline{X} + Ks$ (or greater than $\overline{X} - Ks$), where $\overline{X}$ and s are estimates of the mean and the standard deviation computed from a sample size of n.

	$\gamma = 0.75$					$\gamma = 0.90$				
P \ n	0.75	0.90	0.95	0.99	0.999	0.75	0.90	0.95	0.99	0.999
3	1.464	2.501	3.152	4.396	5.805	2.602	4.258	5.310	7.340	9.651
4	1.256	2.134	2.680	3.726	4.910	1.972	3.187	3.957	5.437	7.128
5	1.152	1.961	2.463	3.421	4.507	1.698	2.742	3.400	4.666	6.112
6	1.087	1.860	2.336	3.243	4.273	1.540	2.494	3.091	4.242	5.556
7	1.043	1.791	2.250	3.126	4.118	1.435	2.333	2.894	3.972	5.201
8	1.010	1.740	2.190	3.042	4.008	1.360	2.219	2.755	3.783	4.955
9	0.984	1.702	2.141	2.977	3.924	1.302	2.133	2.649	3.641	4.772
10	0.964	1.671	2.103	2.927	3.858	1.257	2.065	2.568	3.532	4.629
11	0.947	1.646	2.073	2.885	3.804	1.219	2.012	2.503	3.444	4.515
12	0.933	1.624	2.048	2.851	3.760	1.188	1.966	2.448	3.371	4.420
13	0.919	1.606	2.026	2.822	3.722	1.162	1.928	2.403	3.310	4.341
14	0.909	1.591	2.007	2.796	3.690	1.139	1.895	2.363	3.257	4.274
15	0.899	1.577	1.991	2.776	3.661	1.119	1.866	2.329	3.212	4.215
16	0.891	1.566	1.977	2.756	3.637	1.101	1.842	2.299	3.172	4.164
17	0.883	1.554	1.964	2.739	3.615	1.085	1.820	2.272	3.136	4.118
18	0.876	1.544	1.951	2.723	3.595	1.071	1.800	2.249	3.106	4.078
19	0.870	1.536	1.942	2.710	3.577	1.058	1.781	2.228	3.078	4.041
20	0.865	1.528	1.933	2.697	3.561	1.046	1.765	2.208	3.052	4.009
21	0.859	1.520	1.923	2.686	3.545	1.035	1.750	2.190	3.028	3.979
22	0.854	1.514	1.916	2.675	3.532	1.025	1.736	2.174	3.007	3.952
23	0.849	1.508	1.907	2.665	3.520	1.016	1.724	2.159	2.987	3.927
24	0.845	1.502	1.901	2.656	3.509	1.007	1.712	2.145	2.969	3.904
25	0.842	1.496	1.895	2.647	3.497	0.999	1.702	2.132	2.952	3.882
30	0.825	1.475	1.869	2.613	3.454	0.966	1.657	2.080	2.884	3.794
35	0.812	1.458	1.849	2.588	3.421	0.942	1.623	2.041	2.833	3.730
40	0.803	1.445	1.834	2.568	3.395	0.923	1.598	2.010	2.793	3.679
45	0.795	1.435	1.821	2.552	3.375	0.908	1.577	1.986	2.762	3.638
50	0.788	1.426	1.811	2.538	3.358	0.894	1.560	1.965	2.735	3.604

Adapted by permission from *Industrial Quality Control*, Vol. XIV, No. 10, April 1958, from article entitled "Tables for One-Sided Statistical Tolerance Limits" by G. J. Lieberman.

TABLE A-7 (Continued). FACTORS FOR ONE-SIDED TOLERANCE LIMITS FOR NORMAL DISTRIBUTIONS

*The two starred values have been corrected to the values given by D. B. Owen in "Factors for One-Sided Tolerance Limits and for Variables Sampling Plans", Sandia Corporation Monograph SCR–607, available from the Clearing House for Federal Scientific and Technical Information, U.S. Department of Commerce, Springfield, Va. 22151. The Owen Tables indicate other errors in the table below, not exceeding 4 in the last digit.

| | γ = 0.95 | | | | | γ = 0.99 | | | | |
n \ P	0.75	0.90	0.95	0.99	0.999	0.75	0.90	0.95	0.99	0.999
3	3.804	6.158	7.655	10.552	13.857	—	—	—	—	—
4	2.619	4.163	5.145	7.042	9.215	—	—	—	—	—
5	2.149	3.407	4.202	5.741	7.501	—	—	—	—	—
6	1.895	3.006	3.707	5.062	6.612	2.849	4.408	5.409	7.334	9.550*
7	1.732	2.755	3.399	4.641	6.061	2.490	3.856	4.730	6.411	8.348
8	1.617	2.582	3.188	4.353	5.686	2.252	3.496	4.287	5.811	7.566
9	1.532	2.454	3.031	4.143	5.414	2.085	3.242	3.971	5.389	7.014
10	1.465	2.355	2.911	3.981	5.203	1.954	3.048	3.739	5.075	6.603
11	1.411	2.275	2.815	3.852	5.036	1.854	2.897	3.557	4.828	6.284
12	1.366	2.210	2.736	3.747	4.900	1.771	2.773	3.410	4.633	6.032
13	1.329	2.155	2.670	3.659	4.787	1.702	2.677	3.290	4.472	5.826
14	1.296	2.108	2.614	3.585	4.690	1.645	2.592	3.189	4.336	5.651
15	1.268	2.068	2.566	3.520	4.607	1.596	2.521	3.102	4.224	5.507
16	1.242	2.032	2.523	3.463	4.534	1.553	2.458	3.028	4.124	5.374
17	1.220	2.001	2.486	3.415	4.471	1.514	2.405	2.962	4.038	5.268
18	1.200	1.974	2.453	3.370	4.415	1.481	2.357	2.906	3.961	5.167
19	1.183	1.949	2.423	3.331	4.364	1.450	2.315	2.855	3.893	5.078
20	1.167	1.926	2.396	3.295	4.319	1.424	2.275	2.807	3.832	5.003
21	1.152	1.905	2.371	3.262	4.276	1.397	2.241	2.768	3.776	4.932
22	1.138	1.887	2.350	3.233	4.238	1.376	2.208	2.729	3.727	4.866
23	1.126	1.869	2.329	3.206	4.204	1.355	2.179	2.693	3.680	4.806
24	1.114	1.853	2.309	3.181	4.171	1.336	2.154	2.663	3.638	4.755
25	1.103	1.838	2.292	3.158	4.143	1.319	2.129	2.632	3.601	4.706
30	1.059	1.778	2.220	3.064	4.022	1.249	2.029	2.516	3.446	4.508
35	1.025	1.732	2.166	2.994	3.934	1.195	1.957	2.431	3.334	4.364
40	0.999	1.697	2.126	2.941	3.866	1.154	1.902	2.365	3.250	4.255
45	0.978	1.669	2.092	2.897	3.811	1.122	1.857	2.313	3.181	4.168
50	0.961	1.646	2.065	2.863	3.766	1.096	1.821	2.269*	3.124	4.096

TABLE A-8. SAMPLE SIZES REQUIRED TO DETECT PRESCRIBED DIFFERENCES BETWEEN AVERAGES WHEN THE SIGN OF THE DIFFERENCE IS NOT IMPORTANT

The table entry is the sample size (n) required to detect, with probability $1 - \beta$, that the average m of a new product differs from the standard m_O (or that two product averages m_A and m_B differ). The standardized difference is d, where

$$d = \frac{|m - m_O|}{\sigma} \text{ (or } d = \frac{|m_A - m_B|}{\sqrt{\sigma_A^2 + \sigma_B^2}} \text{ if we are comparing two products).}$$

The standard deviations are assumed to be known, and n is determined by the formula:

$$n = \frac{(z_{1-\alpha/2} + z_{1-\beta})^2}{d^2}$$

$$\alpha = .01$$

d \ $1-\beta$	.50	.60	.70	.80	.90	.95	.99
.1	664	801	962	1168	1488	1782	2404
.2	166	201	241	292	372	446	601
.4	42	51	61	73	93	112	151
.6	19	23	27	33	42	50	67
.8	11	13	16	19	24	28	38
1.0	7	9	10	12	15	18	25
1.2	5	6	7	9	11	13	17
1.4	4	5	5	6	8	10	13
1.6	3	4	4	5	6	7	10
1.8	3	3	3	4	5	6	8
2.0	2	3	3	3	4	5	7
3.0	1	1	2	2	2	2	3

If we must estimate σ from our sample and use Student's t, then we should add 4 to the tabulated values to obtain the approximate required sample size. (If we are comparing two product averages, add 2 to the tabulated values, to obtain the required size of each sample. For this case, we must have $\sigma_A = \sigma_B$).

$$\alpha = .05$$

d \ $1-\beta$	.50	.60	.70	.80	.90	.95	.99
.1	385	490	618	785	1051	1300	1838
.2	97	123	155	197	263	325	460
.4	25	31	39	50	66	82	115
.6	11	14	18	22	30	37	52
.8	7	8	10	13	17	21	29
1.0	4	5	7	8	11	13	19
1.2	3	4	5	6	8	10	13
1.4	2	3	4	5	6	7	10
1.6	2	2	3	4	5	6	8
1.8	2	2	2	3	4	5	6
2.0	1	2	2	2	3	4	5
3.0	1	1	1	1	2	2	3

If we must estimate σ from our sample and use Student's t, then we should add 2 to the tabulated values to obtain the approximate required sample size. (If we are comparing two product averages, add 1 to the tabulated values to obtain the required size of each sample. For this case, we must have $\sigma_A = \sigma_B$.).

TABLE A-9. SAMPLE SIZES REQUIRED TO DETECT PRESCRIBED DIFFERENCES BETWEEN AVERAGES WHEN THE SIGN OF THE DIFFERENCE IS IMPORTANT

The table entry is the sample size (n) required to detect with probability $1 - \beta$ that:

(a) the average m of a new product exceeds that of a standard m_0

(b) the average m of a new product is less than that of a standard m_0

(c) the average of a specified product m_A exceeds the average of another specified product m_B.

The standardized difference is d, where:

$$\text{(a)} \quad d = \frac{m - m_0}{\sigma}$$

$$\text{(b)} \quad d = \frac{m_0 - m}{\sigma}$$

$$\text{(c)} \quad d = \frac{m_A - m_B}{\sqrt{\sigma_A^2 + \sigma_B^2}}$$

The standard deviations are assumed to be known, and n is calculated from the following formula:

$$n = \frac{(z_{1-\alpha} + z_{1-\beta})^2}{d^2}$$

$$\alpha = .01$$

d \ $1-\beta$	.50	.60	.70	.80	.90	.95	.99
.1	542	666	813	1004	1302	1578	2165
.2	136	167	204	251	326	395	542
.4	34	42	51	63	82	99	136
.6	16	19	23	28	37	44	61
.8	9	11	13	16	21	25	34
1.0	6	7	9	11	14	16	22
1.2	4	5	6	7	10	11	16
1.4	3	4	5	6	7	9	12
1.6	3	3	4	4	6	7	9
1.8	2	3	3	4	5	5	7
2.0	2	2	3	3	4	4	6
3.0	1	1	1	2	2	2	3

If we must estimate σ from our sample, and use Student's t, add 3 to the tabulated values to obtain the approximate required sample size. (If we are comparing two product averages, add 2 to the tabulated values to obtain the required size of each sample. For this case, we must have $\sigma_A = \sigma_B$).

$$\alpha = .05$$

d \ $1-\beta$	.50	.60	.70	.80	.90	.95	.99
.1	271	361	471	619	857	1083	1578
.2	68	91	118	155	215	271	395
.4	17	23	30	39	54	68	99
.6	8	11	14	18	24	31	44
.8	5	6	8	10	14	17	25
1.0	3	4	5	7	9	11	16
1.2	2	3	4	5	6	8	11
1.4	2	2	3	4	5	6	9
1.6	2	2	2	3	4	5	7
1.8	1	2	2	2	3	4	5
2.0	1	1	2	2	3	3	4
3.0	1	1	1	1	1	2	2

If we must estimate σ from our sample, and use Student's t, add 2 to the tabulated values to obtain the approximate required sample size. (If we are comparing two product averages, add 1 to the tabulated values to obtain the required size of each sample. For this case, we must have $\sigma_A = \sigma_B$).

TABLE A-10.   PERCENTILES OF THE STUDENTIZED RANGE, q

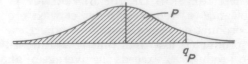

$q = w/s$ where w is the range of t observations, and ν is the number
of degrees of freedom associated with the standard deviation s.

$$q_{.90}$$

ν \ t	2	3	4	5	6	7	8	9	10
1	8.93	13.44	16.36	18.49	20.15	21.51	22.64	23.62	24.48
2	4.13	5.73	6.77	7.54	8.14	8.63	9.05	9.41	9.72
3	3.33	4.47	5.20	5.74	6.16	6.51	6.81	7.06	7.29
4	3.01	3.98	4.59	5.03	5.39	5.68	5.93	6.14	6.33
5	2.85	3.72	4.26	4.66	4.98	5.24	5.46	5.65	5.82
6	2.75	3.56	4.07	4.44	4.73	4.97	5.17	5.34	5.50
7	2.68	3.45	3.93	4.28	4.55	4.78	4.97	5.14	5.28
8	2.63	3.37	3.83	4.17	4.43	4.65	4.83	4.99	5.13
9	2.59	3.32	3.76	4.08	4.34	4.54	4.72	4.87	5.01
10	2.56	3.27	3.70	4.02	4.26	4.47	4.64	4.78	4.91
11	2.54	3.23	3.66	3.96	4.20	4.40	4.57	4.71	4.84
12	2.52	3.20	3.62	3.92	4.16	4.35	4.51	4.65	4.78
13	2.50	3.18	3.59	3.88	4.12	4.30	4.46	4.60	4.72
14	2.49	3.16	3.56	3.85	4.08	4.27	4.42	4.56	4.68
15	2.48	3.14	3.54	3.83	4.05	4.23	4.39	4.52	4.64
16	2.47	3.12	3.52	3.80	4.03	4.21	4.36	4.49	4.61
17	2.46	3.11	3.50	3.78	4.00	4.18	4.33	4.46	4.58
18	2.45	3.10	3.49	3.77	3.98	4.16	4.31	4.44	4.55
19	2.45	3.09	3.47	3.75	3.97	4.14	4.29	4.42	4.53
20	2.44	3.08	3.46	3.74	3.95	4.12	4.27	4.40	4.51
24	2.42	3.05	3.42	3.69	3.90	4.07	4.21	4.34	4.44
30	2.40	3.02	3.39	3.65	3.85	4.02	4.16	4.28	4.38
40	2.38	2.99	3.35	3.60	3.80	3.96	4.10	4.21	4.32
60	2.36	2.96	3.31	3.56	3.75	3.91	4.04	4.16	4.25
120	2.34	2.93	3.28	3.52	3.71	3.86	3.99	4.10	4.19
∞	2.33	2.90	3.24	3.48	3.66	3.81	3.93	4.04	4.13

Adapted by permission from *Biometrika*, Vol. 46, Dec. 1959, from article entitled "Tables of the Upper 10 % Points of the Studentized Range (Accompanied by Revised Tables of 5 % and 1 % Points)," by James Pachares.

TABLE A-10 (Continued). PERCENTILES OF THE STUDENTIZED RANGE, q

$q_{.90}$

ν \ t	11	12	13	14	15	16	17	18	19	20
1	25.24	25.92	26.54	27.10	27.62	28.10	28.54	28.96	29.35	29.71
2	10.01	10.26	10.49	10.70	10.89	11.07	11.24	11.39	11.54	11.68
3	7.49	7.67	7.83	7.98	8.12	8.25	8.37	8.48	8.58	8.68
4	6.49	6.65	6.78	6.91	7.02	7.13	7.23	7.33	7.41	7.50
5	5.97	6.10	6.22	6.34	6.44	6.54	6.63	6.71	6.79	6.86
6	5.64	5.76	5.87	5.98	6.07	6.16	6.25	6.32	6.40	6.47
7	5.41	5.53	5.64	5.74	5.83	5.91	5.99	6.06	6.13	6.19
8	5.25	5.36	5.46	5.56	5.64	5.72	5.80	5.87	5.93	6.00
9	5.13	5.23	5.33	5.42	5.51	5.58	5.66	5.72	5.79	5.85
10	5.03	5.13	5.23	5.32	5.40	5.47	5.54	5.61	5.67	5.73
11	4.95	5.05	5.15	5.23	5.31	5.38	5.45	5.51	5.57	5.63
12	4.89	4.99	5.08	5.16	5.24	5.31	5.37	5.44	5.49	5.55
13	4.83	4.93	5.02	5.10	5.18	5.25	5.31	5.37	5.43	5.48
14	4.79	4.88	4.97	5.05	5.12	5.19	5.26	5.32	5.37	5.43
15	4.75	4.84	4.93	5.01	5.08	5.15	5.21	5.27	5.32	5.38
16	4.71	4.81	4.89	4.97	5.04	5.11	5.17	5.23	5.28	5.33
17	4.68	4.77	4.86	4.93	5.01	5.07	5.13	5.19	5.24	5.30
18	4.65	4.75	4.83	4.90	4.98	5.04	5.10	5.16	5.21	5.26
19	4.63	4.72	4.80	4.88	4.95	5.01	5.07	5.13	5.18	5.23
20	4.61	4.70	4.78	4.85	4.92	4.99	5.05	5.10	5.16	5.20
24	4.54	4.63	4.71	4.78	4.85	4.91	4.97	5.02	5.07	5.12
30	4.47	4.56	4.64	4.71	4.77	4.83	4.89	4.94	4.99	5.03
40	4.41	4.49	4.56	4.63	4.69	4.75	4.81	4.86	4.90	4.95
60	4.34	4.42	4.49	4.56	4.62	4.67	4.73	4.78	4.82	4.86
120	4.28	4.35	4.42	4.48	4.54	4.60	4.65	4.69	4.74	4.78
∞	4.21	4.28	4.35	4.41	4.47	4.52	4.57	4.61	4.65	4.69

TABLE A-10 (Continued). PERCENTILES OF THE STUDENTIZED RANGE, q

$q_{.95}$

ν \ t	2	3	4	5	6	7	8	9	10
1	17.97	26.98	32.82	37.08	40.41	43.12	45.40	47.36	49.07
2	6.08	8.33	9.80	10.88	11.74	12.44	13.03	13.54	13.99
3	4.50	5.91	6.82	7.50	8.04	8.48	8.85	9.18	9.46
4	3.93	5.04	5.76	6.29	6.71	7.05	7.35	7.60	7.83
5	3.64	4.60	5.22	5.67	6.03	6.33	6.58	6.80	6.99
6	3.46	4.34	4.90	5.30	5.63	5.90	6.12	6.32	6.49
7	3.34	4.16	4.68	5.06	5.36	5.61	5.82	6.00	6.16
8	3.26	4.04	4.53	4.89	5.17	5.40	5.60	5.77	5.92
9	3.20	3.95	4.41	4.76	5.02	5.24	5.43	5.59	5.74
10	3.15	3.88	4.33	4.65	4.91	5.12	5.30	5.46	5.60
11	3.11	3.82	4.26	4.57	4.82	5.03	5.20	5.35	5.49
12	3.08	3.77	4.20	4.51	4.75	4.95	5.12	5.27	5.39
13	3.06	3.73	4.15	4.45	4.69	4.88	5.05	5.19	5.32
14	3.03	3.70	4.11	4.41	4.64	4.83	4.99	5.13	5.25
15	3.01	3.67	4.08	4.37	4.59	4.78	4.94	5.08	5.20
16	3.00	3.65	4.05	4.33	4.56	4.74	4.90	5.03	5.15
17	2.98	3.63	4.02	4.30	4.52	4.70	4.86	4.99	5.11
18	2.97	3.61	4.00	4.28	4.49	4.67	4.82	4.96	5.07
19	2.96	3.59	3.98	4.25	4.47	4.65	4.79	4.92	5.04
20	2.95	3.58	3.96	4.23	4.45	4.62	4.77	4.90	5.01
24	2.92	3.53	3.90	4.17	4.37	4.54	4.68	4.81	4.92
30	2.89	3.49	3.85	4.10	4.30	4.46	4.60	4.72	4.82
40	2.86	3.44	3.79	4.04	4.23	4.39	4.52	4.63	4.73
60	2.83	3.40	3.74	3.98	4.16	4.31	4.44	4.55	4.65
120	2.80	3.36	3.68	3.92	4.10	4.24	4.36	4.47	4.56
∞	2.77	3.31	3.63	3.86	4.03	4.17	4.29	4.39	4.47

TABLE A-10 (Continued). PERCENTILES OF THE STUDENTIZED RANGE, q

$$q_{.95}$$

ν	11	12	13	14	15	16	17	18	19	20
1	50.59	51.96	53.20	54.33	55.36	56.32	57.22	58.04	58.83	59.56
2	14.39	14.75	15.08	15.38	15.65	15.91	16.14	16.37	16.57	16.77
3	9.72	9.95	10.15	10.35	10.52	10.69	10.84	10.98	11.11	11.24
4	8.03	8.21	8.37	8.52	8.66	8.79	8.91	9.03	9.13	9.23
5	7.17	7.32	7.47	7.60	7.72	7.83	7.93	8.03	8.12	8.21
6	6.65	6.79	6.92	7.03	7.14	7.24	7.34	7.43	7.51	7.59
7	6.30	6.43	6.55	6.66	6.76	6.85	6.94	7.02	7.10	7.17
8	6.05	6.18	6.29	6.39	6.48	6.57	6.65	6.73	6.80	6.87
9	5.87	5.98	6.09	6.19	6.28	6.36	6.44	6.51	6.58	6.64
10	5.72	5.83	5.93	6.03	6.11	6.19	6.27	6.34	6.40	6.47
11	5.61	5.71	5.81	5.90	5.98	6.06	6.13	6.20	6.27	6.33
12	5.51	5.61	5.71	5.80	5.88	5.95	6.02	6.09	6.15	6.21
13	5.43	5.53	5.63	5.71	5.79	5.86	5.93	5.99	6.05	6.11
14	5.36	5.46	5.55	5.64	5.71	5.79	5.85	5.91	5.97	6.03
15	5.31	5.40	5.49	5.57	5.65	5.72	5.78	5.85	5.90	5.96
16	5.26	5.35	5.44	5.52	5.59	5.66	5.73	5.79	5.84	5.90
17	5.21	5.31	5.39	5.47	5.54	5.61	5.67	5.73	5.79	5.84
18	5.17	5.27	5.35	5.43	5.50	5.57	5.63	5.69	5.74	5.79
19	5.14	5.23	5.31	5.39	5.46	5.53	5.59	5.65	5.70	5.75
20	5.11	5.20	5.28	5.36	5.43	5.49	5.55	5.61	5.66	5.71
24	5.01	5.10	5.18	5.25	5.32	5.38	5.44	5.49	5.55	5.59
30	4.92	5.00	5.08	5.15	5.21	5.27	5.33	5.38	5.43	5.47
40	4.82	4.90	4.98	5.04	5.11	5.16	5.22	5.27	5.31	5.36
60	4.73	4.81	4.88	4.94	5.00	5.06	5.11	5.15	5.20	5.24
120	4.64	4.71	4.78	4.84	4.90	4.95	5.00	5.04	5.09	5.13
∞	4.55	4.62	4.68	4.74	4.80	4.85	4.89	4.93	4.97	5.01

TABLE A-10 (Continued). PERCENTILES OF THE STUDENTIZED RANGE, q

$$q_{.99}$$

ν \ t	2	3	4	5	6	7	8	9	10
1	90.03	135.0	164.3	185.6	202.2	215.8	227.2	237.0	245.6
2	14.04	19.02	22.29	24.72	26.63	28.20	29.53	30.68	31.69
3	8.26	10.62	12.17	13.33	14.24	15.00	15.64	16.20	16.69
4	6.51	8.12	9.17	9.96	10.58	11.10	11.55	11.93	12.27
5	5.70	6.98	7.80	8.42	8.91	9.32	9.67	9.97	10.24
6	5.24	6.33	7.03	7.56	7.97	8.32	8.61	8.87	9.10
7	4.95	5.92	6.54	7.01	7.37	7.68	7.94	8.17	8.37
8	4.75	5.64	6.20	6.62	6.96	7.24	7.47	7.68	7.86
9	4.60	5.43	5.96	6.35	6.66	6.91	7.13	7.33	7.49
10	4.48	5.27	5.77	6.14	6.43	6.67	6.87	7.05	7.21
11	4.39	5.15	5.62	5.97	6.25	6.48	6.67	6.84	6.99
12	4.32	5.05	5.50	5.84	6.10	6.32	6.51	6.67	6.81
13	4.26	4.96	5.40	5.73	5.98	6.19	6.37	6.53	6.67
14	4.21	4.89	5.32	5.63	5.88	6.08	6.26	6.41	6.54
15	4.17	4.84	5.25	5.56	5.80	5.99	6.16	6.31	6.44
16	4.13	4.79	5.19	5.49	5.72	5.92	6.08	6.22	6.35
17	4.10	4.74	5.14	5.43	5.66	5.85	6.01	6.15	6.27
18	4.07	4.70	5.09	5.38	5.60	5.79	5.94	6.08	6.20
19	4.05	4.67	5.05	5.33	5.55	5.73	5.89	6.02	6.14
20	4.02	4.64	5.02	5.29	5.51	5.69	5.84	5.97	6.09
24	3.96	4.55	4.91	5.17	5.37	5.54	5.69	5.81	5.92
30	3.89	4.45	4.80	5.05	5.24	5.40	5.54	5.65	5.76
40	3.82	4.37	4.70	4.93	5.11	5.26	5.39	5.50	5.60
60	3.76	4.28	4.59	4.82	4.99	5.13	5.25	5.36	5.45
120	3.70	4.20	4.50	4.71	4.87	5.01	5.12	5.21	5.30
∞	3.64	4.12	4.40	4.60	4.76	4.88	4.99	5.08	5.16

TABLE A-10 (Continued). PERCENTILES OF THE STUDENTIZED RANGE, q

$$q_{.99}$$

ν \ t	11	12	13	14	15	16	17	18	19	20
1	253.2	260.0	266.2	271.8	277.0	281.8	286.3	290.4	294.3	298.0
2	32.59	33.40	34.13	34.81	35.43	36.00	36.53	37.03	37.50	37.95
3	17.13	17.53	17.89	18.22	18.52	18.81	19.07	19.32	19.55	19.77
4	12.57	12.84	13.09	13.32	13.53	13.73	13.91	14.08	14.24	14.40
5	10.48	10.70	10.89	11.08	11.24	11.40	11.55	11.68	11.81	11.93
6	9.30	9.48	9.65	9.81	9.95	10.08	10.21	10.32	10.43	10.54
7	8.55	8.71	8.86	9.00	9.12	9.24	9.35	9.46	9.55	9.65
8	8.03	8.18	8.31	8.44	8.55	8.66	8.76	8.85	8.94	9.03
9	7.65	7.78	7.91	8.03	8.13	8.23	8.33	8.41	8.49	8.57
10	7.36	7.49	7.60	7.71	7.81	7.91	7.99	8.08	8.15	8.23
11	7.13	7.25	7.36	7.46	7.56	7.65	7.73	7.81	7.88	7.95
12	6.94	7.06	7.17	7.26	7.36	7.44	7.52	7.59	7.66	7.73
13	6.79	6.90	7.01	7.10	7.19	7.27	7.35	7.42	7.48	7.55
14	6.66	6.77	6.87	6.96	7.05	7.13	7.20	7.27	7.33	7.39
15	6.55	6.66	6.76	6.84	6.93	7.00	7.07	7.14	7.20	7.26
16	6.46	6.56	6.66	6.74	6.82	6.90	6.97	7.03	7.09	7.15
17	6.38	6.48	6.57	6.66	6.73	6.81	6.87	6.94	7.00	7.05
18	6.31	6.41	6.50	6.58	6.65	6.73	6.79	6.85	6.91	6.97
19	6.25	6.34	6.43	6.51	6.58	6.65	6.72	6.78	6.84	6.89
20	6.19	6.28	6.37	6.45	6.52	6.59	6.65	6.71	6.77	6.82
24	6.02	6.11	6.19	6.26	6.33	6.39	6.45	6.51	6.56	6.61
30	5.85	5.93	6.01	6.08	6.14	6.20	6.26	6.31	6.36	6.41
40	5.69	5.76	5.83	5.90	5.96	6.02	6.07	6.12	6.16	6.21
60	5.53	5.60	5.67	5.73	5.78	5.84	5.89	5.93	5.97	6.01
120	5.37	5.44	5.50	5.56	5.61	5.66	5.71	5.75	5.79	5.83
∞	5.23	5.29	5.35	5.40	5.45	5.49	5.54	5.57	5.61	5.65

TABLE A-11.   PERCENTILES OF $F' = \dfrac{w_A}{w_B}$

n_B	Cum. Prop.	n_A 2	3	4	5	6	7	8	9	10
2	.005	.0078	.096	.21	.30	.38	.44	.49	.54	.57
	.01	.0157	.136	.26	.38	.46	.53	.59	.64	.68
	.025	.039	.217	.37	.50	.60	.68	.74	.79	.83
	.05	.079	.31	.50	.62	.74	.80	.86	.91	.95
	.95	12.7	19.1	23	26	29	30	32	34	35
	.975	25.5	38.2	52	57	60	62	64	67	68
	.99	63.7	95	116	132	142	153	160	168	174
	.995	127	191	230	250	260	270	280	290	290
3	.005	.0052	.071	.16	.24	.32	.38	.43	.47	.50
	.01	.0105	.100	.20	.30	.37	.43	.49	.53	.57
	.025	.026	.160	.28	.39	.47	.54	.59	.64	.68
	.05	.052	.23	.37	.49	.57	.64	.70	.75	.80
	.95	3.19	4.4	5.0	5.7	6.2	6.6	6.9	7.2	7.4
	.975	4.61	6.3	7.3	8.0	8.7	9.3	9.8	10.2	10.5
	.99	7.37	10	12	13	14	15	15	16	17
	.995	10.4	14	17	18	20	21	22	23	25
4	.005	.0043	.059	.14	.22	.28	.34	.39	.43	.46
	.01	.0086	.084	.18	.26	.33	.39	.44	.48	.52
	.025	.019	.137	.25	.34	.42	.48	.53	.57	.61
	.05	.043	.20	.32	.42	.50	.57	.62	.67	.70
	.95	2.02	2.7	3.1	3.4	3.6	3.8	4.0	4.2	4.4
	.975	2.72	3.5	4.0	4.4	4.7	5.0	5.2	5.4	5.6
	.99	3.83	5.0	5.5	6.0	6.4	6.7	7.0	7.2	7.5
	.995	4.85	6.1	7.0	7.6	8.1	8.5	8.8	9.3	9.6
5	.005	.0039	.054	.13	.20	.26	.32	.36	.40	.44
	.01	.0076	.079	.17	.24	.31	.36	.41	.45	.49
	.025	.018	.124	.23	.32	.38	.44	.49	.53	.57
	.05	.038	.18	.29	.40	.46	.52	.57	.61	.65
	.95	1.61	2.1	2.4	2.6	2.8	2.9	3.0	3.1	3.2
	.975	2.01	2.6	2.9	3.2	3.4	3.6	3.7	3.8	3.9
	.99	2.64	3.4	3.8	4.1	4.3	4.6	4.7	4.9	5.0
	.995	3.36	4.1	4.6	4.9	5.2	5.5	5.7	5.9	6.1

Adapted with permission from *Introduction to Statistical Analysis* (2d ed.) by W. J. Dixon and F. J. Massey, Jr., Copyright, 1957, McGraw-Hill Book Company, Inc.

TABLE A-11 (Continued). PERCENTILES OF $F' = \dfrac{w_A}{w_B}$

n_B	Cum. Prop.	n_A								
		2	3	4	5	6	7	8	9	10
6	.005	.0038	.051	.12	.19	.25	.30	.35	.38	.42
	.01	.0070	.073	.16	.23	.29	.34	.39	.43	.46
	.025	.017	.115	.21	.30	.36	.42	.46	.50	.54
	.05	.035	.16	.27	.36	.43	.49	.54	.58	.61
	.95	1.36	1.8	2.0	2.2	2.3	2.4	2.5	2.6	2.7
	.975	1.67	2.1	2.4	2.6	2.8	2.9	3.0	3.1	3.2
	.99	2.16	2.7	3.0	3.2	3.4	3.6	3.7	3.8	3.9
	.995	2.67	3.1	3.5	3.8	4.0	4.1	4.3	4.5	4.6
7	.005	.0037	.048	.12	.18	.24	.29	.33	.37	.40
	.01	.0066	.069	.15	.22	.28	.33	.37	.41	.45
	.025	.016	.107	.20	.28	.34	.40	.44	.48	.52
	.05	.032	.15	.26	.35	.41	.47	.51	.55	.59
	.95	1.26	1.6	1.8	1.9	2.0	2.1	2.2	2.3	2.4
	.975	1.48	1.9	2.1	2.3	2.4	2.5	2.6	2.7	2.8
	.99	1.87	2.3	2.6	2.8	2.9	3.0	3.1	3.2	3.3
	.995	2.28	2.7	2.9	3.1	3.3	3.5	3.6	3.7	3.8
8	.005	.0036	.045	.11	.18	.23	.28	.32	.36	.39
	.01	.0063	.065	.14	.21	.27	.32	.36	.40	.43
	.025	.016	.102	.19	.27	.33	.38	.43	.47	.50
	.05	.031	.14	.25	.33	.40	.45	.50	.53	.57
	.95	1.17	1.4	1.6	1.8	1.9	1.9	2.0	2.1	2.1
	.975	1.36	1.7	1.9	2.0	2.2	2.3	2.3	2.4	2.5
	.99	1.69	2.1	2.3	2.4	2.6	2.7	2.8	2.8	2.9
	.995	2.03	2.3	2.6	2.7	2.9	3.0	3.1	3.2	3.3
9	.005	.0035	.042	.11	.17	.22	.27	.31	.35	.38
	.01	.0060	.062	.14	.21	.26	.31	.35	.39	.42
	.025	.015	.098	.18	.26	.32	.37	.42	.46	.49
	.05	.030	.14	.24	.32	.38	.44	.48	.52	.55
	.95	1.10	1.3	1.5	1.6	1.7	1.8	1.9	1.9	2.0
	.975	1.27	1.6	1.8	1.9	2.0	2.1	2.1	2.2	2.3
	.99	1.56	1.9	2.1	2.2	2.3	2.4	2.5	2.6	2.6
	.995	1.87	2.1	2.3	2.5	2.6	2.7	2.8	2.9	3.0
10	.005	.0034	.041	.10	.16	.22	.26	.30	.34	.37
	.01	.0058	.060	.13	.20	.26	.30	.34	.38	.41
	.025	.015	.095	.18	.25	.31	.36	.41	.44	.48
	.05	.029	.13	.23	.31	.37	.43	.47	.51	.54
	.95	1.05	1.3	1.4	1.5	1.6	1.7	1.8	1.8	1.9
	.975	1.21	1.5	1.6	1.8	1.9	1.9	2.0	2.0	2.1
	.99	1.47	1.8	1.9	2.1	2.2	2.2	2.3	2.4	2.4
	.995	1.75	2.0	2.2	2.3	2.4	2.5	2.6	2.6	2.7

TABLE A-12. PERCENTILES FOR $\phi = \dfrac{\overline{X} - m_0}{w}$

Sample Size	$\phi_{.95}$	$\phi_{.975}$	$\phi_{.99}$	$\phi_{.995}$	$\phi_{.999}$	$\phi_{.9995}$
2	3.175	6.353	15.910	31.828	159.16	318.31
3	.885	1.304	2.111	3.008	6.77	9.58
4	.529	.717	1.023	1.316	2.29	2.85
5	.388	.507	.685	.843	1.32	1.58
6	.312	.399	.523	.628	.92	1.07
7	.263	.333	.429	.507	.71	.82
8	.230	.288	.366	.429	.59	.67
9	.205	.255	.322	.374	.50	.57
10	.186	.230	.288	.333	.44	.50
11	.170	.210	.262	.302	.40	.44
12	.158	.194	.241	.277	.36	.40
13	.147	.181	.224	.256	.33	.37
14	.138	.170	.209	.239	.31	.34
15	.131	.160	.197	.224	.29	.32
16	.124	.151	.186	.212	.27	.30
17	.118	.144	.177	.201	.26	.28
18	.113	.137	.168	.191	.24	.26
19	.108	.131	.161	.182	.23	.25
20	.104	.126	.154	.175	.22	.24

Adapted with permission from *Biometrika*, Vol. 34 (1947) from article entitled "The Use of the Range in Place of the Standard Deviation in the *t* Test" by E. Lord.

TABLE A-13. PERCENTILES FOR $\phi' = \dfrac{\overline{X}_A - \overline{X}_B}{\frac{1}{2}(w_A + w_B)}$

$n = n_A = n_B$	$\phi'_{.95}$	$\phi'_{.975}$	$\phi'_{.99}$	$\phi'_{.995}$	$\phi'_{.999}$	$\phi'_{.9995}$
2	2.322	3.427	5.553	7.916	17.81	25.23
3	.974	1.272	1.715	2.093	3.27	4.18
4	.644	.813	1.047	1.237	1.74	1.99
5	.493	.613	.772	.896	1.21	1.35
6	.405	.499	.621	.714	.94	1.03
7	.347	.426	.525	.600	.77	.85
8	.306	.373	.459	.521	.67	.73
9	.275	.334	.409	.464	.59	.64
10	.250	.304	.371	.419	.53	.58
11	.233	.280	.340	.384	.48	.52
12	.214	.260	.315	.355	.44	.48
13	.201	.243	.294	.331	.41	.45
14	.189	.228	.276	.311	.39	.42
15	.179	.216	.261	.293	.36	.39
16	.170	.205	.247	.278	.34	.37
17	.162	.195	.236	.264	.33	.35
18	.155	.187	.225	.252	.31	.34
19	.149	.179	.216	.242	.30	.32
20	.143	.172	.207	.232	.29	.31

Adapted with permission from *Biometrika*, Vol. 34 (1947) from article entitled "The Use of the Range in Place of the Standard Deviation in the *t* Test" by E. Lord.

TABLE A-14. CRITERIA FOR REJECTION OF OUTLYING OBSERVATIONS

Statistic	Number of Observations, n	Upper Percentiles						
		.70	.80	.90	.95	.98	.99	.995
r_{10}	3	.684	.781	.886	.941	.976	.988	.994
	4	.471	.560	.679	.765	.846	.889	.926
	5	.373	.451	.557	.642	.729	.780	.821
	6	.318	.386	.482	.560	.644	.698	.740
	7	.281	.344	.434	.507	.586	.637	.680
r_{11}	8	.318	.385	.479	.554	.631	.683	.725
	9	.288	.352	.441	.512	.587	.635	.677
	10	.265	.325	.409	.477	.551	.597	.639
r_{21}	11	.391	.442	.517	.576	.638	.679	.713
	12	.370	.419	.490	.546	.605	.642	.675
	13	.351	.399	.467	.521	.578	.615	.649
r_{22}	14	.370	.421	.492	.546	.602	.641	.674
	15	.353	.402	.472	.525	.579	.616	.647
	16	.338	.386	.454	.507	.559	.595	.624
	17	.325	.373	.438	.490	.542	.577	.605
	18	.314	.361	.424	.475	.527	.561	.589
	19	.304	.350	.412	.462	.514	.547	.575
	20	.295	.340	.401	.450	.502	.535	.562
	21	.287	.331	.391	.440	.491	.524	.551
	22	.280	.323	.382	.430	.481	.514	.541
	23	.274	.316	.374	.421	.472	.505	.532
	24	.268	.310	.367	.413	.464	.497	.524
	25	.262	.304	.360	.406	.457	.489	.516

Adapted by permission from *Introduction to Statistical Analysis* (2d ed.) by W. J. Dixon and F. J. Massey, Jr., Copyright, 1957, McGraw-Hill Book Company, Inc.

TABLE A-15. CRITICAL VALUES OF *L* FOR LINK-WALLACE TEST

$\alpha = .05$

t = number of groups = number of ranges

n = number in group = number per range

n \ t	2	3	4	5	6	7	8	9	10
2	3.43	2.37	1.78	1.40	1.16	1.00	.87	.78	.70
3	1.91	1.44	1.13	.94	.80	.70	.62	.56	.51
4	1.63	1.25	1.01	.84	.72	.63	.57	.51	.47
5	1.53	1.19	.96	.81	.70	.61	.55	.50	.45
6	1.50	1.18	.95	.80	.69	.61	.55	.49	.45
7	1.49	1.17	.95	.80	.69	.61	.55	.50	.45
8	1.49	1.17	.96	.81	.70	.62	.55	.50	.46
9	1.50	1.18	.97	.82	.71	.62	.56	.51	.47
10	1.52	1.20	.98	.83	.72	.63	.57	.52	.47
11	1.54	1.21	.99	.84	.73	.64	.58	.52	.48
12	1.56	1.23	1.00	.85	.74	.65	.59	.53	.49
13	1.58	1.25	1.02	.86	.75	.66	.59	.54	.49
14	1.60	1.26	1.03	.87	.76	.67	.60	.55	.50
15	1.62	1.28	1.05	.89	.77	.68	.61	.56	.51
16	1.64	1.30	1.06	.90	.78	.69	.62	.56	.52
17	1.66	1.31	1.08	.91	.79	.70	.63	.57	.52
18	1.68	1.33	1.09	.92	.80	.71	.64	.58	.53
19	1.70	1.34	1.10	.93	.81	.72	.65	.59	.54
20	1.72	1.36	1.11	.95	.82	.73	.65	.59	.54

n \ t	11	12	13	14	15	16	17	18	19	20
2	.66	.63	.58	.50	.47	.44	.42	.40	.38	.36
3	.47	.43	.40	.38	.36	.33	.32	.30	.29	.27
4	.43	.40	.37	.35	.33	.31	.29	.28	.27	.25
5	.42	.39	.36	.34	.32	.30	.29	.27	.26	.25
6	.42	.39	.36	.34	.32	.30	.29	.27	.26	.25
7	.42	.39	.36	.34	.32	.30	.29	.28	.26	.25
8	.42	.39	.37	.35	.33	.31	.29	.28	.27	.25
9	.43	.40	.37	.35	.33	.31	.30	.28	.27	.26
10	.44	.41	.38	.35	.34	.32	.30	.29	.27	.26
11	.44	.41	.38	.36	.34	.32	.31	.29	.28	.27
12	.45	.42	.39	.37	.35	.33	.31	.30	.28	.27
13	.46	.42	.40	.37	.35	.33	.32	.30	.29	.27
14	.46	.43	.40	.38	.36	.34	.32	.31	.29	.28
15	.47	.44	.41	.38	.36	.34	.33	.31	.30	.28
16	.48	.44	.41	.39	.37	.35	.33	.31	.30	.29
17	.48	.45	.42	.39	.37	.35	.33	.32	.30	.29
18	.49	.46	.43	.40	.38	.36	.34	.32	.31	.30
19	.50	.46	.43	.40	.38	.36	.34	.33	.31	.30
20	.50	.47	.44	.41	.39	.37	.35	.33	.32	.30

Adapted by permission from "Some Short Cuts to Allowances," Table 1, by R. F. Link and D. L. Wallace, Princeton University, (unpublished manuscript).

TABLE A-15 (Continued). CRITICAL VALUES OF L FOR LINK-WALLACE TEST

$\alpha = .01$

t = number of groups = number of ranges

n \ t	2	3	4	5	6	7	8	9	10
2	7.92	4.42	2.96	2.06	1.69	1.39	1.20	1.03	.91
3	3.14	2.14	1.57	1.25	1.04	.89	.78	.69	.62
4	2.47	1.74	1.33	1.08	.91	.78	.69	.62	.56
5	2.24	1.60	1.24	1.02	.86	.75	.66	.59	.54
6	2.14	1.55	1.21	.99	.85	.74	.65	.59	.53
7	2.10	1.53	1.21	.99	.84	.74	.65	.59	.53
8	2.08	1.52	1.21	.99	.85	.74	.66	.59	.54
9	2.09	1.53	1.22	1.00	.85	.75	.66	.60	.54
10	2.10	1.55	1.23	1.01	.86	.75	.67	.61	.55
11	2.11	1.56	1.24	1.02	.88	.77	.68	.61	.56
12	2.13	1.58	1.25	1.03	.89	.78	.69	.62	.57
13	2.15	1.60	1.27	1.05	.90	79	.70	.63	.58
14	2.18	1.62	1.28	1.06	.91	.80	.71	.64	.58
15	2.20	1.64	1.30	1.08	.92	.81	.72	.65	.59
16	2.22	1.65	1.31	1.09	.93	.82	.73	.66	.60
17	2.24	1.67	1.33	1.11	.95	.83	.74	.67	.61
18	2.27	1.69	1.34	1.12	.96	.84	.75	.68	.62
19	2.30	1.71	1.36	1.14	.97	.85	.76	.68	.62
20	2.32	1.73	1.38	1.15	.98	.86	.77	.69	.63

n \ t	11	12	13	14	15	16	17	18	19	20
2	.82	.75	.68	.63	.59	.55	.51	.48	.46	.43
3	.57	.52	.48	.45	.42	.39	.37	.35	.34	.32
4	.51	.47	.44	.41	.38	.36	.34	.32	.31	.29
5	.49	.46	.42	.40	.37	.35	.33	.31	.30	.29
6	.49	.45	.42	.39	.37	.35	.33	.31	.30	.28
7	.49	.45	.42	.40	.37	.35	.33	.32	.30	.29
8	.50	.46	.43	.40	.37	.35	.33	.32	.30	.29
9	.50	.46	.43	.40	.38	.36	.34	.32	.31	.29
10	.51	.47	.44	.41	.38	.36	.34	.33	.31	.30
11	.51	.48	.44	.42	.39	.37	.35	.33	.32	.30
12	.52	.48	.45	.42	.40	.37	.35	.34	.32	.31
13	.53	.49	.46	.43	.40	.38	.36	.34	.33	.31
14	.54	.50	.46	.43	.41	.39	.37	.35	.33	.32
15	.54	50	.47	.44	.41	.39	.97	.85	.34	.32
16	.55	.51	.48	.45	.42	.40	.38	.36	.34	.32
17	.56	.52	.48	.45	.43	.40	.38	.36	.34	.33
18	.57	.53	.49	.46	.43	.41	.39	.37	.35	.33
19	.57	.53	.50	.46	.44	.41	.39	.37	.35	.34
20	.58	.54	.50	.47	.44	.42	.40	.38	.36	.34

n = number in group = number per range

TABLE A-16. PERCENTAGE POINTS OF THE EXTREME STUDENTIZED DEVIATE FROM SAMPLE MEAN,

$$t_n = (X_n - \overline{X})/s_v \text{ (or) } t_1 = (\overline{X} - X_1)/s_v$$

This table is to be used with s_v, an *external* estimate of σ, based on ν degrees of freedom, not with the s computed from the sample in hand.

n	\multicolumn{8}{c}{$\alpha = .05$}	\multicolumn{8}{c}{$\alpha = .01$}
ν	3	4	5	6	7	8	9	12	3	4	5	6	7	8	9	12
10	2.01	2.27	2.46	2.60	2.72	2.81	2.89	3.08	2.78	3.10	3.32	3.48	3.62	3.73	3.82	4.04
11	1.98	2.24	2.42	2.56	2.67	2.76	2.84	3.03	2.72	3.02	3.24	3.39	3.52	3.63	3.72	3.93
12	1.96	2.21	2.39	2.52	2.63	2.72	2.80	2.98	2.67	2.96	3.17	3.32	3.45	3.55	3.64	3.84
13	1.94	2.19	2.36	2.50	2.60	2.69	2.76	2.94	2.63	2.92	3.12	3.27	3.38	3.48	3.57	3.76
14	1.93	2.17	2.34	2.47	2.57	2.66	2.74	2.91	2.60	2.88	3.07	3.22	3.33	3.43	3.51	3.70
15	1.91	2.15	2.32	2.45	2.55	2.64	2.71	2.88	2.57	2.84	3.03	3.17	3.29	3.38	3.46	3.65
16	1.90	2.14	2.31	2.43	2.53	2.62	2.69	2.86	2.54	2.81	3.00	3.14	3.25	3.34	3.42	3.60
17	1.89	2.13	2.29	2.42	2.52	2.60	2.67	2.84	2.52	2.79	2.97	3.11	3.22	3.31	3.38	3.56
18	1.88	2.11	2.28	2.40	2.50	2.58	2.65	2.82	2.50	2.77	2.95	3.08	3.19	3.28	3.35	3.53
19	1.87	2.11	2.27	2.39	2.49	2.57	2.64	2.80	2.49	2.75	2.93	3.06	3.16	3.25	3.33	3.50
20	1.87	2.10	2.26	2.38	2.47	2.56	2.63	2.78	2.47	2.73	2.91	3.04	3.14	3.23	3.30	3.47
24	1.84	2.07	2.23	2.34	2.44	2.52	2.58	2.74	2.42	2.68	2.84	2.97	3.07	3.16	3.23	3.38
30	1.82	2.04	2.20	2.31	2.40	2.48	2.54	2.69	2.38	2.62	2.79	2.91	3.01	3.08	3.15	3.30
40	1.80	2.02	2.17	2.28	2.37	2.44	2.50	2.65	2.34	2.57	2.73	2.85	2.94	3.02	3.08	3.22
60	1.78	1.99	2.14	2.25	2.33	2.41	2.47	2.61	2.29	2.52	2.68	2.79	2.88	2.95	3.01	3.15
120	1.76	1.96	2.11	2.22	2.30	2.37	2.43	2.57	2.25	2.48	2.62	2.73	2.82	2.89	2.95	3.08
∞	1.74	1.94	2.08	2.18	2.27	2.33	2.39	2.52	2.22	2.43	2.57	2.68	2.76	2.83	2.88	3.01

TABLE A-17. CONFIDENCE BELTS FOR THE CORRELATION COEFFICIENT
(CONFIDENCE COEFFICIENT .95)

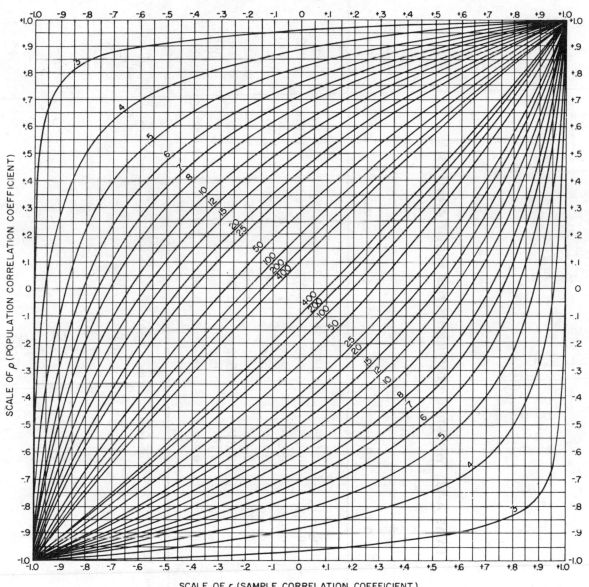

SCALE OF r (SAMPLE CORRELATION COEFFICIENT)
THE NUMBERS ON THE CURVES INDICATE SAMPLE SIZE

TABLE A-18. WEIGHTING COEFFICIENTS FOR PROBIT ANALYSIS

Y	0.0	0.1	0.2	0.3	0.4	0.5	0.6	0.7	0.8	0.9
1	0.001	0.001	0.001	0.002	0.002	0.003	0.005	0.006	0.008	0.011
2	0.015	0.019	0.025	0.031	0.040	0.050	0.062	0.076	0.092	0.110
3	0.131	0.154	0.180	0.208	0.238	0.269	0.302	0.336	0.370	0.405
4	0.439	0.471	0.503	0.532	0.558	0.581	0.601	0.616	0.627	0.634
5	0.637	0.634	0.627	0.616	0.601	0.581	0.558	0.532	0.503	0.471
6	0.439	0.405	0.370	0.336	0.302	0.269	0.238	0.208	0.180	0.154
7	0.131	0.110	0.092	0.076	0.062	0.050	0.040	0.031	0.025	0.019
8	0.015	0.011	0.008	0.006	0.005	0.003	0.002	0.002	0.001	0.001

Adapted with permission from *Statistical Tables for Biological, Agricultural and Medical Research* (5th ed.) by R. A. Fisher and F. Yates, Copyright, 1957, Oliver and Boyd Ltd., Edinburgh. (Published in U. S. by Hafner Publishing Company, Inc.)

TABLE A-19. MAXIMUM AND MINIMUM WORKING PROBITS AND RANGE

Expected Probit Y	Minimum Working Probit y_0	Range $1/Z$	Maximum Working Probit y_{100}	Expected Probit Y
1.1	0.8579	5034	9.1421	8.9
1.2	0.9522	3425	9.0478	8.8
1.3	1.0462	2354	8.9538	8.7
1.4	1.1400	1634	8.8600	8.6
1.5	1.2334	1146	8.7666	8.5
1.6	1.3266	811.5	8.6734	8.4
1.7	1.4194	580.5	8.5806	8.3
1.8	1.5118	419.4	8.4882	8.2
1.9	1.6038	306.1	8.3962	8.1
2.0	1.6954	225.6	8.3046	8.0
2.1	1.7866	168.00	8.2134	7.9
2.2	1.8772	126.34	8.1228	7.8
2.3	1.9673	95.96	8.0327	7.7
2.4	2.0568	73.62	7.9432	7.6
2.5	2.1457	57.05	7.8543	7.5
2.6	2.2339	44.654	7.7661	7.4
2.7	2.3214	35.302	7.6786	7.3
2.8	2.4081	28.189	7.5919	7.2
2.9	2.4938	22.736	7.5062	7.1
3.0	2.5786	18.522	7.4214	7.0
3.1	2.6624	15.240	7.3376	6.9
3.2	2.7449	12.666	7.2551	6.8
3.3	2.8261	10.633	7.1739	6.7
3.4	2.9060	9.015	7.0940	6.6
3.5	2.9842	7.721	7.0158	6.5
3.6	3.0606	6.6788	6.9394	6.4
3.7	3.1351	5.8354	6.8649	6.3
3.8	3.2074	5.1497	6.7926	6.2
3.9	3.2773	4.5903	6.7227	6.1
4.0	3.3443	4.1327	6.6557	6.0
4.1	3.4083	3.7582	6.5917	5.9
4.2	3.4687	3.4519	6.5313	5.8
4.3	3.5251	3.2025	6.4749	5.7
4.4	3.5770	3.0010	6.4230	5.6
4.5	3.6236	2.8404	6.3764	5.5
4.6	3.6643	2.7154	6.3357	5.4
4.7	3.6982	2.6220	6.3018	5.3
4.8	3.7241	2.5573	6.2759	5.2
4.9	3.7407	2.5192	6.2593	5.1
5.0	3.7467	2.5066	6.2533	5.0

Discrepancies between the source table and some other tables were noted in the entries for y_0 corresponding to $Y =$ 1.5 and $Y = 2.6$. These two values were recalculated and altered from the source table in the last place.

Adapted with permission from *Statistical Tables for Biological, Agricultural and Medical Research* (5th ed.) by R. A. Fisher and F. Yates. Copyright, 1957, Oliver and Boyd Ltd., Edinburgh. (Published in U. S. by Hafner Publishing Company, Inc.)

TABLE A-20. FACTORS FOR COMPUTING TWO-SIDED CONFIDENCE LIMITS FOR σ

Degrees of Freedom ν	$\alpha = .05$		$\alpha = .01$		$\alpha = .001$	
	B_U	B_L	B_U	B_L	B_U	B_L
1	17.79	.3576	86.31	.2969	844.4	.2480
2	4.859	.4581	10.70	.3879	33.29	.3291
3	3.183	.5178	5.449	.4453	11.65	.3824
4	2.567	.5590	3.892	.4865	6.938	.4218
5	2.248	.5899	3.175	.5182	5.085	.4529
6	2.052	.6143	2.764	.5437	4.128	.4784
7	1.918	.6344	2.498	.5650	3.551	.5000
8	1.820	.6513	2.311	.5830	3.167	.5186
9	1.746	.6657	2.173	.5987	2.894	.5348
10	1.686	.6784	2.065	.6125	2.689	.5492
11	1.638	.6896	1.980	.6248	2.530	.5621
12	1.598	.6995	1.909	.6358	2.402	.5738
13	1.564	.7084	1.851	.6458	2.298	.5845
14	1.534	.7166	1.801	.6549	2.210	.5942
15	1.509	.7240	1.758	.6632	2.136	.6032
16	1.486	.7308	1.721	.6710	2.073	.6116
17	1.466	.7372	1.688	.6781	2.017	.6193
18	1.448	.7430	1.658	.6848	1.968	.6266
19	1.432	.7484	1.632	.6909	1.925	.6333
20	1.417	.7535	1.609	.6968	1.886	.6397
21	1.404	.7582	1.587	.7022	1.851	.6457
22	1.391	.7627	1.568	.7074	1.820	.6514
23	1.380	.7669	1.550	.7122	1.791	.6568
24	1.370	.7709	1.533	.7169	1.765	.6619
25	1.360	.7747	1.518	.7212	1.741	.6668
26	1.351	.7783	1.504	.7253	1.719	.6713
27	1.343	.7817	1.491	.7293	1.698	.6758
28	1.335	.7849	1.479	.7331	1.679	.6800
29	1.327	.7880	1.467	.7367	1.661	.6841
30	1.321	.7909	1.457	.7401	1.645	.6880
31	1.314	.7937	1.447	.7434	1.629	.6917
32	1.308	.7964	1.437	.7467	1.615	.6953
33	1.302	.7990	1.428	.7497	1.601	.6987
34	1.296	.8015	1.420	.7526	1.588	.7020
35	1.291	.8039	1.412	.7554	1.576	.7052
36	1.286	.8062	1.404	.7582	1.564	.7083
37	1.281	.8085	1.397	.7608	1.553	.7113
38	1.277	.8106	1.390	.7633	1.543	.7141
39	1.272	.8126	1.383	.7658	1.533	.7169
40	1.268	.8146	1.377	.7681	1.523	.7197
41	1.264	.8166	1.371	.7705	1.515	.7223
42	1.260	.8184	1.365	.7727	1.506	.7248
43	1.257	.8202	1.360	.7748	1.498	.7273
44	1.253	.8220	1.355	.7769	1.490	.7297
45	1.249	.8237	1.349	.7789	1.482	.7320
46	1.246	.8253	1.345	.7809	1.475	.7342
47	1.243	.8269	1.340	.7828	1.468	.7364
48	1.240	.8285	1.335	.7847	1.462	.7386
49	1.237	.8300	1.331	.7864	1.455	.7407
50	1.234	.8314	1.327	.7882	1.449	.7427

Adapted with permission from *Biometrika*, Vol. 47, (1960), from article entitled "Tables for Making Inferences About the Variance of a Normal Distribution" by D. V. Lindley, D. A. East, and P. A. Hamilton.

TABLE A-20 (Continued). FACTORS FOR COMPUTING TWO-SIDED CONFIDENCE LIMITS FOR σ

Degrees of Freedom ν	$\alpha = .05$		$\alpha = .01$		$\alpha = .001$	
	B_U	B_L	B_U	B_L	B_U	B_L
51	1.232	.8329	1.323	.7899	1.443	.7446
52	1.229	.8343	1.319	.7916	1.437	.7466
53	1.226	.8356	1.315	.7932	1.432	.7485
54	1.224	.8370	1.311	.7949	1.426	.7503
55	1.221	.8383	1.308	.7964	1.421	.7521
56	1.219	.8395	1.304	.7979	1.416	.7539
57	1.217	.8408	1.301	.7994	1.411	.7556
58	1.214	.8420	1.298	.8008	1.406	.7573
59	1.212	.8431	1.295	.8022	1.402	.7589
60	1.210	.8443	1.292	.8036	1.397	.7605
61	1.208	.8454	1.289	.8050	1.393	.7621
62	1.206	.8465	1.286	.8063	1.389	.7636
63	1.204	.8475	1.283	.8076	1.385	.7651
64	1.202	.8486	1.280	.8088	1.381	.7666
65	1.200	.8496	1.277	.8101	1.377	.7680
66	1.199	.8506	1.275	.8113	1.374	.7694
67	1.197	.8516	1.272	.8125	1.370	.7708
68	1.195	.8525	1.270	.8137	1.366	.7722
69	1.194	.8535	1.268	.8148	1.363	.7735
70	1.192	.8544	1.265	.8159	1.360	.7749
71	1.190	.8553	1.263	.8170	1.356	.7761
72	1.189	.8562	1.261	.8181	1.353	.7774
73	1.187	.8571	1.259	.8191	1.350	.7787
74	1.186	.8580	1.257	.8202	1.347	.7799
75	1.184	.8588	1.255	.8212	1.344	.7811
76	1.183	.8596	1.253	.8222	1.341	.7822
77	1.182	.8604	1.251	.8232	1.338	.7834
78	1.181	.8612	1.249	.8242	1.336	.7845
79	1.179	.8620	1.247	.8252	1.333	.7856
80	1.178	.8627	1.245	.8261	1.330	.7868
81	1.176	.8635	1.243	.8270	1.328	.7878
82	1.176	.8642	1.241	.8279	1.325	.7889
83	1.174	.8650	1.239	.8288	1.323	.7899
84	1.173	.8657	1.238	.8297	1.320	.7909
85	1.172	.8664	1.236	.8305	1.318	.7920
86	1.171	.8671	1.235	.8314	1.316	.7930
87	1.170	.8678	1.233	.8322	1.313	.7939
88	1.168	.8684	1.231	.8331	1.311	.7949
89	1.167	.8691	1.230	.8338	1.309	.7959
90	1.166	.8697	1.228	.8346	1.307	.7968
91	1.165	.8704	1.227	.8354	1.305	.7977
92	1.164	.8710	1.225	.8362	1.303	.7987
93	1.163	.8716	1.224	.8370	1.301	.7996
94	1.162	.8722	1.222	.8377	1.298	.8004
95	1.161	.8729	1.221	.8385	1.297	.8013
96	1.160	.8734	1.219	.8392	1.295	.8022
97	1.159	.8741	1.218	.8399	1.293	.8031
98	1.158	.8746	1.217	.8406	1.291	.8039
99	1.158	.8752	1.216	.8413	1.289	.8047
100	1.157	.8757	1.214	.8420	1.288	.8055

TABLE A-21. FACTORS FOR COMPUTING ONE-SIDED CONFIDENCE LIMITS FOR σ

Degrees of Freedom ν	$A_{.05}$	$A_{.95}$	$A_{.025}$	$A_{.975}$	$A_{.01}$	$A_{.99}$	$A_{.005}$	$A_{.995}$
1	.5103	15.947	.4461	31.910	.3882	79.786	.3562	159.576
2	.5778	4.415	.5207	6.285	.4660	9.975	.4344	14.124
3	.6196	2.920	.5665	3.729	.5142	5.111	.4834	6.467
4	.6493	2.372	.5992	2.874	.5489	3.669	.5188	4.396
5	.6721	2.089	.6242	2.453	.5757	3.003	.5464	3.485
6	.6903	1.915	.6444	2.202	.5974	2.623	.5688	2.980
7	.7054	1.797	.6612	2.035	.6155	2.377	.5875	2.660
8	.7183	1.711	.6754	1.916	.6310	2.204	.6037	2.439
9	.7293	1.645	.6878	1.826	.6445	2.076	.6177	2.278
10	.7391	1.593	.6987	1.755	.6564	1.977	.6301	2.154
11	.7477	1.551	.7084	1.698	.6670	1.898	.6412	2.056
12	.7554	1.515	.7171	1.651	.6765	1.833	.6512	1.976
13	.7624	1.485	.7250	1.611	.6852	1.779	.6603	1.909
14	.7688	1.460	.7321	1.577	.6931	1.733	.6686	1.854
15	.7747	1.437	.7387	1.548	.7004	1.694	.6762	1.806
20	.7979	1.358	.7650	1.444	.7297	1.556	.7071	1.640
25	.8149	1.308	.7843	1.380	.7511	1.473	.7299	1.542
30	.8279	1.274	.7991	1.337	.7678	1.416	.7477	1.475
40	.8470	1.228	.8210	1.279	.7925	1.343	.7740	1.390
50	.8606	1.199	.8367	1.243	.8103	1.297	.7931	1.337
60	.8710	1.179	.8487	1.217	.8239	1.265	.8078	1.299
70	.8793	1.163	.8583	1.198	.8349	1.241	.8196	1.272
80	.8861	1.151	.8662	1.183	.8439	1.222	.8293	1.250
90	.8919	1.141	.8728	1.171	.8515	1.207	.8376	1.233
100	.8968	1.133	.8785	1.161	.8581	1.195	.8446	1.219

For large degrees of freedom, we may use the approximate formula:

$$A_P = \sqrt{2\nu}/(z_P + \sqrt{2\nu - 1}),$$

where z_P is found in Table A-2.

TABLE A-22. CONFIDENCE LIMITS FOR A PROPORTION (TWO-SIDED)

For confidence limits for $n > 30$, see Table A-24.

Upper limits are in boldface. The observed proportion in a random sample is r/n

n = 1

r	90%		95%		99%	
0	0	.900	0	.950	0	.990
1	.100	1	.050	1	.010	1

n = 2

r	90%		95%		99%	
0	0	.684	0	.776	0	.900
1	.051	.949	.025+	.975−	.005+	.995−
2	.316	1	.224	1	.100	1

n = 3

r	90%		95%		99%	
0	0	.536	0	.632	0	.785−
1	.035−	.804	.017	.865−	.003	.941
2	.196	.965+	.135+	.983	.059	.997
3	.464	1	.368	1	.215+	1

n = 4

r	90%		95%		99%	
0	0	.500	0	.527	0	.684
1	.026	.680	.013	.751	.003	.859
2	.143	.857	.098	.902	.042	.958
3	.320	.974	.249	.987	.141	.997
4	.500	1	.473	1	.316	1

n = 5

r	90%		95%		99%	
0	0	.379	0	.500	0	.602
1	.021	.621	.010	.657	.002	.778
2	.112	.753	.076	.811	.033	.894
3	.247	.888	.189	.924	.106	.967
4	.379	.979	.343	.990	.222	.998
5	.621	1	.500	1	.398	1

n = 6

r	90%		95%		99%	
0	0	.345−	0	.402	0	.536
1	.017	.542	.009	.598	.002	.706
2	.093	.667	.063	.729	.027	.827
3	.201	.799	.133	.847	.085−	.915+
4	.333	.907	.271	.937	.173	.973
5	.458	.983	.402	.991	.294	.998
6	.655+	1	.598	1	.464	1

n = 7

r	90%		95%		99%	
0	0	.316	0	.377	0	.500
1	.015−	.500	.007	.554	.001	.643
2	.079	.684	.053	.659	.023	.764
3	.170	.721	.129	.775−	.071	.858
4	.279	.830	.225+	.871	.142	.929
5	.316	.921	.341	.947	.236	.977
6	.500	.985+	.416	.993	.357	.999
7	.684	1	.623	1	.500	1

n = 8

r	90%		95%		99%	
0	0	.255−	0	.315+	0	.451
1	.013	.418	.006	.500	.001	.590
2	.069	.582	.046	.685−	.020	.707
3	.147	.745+	.111	.711	.061	.802
4	.240	.760	.193	.807	.121	.879
5	.255−	.853	.289	.889	.198	.939
6	.418	.931	.315+	.954	.293	.980
7	.582	.987	.500	.994	.410	.999
8	.745+	1	.685−	1	.549	1

n = 9

r	90%		95%		99%	
0	0	.232	0	.289	0	.402
1	.012	.391	.006	.443	.001	.598
2	.061	.515+	.041	.558	.017	.656
3	.129	.610	.098	.711	.053	.750
4	.210	.768	.169	.749	.105+	.829
5	.232	.790	.251	.831	.171	.895−
6	.390	.871	.289	.902	.250	.947
7	.485−	.939	.442	.959	.344	.983
8	.609	.988	.557	.994	.402	.999
9	.768	1	.711	1	.598	1

n = 10

r	90%		95%		99%	
0	0	.222	0	.267	0	.376
1	.010	.352	.005+	.397	.001	.512
2	.055−	.500	.037	.603	.016	.624
3	.116	.648	.087	.619	.048	.703
4	.188	.659	.150	.733	.093	.782
5	.222	.778	.222	.778	.150	.850
6	.341	.812	.267	.850	.218	.907
7	.352	.884	.381	.913	.297	.952
8	.500	.945+	.397	.963	.376	.984
9	.648	.990	.603	.995−	.488	.999
10	.778	1	.733	1	.624	1

n = 11

r	90%		95%		99%	
0	0	.197	0	.250	0	.359
1	.010	.315+	.005−	.369	.001	.500
2	.049	.423	.033	.500	.014	.593
3	.105−	.577	.079	.631	.043	.660
4	.169	.685−	.135+	.667	.084	.738
5	.197	.698	.200	.750	.134	.806
6	.302	.803	.250	.800	.194	.866
7	.315+	.831	.333	.865−	.262	.916
8	.423	.895+	.369	.921	.340	.957
9	.577	.951	.500	.967	.407	.986
10	.685−	.990	.631	.995+	.500	.999
11	.803	1	.750	1	.641	1

n = 12

r	90%		95%		99%	
0	0	.184	0	.236	0	.321
1	.009	.294	.004	.346	.001	.445+
2	.045+	.398	.030	.450	.013	.555−
3	.096	.500	.072	.550	.039	.679
4	.154	.602	.123	.654	.076	.698
5	.184	.706	.181	.706	.121	.765+
6	.271	.729	.236	.764	.175−	.825+
7	.294	.816	.294	.819	.235−	.879
8	.398	.846	.346	.877	.302	.924
9	.500	.904	.450	.928	.321	.961
10	.602	.955−	.550	.970	.445+	.987
11	.706	.991	.654	.996	.555−	.999
12	.816	1	.764	1	.679	1

Reproduced by permission from *Statistics Manual*, NAVORD REPORT 3369, NOTS 948, by E. L. Crow, F. A. Davis, and M. W. Maxfield, 1955, U.S. Naval Ordnance Test Station, China Lake, California.

TABLE A-22 (Continued). CONFIDENCE LIMITS FOR A PROPORTION (TWO-SIDED)

n = 13

r	90%		95%		99%	
0	0	.173	0	.225+	0	.302
1	.008	.276	.004	.327	.001	.429
2	.042	.379	.028	.434	.012	.523
3	.088	.470	.066	.520	.036	.594
4	.142	.545-	.113	.587	.069	.698
5	.173	.621	.166	.673	.111	.727
6	.246	.724	.224	.740	.159	.787
7	.276	.754	.260	.776	.213	.841
8	.379	.827	.327	.834	.273	.889
9	.455+	.858	.413	.887	.302	.931
10	.530	.912	.480	.934	.406	.964
11	.621	.958	.566	.972	.477	.988
12	.724	.992	.673	.996	.571	.999
13	.827	1	.775-	1	.698	1

n = 14

r	90%		95%		99%	
0	0	.163	0	.207	0	.286
1	.007	.261	.004	.312	.001	.392
2	.039	.365+	.026	.389	.011	.500
3	.081	.422	.061	.500	.033	.608
4	.131	.578	.104	.611	.064	.636
5	.163	.594	.153	.629	.102	.714
6	.224	.645+	.206	.688	.146	.751
7	.261	.739	.207	.793	.195-	.805+
8	.355+	.776	.312	.794	.249	.854
9	.406	.837	.371	.847	.286	.898
10	.422	.869	.389	.896	.364	.936
11	.578	.919	.500	.939	.392	.967
12	.635-	.961	.611	.974	.500	.989
13	.739	.993	.688	.996	.608	.999
14	.837	1	.793	1	.714	1

n = 15

r	90%		95%		99%	
0	0	.154	0	.191	0	.273
1	.007	.247	.003	.302	.001	.373
2	.036	.326	.024	.369	.010	.461
3	.076	.400	.057	.448	.031	.539
4	.122	.500	.097	.552	.059	.627
5	.154	.600	.142	.631	.094	.672
6	.205+	.674	.191	.668	.135-	.727
7	.247	.675-	.192	.706	.179	.771
8	.325+	.753	.294	.808	.229	.821
9	.326	.795-	.332	.809	.273	.865+
10	.400	.846	.369	.858	.328	.906
11	.500	.878	.448	.903	.373	.941
12	.600	.924	.552	.943	.461	.969
13	.674	.964	.631	.976	.539	.990
14	.753	.993	.698	.997	.627	.999
15	.846	1	.809	1	.727	1

n = 16

r	90%		95%		99%	
0	0	.147	0	.179	0	.264
1	.007	.235+	.003	.273	.001	.357
2	.034	.305+	.023	.352	.010	.451
3	.071	.381	.053	.429	.029	.525-
4	.114	.450	.090	.500	.055+	.579
5	.147	.550	.132	.571	.088	.643
6	.189	.619	.178	.648	.125+	.705-
7	.235+	.695-	.179	.727	.166	.739
8	.299	.701	.272	.728	.212	.788
9	.305+	.765-	.273	.821	.261	.834
10	.381	.811	.352	.822	.295+	.875-
11	.450	.853	.429	.868	.357	.912
12	.550	.886	.500	.910	.421	.945-
13	.619	.929	.571	.947	.475+	.971
14	.695-	.966	.648	.977	.549	.990
15	.765-	.993	.727	.997	.643	.999
16	.853	1	.821	1	.736	1

n = 17

r	90%		95%		99%	
0	0	.140	0	.167	0	.243
1	.006	.225+	.003	.254	.001	.346
2	.032	.290	.021	.337	.009	.413
3	.067	.364	.050	.417	.027	.500
4	.107	.432	.085-	.489	.052	.587
5	.140	.500	.124	.544	.082	.620
6	.175+	.568	.166	.594	.117	.662
7	.225+	.636	.167	.663	.155+	.757
8	.277	.710	.253	.746	.197	.758
9	.290	.723	.254	.747	.242	.803
10	.364	.775-	.337	.833	.243	.845
11	.432	.825-	.406	.834	.338	.883
12	.500	.860	.456	.876	.380	.918
13	.568	.893	.511	.915+	.413	.948
14	.636	.933	.583	.950	.500	.973
15	.710	.968	.663	.979	.587	.991
16	.775-	.994	.746	.997	.654	.999
17	.860	1	.833	1	.757	1

n = 18

r	90%		95%		99%	
0	0	.135-	0	.157	0	.228
1	.006	.216	.003	.242	.001	.318
2	.030	.277	.020	.325-	.008	.397
3	.063	.349	.047	.381	.025+	.466
4	.101	.419	.080	.444	.049	.534
5	.135-	.482	.116	.556	.077	.603
6	.163	.536	.156	.619	.110	.682
7	.216	.584	.157	.625+	.145+	.686
8	.257	.651	.236	.675-	.184	.772
9	.277	.723	.242	.758	.226	.774
10	.349	.743	.325-	.764	.228	.816
11	.416	.784	.375-	.843	.314	.855-
12	.464	.837	.381	.844	.318	.890
13	.518	.865+	.444	.884	.397	.923
14	.581	.899	.556	.920	.466	.951
15	.651	.937	.619	.953	.534	.975-
16	.723	.970	.675+	.980	.603	.992
17	.784	.994	.758	.997	.682	.999
18	.865+	1	.843	1	.772	1

n = 19

r	90%		95%		99%	
0	0	.130	0	.150	0	.218
1	.006	.209	.003	.232	.001	.305+
2	.028	.265+	.019	.316	.008	.383
3	.059	.337	.044	.365-	.024	.455+
4	.095+	.387	.075+	.426	.046	.515+
5	.130	.440	.110	.500	.073	.564
6	.151	.560	.147	.574	.103	.617
7	.209	.613	.150	.635+	.137	.695-
8	.238	.614	.222	.655+	.173	.707
9	.265+	.663	.232	.688	.212	.782
10	.337	.735-	.312	.768	.218	.788
11	.386	.762	.345-	.778	.293	.827
12	.387	.791	.365-	.850	.305+	.863
13	.440	.849	.426	.853	.383	.897
14	.560	.870	.500	.890	.436	.927
15	.613	.905-	.574	.925-	.485-	.954
16	.663	.941	.635+	.956	.545-	.976
17	.735-	.972	.684	.981	.617	.992
18	.791	.994	.768	.997	.695-	.999
19	.870	1	.850	1	.782	1

n = 20

r	90%		95%		99%	
0	0	.126	0	.143	0	.209
1	.005+	.203	.003	.222	.001	.293
2	.027	.255-	.018	.294	.008	.375-
3	.056	.328	.042	.351	.023	.424
4	.090	.367	.071	.411	.044	.500
5	.126	.422	.104	.467	.069	.576
6	.141	.500	.140	.533	.098	.601
7	.201	.578	.143	.589	.129	.637
8	.221	.633	.209	.649	.163	.707
9	.255+	.642	.222	.706	.200	.726
10	.325	.675+	.293	.707	.209	.791
11	.358	.745+	.294	.778	.274	.800
12	.367	.779	.351	.791	.293	.837
13	.422	.799	.411	.857	.363	.871
14	.500	.859	.467	.860	.399	.902
15	.578	.874	.533	.896	.424	.931
16	.633	.910	.589	.929	.500	.956
17	.672	.944	.649	.958	.576	.977
18	.745+	.973	.706	.982	.625+	.992
19	.797	.995-	.778	.997	.707	.999
20	.874	1	.857	1	.791	1

TABLE A-22 (Continued). CONFIDENCE LIMITS FOR A PROPORTION (TWO-SIDED)

r	90%		95%		99%		r	90%		95%		99%	
				n = 21							n = 22		
0	0	.123	0	.137	0	.201	0	0	.116	0	.132	0	.194
1	.005 +	.192	.002	.213	.000	.283	1	.005 −	.182	.002	.205 +	.000	.273
2	.026	.245 −	.017	.277	.007	.347	2	.024	.236	.016	.264	.007	.334
3	.054	.307	.040	.338	.022	.409	3	.051	.289	.038	.326	.021	.396
4	.086	.353	.068	.398	.041	.466	4	.082	.340	.065 −	.389	.039	.454
5	.121	.407	.099	.455 +	.065 +	.534	5	.115 −	.393	.094	.424	.062	.505 −
6	.130	.458	.132	.506	.092	.591	6	.116	.444	.126	.500	.088	.550
7	.191	.542	.137	.551	.122	.653	7	.181	.500	.132	.576	.116	.604
8	.192	.593	.197	.602	.155 −	.661	8	.182	.556	.187	.582	.147	.666
9	.245 −	.647	.213	.662	.189	.717	9	.236	.607	.205 +	.617	.179	.682
10	.306	.693	.276	.723	.201	.743	10	.289	.660	.260	.674	.194	.727
11	.307	.694	.277	.724	.257	.799	11	.290	.710	.264	.736	.242	.758
12	.353	.755 +	.338	.787	.283	.811	12	.340	.711	.326	.740	.273	.806
13	.407	.808	.398	.803	.339	.845 +	13	.393	.764	.383	.795 −	.318	.821
14	.458	.809	.449	.863	.347	.878	14	.444	.818	.418	.813	.334	.853
15	.542	.870	.494	.868	.409	.908	15	.500	.819	.424	.868	.396	.884
16	.593	.879	.545 −	.901	.466	.935 −	16	.556	.884	.500	.874	.450	.912
17	.647	.914	.602	.932	.534	.959	17	.607	.885 +	.576	.906	.495 +	.938
18	.693	.946	.662	.960	.591	.978	18	.660	.918	.611	.935 +	.540	.961
19	.755 +	.974	.723	.983	.653	.993	19	.711	.949	.674	.962	.604	.979
20	.808	.995 −	.787	.998	.717	1.000	20	.764	.976	.736	.984	.666	.993
21	.877	1	.863	1	.799	1	21	.818	.995 +	.795 −	.998	.727	1.000
							22	.884	1	.868	1	.806	1
				n = 23							n = 24		
0	0	.111	0	.127	0	.187	0	0	.103 +	0	.122	0	.181
1	.005 −	.174	.002	.198	.000	.265 +	1	.004	.165 +	.002	.191	.000	.259
2	.023	.228	.016	.255 −	.007	.323	2	.022	.221	.015 +	.246	.006	.313
3	.049	.274	.037	.317	.020	.386	3	.047	.264	.035 −	.308	.019	.364
4	.078	.328	.062	.361	.038	.429	4	.075 −	.317	.059	.347	.036	.416
5	.110	.381	.090	.409	.059	.500	5	.105 −	.370	.086	.396	.057	.464
6	.111	.431	.120	.457	.084	.571	6	.105 +	.423	.115 −	.443	.080	.536
7	.173	.479	.127	.543	.111	.580	7	.165 −	.448	.122	.500	.106	.584
8	.174	.522	.178	.591	.140	.616	8	.165 +	.552	.169	.557	.133	.636
9	.228	.569	.198	.639	.171	.677	9	.221	.553	.191	.604	.163	.638
10	.273	.619	.247	.640	.187	.702	10	.259	.587	.234	.653	.181	.687
11	.274	.672	.255 −	.683	.229	.735 −	11	.264	.630	.246	.661	.216	.720
12	.328	.726	.317	.745 +	.265 +	.771	12	.317	.683	.308	.692	.257	.743
13	.381	.727	.360	.753	.298	.813	13	.370	.736	.339	.754	.280	.784
14	.431	.772	.361	.802	.323	.829	14	.413	.741	.347	.766	.313	.819
15	.478	.826	.409	.822	.384	.860	15	.447	.779	.396	.809	.362	.837
16	.521	.827	.457	.873	.420	.889	16	.448	.835 −	.443	.831	.364	.867
17	.569	.889	.543	.880	.429	.916	17	.552	.835 +	.500	.878	.416	.894
18	.619	.890	.591	.910	.500	.941	18	.577	.895 −	.557	.885 +	.464	.920
19	.672	.922	.639	.938	.571	.962	19	.630	.895 +	.604	.914	.536	.943
20	.726	.951	.683	.963	.614	.980	20	.683	.925 +	.653	.941	.584	.964
21	.772	.977	.745 +	.984	.677	.993	21	.736	.953	.692	.965 +	.636	.981
22	.826	.995 +	.802	.998	.735 −	1.000	22	.779	.978	.754	.985 −	.687	.994
23	.889	1	.873	1	.813	1	23	.835 −	.996	.809	.998	.741	1.000
							24	.895 −	1	.878	1	.819	1
				n = 25							n = 26		
0	0	.102	0	.118	0	.175 +	0	0	.098	0	.114	0	.170
1	.004	.159	.002	.185 +	.000	.246	1	.004	.152	.002	.180	.000	.235 −
2	.021	.214	.014	.238	.006	.305 −	2	.021	.209	.014	.230	.006	.298
3	.045 −	.255 −	.034	.303	.018	.352	3	.043	.247	.032	.283	.017	.342
4	.072	.307	.057	.336	.034	.403	4	.069	.299	.054	.325 +	.033	.393
5	.101	.362	.082	.384	.054	.431	5	.097	.343	.079	.374	.052	.442
6	.102	.390	.110	.431	.077	.500	6	.098	.377	.106	.421	.073	.487
7	.158	.432	.118	.475 −	.101	.549	7	.151	.419	.114	.465 −	.097	.526
8	.159	.500	.161	.525 +	.127	.597	8	.152	.460	.154	.506	.122	.562
9	.214	.568	.185 +	.569	.155 +	.648	9	.209	.540	.180	.542	.149	.607
10	.246	.610	.222	.616	.175 +	.658	10	.233	.581	.212	.579	.170	.658
11	.255 −	.611	.238	.664	.205 +	.695 +	11	.247	.623	.230	.626	.195 −	.678
12	.307	.640	.296	.683	.245 +	.754	12	.299	.657	.282	.675 −	.234	.702
13	.360	.693	.317	.704	.246	.755 −	13	.342	.658	.283	.717	.235 −	.765 +
14	.389	.745 +	.336	.762	.305 +	.795	14	.343	.701	.325 +	.718	.298	.766
15	.390	.754	.384	.778	.342	.825 −	15	.377	.753	.374	.770	.322	.805 +
16	.432	.786	.431	.815 −	.352	.845 −	16	.419	.767	.421	.788	.342	.830
17	.500	.841	.475 −	.839	.403	.873	17	.460	.791	.458	.820	.393	.851
18	.568	.842	.525 +	.882	.451	.899	18	.540	.848	.494	.846	.438	.878
19	.610	.898	.569	.890	.500	.923	19	.581	.849	.535 −	.886	.474	.903
20	.638	.899	.616	.918	.549	.946	20	.623	.902	.579	.894	.513	.927
21	.693	.928	.664	.943	.597	.966	21	.657	.903	.626	.921	.558	.948
22	.745 +	.955 +	.697	.966	.648	.982	22	.701	.931	.675 −	.946	.607	.967
23	.786	.979	.762	.986	.695 +	.994	23	.753	.957	.717	.968	.658	.983
24	.841	.996	.815 −	.998	.754	1.000	24	.791	.979	.770	.986	.702	.994
25	.898	1	.882	1	.825 −	1	25	.848	.996	.820	.998	.765 +	1.000
							26	.902	1	.886	1	.830	1

TABLE A-22 (Continued). CONFIDENCE LIMITS FOR A PROPORTION (TWO-SIDED)

n = 27

r	90%		95%		99%	
0	0	.093	0	.110	0	.166
1	.004	.146	.002	.175−	.000	.225−
2	.020	.204	.013	.223	.006	.297
3	.042	.239	.031	.270	.017	.332
4	.066	.291	.052	.316	.032	.384
5	.093	.327	.076	.364	.050	.419
6	.094	.365+	.101	.415−	.070	.461
7	.145+	.407	.110	.437	.093	.539
8	.146	.447	.148	.500	.117	.581
9	.204	.500	.175−	.563	.143	.587
10	.221	.553	.202	.570	.166	.617
11	.239	.593	.223	.598	.185−	.668
12	.291	.635−	.269	.636	.224	.702
13	.326	.673	.270	.684	.225−	.716
14	.327	.674	.316	.730	.284	.775+
15	.365+	.709	.364	.731	.298	.776
16	.407	.761	.402	.777	.332	.815+
17	.447	.779	.430	.798	.383	.834
18	.500	.796	.437	.825+	.413	.857
19	.553	.854	.500	.852	.419	.883
20	.593	.855−	.563	.890	.461	.907
21	.635−	.906	.585+	.899	.539	.930
22	.673	.907	.636	.924	.581	.950
23	.709	.934	.684	.948	.616	.968
24	.761	.958	.730	.969	.668	.983
25	.796	.980	.777	.987	.703	.994
26	.854	.996	.825+	.998	.775+	1.000
27	.907	1	.890	1	.834	1

n = 28

r	90%		95%		99%	
0	0	.090	0	.106	0	.162
1	.004	.140	.002	.170	.000	.218
2	.019	.201	.013	.217	.005+	.273
3	.040	.232	.030	.259	.016	.323
4	.064	.284	.050	.307	.031	.365−
5	.089	.312	.073	.357	.048	.408
6	.090	.355−	.098	.384	.068	.449
7	.139	.396	.106	.424	.089	.500
8	.140	.435+	.142	.463	.112	.551
9	.197	.473	.170	.537	.137	.592
10	.208	.527	.192	.576	.162	.635+
11	.232	.565−	.217	.616	.175+	.636
12	.284	.604	.258	.619	.214	.677
13	.310	.645+	.259	.645+	.218	.727
14	.312	.688	.307	.693	.272	.728
15	.355−	.690	.355−	.741	.273	.782
16	.396	.716	.381	.742	.323	.786
17	.435+	.768	.384	.783	.364	.825−
18	.473	.792	.424	.808	.365−	.838
19	.527	.803	.463	.830	.408	.863
20	.565−	.860	.537	.858	.449	.888
21	.604	.861	.576	.894	.500	.911
22	.645+	.910	.616	.902	.551	.932
23	.688	.911	.643	.927	.592	.952
24	.716	.936	.693	.950	.635+	.969
25	.768	.960	.741	.970	.677	.984
26	.799	.981	.783	.987	.727	.995−
27	.860	.996	.830	.998	.782	1.000
28	.910	1	.894	1	.838	1

n = 29

r	90%		95%		99%	
0	0	.087	0	.103	0	.160
1	.004	.135−	.002	.166	.000	.211
2	.018	.190	.012	.211	.005+	.263
3	.039	.225−	.029	.251	.015−	.316
4	.062	.279	.049	.299	.030	.354
5	.086	.303	.070	.340	.046	.397
6	.087	.345−	.094	.374	.065+	.438
7	.134	.385+	.103	.413	.086	.477
8	.135−	.425−	.136	.451	.108	.523
9	.189	.463	.166	.500	.132	.562
10	.190	.500	.184	.549	.157	.603
11	.225−	.537	.211	.587	.165+	.646
12	.276	.575+	.247	.626	.206	.654
13	.294	.615−	.251	.660	.211	.684
14	.303	.655+	.299	.661	.260	.737
15	.345−	.697	.339	.701	.263	.740
16	.385+	.706	.340	.749	.316	.789
17	.425−	.724	.374	.753	.346	.794
18	.463	.775+	.413	.789	.354	.835−
19	.500	.810	.451	.816	.397	.843
20	.537	.811	.500	.834	.438	.868
21	.575+	.865+	.549	.864	.477	.892
22	.615−	.866	.587	.897	.523	.914
23	.655−	.913	.626	.906	.562	.935−
24	.697	.914	.660	.930	.603	.954
25	.721	.938	.701	.951	.646	.970
26	.775+	.961	.749	.971	.684	.985−
27	.810	.982	.789	.988	.737	.995−
28	.865+	.996	.834	.998	.789	1.000
29	.913	1	.897	1	.840	1

n = 30

r	90%		95%		99%	
0	0	.084	0	.100	0	.152
1	.004	.130	.002	.163	.000	.206
2	.018	.183	.012	.205+	.005+	.256
3	.037	.219	.028	.244	.015−	.310
4	.059	.266	.047	.292	.028	.345−
5	.083	.295−	.068	.325−	.045−	.388
6	.084	.336	.091	.364	.063	.430
7	.129	.376	.100	.403	.083	.469
8	.130	.416	.131	.440	.104	.505+
9	.182	.455+	.163	.476	.127	.538
10	.183	.492	.175+	.524	.151	.570
11	.219	.524	.205+	.560	.152	.612
12	.265−	.554	.236	.597	.198	.655+
13	.266	.584	.244	.636	.206	.671
14	.295−	.624	.292	.675+	.249	.692
15	.336	.664	.324	.676	.256	.744
16	.376	.705+	.325−	.708	.308	.751
17	.416	.734	.364	.756	.329	.794
18	.446	.735+	.403	.764	.345−	.802
19	.476	.781	.440	.795−	.388	.848
20	.508	.817	.476	.825−	.430	.849
21	.545−	.818	.524	.837	.462	.873
22	.584	.870	.560	.869	.495−	.896
23	.624	.871	.597	.900	.531	.917
24	.664	.916	.636	.909	.570	.937
25	.705+	.917	.675+	.932	.612	.955+
26	.734	.941	.708	.953	.655+	.972
27	.781	.963	.756	.972	.690	.985+
28	.817	.982	.795−	.988	.744	.995−
29	.870	.996	.837	.998	.794	1.000
30	.916	1	.900	1	.848	1

TABLE A-23. CONFIDENCE LIMITS FOR A PROPORTION (ONE-SIDED)

For confidence limits for $n > 30$, see Table A-24.

If the observed proportion is r/n, enter the table with n and r for an upper one-sided limit.
For a lower one-sided limit, enter the table with n and $n - r$ and subtract the table entry from 1.

r	90%	95%	99%	r	90%	95%	99%	r	90%	95%	99%
	n = 2				n = 3				n = 4		
0	.684	.776	.900	0	.536	.632	.785−	0	.438	.527	.684
1	.949	.975−	.995−	1	.804	.865−	.941	1	.680	.751	.859
				2	.965+	.983	.997	2	.857	.902	.958
								3	.974	.987	.997

r	90%	95%	99%	r	90%	95%	99%	r	90%	95%	99%
	n = 5				n = 6				n = 7		
0	.369	.451	.602	0	.319	.393	.536	0	.280	.348	.482
1	.584	.657	.778	1	.510	.582	.706	1	.453	.521	.643
2	.753	.811	.894	2	.667	.729	.827	2	.596	.659	.764
3	.888	.924	.967	3	.799	.847	.915+	3	.721	.775−	.858
4	.979	.990	.998	4	.907	.937	.973	4	.830	.871	.929
				5	.983	.991	.998	5	.921	.947	.977
								6	.985+	.993	.999

r	90%	95%	99%	r	90%	95%	99%	r	90%	95%	99%
	n = 8				n = 9				n = 10		
0	.250	.312	.438	0	.226	.283	.401	0	.206	.259	.369
1	.406	.471	.590	1	.368	.429	.544	1	.337	.394	.504
2	.538	.600	.707	2	.490	.550	.656	2	.450	.507	.612
3	.655+	.711	.802	3	.599	.655+	.750	3	.552	.607	.703
4	.760	.807	.879	4	.699	.749	.829	4	.646	.696	.782
5	.853	.889	.939	5	.790	.831	.895−	5	.733	.778	.850
6	.931	.954	.980	6	.871	.902	.947	6	.812	.850	.907
7	.987	.994	.999	7	.939	.959	.983	7	.884	.913	.952
				8	.988	.994	.999	8	.945+	.963	.984
								9	.990	.995−	.999

r	90%	95%	99%	r	90%	95%	99%	r	90%	95%	99%
	n = 11				n = 12				n = 13		
0	.189	.238	.342	0	.175−	.221	.319	0	.162	.206	.298
1	.310	.364	.470	1	.287	.339	.440	1	.268	.316	.413
2	.415+	.470	.572	2	.386	.438	.537	2	.360	.410	.506
3	.511	.564	.660	3	.475+	.527	.622	3	.444	.495−	.588
4	.599	.650	.738	4	.559	.609	.698	4	.523	.573	.661
5	.682	.729	.806	5	.638	.685−	.765+	5	.598	.645+	.727
6	.759	.800	.866	6	.712	.755−	.825+	6	.669	.713	.787
7	.831	.865−	.916	7	.781	.819	.870	7	.736	.776	.841
8	.895+	.921	.957	8	.846	.877	.924	8	.799	.834	.889
9	.951	.967	.986	9	.904	.928	.961	9	.858	.887	.931
10	.990	.995+	.999	10	.955−	.970	.987	10	.912	.934	.964
				11	.991	.996	.999	11	.958	.972	.988
								12	.992	.996	.999

r	90%	95%	99%	r	90%	95%	99%	r	90%	95%	99%
	n = 14				n = 15				n = 16		
0	.152	.193	.280	0	.142	.181	.264	0	.134	.171	.250
1	.251	.297	.389	1	.236	.279	.368	1	.222	.264	.349
2	.337	.385+	.478	2	.317	.363	.453	2	.300	.344	.430
3	.417	.466	.557	3	.393	.440	.529	3	.371	.417	.503
4	.492	.540	.627	4	.464	.511	.597	4	.439	.484	.569
5	.563	.610	.692	5	.532	.577	.660	5	.504	.548	.630

TABLE A-23 (Continued). CONFIDENCE LIMITS FOR A PROPORTION (ONE-SIDED)

r	90%	95%	99%	r	90%	95%	99%	r	90%	95%	99%
	n = 14 (Continued)				n = 15 (Continued)				n = 16 (Continued)		
6	.631	.675−	.751	6	.596	.640	.718	6	.565+	.609	.687
7	.695+	.736	.805+	7	.658	.700	.771	7	.625−	.667	.739
8	.757	.794	.854	8	.718	.756	.821	8	.682	.721	.788
9	.815−	.847	.898	9	.774	.809	.865+	9	.737	.773	.834
10	.869	.896	.936	10	.828	.858	.906	10	.790	.822	.875−
11	.919	.939	.967	11	.878	.903	.941	11	.839	.868	.912
12	.961	.974	.989	12	.924	.943	.969	12	.886	.910	.945−
13	.993	.996	.999	13	.964	.976	.990	13	.929	.947	.971
				14	.993	.997	.999	14	.966	.977	.990
								15	.993	.997	.999
	n = 17				n = 18				n = 19		
0	.127	.162	.237	0	.120	.153	.226	0	.114	.146	.215+
1	.210	.250	.332	1	.199	.238	.316	1	.190	.226	.302
2	.284	.326	.410	2	.269	.310	.391	2	.257	.296	.374
3	.352	.396	.480	3	.334	.377	.458	3	.319	.359	.439
4	.416	.461	.543	4	.396	.439	.520	4	.378	.419	.498
5	.478	.522	.603	5	.455+	.498	.577	5	.434	.476	.554
6	.537	.580	.658	6	.512	.554	.631	6	.489	.530	.606
7	.594	.636	.709	7	.567	.608	.681	7	.541	.582	.655+
8	.650	.689	.758	8	.620	.659	.729	8	.592	.632	.702
9	.703	.740	.803	9	.671	.709	.774	9	.642	.680	.746
10	.754	.788	.845−	10	.721	.756	.816	10	.690	.726	.788
11	.803	.834	.883	11	.769	.801	.855−	11	.737	.770	.827
12	.849	.876	.918	12	.815−	.844	.890	12	.782	.812	.863
13	.893	.915+	.948	13	.858	.884	.923	13	.825−	.853	.897
14	.933	.950	.973	14	.899	.920	.951	14	.866	.890	.927
15	.968	.979	.991	15	.937	.953	.975−	15	.905−	.925−	.954
16	.994	.997	.999	16	.970	.980	.992	16	.941	.956	.976
				17	.994	.997	.999	17	.972	.981	.992
								18	.994	.997	.999
	n = 20				n = 21				n = 22		
0	.109	.139	.206	0	.104	.133	.197	0	.099	.127	.189
1	.181	.216	.289	1	.173	.207	.277	1	.166	.198	.266
2	.245−	.283	.358	2	.234	.271	.344	2	.224	.259	.330
3	.304	.344	.421	3	.291	.329	.404	3	.279	.316	.389
4	.361	.401	.478	4	.345+	.384	.460	4	.331	.369	.443
5	.415−	.456	.532	5	.397	.437	.512	5	.381	.420	.493
6	.467	.508	.583	6	.448	.487	.561	6	.430	.468	.541
7	.518	.558	.631	7	.497	.536	.608	7	.477	.515+	.587
8	.567	.606	.677	8	.544	.583	.653	8	.523	.561	.630
9	.615+	.653	.720	9	.590	.628	.695+	9	.568	.605−	.672
10	.662	.698	.761	10	.636	.672	.736	10	.611	.647	.712
11	.707	.741	.800	11	.679	.714	.774	11	.654	.689	.750
12	.751	.783	.837	12	.722	.755+	.811	12	.695+	.729	.786
13	.793	.823	.871	13	.764	.794	.845+	13	.736	.767	.821
14	.834	.860	.902	14	.804	.832	.878	14	.775+	.804	.853
15	.873	.896	.931	15	.842	.868	.908	15	.813	.840	.884
16	.910	.929	.956	16	.879	.901	.935−	16	.850	.874	.912
17	.944	.958	.977	17	.914	.932	.959	17	.885+	.906	.938
18	.973	.982	.992	18	.946	.960	.978	18	.918	.935+	.961
19	.995−	.997	.999	19	.974	.983	.993	19	.949	.962	.979
				20	.995−	.988	1.000	20	.976	.984	.993
								21	.995+	.998	1.000

TABLE A-23 (Continued). CONFIDENCE LIMITS FOR A PROPORTION (ONE-SIDED)

r	90%	95%	99%	r	90%	95%	99%	r	90%	95%	99%
	n = 23				**n = 24**				**n = 25**		
0	.095+	.122	.181	0	.091	.117	.175−	0	.088	.113	.168
1	.159	.190	.256	1	.153	.183	.246	1	.147	.176	.237
2	.215+	.249	.318	2	.207	.240	.307	2	.199	.231	.296
3	.268	.304	.374	3	.258	.292	.361	3	.248	.282	.349
4	.318	.355−	.427	4	.306	.342	.412	4	.295−	.330	.398
5	.366	.404	.476	5	.352	.389	.460	5	.340	.375+	.444
6	.413	.451	.522	6	.398	.435−	.505−	6	.383	.420	.488
7	.459	.496	.567	7	.442	.479	.548	7	.426	.462	.531
8	.503	.540	.609	8	.484	.521	.590	8	.467	.504	.571
9	.546	.583	.650	9	.526	.563	.630	9	.508	.544	.610
10	.589	.625−	.689	10	.567	.603	.668	10	.548	.583	.648
11	.630	.665−	.727	11	.608	.642	.705−	11	.587	.621	.684
12	.670	.704	.763	12	.647	.681	.740	12	.625−	.659	.719
13	.710	.742	.797	13	.685+	.718	.774	13	.662	.695−	.752
14	.748	.778	.829	14	.723	.754	.806	14	.699	.730	.784
15	.786	.814	.860	15	.759	.788	.837	15	.735−	.764	.815+
16	.822	.848	.889	16	.795+	.822	.867	16	.770	.798	.845+
17	.857	.880	.916	17	.830	.854	.894	17	.804	.830	.873
18	.890	.910	.941	18	.863	.885+	.920	18	.837	.861	.899
19	.922	.938	.962	19	.895+	.914	.943	19	.869	.890	.923
20	.951	.963	.980	20	.925+	.941	.964	20	.899	.918	.946
21	.977	.984	.993	21	.953	.965+	.981	21	.928	.943	.966
22	.995+	.998	1.000	22	.978	.985−	.994	22	.955+	.966	.982
				23	.996	.998	1.000	23	.979	.986	.994
								24	.996	.998	1.000
	n = 26				**n = 27**				**n = 28**		
0	.085−	.109	.162	0	.082	.105+	.157	0	.079	.101	.152
1	.142	.170	.229	1	.137	.164	.222	1	.132	.159	.215−
2	.192	.223	.286	2	.185+	.215+	.277	2	.179	.208	.268
3	.239	.272	.337	3	.231	.263	.326	3	.223	.254	.316
4	.284	.318	.385−	4	.275−	.308	.373	4	.265+	.298	.361
5	.328	.363	.430	5	.317	.351	.417	5	.306	.339	.404
6	.370	.405+	.473	6	.358	.392	.458	6	.346	.380	.445−
7	.411	.447	.514	7	.397	.432	.498	7	.385−	.419	.484
8	.451	.487	.554	8	.436	.471	.537	8	.422	.457	.521
9	.491	.526	.592	9	.475−	.509	.574	9	.459	.494	.558
10	.529	.564	.628	10	.512	.547	.610	10	.496	.530	.593
11	.567	.602	.664	11	.549	.583	.645+	11	.532	.565+	.627
12	.604	.638	.698	12	.585−	.618	.679	12	.567	.600	.660
13	.641	.673	.731	13	.620	.653	.711	13	.601	.634	.692
14	.676	.708	.763	14	.655+	.687	.743	14	.635+	.667	.723
15	.711	.742	.794	15	.689	.720	.773	15	.669	.699	.753
16	.746	.774	.823	16	.723	.752	.802	16	.701	.731	.782
17	.779	.806	.851	17	.756	.783	.831	17	.733	.762	.810
18	.812	.837	.878	18	.788	.814	.857	18	.765−	.792	.837
19	.843	.866	.903	19	.819	.843	.883	19	.796	.821	.863
20	.874	.894	.927	20	.849	.871	.907	20	.826	.849	.888
21	.903	.921	.948	21	.879	.899	.930	21	.855+	.876	.911
22	.931	.946	.967	22	.907	.924	.950	22	.883	.902	.932
23	.957	.968	.983	23	.934	.948	.968	23	.911	.927	.952
24	.979	.986	.994	24	.958	.969	.983	24	.936	.950	.969
25	.996	.998	1.000	25	.980	.987	.994	25	.960	.970	.984
				26	.996	.998	1.000	26	.981	.987	.995−
								27	.996	.998	1.000

TABLE A-23 (Continued). CONFIDENCE LIMITS FOR A PROPORTION (ONE-SIDED)

r	90%	95%	99%	r	90%	95%	99%
		n = 29				n = 30	
0	.076	.098	.147	0	.074	.095 +	.142
1	.128	.153	.208	1	.124	.149	.202
2	.173	.202	.260	2	.168	.195 +	.252
3	.216	.246	.307	3	.209	.239	.298
4	.257	.288	.350	4	.249	.280	.340
5	.297	.329	.392	5	.287	.319	.381
6	.335 −	.368	.432	6	.325 −	.357	.420
7	.372	.406	.470	7	.361	.394	.457
8	.409	.443	.507	8	.397	.430	.493
9	.445 +	.479	.542	9	.432	.465 +	.527
10	.481	.514	.577	10	.466	.499	.561
11	.515 +	.549	.610	11	.500	.533	.594
12	.550	.583	.643	12	.533	.566	.626
13	.583	.616	.674	13	.566	.598	.657
14	.616	.648	.705 −	14	.599	.630	.687
15	.649	.680	.734	15	.630	.661	.716
16	.681	.711	.763	16	.662	.692	.744
17	.712	.741	.791	17	.692	.721	.772
18	.743	.771	.818	18	.723	.750	.799
19	.774	.800	.843	19	.752	.779	.824
20	.803	.828	.868	20	.782	.807	.849
21	.832	.855 −	.892	21	.810	.834	.873
22	.860	.881	.914	22	.838	.860	.896
23	.888	.906	.935 −	23	.865 +	.885 +	.917
24	.914	.930	.954	24	.891	.909	.937
25	.938	.951	.970	25	.917	.932	.955 +
26	.961	.971	.985 −	26	.941	.953	.972
27	.982	.988	.995 −	27	.963	.972	.985 +
28	.996	.998	1.000	28	.982	.988	.995 −
				29	.996	.998	1.000

TABLE A-24. CONFIDENCE BELTS FOR PROPORTIONS FOR $n > 30$
(CONFIDENCE COEFFICIENT .90)
For tables of confidence limits for $n \leq 30$, see Tables A-22 and A-23

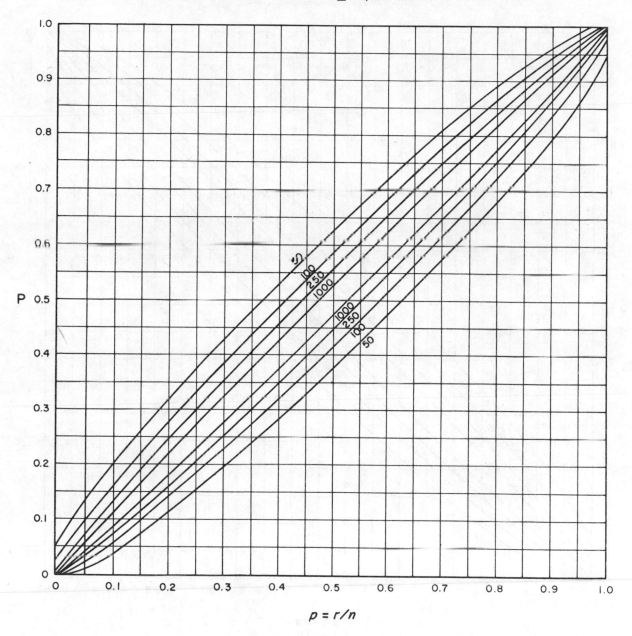

$$p = r/n$$

Reproduced, in part, by permission from *Introduction to Statistical Analysis* (2d ed.) by W. J. Dixon and F. J. Massey, Jr., Copyright, 1957, McGraw-Hill Book Company, Inc.

TABLE A-24 (Continued).   CONFIDENCE BELTS FOR PROPORTIONS FOR $n > 30$
(CONFIDENCE COEFFICIENT .95)

For tables of confidence limits for $n \leq 30$, see Tables A-22 and A-23

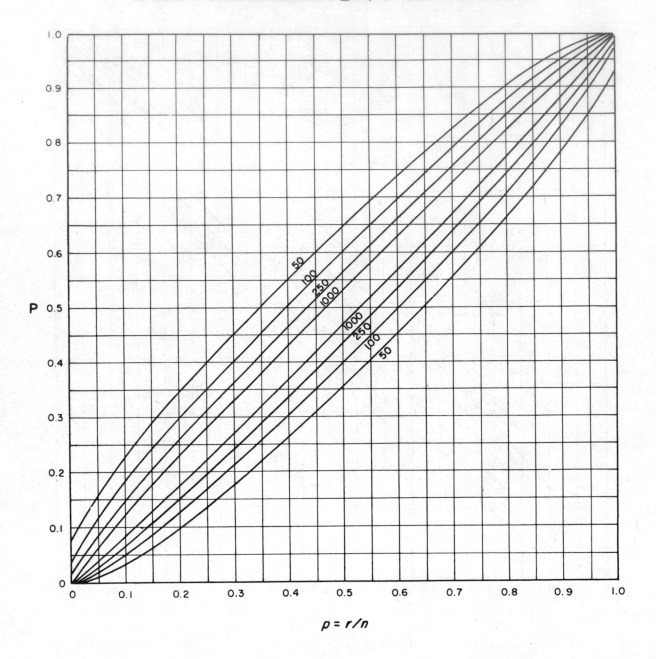

$p = r/n$

Reproduced, in part, with permission from *Biometrika*, Vol. 26, (1934), from article entitled "The Use of Confidence or Fiducial Limits Illustrated
in the Case of the Binomial" by C. J. Clopper and E. S. Pearson.

TABLE A-24 (Continued).   CONFIDENCE BELTS FOR PROPORTIONS FOR $n > 30$
(CONFIDENCE COEFFICIENT .99)
For tables of confidence limits for $n \leq 30$, see Tables A-22 and A-23

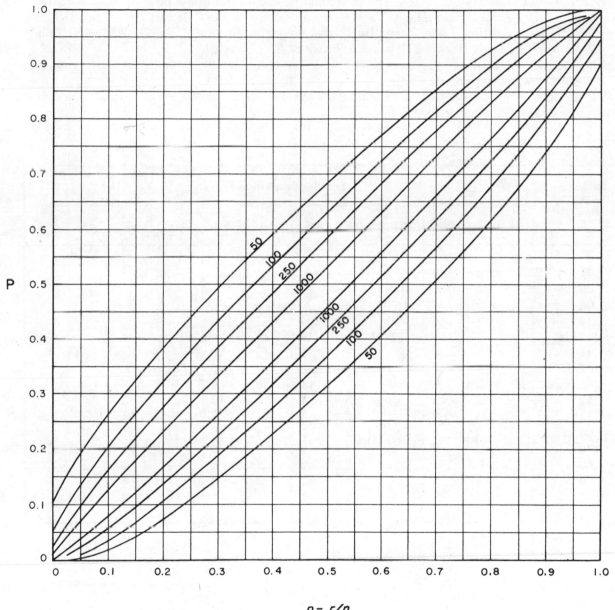

$$p = r/n$$

Reproduced, in part, with permission from *Biometrika*, Vol. 26, (1934), from article entitled "The Use of Confidence or Fiducial Limits Illustrated in the Case of the Binomial" by C. J. Clopper and E. S. Pearson.

TABLE A-25. SAMPLE SIZE REQUIRED FOR COMPARING A PROPORTION WITH A STANDARD PROPORTION WHEN THE SIGN OF THE DIFFERENCE IS NOT IMPORTANT

The use of Table A-25 (or equivalent use of Tables A-27 and A-8) is based on the inverse-sine transformation of the binomial to an approximately normal distribution.

Exact determination of required sample size could be made from tables of the binomial distribution, so far as the tables are available. (See *Tables of the Cumulative Binomial Probability Distribution*, Staff, Computation Laboratory, Harvard University, Section IV of the "Introduction" entitled "Applications", Harvard University Press, 1955.)

The entries computed for the tables were rounded to three significant figures, and the rounding was always upward.

These tables also may be used to determine the sample size required for comparing two proportions, as discussed in Chapter 8.

$$\alpha = .05, \quad 1 - \beta = .50$$

Larger Propor- tion	Smaller Proportion											
	.001	.002	.005	.01	.02	.05	.10	.20	.30	.40	.45	.50
.01	205	313	1120	—	—	—	—	—	—	—	—	—
.02	80	102	190	551	—	—	—	—	—	—	—	—
.05	26	30	41	62	138	—	—	—	—	—	—	—
.10	12	13	16	20	30	104	—	—	—	—	—	—
.20	6	6	7	8	10	17	48	—	—	—	—	—
.30	4	4	4	5	6	8	15	72	—	—	—	—
.40	3	3	3	3	4	5	8	20	88	—	—	—
.45	2	3	3	3	3	4	6	14	40	376	—	—
.50	2	2	2	3	3	4	5	10	23	95	383	—
.55	2	2	2	2	2	3	4	7	15	43	96	383
.60	2	2	2	2	2	3	4	6	11	24	43	95
.70	2	2	2	2	2	2	3	4	6	11	15	23
.80	1	1	1	1	2	2	2	3	4	6	7	10
.90	1	1	1	1	1	1	2	2	3	4	4	5
1.00	1	1	1	1	1	1	1	1	1	2	2	2

TABLE A-25 (Continued). SAMPLE SIZE REQUIRED FOR COMPARING A PROPORTION WITH A STANDARD PROPORTION WHEN THE SIGN OF THE DIFFERENCE IS NOT IMPORTANT

$\alpha = .05, \quad 1 - \beta = .80$

Larger Proportion	Smaller Proportion											
	.001	.002	.005	.01	.02	.05	.10	.20	.30	.40	.45	.50
.01	419	640	2280	—	—	—	—	—	—	—	—	—
.02	162	208	388	1130	—	—	—	—	—	—	—	—
.05	53	61	82	125	281	—	—	—	—	—	—	—
.10	24	26	32	40	61	212	—	—	—	—	—	—
.20	11	12	13	15	19	35	98	—	—	—	—	—
.30	7	7	8	9	11	16	30	146	—	—	—	—
.40	5	5	6	6	7	10	15	41	178	—	—	—
.45	4	5	5	5	6	8	12	27	82	767	—	—
.50	4	4	4	5	5	7	10	19	47	194	782	—
.55	4	4	4	4	5	6	8	15	30	87	196	782
.60	3	3	3	4	4	5	7	11	21	49	87	194
.70	3	3	3	3	3	4	5	8	12	21	30	47
.80	2	2	2	2	3	3	4	5	8	11	15	19
.90	2	2	2	2	2	2	3	4	5	7	8	10
1.00	1	1	1	1	1	2	2	2	2	3	3	4

$\alpha = .05, \quad 1 - \beta = .90$

Larger Proportion	Smaller Proportion											
	.001	.002	.005	.01	.02	.05	.10	.20	.30	.40	.45	.50
.01	560	857	3040	—	—	—	—	—	—	—	—	—
.02	217	279	520	1510	—	—	—	—	—	—	—	—
.05	70	81	110	168	376	—	—	—	—	—	—	—
.10	32	35	42	54	82	284	—	—	—	—	—	—
.20	15	15	18	20	26	47	131	—	—	—	—	—
.30	9	10	11	12	14	21	40	196	—	—	—	—
.40	7	7	7	8	9	13	20	54	239	—	—	—
.45	6	6	6	7	8	11	16	36	109	1030	—	—
.50	5	5	6	6	7	9	13	26	63	260	1050	—
.55	5	5	5	5	6	8	10	20	41	116	262	1050
.60	4	4	4	5	5	7	9	15	28	65	116	260
.70	3	3	4	4	4	5	6	10	16	28	41	63
.80	3	3	3	3	3	4	5	7	10	15	20	26
.90	2	2	2	2	3	3	4	5	6	9	10	13
1.00	2	2	2	2	2	2	2	3	3	4	4	5

TABLE A-25 (Continued).　SAMPLE SIZE REQUIRED FOR COMPARING A PROPORTION WITH A STANDARD PROPORTION WHEN THE SIGN OF THE DIFFERENCE IS NOT IMPORTANT

$\alpha = .05, \quad 1 - \beta = .95$

Larger Propor-tion	Smaller Proportion											
	.001	.002	.005	.01	.02	.05	.10	.20	.30	.40	.45	.50
.01	693	1060	3760	—	—	—	—	—	—	—	—	—
.02	268	345	642	1870	—	—	—	—	—	—	—	—
.05	87	100	136	207	465	—	—	—	—	—	—	—
.10	39	43	52	67	101	351	—	—	—	—	—	—
.20	18	19	22	25	32	58	162	—	—	—	—	—
.30	11	12	13	15	17	26	49	242	—	—	—	—
.40	8	8	9	10	12	16	25	67	295	—	—	—
.45	7	7	8	9	10	13	19	45	135	1270	—	—
.50	6	6	7	7	8	11	16	32	77	321	1300	—
.55	6	6	6	7	7	9	13	24	50	143	324	1300
.60	5	5	5	6	6	8	11	19	35	81	143	321
.70	4	4	4	5	5	6	8	12	20	35	50	77
.80	3	3	4	4	4	5	6	8	12	19	24	32
.90	3	3	3	3	3	4	4	6	8	11	13	16
1.00	2	2	2	2	2	2	3	3	4	5	5	6

$\alpha = .05, \quad 1 - \beta = .99$

Larger Propor-tion	Smaller Proportion											
	.001	.002	.005	.01	.02	.05	.10	.20	.30	.40	.45	.50
.01	979	1500	5320	—	—	—	—	—	—	—	—	—
.02	378	487	908	2640	—	—	—	—	—	—	—	—
.05	123	141	192	293	658	—	—	—	—	—	—	—
.10	55	60	73	94	142	496	—	—	—	—	—	—
.20	25	27	30	35	45	81	229	—	—	—	—	—
.30	16	17	18	20	24	37	70	342	—	—	—	—
.40	11	12	13	14	16	22	35	94	417	—	—	—
.45	10	10	11	12	14	18	27	63	190	1800	—	—
.50	9	9	9	10	12	15	22	45	109	453	1830	—
.55	8	8	8	9	10	13	18	34	71	202	458	1830
.60	7	7	7	8	9	11	15	26	49	114	202	453
.70	5	6	6	6	7	8	11	17	28	49	71	109
.80	4	5	5	5	5	6	8	12	17	26	34	45
.90	4	4	4	4	4	5	6	8	11	15	18	22
1.00	2	2	3	3	3	3	3	4	5	6	7	8

TABLE A-26. SAMPLE SIZE REQUIRED FOR COMPARING A PROPORTION WITH A STANDARD PROPORTION WHEN THE SIGN OF THE DIFFERENCE IS IMPORTANT

The use of Table A-26 (or the equivalent use of Tables A-27 and A-9) is based on the inverse-sine transformation of the binomial to an approximately normal distribution.

Exact determination of required sample size could be made from tables of the binomial distribution, so far as the tables are available. (See *Tables of the Cumulative Binomial Distribution*, Staff, Computation Laboratory, Harvard University, Section IV of the "Introduction" entitled "Applications", Harvard University Press, 1955.)

The entries computed for the tables were rounded to three significant figures, and the rounding was always upward.

These tables may also be used to determine the sample size required for comparing two proportions, as discussed in Chapter 8.

$$\alpha = .05, \quad 1 - \beta = .50$$

Larger Proportion	Smaller Proportion											
	.001	.002	.005	.01	.02	.05	.10	.20	.30	.40	.45	.50
.01	145	221	783	—	—	—	—	—	—	—	—	—
.02	56	72	134	389	—	—	—	—	—	—	—	—
.05	19	21	29	44	97	—	—	—	—	—	—	—
.10	9	9	11	14	21	74	—	—	—	—	—	—
.20	4	4	5	6	7	12	34	—	—	—	—	—
.30	3	3	3	3	4	6	11	51	—	—	—	—
.40	2	2	2	2	3	4	6	14	62	—	—	—
.45	2	2	2	2	2	3	4	10	28	265	—	—
.50	2	2	2	2	2	3	4	7	16	67	270	—
.55	2	2	2	2	2	2	3	5	11	30	68	270
.60	1	1	2	2	2	2	3	4	8	17	30	67
.70	1	1	1	1	1	2	2	3	4	8	11	16
.80	1	1	1	1	1	1	2	2	3	4	5	7
.90	1	1	1	1	1	1	1	2	2	3	3	4
1.00	1	1	1	1	1	1	1	1	1	1	1	2

TABLE A-26 (Continued). SAMPLE SIZE REQUIRED FOR COMPARING A PROPORTION WITH A STANDARD PROPORTION WHEN THE SIGN OF THE DIFFERENCE IS IMPORTANT

$$\alpha = .05, \quad 1 - \beta = .80$$

Larger Propor-tion	Smaller Proportion											
	.001	.002	.005	.01	.02	.05	.10	.20	.30	.40	.45	.50
.01	330	504	1790	—	—	—	—	—	—	—	—	—
.02	128	164	306	888	—	—	—	—	—	—	—	—
.05	42	48	65	99	222	—	—	—	—	—	—	—
.10	19	21	25	32	48	167	—	—	—	—	—	—
.20	9	9	11	12	15	28	77	—	—	—	—	—
.30	6	6	6	7	9	13	24	115	—	—	—	—
.40	4	4	5	5	6	8	12	32	141	—	—	—
.45	4	4	4	4	5	6	10	21	64	604	—	—
.50	3	3	4	4	4	5	8	15	37	153	617	—
.55	3	3	3	3	4	5	6	12	24	68	155	617
.60	3	3	3	3	3	4	5	9	17	39	68	153
.70	2	2	2	2	3	3	4	6	10	17	24	37
.80	2	2	2	2	2	2	3	4	6	9	12	15
.90	2	2	2	2	2	2	2	3	4	5	6	8
1.00	1	1	1	1	1	1	1	2	2	2	3	3

$$\alpha = .05, \quad 1 - \beta = .90$$

Larger Propor-tion	Smaller Proportion											
	.001	.002	.005	.01	.02	.05	.10	.20	.30	.40	.45	.50
.01	457	698	2480	—	—	—	—	—	—	—	—	—
.02	177	227	424	1230	—	—	—	—	—	—	—	—
.05	57	66	90	137	307	—	—	—	—	—	—	—
.10	26	28	34	44	67	232	—	—	—	—	—	—
.20	12	13	14	17	21	38	107	—	—	—	—	—
.30	8	8	9	10	12	18	33	160	—	—	—	—
.40	6	6	6	7	8	11	17	44	195	—	—	—
.45	5	5	5	6	7	9	13	30	89	837	—	—
.50	4	4	5	5	6	7	10	21	51	212	854	—
.55	4	4	4	4	5	6	9	16	33	95	214	854
.60	3	4	4	4	4	5	7	13	23	53	95	212
.70	3	3	3	3	3	4	5	8	13	23	33	51
.80	2	2	2	3	3	3	4	6	8	13	16	21
.90	2	2	2	2	2	3	3	4	5	7	9	10
1.00	1	1	1	1	2	2	2	2	3	3	4	4

TABLE A-26 (Continued). SAMPLE SIZE REQUIRED FOR COMPARING A PROPORTION WITH A STANDARD PROPORTION WHEN THE SIGN OF THE DIFFERENCE IS IMPORTANT

$\alpha = .05, \quad 1 - \beta = .95$

Larger Propor- tion	Smaller Proportion											
	.001	.002	.005	.01	.02	.05	.10	.20	.30	.40	.45	.50
.01	577	882	3140	—	—	—	—	—	—	—	—	—
.02	223	287	535	1560	—	—	—	—	—	—	—	—
.05	73	83	113	173	388	—	—	—	—	—	—	—
.10	33	36	43	56	84	293	—	—	—	—	—	—
.20	15	16	18	21	27	48	135	—	—	—	—	—
.30	10	10	11	12	15	22	41	202	—	—	—	—
.40	7	7	8	8	10	13	21	56	246	—	—	—
.45	6	6	7	7	8	11	16	37	112	1060	—	—
.50	5	5	6	6	7	9	13	27	64	267	1080	—
.55	5	5	5	6	6	8	11	20	42	119	270	1080
.60	4	4	5	5	5	7	9	16	29	67	119	267
.70	3	4	4	4	4	5	7	10	16	29	42	64
.80	3	3	3	3	3	4	5	7	10	16	20	27
.90	2	2	2	3	3	3	4	5	7	9	11	13
1.00	2	2	2	2	2	2	2	3	3	4	4	5

$\alpha - .05, \quad 1 - \beta = .99$

Larger Propor- tion	Smaller Proportion											
	.001	.002	.005	.01	.02	.05	.10	.20	.30	.40	.45	.50
.01	841	1290	4570	—	—	—	—	—	—	—	—	—
.02	325	418	779	2270	—	—	—	—	—	—	—	—
.05	105	121	165	251	565	—	—	—	—	—	—	—
.10	47	52	63	81	122	426	—	—	—	—	—	—
.20	22	23	26	30	39	70	196	—	—	—	—	—
.30	14	14	16	18	21	32	60	293	—	—	—	—
.40	10	10	11	12	14	19	30	81	358	—	—	—
.45	8	9	9	10	12	16	24	54	163	1540	—	—
.50	7	8	8	9	10	13	19	39	94	389	1580	—
.55	7	7	7	8	9	11	15	29	61	174	393	1580
.60	6	6	6	7	8	10	13	23	42	98	174	389
.70	5	5	5	5	6	7	9	15	24	42	61	94
.80	4	4	4	4	5	6	7	10	15	23	29	39
.90	3	3	3	3	4	4	5	7	9	13	15	19
1.00	2	2	2	2	2	3	3	4	5	6	6	7

TABLE A-27.　TABLE OF ARC SINE TRANSFORMATION FOR PROPORTIONS

$$\theta = 2 \text{ arc sin } \sqrt{P}$$

P	θ	P	θ	P	θ	P	θ
.00	.00	.25	1.05	.50	1.57	.75	2.09
.01	.20	.26	1.07	.51	1.59	.76	2.12
.02	.28	.27	1.09	.52	1.61	.77	2.14
.03	.35	.28	1.12	.53	1.63	.78	2.17
.04	.40	.29	1.14	.54	1.65	.79	2.19
.05	.45	.30	1.16	.55	1.67	.80	2.21
.06	.49	.31	1.18	.56	1.69	.81	2.24
.07	.54	.32	1.20	.57	1.71	.82	2.27
.08	.57	.33	1.22	.58	1.73	.83	2.29
.09	.61	.34	1.25	.59	1.75	.84	2.32
.10	.64	.35	1.27	.60	1.77	.85	2.35
.11	.68	.36	1.29	.61	1.79	.86	2.37
.12	.71	.37	1.31	.62	1.81	.87	2.40
.13	.74	.38	1.33	.63	1.83	.88	2.43
.14	.77	.39	1.35	.64	1.85	.89	2.47
.15	.80	.40	1.37	.65	1.88	.90	2.50
.16	.82	.41	1.39	.66	1.90	.91	2.53
.17	.85	.42	1.41	.67	1.92	.92	2.57
.18	.88	.43	1.43	.68	1.94	.93	2.61
.19	.90	.44	1.45	.69	1.96	.94	2.65
.20	.93	.45	1.47	.70	1.98	.95	2.69
.21	.95	.46	1.49	.71	2.00	.96	2.74
.22	.98	.47	1.51	.72	2.03	.97	2.79
.23	1.00	.48	1.53	.73	2.05	.98	2.86
.24	1.02	.49	1.55	.74	2.07	.99	2.94
						1.00	3.14

TABLE A-28. MINIMUM CONTRASTS REQUIRED FOR SIGNIFICANCE IN 2 × 2 TABLES WITH EQUAL SAMPLES

Note that some entries in this table have been omitted in instances where they are easy to supply. For example, see $n_A = n_B = 80$, 5% Level. There is an entry (16,29) followed by an entry (23,36). The difference between the first numbers of these pairs is the same as the difference between the second numbers of the pairs. Thus contrast pairs (17,30), (18,31), (19,32), etc., are also significant contrasts, but have been omitted to save space.

In many cases this table can be used to give a good idea of the significance of an observed contrast for values of n intermediate to those tabulated. For example, consider two samples of $n = 320$ items each:

	Class I	Class II	Total
Sample A	92	228	320
Sample B	117	203	320

We find the entry (95,119) in the table for $n = 300$, hence (92,116) is a significant contrast for $n = 300$. For $n = 400$, we find (100,126), hence (92,118) is a significant contrast for $n = 400$. We conclude that the observed contrast (92,117) is approximately significant at the 5% level.

If this method is not considered sufficient in a particular case, use the χ^2 method described in Chapter 8. The χ^2 method is an approximation which gives good results for cases not covered by this table.

5% Level, Two-Sided (Is P_A different from P_B?) 2.5% Level, One-Sided (Is P_A larger than P_B?)					1% Level, Two-Sided (Is P_A different from P_B?) 0.5% Level, One-Sided (Is P_A larger than P_B?)				
Sample Size $n_A = n_B$	A_1, A_2				Sample Size $n_A = n_B$	A_1, A_2			
4	0,4								
5	0,4				5	0,5			
6	0,5				6	0,6			
7	0,5	1,6			7	0,6			
8	0,5	1,6			8	0,6			
9	0,5	1,6			9	0,6	1,8		
10	0,5	1,7	2,8		10	0,7	1,8		
11	0,5	1,7	2,8		11	0,7	1,8	2,9	
12	0,5	1,7	2,8	3,9	12	0,7	1,8	2,10	

Adapted with permission from *Tables for Use with Binomial Samples* by D. Mainland, L. Herrera, and M. Sutcliffe, Copyright, 1956, Department of Medical Statistics, New York University College of Medicine.

TABLE A-28 (Continued). MINIMUM CONTRASTS REQUIRED FOR SIGNIFICANCE IN 2 × 2 TABLES WITH EQUAL SAMPLES

5% Level, Two-Sided (Is P_A different from P_B?) 2.5% Level, One-Sided (Is P_A larger than P_B?)					1% Level, Two-Sided (Is P_A different from P_B?) 0.5% Level, One-Sided (Is P_A larger than P_B?)				
Sample Size $n_A = n_B$	A_1, A_2				Sample Size $n_A = n_B$	A_1, A_2			
13	0,5	1,7	2,8	3,9	13	0,7	1,9	2,10	
14	0,5	1,7	2,8	3,10	14	0,7	1,9	2,10	3,11
15	0,5	1,7	2,9	3,10 4,11	15	0,7	1,9	2,10	3,11
16	0,5 4,11	1,7	2,9	3,10	16	0,7	1,9	2,10	3,12
17	0,5 4,11	1,7 5,12	2,9	3,10	17	0,7 4,13	1,9	2,11	3,12
18	0,5 4,11	1,7 5,12	2,9	3,10	18	0,7 4,13	1,9	2,11	3,12
19	0,5 4,11	1,7 5,12	2,9	3,10	19	0,7 4,13	1,9 5,14	2,11	3,12
20	0,5 4,11	1,7 5,13	2,9 6,14	3,10	20	0,7 4,13	1,9 5,15	2,11	3,12
30	0,6 4,12 8,17	1,8 5,13 9,18	2,9 6,15 10,19	3,11 7,16	30	0,8 4,15	1,10 9,20	2,12	3,13
40	0,6 4,12 8,18	1,8 5,14 9,19	2,9 6,15 10,20	3,11 7,16 15,25	40	0,8 4,15 13,26	1,10 5,17	2,12 8,20	3,14 9,22
50	0,6 4,13 8,18 19,30	1,8 5,14 9,19	2,10 6,15 10,20	3,11 7,17 11,22	50	0,8 4,15 9,22	1,10 5,17 10,24	2,12 6,18 18,32	3,14 7,20
60	0,6 4,13 8,18 12,23	1,8 5,14 9,20 13,24	2,10 6,16 10,21 14,26	3,11 7,17 11,22 24,36	60	0,8 4,16 9,23 20,36	1,10 5,17 11,25 22,38	2,12 6,19 12,27	3,14 8,21 19,34

TABLE A-28 (Continued). MINIMUM CONTRASTS REQUIRED FOR SIGNIFICANCE IN 2 × 2 TABLES WITH EQUAL SAMPLES

5% Level, Two-Sided (Is P_A different from P_B?) 2.5% Level, One-Sided (Is P_A larger than P_B?)				1% Level, Two-Sided (Is P_A different from P_B?) 0.5% Level, One-Sided (Is P_A larger than P_B?)			
Sample Size $n_A = n_B$	A_1, A_2			**Sample Size** $n_A = n_B$	A_1, A_2		
70	0,6	1,8	2,10	3,11	**70**	0,8	1,10	2,12	3,14
	4,13	5,14	6,16	7,17		4,16	5,17	6,19	7,20
	8,18	9,20	10,21	11,22		8,22	10,24	11,26	14,29
	12,23	13,25	18,30	19,32		15,31	21,37	22,39	26,43
	20,33	28,41						
80	0,6	1,8	2,10	3,11	**80**	0,8	1,10	2,12	3,14
	4,13	5,14	6,16	7,17		4,16	5,18	6,19	7,21
	8,19	9,20	10,21	11,22		9,23	10,25	12,27	13,29
	12,24	13,25	14,26	15,27		16,32	17,34	24,41	25,43
	16,29	23,36	24,38	33,47		31,49			
90	0,6	1,8	2,10	3,11	**90**	0,8	1,10	2,12	3,14
	4,13	5,14	6,16	7,17		4,16	5,18	6,19	7,21
	8,19	9,20	10,21	11,23		8,22	9,24	11,26	12,28
	12,24	13,25	14,26	15,28		15,31	16,33	19,36	20,38
	20,33	21,35	31,45	32,47		28,46	29,48	35,54	
	37,52							
100	0,6	1,8	2,10	3,11	**100**	0,8	1,10	2,13	3,14
	4,13	5,15	6,16	7,17		4,16	5,18	6,19	7,21
	8,19	9,20	10,21	11,23		8,22	9,24	10,25	11,27
	12,24	13,25	14,27	18,31		14,30	15,32	18,35	19,37
	19,33	25,39	26,41	42,57		23,41	24,43	33,52	34,54
						40,60		
150	0,6	1,8	2,10	3,12	**150**	0,8	1,11	2,13	3,15
	4,13	5,15	6,16	7,18		4,16	5,18	6,20	7,21
	8,19	9,20	10,22	11,23		8,23	9,24	10,26	11,27
	12,24	13,26	14,27	15,28		12,29	14,31	15,33	17,35
	16,30	19,33	20,35	25,40		18,37	21,40	22,42	26,46
	26,42	32,48	33,50	41,58		27,48	31,52	32,54	39,61
	42,60	66,84				40,63	51,74	52,76	63,87
200	0,6	1,8	2,10	3,12	**200**	0,8	1,11	2,13	3,15
	4,13	5,15	6,16	7,18		4,16	5,18	6,20	7,21
	8,19	9,21	10,22	11,23		8,23	9,24	10,26	11,27
	12,25	13,26	14,27	15,29		12,29	13,30	14,32	16,34
	18,32	19,34	22,37	23,39		17,36	19,38	20,40	23,43
	27,43	28,45	33,50	34,52		24,45	26,47	27,49	31,53
	41,59	42,61	51,70	52,72		32,55	36,59	37,61	43,67
	65,85	66,87	89,110			44,69	51,76	52,78	63,89
						64,91	86,113		

TABLE A-28 (Continued). MINIMUM CONTRASTS REQUIRED FOR SIGNIFICANCE IN 2 × 2 TABLES WITH EQUAL SAMPLES

5% Level, Two-Sided (Is P_A different from P_B?)
2.5% Level, One-Sided (Is P_A larger than P_B?)

Sample Size $n_A = n_B$	A_1, A_2			
300	0,6	1,8	2,10	3,12
	4,13	5,15	6,16	7,18
	8,19	9,21	10,22	11,24
	12,25	13,26	14,28	15,29
	16,30	17,31	18,33	19,34
	20,35	21,37	24,40	25,42
	29,46	30,48	35,53	36,55
	41,60	42,62	48,68	49,70
	56,77	57,79	66,88	67,90
	78,101	79,103	95,119	96,121
	137,162			
400	0,6	1,8	2,10	3,12
	4,13	5,15	6,17	7,18
	8,19	9,21	10,22	11,24
	12,25	13,26	14,28	15,29
	16,30	17,32	20,35	21,37
	24,40	25,42	28,45	29,47
	33,51	34,53	38,57	39,59
	44,64	45,66	51,72	52,74
	58,80	59,82	67,90	68,92
	76,100	77,102	87,112	88,114
	100,126	101,128	117,144	118,146
	141,169	142,171	185,214	
500	0,6	1,8	2,10	3,12
	4,13	5,15	6,17	7,18
	8,19	9,21	10,22	11,24
	12,25	13,26	14,28	15,29
	16,30	17,32	18,33	19,34
	20,36	23,39	24,41	27,44
	28,46	32,50	33,52	37,56
	38,58	42,62	43,64	48,69
	49,71	55,77	56,79	62,85
	63,87	70,94	71,96	79,104
	80,106	89,115	90,117	100,127
	101,129	113,141	114,143	128,157
	129,159	147,177	148,179	172,203
	173,205	234,266		

1% Level, Two-Sided (Is P_A different from P_B?)
0.5% Level, One-Sided (Is P_A larger than P_B?)

Sample Size $n_A = n_B$	A_1, A_2			
300	0,8	1,11	2,13	3,15
	4,17	5,18	6,20	7,22
	8,23	9,25	10,26	11,28
	12,29	13,31	15,33	16,35
	17,36	18,38	20,40	21,42
	23,44	24,46	27,49	28,51
	31,54	32,56	35,59	36,61
	40,65	41,67	45,71	46,73
	51,78	52,80	58,86	59,88
	66,95	67,97	76,106	77,108
	88,119	89,121	107.139	108,141
	133,166			
400	0,8	1,11	2,13	3,15
	4,17	5,18	6,20	7,22
	8,23	9,25	10,26	11,28
	12,29	13,31	14,32	15,34
	17,36	18,38	19,39	20,41
	22,43	23,45	26,48	27,50
	29,52	30,54	33,57	34,59
	37,62	38,64	41,67	42,69
	46,73	47,75	52,80	53,82
	57,86	58,88	64,94	65,96
	71,102	72,104	79,111	80,113
	88,121	89,123	98,132	99,134
	111,146	112,148	127,163	128,165
	152,189	153,191	181,219	
500	0,8	1,11	2,13	3,15
	4,17	5,18	6,20	7,22
	8,24	9,25	10,27	11,28
	12,30	14,32	15,34	16,35
	17,37	19,39	20,41	22,43
	23,45	25,47	26,49	28,51
	29,53	32,56	33,58	35,60
	36,62	40,66	41,68	44,71
	45,73	49,77	50,79	54,83
	55,85	59,89	60,91	65,96
	66,98	72,104	73,106	79,112
	80,114	86,120	87,122	95,130
	96,132	104,140	105,142	115,152
	116,154	127,165	128,167	141,180
	142,182	159,199	160,201	184,225
	185,227	229,271		

TABLE A-29. TABLES FOR TESTING SIGNIFICANCE IN 2 × 2 TABLES WITH UNEQUAL SAMPLES

Table A-29 shows (1) in bold type for given a_1, n_1, and n_2, the value of a_2 which is just significant at the probability level quoted in parentheses for a two-sided test and without parentheses for a one-sided test, (2) in small type, for given n_1, n_2 and $a_1 + a_2$, the exact probability (if there is independence) that a_2 is equal to or less than the integer shown in bold type.

n_1	n_2	a_1	0.05 (0.10)	0.025 (0.05)	0.01 (0.02)	0.005 (0.01)
3	3	3	0 .050	—	—	—
4	4	4	0 .014	0 .014	—	—
	3	4	0 .029	—	—	—
5	5	5	1 .024	1 .024	0 .004	0 .004
		4	0 .024	0 .024	—	—
	4	5	1 .048	0 .008	0 .008	—
		4	0 .040	—	—	—
	3	5	0 .018	0 .018	—	—
	2	5	0 .048	—	—	—
6	6	6	2 .030	1 .008	1 .008	0 .001
		5	1 .040	0 .008	0 .008	—
		4	0 .030	—	—	—
	5	6	1 .015+	1 .015+	0 .002	0 .002
		5	0 .013	0 .013	—	—
		4	0 .045+	—	—	—
	4	6	1 .033	0 .005−	0 .005−	0 .005−
		5	0 .024	0 .024	—	—
	3	6	0 .012	0 .012	—	—
		5	0 .048	—	—	—
	2	6	0 .036	—	—	—
7	7	7	3 .035−	2 .010+	1 .002	1 .002
		6	1 .015−	1 .015−	0 .002	0 .002
		5	0 .010+	0 .010+	—	—
		4	0 .035	—	—	—
	6	7	2 .021	2 .021	1 .005−	1 .005−
		6	1 .025+	0 .004	0 .004	0 .004
		5	0 .010	0 .016	—	—
		4	0 .049	—	—	—
	5	7	2 .045+	1 .010+	0 .001	0 .001
		6	1 .045+	0 .008	0 .008	—
		5	0 .027	—	—	—
	4	7	1 .024	1 .024	0 .003	0 .003
		6	0 .015+	0 .015+	—	—
		5	0 .045+	—	—	—
	3	7	0 .008	0 .008	0 .008	—
		6	0 .033	—	—	—
	2	7	0 .028	—	—	—

n_1	n_2	a_1	0.05 (0.10)	0.025 (0.05)	0.01 (0.02)	0.005 (0.01)
8	8	8	4 .038	3 .013	2 .003	2 .003
		7	2 .020	2 .020	1 .005+	0 .001
		6	1 .020	1 .020	0 .003	0 .003
		5	0 .013	0 .013	—	—
		4	0 .038	—	—	—
	7	8	3 .026	2 .007	2 .007	1 .001
		7	2 .035−	1 .009	1 .009	0 .001
		6	1 .032	0 .006	0 .006	—
		5	0 .019	0 .019	—	—
	6	8	2 .015−	2 .015−	1 .003	1 .003
		7	1 .016	1 .016	0 .002	0 .002
		6	0 .009	0 .009	0 .009	—
		5	0 .028	—	—	—
	5	8	2 .035−	1 .007	1 .007	0 .001
		7	1 .032	0 .005−	0 .005−	0 .005−
		6	0 .016	0 .016	—	—
		5	0 .044	—	—	—
	4	8	1 .018	1 .018	0 .002	0 .002
		7	0 .010+	0 .010+	—	—
		6	0 .030	—	—	—
	3	8	0 .006	0 .006	0 .006	—
		7	0 .024	0 .024	—	—
	2	8	0 .022	0 .022	—	—
9	9	9	5 .041	4 .015−	3 .005−	3 .005−
		8	3 .025−	3 .025−	2 .008	1 .002
		7	2 .028	1 .008	1 .008	0 .001
		6	1 .025−	1 .025−	0 .005−	0 .005−
		5	0 .015−	0 .015−	—	—
		4	0 .041	—	—	—
	8	9	4 .029	3 .009	3 .009	2 .002
		8	3 .043	2 .013	1 .003	1 .003
		7	2 .044	1 .012	0 .002	0 .002
		6	1 .036	0 .007	0 .007	—
		5	0 .020	0 .020	—	—
	7	9	3 .019	3 .019	2 .005−	2 .005−
		8	2 .024	2 .024	1 .006	0 .001
		7	1 .020	1 .020	0 .003	0 .003
		6	0 .010+	0 .010+	—	—
		5	0 .029	—	—	—
	6	9	2 .044	2 .011	1 .002	1 .002
		8	2 .047	1 .011	0 .001	0 .001
		7	1 .035−	0 .006	0 .006	—
		6	0 .017	0 .017	—	—
		5	0 .042	—	—	—

Adapted from a table of the same form with probabilities to 4 decimals prepared in the Statistical Engineering Laboratory, National Bureau of Standards, by Anna M. Glinski and John Van Dyke from *Tables of the Hypergeometric Probability Distribution* by Gerald J. Lieberman and Donald B. Owen, Technical Report No. 50 (Contract Nonr–225(53) (NR 042 002)), Applied Mathematics and Statistics Laboratories, Stanford University, Stanford, California.

TABLE A-29 (Continued). TABLES FOR TESTING SIGNIFICANCE IN 2 × 2 TABLES WITH UNEQUAL SAMPLES

Left panel

			Significance Level			
		a_1	0.05 (0.10)	0.025 (0.05)	0.01 (0.02)	0.005 (0.01)
$n_1=9$ $n_2=5$	9	9	2 .027	1 .005 −	1 .005 −	1 .005 −
		8	1 .023	1 .023	0 .003	0 .003
		7	0 .010 +	0 .010 +	—	—
		6	0 .028	—	—	—
	4	9	1 .014	1 .014	0 .001	0 .001
		8	0 .007	0 .007	0 .007	—
		7	0 .021	0 .021	—	—
		6	0 .049	—	—	—
	3	9	1 .045 +	0 .005 −	0 .005 −	0 .005 −
		8	0 .018	0 .018	—	—
		7	0 .045 +	—	—	—
	2	9	0 .018	0 .018	—	—
$n_1=10$ $n_2=10$	10	10	6 .043	5 .016	4 .005 +	3 .002
		9	4 .029	3 .010 −	3 .010 −	2 .003
		8	3 .035 −	2 .012	1 .003	1 .003
		7	2 .035 −	1 .010 −	1 .010 −	0 .002
		6	1 .029	0 .005 +	0 .005 +	—
		5	0 .016	0 .016	—	—
		4	0 .043	—	—	—
	9	10	5 .033	4 .011	3 .003	3 .003
		9	4 .050 −	3 .017	2 .005 −	2 .005 −
		8	2 .019	2 .019	1 .004	1 .004
		7	1 .015 −	1 .015 −	0 .002	0 .002
		6	1 .040	0 .008	0 .008	—
		5	0 .022	0 .022	—	—
	8	10	4 .023	4 .023	3 .007	2 .002
		9	3 .032	2 .009	2 .009	1 .002
		8	2 .031	1 .008	1 .008	0 .001
		7	1 .023	1 .023	0 .004	0 .004
		6	0 .011	0 .011	—	—
		5	0 .029	—	—	—
	7	10	3 .015 −	3 .015 −	2 .003	2 .003
		9	2 .018	2 .018	1 .004	1 .004
		8	1 .013	1 .013	0 .002	0 .002
		7	1 .036	0 .006	0 .006	—
		6	0 .017	0 .017	—	—
		5	0 .041	—	—	—
	6	10	3 .036	2 .008	2 .008	1 .001
		9	2 .036	1 .008	1 .008	0 .001
		8	1 .024	1 .024	0 .003	0 .003
		7	0 .010 +	0 .010 +	—	—
		6	0 .026	—	—	—
	5	10	2 .022	2 .022	1 .004	1 .004
		9	1 .017	1 .017	0 .002	0 .002
		8	1 .047	0 .007	0 .007	—
		7	0 .019	0 .019	—	—
		6	0 .042	—	—	—

Right panel

			Significance Level			
		a_1	0.05 (0.10)	0.025 (0.05)	0.01 (0.02)	0.005 (0.01)
$n_1=10$ $n_2=4$	10	10	1 .011	1 .011	0 .001	0 .001
		9	1 .041	0 .005 −	0 .005 −	0 .005 −
		8	0 .015 −	0 .015 −	—	—
		7	0 .035 −	—	—	—
	3	10	1 .038	0 .003	0 .003	0 .003
		9	0 .014	0 .014	—	—
		8	0 .035 −	—	—	—
	2	10	0 .015 +	0 .015 +	—	—
		9	0 .045 +	—	—	—
$n_1=11$ $n_2=11$	11	11	7 .045 +	6 .018	5 .006	4 .002
		10	5 .032	4 .012	3 .004	3 .004
		9	4 .040	3 .015 −	2 .004	2 .004
		8	3 .043	2 .015 −	1 .004	1 .004
		7	2 .040	1 .012	0 .002	0 .002
		6	1 .032	0 .006	0 .006	—
		5	0 .018	0 .018	—	—
		4	0 .045 +	—	—	—
	10	11	6 .035 +	5 .012	4 .004	4 .004
		10	4 .021	4 .021	3 .007	2 .002
		9	3 .024	3 .024	2 .007	1 .002
		8	2 .023	2 .023	1 .006	0 .001
		7	1 .017	1 .017	0 .003	0 .003
		6	1 .043	0 .009	0 .009	—
		5	0 .023	0 .023	—	—
	9	11	5 .026	4 .008	4 .008	3 .002
		10	4 .038	3 .012	2 .003	2 .003
		9	3 .040	2 .012	1 .003	1 .003
		8	2 .035 −	1 .009	1 .009	0 .001
		7	1 .025 −	1 .025 −	0 .004	0 .004
		6	0 .012	0 .012	—	—
		5	0 .030	—	—	—
	8	11	4 .018	4 .018	3 .005 −	3 .005 −
		10	3 .024	3 .024	2 .006	1 .001
		9	2 .022	2 .022	1 .005 −	1 .005 −
		8	1 .015 −	1 .015 −	0 .002	0 .002
		7	1 .037	0 .007	0 .007	—
		6	0 .017	0 .017	—	—
		5	0 .040	—	—	—
	7	11	4 .043	3 .011	2 .002	2 .002
		10	3 .047	2 .013	1 .002	1 .002
		9	2 .039	1 .009	1 .009	0 .001
		8	1 .025 −	1 .025 −	0 .004	0 .004
		7	0 .010 +	0 .010 +	—	—
		6	0 .025 −	0 .025 −	—	—
	6	11	3 .029	2 .006	2 .006	1 .001
		10	2 .028	1 .005 +	1 .005 +	0 .001
		9	1 .018	1 .018	0 .002	0 .002

TABLE A-29 (Continued).   TABLES FOR TESTING SIGNIFICANCE IN 2 × 2 TABLES WITH UNEQUAL SAMPLES

Left half

	a	a_1	Significance Level 0.05 (0.10)	0.025 (0.05)	0.01 (0.02)	0.005 (0.01)
$n_1=11$ $n_2=6$	8	8	1 .043	0 .007	0 .007	—
		7	0 .017	0 .017	—	—
		6	0 .037	—	—	—
	5	11	2 .018	2 .018	1 .003	1 .003
		10	1 .013	1 .013	0 .001	0 .001
		9	1 .036	0 .005 −	0 .005 −	0 .005 −
		8	0 .013	0 .013	—	—
		7	0 .029	—	—	—
	4	11	1 .009	1 .009	1 .009	0 .001
		10	1 .033	0 .004	0 .004	0 .004
		9	0 .011	0 .011	—	—
		8	0 .026	—	—	—
	3	11	1 .033	0 .003	0 .003	0 .003
		10	0 .011	0 .011	—	—
		9	0 .027	—	—	—
	2	11	0 .013	0 .013	—	—
		10	0 .038	—	—	—
$n_1=12$ $n_2=12$	12	12	8 .047	7 .019	6 .007	5 .002
		11	6 .034	5 .014	4 .005 −	4 .005 −
		10	5 .045 −	4 .018	3 .006	2 .002
		9	4 .050 −	3 .020	2 .006	1 .001
		8	3 .050 −	2 .018	1 .005 −	1 .005 −
		7	2 .045 −	1 .014	0 .002	0 .002
		6	1 .034	0 .007	0 .007	—
		5	0 .019	0 .019	—	—
		4	0 .047	—	—	—
	11	12	7 .037	6 .014	5 .005 −	5 .005 −
		11	5 .024	5 .024	4 .008	3 .002
		10	4 .029	3 .010 +	2 .003	2 .003
		9	3 .030	2 .009	2 .009	1 .002
		8	2 .026	1 .007	1 .007	0 .001
		7	1 .019	0 .003	0 .003	0 .003
		6	1 .045 −	0 .009	0 .009	—
		5	0 .024	0 .024	—	—
	10	12	6 .029	5 .010 −	5 .010 −	4 .003
		11	5 .043	4 .015 +	3 .005 −	3 .005 −
		10	4 .048	3 .017	2 .005 −	2 .005 −
		9	3 .046	2 .015 −	1 .004	1 .004
		8	2 .038	1 .010 +	0 .002	0 .002
		7	1 .026	0 .005 −	0 .005 −	0 .005 −
		6	0 .012	0 .012	—	—
		5	0 .030	—	—	—
	9	12	5 .021	5 .021	4 .006	3 .002
		11	4 .029	3 .009	3 .009	2 .002
		10	3 .029	2 .008	2 .008	1 .002
		9	2 .024	2 .024	1 .006	0 .001
		8	1 .016	1 .016	0 .002	0 .002

Right half

	a	a_1	Significance Level 0.05 (0.10)	0.025 (0.05)	0.01 (0.02)	0.005 (0.01)
$n_1=12$ $n_2=9$	7	7	1 .037	0 .007	0 .007	—
		6	0 .017	0 .017	—	—
		5	0 .039	—	—	—
	8	12	5 .049	4 .014	3 .004	3 .004
		11	3 .018	3 .018	2 .004	2 .004
		10	2 .015 +	2 .015 +	1 .003	1 .003
		9	2 .040	1 .010 −	1 .010 −	0 .001
		8	1 .025 −	1 .025 −	0 .004	0 .004
		7	0 .010 +	0 .010 +	—	—
		6	0 .024	0 .024	—	—
	7	12	4 .036	3 .009	3 .009	2 .002
		11	3 .038	2 .010 −	2 .010 −	1 .002
		10	2 .029	1 .006	1 .006	0 .001
		9	1 .017	1 .017	0 .002	0 .002
		8	1 .040	0 .007	0 .007	—
		7	0 .016	0 .016	—	—
		6	0 .034	—	—	—
	6	12	3 .025 −	3 .025 −	2 .005 −	2 .005 −
		11	2 .022	2 .022	1 .004	1 .004
		10	1 .013	1 .013	0 .002	0 .002
		9	1 .032	0 .005 −	0 .005 −	0 .005 −
		8	0 .011	0 .011	—	—
		7	0 .025 −	0 .025 −	—	—
		6	0 .050 −	—	—	—
	5	12	2 .015 −	2 .015 −	1 .002	1 .002
		11	1 .010 −	1 .010 −	1 .010 −	0 .001
		10	1 .038	0 .003	0 .003	0 .003
		9	0 .009	0 .009	0 .009	—
		8	0 .020	0 .020	—	—
		7	0 .041	—	—	—
	4	12	2 .050	1 .007	1 .007	0 .001
		11	1 .027	0 .003	0 .003	0 .003
		10	0 .008	0 .008	0 .008	—
		9	0 .019	0 .019	—	—
		8	0 .038	—	—	—
	3	12	1 .029	0 .002	0 .002	0 .002
		11	0 .009	0 .009	0 .009	—
		10	0 .022	0 .022	—	—
		9	0 .044	—	—	—
	2	12	0 .011	0 .011	—	—
		11	0 .033	—	—	—
$n_1=13$ $n_2=13$	13	13	9 .048	8 .020	7 .007	6 .003
		12	7 .037	6 .015 +	5 .006	4 .002
		11	6 .048	5 .021	4 .008	3 .002
		10	4 .024	4 .024	3 .008	2 .002
		9	3 .024	3 .024	2 .008	1 .002
		8	2 .021	2 .021	1 .006	0 .001

TABLE A-29 (Continued). TABLES FOR TESTING SIGNIFICANCE IN 2 × 2 TABLES WITH UNEQUAL SAMPLES

Left

			Significance Level			
		a_1	0.05 (0.10)	0.025 (0.05)	0.01 (0.02)	0.005 (0.01)
$n_1=13$ $n_2=13$		7	2 .048	1 .015 +	0 .003	0 .003
		6	1 .037	0 .007	0 .007	—
		5	0 .020	0 .020	—	—
		4	0 .048	—	—	—
	12	13	8 .039	7 .015 −	6 .005 +	5 .002
		12	6 .027	5 .010 −	5 .010 −	4 .003
		11	5 .033	4 .013	3 .004	3 .004
		10	4 .036	3 .013	2 .004	2 .004
		9	3 .034	2 .011	1 .003	1 .003
		8	2 .029	1 .008	1 .008	0 .001
		7	1 .020	1 .020	0 .004	0 .004
		6	1 .046	0 .010 −	0 .010 −	—
		5	0 .024	0 .024	—	—
	11	13	7 .031	6 .011	5 .003	5 .003
		12	6 .048	5 .018	4 .006	3 .002
		11	4 .021	4 .021	3 .007	2 .002
		10	3 .021	3 .021	2 .006	1 .001
		9	3 .050 −	2 .017	1 .004	1 .004
		8	2 .040	1 .011	0 .002	0 .002
		7	1 .027	0 .005 −	0 .005 −	0 .005 −
		6	0 .013	0 .013	—	—
		5	0 .030	—	—	—
	10	13	6 .024	6 .024	5 .007	4 .002
		12	5 .035 −	4 .012	3 .003	3 .003
		11	4 .037	3 .012	2 .003	2 .003
		10	3 .033	2 .010 +	1 .002	1 .002
		9	2 .026	1 .006	1 .006	0 .001
		8	1 .017	1 .017	0 .003	0 .003
		7	1 .038	0 .007	0 .007	—
		6	0 .017	0 .017	—	—
		5	0 .038	—	—	—
	9	13	5 .017	5 .017	4 .005 −	4 .005 −
		12	4 .023	4 .023	3 .007	2 .001
		11	3 .022	3 .022	2 .006	1 .001
		10	2 .017	2 .017	1 .004	1 .004
		9	2 .040	1 .010 +	0 .001	0 .001
		8	1 .025 −	1 .025 −	0 .004	0 .004
		7	0 .010 +	0 .010 +	—	—
		6	0 .023	0 .023	—	—
		5	0 .049	—	—	—
	8	13	5 .042	4 .012	3 .003	3 .003
		12	4 .047	3 .014	2 .003	2 .003
		11	3 .041	2 .011	1 .002	1 .002
		10	2 .029	1 .007	1 .007	0 .001
		9	1 .017	1 .017	0 .002	0 .002
		8	1 .037	0 .006	0 .006	—
		7	0 .015 −	0 .015 −	—	—
		6	0 .032	—	—	—
	7	13	4 .031	3 .007	3 .007	2 .001
		12	3 .031	2 .007	2 .007	1 .001

Right

			Significance Level			
		a_1	0.05 (0.10)	0.025 (0.05)	0.01 (0.02)	0.005 (0.01)
$n_1=13$ $n_2=7$		11	2 .022	2 .022	1 .004	1 .004
		10	1 .012	1 .012	0 .002	0 .002
		9	1 .029	0 .004	0 .004	0 .004
		8	0 .010 +	0 .010 +	—	—
		7	0 .022	0 .022	—	—
		6	0 .044	—	—	—
	6	13	3 .021	3 .021	2 .004	2 .004
		12	2 .017	2 .017	1 .003	1 .003
		11	2 .046	1 .010 −	1 .010 −	0 .001
		10	1 .024	1 .024	0 .003	0 .003
		9	1 .050 −	0 .008	0 .008	—
		8	0 .017	0 .017	—	—
		7	0 .034	—	—	—
	5	13	2 .012	2 .012	1 .002	1 .002
		12	2 .044	1 .008	1 .008	0 .001
		11	1 .022	1 .022	0 .002	0 .022
		10	1 .047	0 .007	0 .007	—
		9	0 .015 −	0 .015 −	—	—
		8	0 .029	—	—	—
	4	13	2 .044	1 .006	1 .006	0 .000
		12	1 .022	1 .022	0 .002	0 .002
		11	0 .006	0 .006	0 .006	—
		10	0 .015 −	0 .015 −	—	—
		9	0 .029	—	—	—
	3	13	1 .025	1 .025	0 .002	0 .002
		12	0 .007	0 .007	0 .007	—
		11	0 .018	0 .018	—	—
		10	0 .036	—	—	—
	2	13	0 .010 −	0 .010 −	0 .010 −	—
		12	0 .029	—	—	—
$n_1=14$ $n_2=14$		14	10 .049	9 .020	8 .008	7 .003
		13	8 .038	7 .016	6 .006	5 .002
		12	6 .023	6 .023	5 .009	4 .003
		11	5 .027	4 .011	3 .004	3 .004
		10	4 .028	3 .011	2 .003	2 .003
		9	3 .027	2 .009	2 .009	1 .002
		8	2 .023	2 .023	1 .006	0 .001
		7	1 .016	1 .016	0 .003	0 .003
		6	1 .038	0 .008	0 .008	—
		5	0 .020	0 .020	—	—
		4	0 .049	—	—	—
	13	14	9 .041	8 .016	7 .006	6 .002
		13	7 .029	6 .011	5 .004	5 .004
		12	6 .037	5 .015 +	4 .005 +	3 .002
		11	5 .041	4 .017	3 .006	2 .001
		10	4 .041	3 .016	2 .005 −	2 .005 −
		9	3 .038	2 .013	1 .003	1 .003
		8	2 .031	1 .009	1 .009	0 .001

TABLE A-29 (Continued). TABLES FOR TESTING SIGNIFICANCE IN 2 × 2 TABLES WITH UNEQUAL SAMPLES

	a_1	Significance Level 0.05 (0.10)	0.025 (0.05)	0.01 (0.02)	0.005 (0.01)
$n_1=14$ $n_2=13$	7	1 .021	1 .021	0 .004	0 .004
	6	1 .048	0 .010 +	—	—
	5	0 .025 −	0 .025 −	—	—
12	14	8 .033	7 .012	6 .004	6 .004
	13	6 .021	6 .021	5 .007	4 .002
	12	5 .025 +	4 .009	4 .009	3 .003
	11	4 .026	3 .009	3 .009	2 .002
	10	3 .024	3 .024	2 .007	1 .002
	9	2 .019	2 .019	1 .005 −	1 .005 −
	8	2 .042	1 .012	0 .002	0 .002
	7	1 .028	0 .005 +	0 .005 +	—
	6	0 .013	0 .013	—	—
	5	0 .030	—	—	—
11	14	7 .026	6 .009	6 .009	5 .003
	13	6 .039	5 .014	4 .004	4 .004
	12	5 .043	4 .016	3 .005 −	3 .005 −
	11	4 .042	3 .015 −	2 .004	2 .004
	10	3 .036	2 .011	1 .003	1 .003
	9	2 .027	1 .007	1 .007	0 .001
	8	1 .017	1 .017	0 .003	0 .003
	7	1 .038	0 .007	0 .007	—
	6	0 .017	0 .017	—	—
	5	0 .038	—	—	—
10	14	6 .020	6 .020	5 .006	4 .002
	13	5 .028	4 .009	4 .009	3 .002
	12	4 .028	3 .009	3 .009	2 .002
	11	3 .024	3 .024	2 .007	1 .001
	10	2 .018	2 .018	1 .004	1 .004
	9	2 .040	1 .011	0 .002	0 .002
	8	1 .024	1 .024	0 .004	0 .004
	7	0 .010 −	0 .010 −	0 .010 −	—
	6	0 .022	0 .022	—	—
	5	0 .047	—	—	—
9	14	6 .047	5 .014	4 .004	4 .004
	13	4 .018	4 .018	3 .005 −	3 .005 −
	12	3 .017	3 .017	2 .004	2 .004
	11	3 .042	2 .012	1 .002	1 .002
	10	2 .029	1 .007	1 .007	0 .001
	9	1 .017	1 .017	0 .002	0 .002
	8	1 .036	0 .006	0 .006	—
	7	0 .014	0 .014	—	—
	6	0 .030	—	—	—
8	14	5 .036	4 .010 −	4 .010 −	3 .002
	13	4 .039	3 .011	2 .002	2 .002
	12	3 .032	2 .008	2 .008	1 .001
	11	2 .022	2 .022	1 .005 −	1 .005 −
	10	2 .048	1 .012	0 .002	0 .002
	9	1 .026	0 .004	0 .004	0 .001
	8	0 .009	0 .009	0 .009	—
	7	0 .020	0 .020	—	—
	6	0 .040	—	—	—

	a_1	Significance Level 0.05 (0.10)	0.025 (0.05)	0.01 (0.02)	0.005 (0.01)
$n_1=14$ $n_2=7$	14	4 .026	3 .006	3 .006	2 .001
	13	3 .025	2 .006	2 .006	1 .001
	12	2 .017	2 .017	1 .003	1 .003
	11	2 .041	1 .009	1 .009	0 .001
	10	1 .021	1 .021	0 .003	0 .003
	9	1 .043	0 .007	0 .007	—
	8	0 .015 −	0 .015 −	—	—
	7	0 .030	—	—	—
6	14	3 .018	3 .018	2 .003	2 .003
	13	2 .014	2 .014	1 .002	1 .002
	12	2 .037	1 .007	1 .007	0 .001
	11	1 .018	1 .018	0 .002	0 .002
	10	1 .038	0 .005 +	0 .005 +	—
	9	0 .012	0 .012	—	—
	8	0 .024	0 .024	—	—
	7	0 .044	—	—	—
5	14	2 .010 +	2 .010 +	1 .001	1 .001
	13	2 .037	1 .006	1 .006	0 .001
	12	1 .017	1 .017	0 .002	0 .002
	11	1 .038	0 .005 −	0 .005 −	0 .005 −
	10	0 .011	0 .011	—	—
	9	0 .022	0 .022	—	—
	8	0 .040	—	—	—
4	14	2 .039	1 .005 −	1 .005 −	1 .005 −
	13	1 .019	1 .019	0 .002	0 .002
	12	1 .044	0 .005 −	0 .005 −	0 .005 −
	11	0 .011	0 .011	—	—
	10	0 .023	0 .023	—	—
	9	0 .041	—	—	—
3	14	1 .022	1 .022	0 .001	0 .001
	13	0 .006	0 .006	0 .006	—
	12	0 .015 −	0 .015 −	—	—
	11	0 .029	—	—	—
2	14	0 .008	0 .008	0 .008	—
	13	0 .025	0 .025	—	—
	12	0 .050	—	—	—
$n_1=15$ $n_2=15$	15	11 .050 −	10 .021	9 .008	8 .003
	14	9 .040	8 .018	7 .007	6 .003
	13	7 .025 +	6 .010 +	5 .004	5 .004
	12	6 .030	5 .013	4 .005 −	4 .005 −
	11	5 .033	4 .013	3 .005 −	3 .005 −
	10	4 .033	3 .013	2 .004	2 .004
	9	3 .030	2 .010 +	1 .003	1 .003
	8	2 .025 +	1 .007	1 .007	0 .001
	7	1 .018	1 .018	0 .003	0 .003
	6	1 .040	0 .008	0 .008	—
	5	0 .021	0 .021	—	—
	4	0 .050 −	—	—	—

TABLE A-29 (Continued). TABLES FOR TESTING SIGNIFICANCE IN 2 × 2 TABLES WITH UNEQUAL SAMPLES

Left table: $n_1 = 15$, $n_2 = 14$

		a_1	0.05 (0.10)	0.025 (0.05)	0.01 (0.02)	0.005 (0.01)
$n_1=15$ $n_2=14$	15	10	10 .042	9 .017	8 .006	7 .002
		14	8 .031	7 .013	6 .005 −	6 .005 −
		13	7 .041	6 .017	5 .007	4 .002
		12	6 .046	5 .020	4 .007	3 .002
		11	5 .048	4 .020	3 .007	2 .002
		10	4 .046	3 .018	2 .006	1 .001
		9	3 .041	2 .014	1 .004	1 .004
		8	2 .033	1 .009	1 .009	0 .001
		7	1 .022	1 .022	0 .004	0 .004
		6	1 .049	0 .011	—	—
		5	0 .025 +	—	—	—
	13	15	9 .035 −	8 .013	7 .005 −	7 .005 −
		14	7 .023	7 .023	6 .009	5 .003
		13	6 .029	5 .011	4 .004	4 .004
		12	5 .031	4 .012	3 .004	3 .004
		11	4 .030	3 .011	2 .003	2 .003
		10	3 .026	2 .008	2 .008	1 .002
		9	2 .020	2 .020	1 .005 +	0 .001
		8	2 .043	1 .013	0 .002	0 .002
		7	1 .029	0 .005 +	0 .005 +	—
		6	0 .013	0 .013	—	—
		5	0 .031	—	—	—
	12	15	8 .028	7 .010 −	7 .010 −	6 .003
		14	7 .043	6 .016	5 .006	4 .002
		13	6 .049	5 .019	4 .007	3 .002
		12	5 .049	4 .019	3 .006	2 .002
		11	4 .045 +	3 .017	2 .005 −	2 .005 −
		10	3 .038	2 .012	1 .003	1 .003
		9	2 .028	1 .007	1 .007	0 .001
		8	1 .018	1 .018	0 .003	0 .003
		7	1 .038	0 .007	0 .007	—
		6	0 .017	0 .017	—	—
		5	0 .037	—	—	—
	11	15	7 .022	7 .022	6 .007	5 .002
		14	6 .032	5 .011	4 .003	4 .003
		13	5 .034	4 .012	3 .003	3 .003
		12	4 .032	3 .010 +	2 .003	2 .003
		11	3 .026	2 .008	2 .008	1 .002
		10	2 .019	2 .019	1 .004	1 .004
		9	2 .040	1 .011	0 .002	0 .002
		8	1 .024	1 .024	0 .004	0 .004
		7	1 .049	0 .010 −	0 .010 −	—
		6	0 .022	0 .022	—	—
		5	0 .046	—	—	—
	10	15	6 .017	6 .017	5 .005 −	5 .005 −
		14	5 .023	5 .023	4 .007	3 .002
		13	4 .022	4 .022	3 .007	2 .001
		12	3 .018	3 .018	2 .005 −	2 .005 −
		11	3 .042	2 .013	1 .003	1 .003
		10	2 .029	1 .007	1 .007	0 .001
		9	1 .016	1 .016	0 .002	0 .002
		8	1 .034	0 .006	0 .006	—
		7	0 .013	0 .013	—	—
		6	0 .028	—	—	—
	9	15	6 .042	5 .012	4 .003	4 .003
		14	5 .047	4 .015 −	3 .004	3 .004

Right table: $n_1 = 15$, $n_2 = 9$

		a_1	0.05 (0.10)	0.025 (0.05)	0.01 (0.02)	0.005 (0.01)
$n_1=15$ $n_2=9$		13	4 .042	3 .013	2 .003	2 .003
		12	3 .032	2 .009	2 .009	1 .002
		11	2 .021	2 .021	1 .005 −	1 .005 −
		10	2 .045 −	1 .011	0 .002	0 .002
		9	1 .024	1 .024	0 .004	0 .004
		8	1 .048	0 .009	0 .009	—
		7	0 .019	0 .019	—	—
		6	0 .037	—	—	—
	8	15	5 .032	4 .008	4 .008	3 .002
		14	4 .033	3 .009	3 .009	2 .002
		13	3 .026	2 .006	2 .006	1 .001
		12	2 .017	2 .017	1 .003	1 .003
		11	2 .037	1 .008	1 .008	0 .001
		10	1 .019	1 .019	0 .003	0 .003
		9	1 .038	0 .006	0 .006	—
		8	0 .013	0 .013	—	—
		7	0 .026	—	—	—
		6	0 .050 −	—	—	—
	7	15	4 .023	4 .023	3 .005 −	3 .005 −
		14	3 .021	3 .021	2 .004	2 .004
		13	2 .014	2 .014	1 .002	1 .002
		12	2 .032	1 .007	1 .007	0 .001
		11	1 .015 +	1 .015 +	0 .002	0 .002
		10	1 .032	0 .005 −	0 .005 −	0 .005 −
		9	0 .010 +	0 .010 +	—	—
		8	0 .020	0 .020	—	—
		7	0 .038	—	—	—
	6	15	3 .015 +	3 .015 +	2 .003	2 .003
		14	2 .011	2 .011	1 .002	1 .002
		13	2 .031	1 .006	1 .006	0 .001
		12	1 .014	1 .014	0 .002	0 .002
		11	1 .029	0 .004	0 .004	0 .004
		10	0 .009	0 .009	0 .009	—
		9	0 .017	0 .017	—	—
		8	0 .032	—	—	—
	5	15	2 .009	2 .009	2 .009	1 .001
		14	2 .032	1 .005 −	1 .005 −	1 .005 −
		13	1 .014	1 .014	0 .001	0 .001
		12	1 .031	0 .004	0 .004	0 .004
		11	0 .008	0 .008	0 .008	—
		10	0 .016	0 .016	—	—
		9	0 .030	—	—	—
	4	15	2 .035 +	1 .004	1 .004	1 .004
		14	1 .016	1 .016	0 .001	0 .001
		13	1 .037	0 .004	0 .004	0 .004
		12	0 .009	0 .009	0 .009	—
		11	0 .018	0 .018	—	—
		10	0 .033	—	—	—
	3	15	1 .020	1 .020	0 .001	0 .001
		14	0 .005 −	0 .005 −	0 .005 −	0 .005 −
		13	0 .012	0 .012	—	—
		12	0 .025 −	0 .025 −	—	—
		11	0 .043	—	—	—
	2	15	0 .007	0 .007	0 .007	—
		14	0 .022	0 .022	—	—
		13	0 .044	—	—	—

TABLE A-29 (Continued).   TABLES FOR TESTING SIGNIFICANCE IN 2 × 2 TABLES WITH UNEQUAL SAMPLES

		a_1	Significance Level 0.05 (0.10)	0.025 (0.05)	0.01 (0.02)	0.005 (0.01)			a_1	Significance Level 0.05 (0.10)	0.025 (0.05)	0.01 (0.02)	0.005 (0.01)
$n_1=16$	$n_2=16$	16	11 .022	11 .022	10 .009	9 .003	$n_1=16$	$n_2=12$	16	8 .024	8 .024	7 .008	6 .002
		15	10 .041	9 .019	8 .008	7 .003			15	7 .036	6 .013	5 .004	5 .004
		14	8 .027	7 .012	6 .005−	6 .005−			14	6 .040	5 .015−	4 .005−	4 .005−
		13	7 .033	6 .015−	5 .006	4 .002			13	5 .039	4 .014	3 .004	3 .004
		12	6 .037	5 .016	4 .006	3 .002			12	4 .034	3 .012	2 .003	2 .003
		11	5 .038	4 .016	3 .006	2 .002			11	3 .027	2 .008	2 .008	1 .002
		10	4 .037	3 .015−	2 .005−	2 .005−			10	2 .019	2 .019	1 .005−	1 .005−
		9	3 .033	2 .012	1 .003	1 .003			9	2 .040	1 .011	0 .002	0 .002
		8	2 .027	1 .008	1 .008	0 .001			8	1 .024	1 .024	0 .004	0 .004
		7	1 .019	1 .019	0 .003	0 .003			7	1 .048	0 .010−	0 .010−	—
		6	1 .041	0 .009	0 .009	—			6	0 .021	0 .021	—	—
		5	0 .022	0 .022	—	—			5	0 .044	—	—	—
	15	16	11 .043	10 .018	9 .007	8 .002		11	16	7 .019	7 .019	6 .006	5 .002
		15	9 .033	8 .014	7 .005+	6 .002			15	6 .027	5 .009	5 .009	4 .002
		14	8 .044	7 .019	6 .008	5 .003			14	5 .027	4 .009	4 .009	3 .002
		13	6 .023	6 .023	5 .009	4 .003			13	4 .024	4 .024	3 .008	2 .002
		12	5 .024	5 .024	4 .009	3 .003			12	3 .019	3 .019	2 .005+	1 .001
		11	4 .023	4 .023	3 .008	2 .002			11	3 .041	2 .013	1 .003	1 .003
		10	4 .049	3 .020	2 .006	1 .001			10	2 .028	1 .007	1 .007	0 .001
		9	3 .043	2 .016	1 .004	1 .004			9	1 .016	1 .016	0 .002	0 .002
		8	2 .035−	1 .010+	0 .002	0 .002			8	1 .033	0 .006	0 .006	—
		7	1 .023	1 .023	0 .004	0 .004			7	0 .013	0 .013	—	—
		6	0 .011	0 .011	—	—			6	0 .027	—	—	—
		5	0 .026	—	—	—							
	14	16	10 .037	9 .014	8 .005+	7 .002		10	16	7 .046	6 .014	5 .004	5 .004
		15	8 .025+	7 .010−	7 .010−	6 .003			15	5 .018	5 .018	4 .005+	3 .001
		14	7 .032	6 .013	5 .005−	5 .005−			14	4 .017	4 .017	3 .005−	3 .005−
		13	6 .035+	5 .014	4 .005+	3 .001			13	4 .042	3 .014	2 .003	2 .003
		12	5 .035+	4 .014	3 .005−	3 .005−			12	3 .032	2 .009	2 .009	1 .002
		11	4 .033	3 .012	2 .004	2 .004			11	2 .021	2 .021	1 .005−	1 .005−
		10	3 .028	2 .009	2 .009	1 .002			10	2 .042	1 .011	0 .002	0 .002
		9	2 .021	2 .021	1 .006	0 .001			9	1 .023	1 .023	0 .004	0 .004
		8	2 .045−	1 .013	0 .002	0 .002			8	1 .045−	0 .008	0 .008	—
		7	1 .030	0 .006	0 .006	—			7	0 .017	0 .017	—	—
		6	0 .013	0 .012	—	—			6	0 .035−	—	—	—
		5	0 .031	—	—	—							
	13	16	9 .030	8 .011	7 .004	7 .004		9	16	6 .037	5 .010−	5 .010−	4 .002
		15	8 .047	7 .019	6 .007	5 .002			15	5 .040	4 .012	3 .003	3 .003
		14	6 .023	6 .023	5 .008	4 .003			14	4 .034	3 .010−	3 .010−	2 .002
		13	5 .023	5 .023	4 .008	3 .003			13	3 .025+	2 .007	2 .007	1 .001
		12	4 .022	4 .022	3 .007	2 .002			12	2 .016	2 .016	1 .003	1 .003
		11	4 .018	3 .018	2 .005+	1 .001			11	2 .033	1 .008	1 .008	0 .001
		10	3 .039	2 .013	1 .003	1 .003			10	1 .017	1 .017	0 .002	0 .002
		9	2 .029	1 .008	1 .008	0 .001			9	1 .034	0 .006	0 .006	...
		8	1 .018	1 .018	0 .003	0 .003			8	0 .012	0 .012	...	...
		7	1 .038	0 .007	0 .007	—			7	0 .024	0 .024	--	...
		6	0 .017	0 .017	—	—			6	0 .045+	—	—	—
		5	0 .037	—	—	—							

TABLE A-29 (Continued). TABLES FOR TESTING SIGNIFICANCE IN 2 × 2 TABLES WITH UNEQUAL SAMPLES

		a_1	Significance Level 0.05 (0.10)	0.025 (0.05)	0.01 (0.02)	0.005 (0.01)
$n_1=16$ $n_2=8$		16	5 .028	4 .007	4 .007	3 .001
		15	4 .028	3 .007	3 .007	2 .001
		14	3 .021	3 .021	2 .005−	2 .005−
		13	3 .047	2 .013	1 .002	1 .002
		12	2 .028	1 .006	1 .006	0 .001
		11	1 .014	1 .014	0 .002	0 .002
		10	1 .027	0 .004	0 .004	0 .004
		9	0 .009	0 .009	0 .009	—
		8	0 .017	0 .017	—	—
		7	0 .033	—	—	—
	7	16	4 .020	4 .020	3 .004	3 .004
		15	3 .017	3 .017	2 .003	2 .003
		14	3 .045+	2 .011	1 .002	1 .002
		13	2 .026	1 .005−	1 .005−	1 .005−
		12	1 .012	1 .012	0 .001	0 .001
		11	1 .024	1 .024	0 .003	0 .003
		10	1 .045−	0 .007	0 .007	—
		9	0 .014	0 .014	—	—
		8	0 .026	—	—	—
		7	0 .047	—	—	—
	6	16	3 .013	3 .013	2 .002	2 .002
		15	3 .046	2 .009	2 .009	1 .001
		14	2 .025+	1 .004	1 .004	1 .004
		13	1 .011	1 .011	0 .001	0 .001
		12	1 .023	1 .023	0 .003	0 .003
		11	1 .043	0 .006	0 .006	—
		10	0 .012	0 .012	—	—
		9	0 .023	0 .023	—	—
		8	0 .040	—	—	—
	5	16	3 .048	2 .008	2 .008	1 .001
		15	2 .028	1 .004	1 .004	1 .004
		14	1 .011	1 .011	0 .001	0 .001
		13	1 .025+	0 .003	0 .003	0 .003
		12	1 .047	0 .006	0 .006	—
		11	0 .012	0 .012	—	—
		10	0 .023	0 .023	—	—
		9	0 .039	—	—	—
	4	16	2 .032	1 .004	1 .004	1 .004
		15	1 .013	1 .013	0 .001	0 .001
		14	1 .032	0 .003	0 .003	0 .003
		13	0 .007	0 .007	0 .007	—
		12	0 .014	0 .014	—	—
		11	0 .026	—	—	—
		10	0 .043	—	—	—

		a_1	Significance Level 0.05 (0.10)	0.025 (0.05)	0.01 (0.02)	0.005 (0.01)
$n_1=16$ $n_2=3$		16	1 .018	1 .018	0 .001	0 .001
		15	0 .004	0 .004	0 .004	0 .004
		14	0 .010+	0 .010+	—	—
		13	0 .021	0 .021	—	—
		12	0 .036	—	—	—
	2	16	0 .007	0 .007	0 .007	—
		15	0 .020	0 .020	—	—
		14	0 .039	—	—	—
$n_1=17$ $n_2=17$		17	12 .022	12 .022	11 .009	10 .004
		16	11 .043	10 .020	9 .008	8 .003
		15	9 .029	8 .013	7 .005+	6 .002
		14	8 .035+	7 .016	6 .007	5 .002
		13	7 .040	6 .019	5 .007	4 .003
		12	6 .042	5 .019	4 .007	3 .002
		11	5 .042	4 .018	3 .007	2 .002
		10	4 .040	3 .016	2 .005+	1 .001
		9	3 .035+	2 .013	1 .003	1 .003
		8	2 .029	1 .008	1 .008	0 .001
		7	1 .020	1 .020	0 .004	0 .004
		6	1 .043	0 .009	0 .009	—
		5	0 .022	0 .022	—	—
	16	17	12 .044	11 .018	10 .007	9 .003
		16	10 .035−	9 .015−	8 .006	7 .002
		15	9 .046	8 .021	7 .009	6 .003
		14	7 .025+	6 .011	5 .004	5 .004
		13	6 .027	5 .011	4 .004	4 .004
		12	5 .027	4 .011	3 .004	3 .004
		11	4 .025+	3 .009	3 .009	2 .003
		10	3 .022	3 .022	2 .007	1 .002
		9	3 .046	2 .017	1 .004	1 .004
		8	2 .036	1 .011	0 .002	0 .002
		7	1 .024	1 .024	0 .005−	0 .005−
		6	0 .011	0 .011	—	—
		5	0 .026	—	—	—
	15	17	11 .038	10 .015−	9 .006	8 .002
		16	9 .027	8 .011	7 .004	7 .004
		15	8 .035+	7 .015−	6 .006	5 .002
		14	7 .040	6 .017	5 .006	4 .002
		13	6 .017	5 .017	4 .006	3 .002
		12	5 .039	4 .016	3 .005+	2 .001
		11	4 .035+	3 .013	2 .004	2 .004
		10	3 .029	2 .010−	2 .010−	1 .002
		9	2 .022	2 .022	1 .006	0 .001
		8	2 .046	1 .014	0 .002	0 .002
		7	1 .030	0 .006	0 .006	—
		6	0 .014	0 .014	—	—
		5	0 .031	—	—	—

TABLE A-29 (Continued). TABLES FOR TESTING SIGNIFICANCE IN 2 × 2 TABLES WITH UNEQUAL SAMPLES

	a_1	Significance Level 0.05 (0.10)	0.025 (0.05)	0.01 (0.02)	0.005 (0.01)		a_1	Significance Level 0.05 (0.10)	0.025 (0.05)	0.01 (0.02)	0.005 (0.01)
$n_1=17$ $n_2=14$	17	10 .032	9 .012	8 .004	8 .004	$n_1=17$ $n_2=11$	13	4 .042	3 .014	2 .004	2 .004
	16	8 .021	8 .021	7 .008	6 .003		12	3 .031	2 .009	2 .009	1 .002
	15	7 .026	6 .010 −	6 .010 −	5 .003		11	2 .020	2 .020	1 .005 −	1 .005 −
	14	6 .028	5 .011	4 .004	4 .004		10	2 .040	1 .011	0 .001	0 .001
	13	5 .027	4 .010 −	4 .010 −	3 .003		9	1 .022	1 .022	0 .004	0 .004
	12	4 .024	4 .024	3 .008	2 .002		8	1 .042	0 .008	0 .008	—
	11	4 .049	3 .019	2 .006	1 .001		7	0 .016	0 .016	—	—
	10	3 .040	2 .014	1 .003	1 .003		6	0 .033	—	—	—
	9	2 .029	1 .008	1 .008	0 .001						
	8	1 .018	1 .018	0 .003	0 .003	10	17	7 .041	6 .012	5 .003	5 .003
	7	1 .038	0 .007	0 .007	—		16	6 .047	5 .015 +	4 .004	4 .004
	6	0 .017	0 .017	—	—		15	5 .043	4 .014	3 .004	3 .004
	5	0 .036	—	—	—		14	4 .034	3 .010 +	2 .002	2 .002
							13	3 .024	3 .024	2 .007	1 .001
13	17	9 .026	8 .009	8 .009	7 .003		12	3 .049	2 .015 +	1 .003	1 .003
	16	8 .040	7 .015 +	6 .005 +	5 .002		11	2 .031	1 .007	1 .007	0 .001
	15	7 .045 +	6 .018	5 .006	4 .002		10	1 .016	1 .016	0 .002	0 .002
	14	6 .045 +	5 .018	4 .006	3 .002		9	1 .031	0 .005 +	0 .005 +	—
	13	5 .042	4 .016	3 .005 +	2 .001		8	0 .011	0 .011	—	—
	12	4 .035 +	3 .013	2 .004	2 .004		7	0 .022	0 .022	—	—
	11	3 .028	2 .009	2 .009	1 .002		6	0 .042	—	—	—
	10	2 .019	2 .019	1 .005 −	1 .005 −						
	9	2 .040	1 .011	0 .002	0 .002	9	17	6 .032	5 .008	5 .008	4 .002
	8	1 .024	1 .024	0 .004	0 .004		16	5 .034	4 .010 −	4 .010 −	3 .002
	7	1 .047	0 .010 −	0 .010 −	—		15	4 .028	3 .008	3 .008	2 .002
	6	0 .021	0 .021	—	—		14	3 .020	3 .020	2 .005 −	2 .005 −
	5	0 .043	—	—	—		13	3 .042	2 .012	1 .002	1 .002
							12	2 .025 +	1 .006	1 .006	0 .001
12	17	8 .021	8 .021	7 .007	6 .002		11	2 .048	1 .012	0 .002	0 .002
	16	7 .030	6 .011	5 .003	5 .003		10	1 .024	1 .024	0 .004	0 .004
	15	6 .033	5 .012	4 .004	4 .004		9	1 .045 −	0 .008	0 .008	—
	14	5 .030	4 .011	3 .003	3 .003		8	0 .016	0 .016	—	—
	13	4 .026	3 .008	3 .008	2 .002		7	0 .030	—	—	—
	12	3 .020	3 .020	2 .006	1 .001						
	11	3 .041	2 .013	1 .003	1 .003	8	17	5 .024	5 .024	4 .006	3 .001
	10	2 .028	1 .007	1 .007	0 .001		16	4 .023	4 .023	3 .006	2 .001
	9	1 .016	1 .016	0 .002	0 .002		15	3 .017	3 .017	2 .004	2 .004
	8	1 .032	0 .006	0 .006	—		14	3 .039	2 .010 −	2 .010 −	1 .002
	7	0 .012	0 .012	—	—		13	2 .022	2 .022	1 .004	1 .004
	6	0 .026	—	—	—		12	2 .043	1 .010 −	1 .010 −	0 .001
							11	1 .020	1 .020	0 .003	0 .003
11	17	7 .016	7 .016	6 .005 −	6 .005 −		10	1 .038	0 .006	0 .006	—
	16	6 .022	6 .022	5 .007	4 .002		9	0 .012	0 .012	—	—
	15	5 .022	5 .022	4 .007	3 .002		8	0 .022	0 .022	—	—
	14	4 .019	4 .019	3 .006	2 .001		7	0 .040	—	—	—

TABLE A-29 (Continued). TABLES FOR TESTING SIGNIFICANCE IN 2 × 2 TABLES WITH UNEQUAL SAMPLES

		a_1	Significance Level 0.05 (0.10)	0.025 (0.05)	0.01 (0.02)	0.005 (0.01)
$n_1=17$ $n_2=7$		17	4 .017	4 .017	3 .003	3 .003
		16	3 .014	3 .014	2 .003	2 .003
		15	3 .038	2 .009	2 .009	1 .001
		14	2 .021	2 .021	1 .004	1 .004
		13	2 .042	1 .009	1 .009	0 .001
		12	1 .018	1 .018	0 .002	0 .002
		11	1 .034	0 .005 −	0 .005 −	0 .005 −
		10	0 .010 −	0 .010 −	0 .010 −	—
		9	0 .019	0 .019	—	—
		8	0 .033	—	—	—
	6	17	3 .011	3 .011	2 .002	2 .002
		16	3 .040	2 .008	2 .008	1 .001
		15	2 .021	2 .021	1 .003	1 .003
		14	2 .045 +	1 .009	1 .009	0 .001
		13	1 .018	1 .018	0 .002	0 .002
		12	1 .035 −	0 .005 −	0 .005 −	0 .005 −
		11	0 .009	0 .009	0 .009	—
		10	0 .017	0 .017	—	—
		9	0 .030	—	—	—
		8	0 .050 −	—	—	—
	5	17	3 .043	2 .006	2 .006	1 .001
		16	2 .024	2 .024	1 .003	1 .003
		15	1 .009	1 .009	1 .009	0 .001
		14	1 .021	1 .021	0 .002	0 .002
		13	1 .039	0 .005 −	0 .005 −	0 .005 −
		12	0 .010 −	0 .010 −	0 .010 −	—
		11	0 .018	0 .018	—	—
		10	0 .030	—	—	—
		9	0 .049	—	—	—
	4	17	2 .029	1 .003	1 .003	1 .003
		16	1 .012	1 .012	0 .001	0 .001
		15	1 .028	0 .003	0 .003	0 .003
		14	0 .006	0 .006	0 .006	—
		13	0 .012	0 .012	—	—
		12	0 .021	0 .021	—	—
		11	0 .035 +	—	—	—
	3	17	1 .016	1 .016	0 .001	0 .001
		16	1 .046	0 .004	0 .004	0 .004
		15	0 .009	0 .009	0 .009	—
		14	0 .018	0 .018	—	—
		13	0 .031	—	—	—
		12	0 .049	—	—	—
	2	17	0 .006	0 .006	0 .006	—
		16	0 .018	0 .018	—	—
		15	0 .035 +	—	—	—

		a_1	Significance Level 0.05 (0.10)	0.025 (0.05)	0.01 (0.02)	0.005 (0.01)
$n_1=18$ $n_2=18$		18	13 .023	13 .023	12 .010 −	11 .004
		17	12 .044	11 .020	10 .009	9 .004
		16	10 .030	9 .014	8 .006	7 .002
		15	9 .038	8 .018	7 .008	6 .003
		14	8 .043	7 .020	6 .009	5 .003
		13	7 .046	6 .022	5 .009	4 .003
		12	6 .047	5 .022	4 .009	3 .003
		11	5 .046	4 .020	3 .008	2 .002
		10	4 .043	3 .018	2 .006	1 .001
		9	3 .038	2 .014	1 .004	1 .004
		8	2 .030	1 .009	1 .009	0 .001
		7	1 .020	1 .020	0 .004	0 .004
		6	1 .044	0 .010 −	0 .010 −	—
		5	0 .023	0 .023	—	—
	17	18	13 .045 +	12 .019	11 .008	10 .003
		17	11 .036	10 .016	9 .007	8 .002
		16	10 .049	9 .023	8 .010 −	7 .004
		15	8 .028	7 .012	6 .005 −	6 .005 −
		14	7 .030	6 .013	5 .005 +	4 .002
		13	6 .031	5 .013	4 .005 −	4 .005 −
		12	5 .030	4 .012	3 .004	3 .004
		11	4 .028	3 .010 +	2 .003	2 .003
		10	3 .023	3 .023	2 .008	1 .002
		9	3 .047	2 .018	1 .005 −	1 .005 −
		8	2 .037	1 .011	0 .002	0 .002
		7	1 .025 −	1 .025 −	0 .005 −	0 .005 −
		6	0 .011	0 .011	—	—
		5	0 .026	—	—	—
	16	18	12 .039	11 .016	10 .006	9 .002
		17	10 .029	9 .012	8 .005 −	8 .005 −
		16	9 .038	8 .017	7 .007	6 .002
		15	8 .043	7 019	6 .008	5 .003
		14	7 .046	6 .020	5 .008	4 .003
		13	6 .045 +	5 .020	4 .007	3 .002
		12	5 .042	4 .018	3 .006	2 .002
		11	4 .037	3 .015 −	2 .004	2 .004
		10	3 .031	2 .011	1 .003	1 .003
		9	2 .023	2 .023	1 .006	0 .001
		8	2 .046	1 .014	0 .002	0 .002
		7	1 .030	0 .006	0 .006	—
		6	0 .014	0 .014	—	—
		5	0 .031	—	—	—
	15	18	11 .033	10 .013	9 .005 −	9 .005 −
		17	9 .023	9 .023	8 .009	7 .003
		16	8 .029	7 .012	6 .004	6 .004
		15	7 .031	6 .013	5 .005 −	5 .005 −
		14	6 .031	5 .013	4 .004	4 .004
		13	5 .029	4 .011	3 .004	3 .004

TABLE A-29 (Continued). TABLES FOR TESTING SIGNIFICANCE IN 2 × 2 TABLES WITH UNEQUAL SAMPLES

		a_1	0.05 (0.10)	0.025 (0.05)	0.01 (0.02)	0.005 (0.01)			a_1	0.05 (0.10)	0.025 (0.05)	0.01 (0.02)	0.005 (0.01)
$n_1=18$ $n_2=15$		12	4 .025+	3 .009	3 .009	2 .003	$n_1=18$ $n_2=12$		10	2 .038	1 .010+	0 .001	0 .001
		11	3 .020	3 .020	2 .006	1 .001			9	1 .021	1 .021	0 .003	0 .003
		10	3 .041	2 .014	1 .004	1 .004			8	1 .040	0 .007	0 .007	—
		9	2 .030	1 .008	1 .008	0 .001			7	0 .016	0 .016	—	—
		8	1 .018	1 .018	0 .003	0 .003			6	0 .031	—	—	—
		7	1 .038	0 .007	0 .007	—		11	18	8 .045+	7 .014	6 .004	6 .004
		6	0 .017	0 .017	—	—			17	6 .018	6 .018	5 .006	4 .001
		5	0 .036	—	—	—			16	5 .018	5 .018	4 .005+	3 .001
	14	18	10 .028	9 .010−	9 .010−	8 .003			15	5 .043	4 .015−	3 .004	3 .004
		17	9 .043	8 .017	7 .006	6 .002			14	4 .033	3 .011	2 .003	2 .003
		16	8 .050−	7 .021	6 .008	5 .003			13	3 .023	3 .023	2 .007	1 .001
		15	6 .022	6 .022	5 .008	4 .003			12	3 .046	2 .014	1 .003	1 .003
		14	6 .049	5 .020	4 .007	3 .002			11	2 .029	1 .007	1 .007	0 .001
		13	5 .044	4 .017	3 .006	2 .001			10	1 .015−	1 .015−	0 .002	0 .002
		12	4 .037	3 .013	2 .004	2 .004			9	1 .029	0 .005−	0 .005−	0 .005−
		11	3 .028	2 .009	2 .009	1 .002			8	0 .010+	0 .010+	—	—
		10	2 .020	2 .020	1 .005−	1 .005−			7	0 .020	0 .020	—	—
		9	2 .039	1 .011	0 .002	0 .002			6	0 .039	—	—	—
		8	1 .024	1 .024	0 .004	0 .004		10	18	7 .037	6 .010+	5 .003	5 .003
		7	1 .047	0 .009	0 .009	—			17	6 .041	5 .013	4 .003	4 .003
		6	0 .020	0 .020	—	—			16	5 .036	4 .011	3 .003	3 .003
		5	0 .043	—	—	—			15	4 .028	3 .008	3 .008	2 .002
	13	18	9 .023	9 .023	8 .008	7 .002			14	3 .019	3 .019	2 .005−	2 .005−
		17	8 .034	7 .012	6 .004	6 .004			13	3 .039	2 .011	1 .002	1 .002
		16	7 .037	6 .014	5 .005−	5 .005−			12	2 .023	2 .023	1 .005+	0 .001
		15	6 .036	5 .014	4 .004	4 .004			11	2 .043	1 .011	0 .001	0 .001
		14	5 .032	4 .012	3 .004	3 .004			10	1 .022	1 .022	0 .003	0 .003
		13	4 .027	3 .009	3 .009	2 .002			9	1 .040	0 .007	0 .007	—
		12	3 .020	3 .020	2 .006	1 .001			8	0 .014	0 .014	—	—
		11	3 .040	2 .013	1 .003	1 .003			7	0 .027	—	—	—
		10	2 .027	1 .007	1 .007	0 .001			6	0 .049	—	—	—
		9	1 .015+	1 .015+	0 .002	0 .002		9	18	6 .029	5 .007	5 .007	4 .002
		8	1 .031	0 .006	0 .006	—			17	5 .030	4 .008	4 .008	3 .002
		7	0 .012	0 .012	—	—			16	4 .023	4 .023	3 .006	2 .001
		6	0 .025+	—	—	—			15	3 .016	3 .016	2 .004	2 .004
	12	18	8 .018	8 .018	7 .006	6 .002			14	3 .034	2 .009	2 .009	1 .002
		17	7 .026	6 .009	6 .009	5 .003			13	2 .019	2 .019	1 .004	1 .004
		16	6 .027	5 .009	5 .009	4 .003			12	2 .037	1 .009	1 .009	0 .001
		15	5 .024	5 .024	4 .008	3 .002			11	1 .018	1 .018	0 .002	0 .002
		14	4 .020	4 .020	3 .006	2 .001			10	1 .033	0 .005+	0 .005+	—
		13	4 .042	3 .014	2 .004	2 .004			9	0 .010+	0 .010+	—	—
		12	3 .030	2 .009	2 .009	1 .002			8	0 .020	0 .020	—	—
		11	2 .019	2 .019	1 .005−	1 .005−			7	0 .036	—	—	—

TABLE A-29 (Continued). TABLES FOR TESTING SIGNIFICANCE IN 2 × 2 TABLES WITH UNEQUAL SAMPLES

			Significance Level			
		a_1	0.05 (0.10)	0.025 (0.05)	0.01 (0.02)	0.005 (0.01)
$n_1=18$ $n_2=8$		18	5 .022	5 .022	4 .005−	4 .005−
		17	4 .020	4 .020	3 .004	3 .004
		16	3 .014	3 .014	2 .003	2 .003
		15	3 .032	2 .008	2 .008	1 .001
		14	2 .017	2 .017	1 .003	1 .003
		13	2 .034	1 .007	1 .007	0 .001
		12	1 .015+	1 .015+	0 .002	0 .002
		11	1 .028	0 .004	0 .004	0 .004
		10	1 .049	0 .008	0 .008	—
		9	0 .016	0 .016	—	—
		8	0 .028	—	—	—
		7	0 .048	—	—	—
	7	18	4 .015+	4 .015+	3 .003	3 .003
		17	3 .012	3 .012	2 .002	2 .002
		16	3 .032	2 .007	2 .007	1 .001
		15	2 .017	2 .017	1 .003	1 .003
		14	2 .034	1 .007	1 .007	0 .001
		13	1 .014	1 .014	0 .002	0 .002
		12	1 .027	0 .004	0 .004	0 .004
		11	1 .046	0 .007	0 .007	—
		10	0 .013	0 .013	—	—
		9	0 .024	0 .024	—	—
		8	0 .040	—	—	—
	6	18	3 .010−	3 .010−	3 .010−	2 .001
		17	3 .035+	2 .006	2 .006	1 .001
		16	2 .018	2 .018	1 .003	1 .003
		15	2 .038	1 .007	1 .007	0 .001
		14	1 .015−	1 .015−	0 .002	0 .002
		13	1 .028	0 .003	0 .003	0 .003
		12	1 .048	0 .007	0 .007	—
		11	0 .013	0 .013	—	—
		10	0 .022	0 .022	—	—
		9	0 .037	—	—	—
	5	18	3 .040	2 .006	2 .006	1 .001
		17	2 .021	2 .021	1 .003	1 .003
		16	2 .048	1 .008	1 .008	0 .001
		15	1 .017	1 .017	0 .002	0 .002
		14	1 .033	0 .004	0 .004	0 .004
		13	0 .007	0 .007	0 .007	—
		12	0 .014	0 .014	—	—
		11	0 .024	0 .024	—	—
		10	0 .038	—	—	—
	4	18	2 .026	1 .003	1 .003	1 .003
		17	1 .010−	1 .010−	1 .010−	0 .001
		16	1 .024	1 .024	0 .002	0 .002
		15	1 .046	0 .005−	0 .005−	0 .005−
		14	0 .010−	0 .010−	0 .010−	—

			Significance Level			
		a_1	0.05 (0.10)	0.025 (0.05)	0.01 (0.02)	0.005 (0.01)
$n_1=18$ $n_2=4$		13	0 .017	0 .017	—	—
		12	0 .029	—	—	—
		11	0 .045+	—	—	—
	3	18	1 .014	1 .014	0 .001	0 .001
		17	1 .041	0 .003	0 .003	0 .003
		16	0 .008	0 .008	0 .008	—
		15	0 .015+	0 .015+	—	—
		14	0 .026	—	—	—
		13	0 .042	—	—	—
	2	18	0 .005+	0 .005+	0 .005+	—
		17	0 .016	0 .016	—	—
		16	0 .032	—	—	—
$n_1=19$ $n_2=19$		19	14 .023	14 .023	13 .010−	12 .004
		18	13 .045−	12 .021	11 .009	10 .004
		17	11 .031	10 .015−	9 .006	8 .003
		16	10 .039	9 .019	8 .009	7 .003
		15	9 .046	8 .022	6 .004	6 .004
		14	8 .050−	7 .024	5 .004	5 .004
		13	6 .025+	5 .011	4 .004	4 .004
		12	5 .024	5 .024	3 .003	3 .003
		11	5 .050−	4 .022	3 .009	2 .003
		10	4 .046	3 .019	2 .006	1 .002
		9	3 .039	2 .015−	1 .004	1 .004
		8	2 .031	1 .009	1 .009	0 .002
		7	1 .021	1 .021	0 .004	0 .004
		6	1 .045−	0 .010−	0 .010−	—
		5	0 .023	0 .023	—	—
	18	19	14 .046	13 .020	12 .008	11 .003
		18	12 .037	11 .017	10 .007	9 .003
		17	10 .024	10 .024	8 .004	8 .004
		16	9 .030	8 .014	7 .006	6 .002
		15	8 .033	7 .015+	6 .006	5 .002
		14	7 .035+	6 .016	5 .006	4 .002
		13	6 .035−	5 .015+	4 .006	3 .002
		12	5 .033	4 .014	3 .005−	3 .005−
		11	4 .030	3 .011	2 .004	2 .004
		10	3 .025−	3 .025−	2 .008	1 .002
		9	3 .049	2 .019	1 .005+	0 .001
		8	2 .038	1 .012	0 .002	0 .002
		7	1 .025+	0 .005−	0 .005−	0 .005−
		6	0 .012	0 .012	—	—
		5	0 .027	—	—	—
	17	19	13 .040	12 .016	11 .006	10 .002
		18	11 .030	10 .013	9 .005+	8 .002
		17	10 .040	9 .018	8 .008	7 .003
		16	9 .047	8 .022	7 .009	6 .003

TABLE A-29 (Continued). TABLES FOR TESTING SIGNIFICANCE IN 2 × 2 TABLES WITH UNEQUAL SAMPLES

$n_1 = 19$, $n_2 = 17$

n_2	a_1	0.05 (0.10)	0.025 (0.05)	0.01 (0.02)	0.005 (0.01)
17	15	8 .050−	7 .023	6 .010−	5 .004
	14	6 .023	6 .023	5 .010−	4 .003
	13	6 .049	5 .022	4 .008	3 .003
	12	5 .045−	4 .019	3 .007	2 .002
	11	4 .039	3 .015+	2 .005−	2 .005−
	10	3 .032	2 .011	1 .003	1 .003
	9	2 .024	2 .024	1 .007	0 .001
	8	2 .047	1 .015−	0 .002	0 .002
	7	1 .031	0 .006	0 .006	—
	6	0 .014	0 .014	—	—
	5	0 .031	—	—	—
16	19	12 .035−	11 .013	10 .005−	10 .005−
	18	10 .024	10 .024	9 .010−	8 .004
	17	9 .031	8 .013	7 .005+	6 .002
	16	8 .035−	7 .015+	6 .006	5 .002
	15	7 .036	6 .015+	5 .006	4 .002
	14	6 .034	5 .014	4 .005+	3 .002
	13	5 .031	4 .012	3 .004	3 .004
	12	4 .027	3 .010−	3 .010−	2 .003
	11	3 .021	3 .021	2 .007	1 .002
	10	3 .042	2 .015−	1 .004	1 .004
	9	2 .030	1 .009	1 .009	0 .001
	8	1 .018	1 .018	0 .003	0 .003
	7	1 .037	0 .007	0 .007	—
	6	0 .017	0 .017	—	—
	5	0 .036	—	—	—
15	19	11 .029	10 .011	9 .004	9 .004
	18	10 .046	9 .019	8 .007	7 .002
	17	8 .023	8 .023	7 .009	6 .003
	16	7 .025−	7 .025−	6 .010−	5 .003
	15	6 .024	6 .024	5 .009	4 .003
	14	5 .022	5 .022	4 .008	3 .002
	13	5 .045+	4 .018	3 .006	2 .002
	12	4 .037	3 .014	2 .004	2 .004
	11	3 .029	2 .009	2 .009	1 .002
	10	2 .020	2 .020	1 .005+	0 .001
	9	2 .039	1 .011	0 .002	0 .002
	8	1 .023	1 .023	0 .004	0 .004
	7	1 .046	0 .009	0 .009	—
	6	0 .020	0 .020	—	—
	5	0 .042	—	—	—
14	19	10 .024	10 .024	9 .008	8 .003
	18	9 .037	8 .014	7 .005−	7 .005−
	17	8 .042	7 .017	6 .006	5 .002
	16	7 .042	6 .017	5 .006	4 .002
	15	6 .039	5 .015+	4 .005+	3 .001
	14	5 .034	4 .013	3 .004	3 .004
	13	4 .027	3 .009	3 .009	2 .003
	12	3 .020	3 .020	2 .006	1 .001
	11	3 .040	2 .013	1 .003	1 .003
	10	2 .027	1 .007	1 .007	0 .001
	9	1 .015−	1 .015−	0 .002	0 .002
	8	1 .030	0 .005+	0 .005+	—
	7	0 .012	0 .012	—	—
	6	0 .024	0 .024	—	—
	5	0 .049	—	—	—

$n_1 = 19$, $n_2 = 13$

n_2	a_1	0.05 (0.10)	0.025 (0.05)	0.01 (0.02)	0.005 (0.01)
13	19	9 .020	9 .020	8 .006	7 .002
	18	8 .029	7 .010+	6 .003	6 .003
	17	7 .031	6 .011	5 .004	5 .004
	16	6 .029	5 .011	4 .003	4 .003
	15	5 .025+	4 .009	4 .009	3 .003
	14	4 .020	4 .020	3 .006	2 .002
	13	4 .041	3 .015−	2 .004	2 .004
	12	3 .020	2 .006	2 .006	1 .002
	11	2 .019	2 .019	1 .005−	1 .005−
	10	2 .036	1 .010−	1 .010−	0 .001
	9	1 .020	1 .020	0 .003	0 .003
	8	1 .038	0 .007	0 .007	—
	7	0 .015−	0 .015−	—	—
	6	0 .030	—	—	—
12	19	9 .049	8 .016	7 .005−	7 .005−
	18	7 .022	7 .022	6 .007	5 .002
	17	6 .022	6 .022	5 .007	4 .002
	16	5 .019	5 .019	4 .006	3 .002
	15	5 .042	4 .015+	3 .004	3 .004
	14	4 .032	3 .011	2 .003	2 .003
	13	3 .023	3 .023	2 .006	1 .001
	12	3 .043	2 .014	1 .003	1 .003
	11	2 .027	1 .007	1 .007	0 .001
	10	2 .050−	1 .014	0 .002	0 .002
	9	1 .027	0 .005−	0 .005−	0 .005−
	8	1 .050−	0 .010−	0 .010−	—
	7	0 .019	0 .019	—	—
	6	0 .037	—	—	—
11	19	8 .041	7 .012	6 .003	6 .003
	18	7 .047	6 .016	5 .004	5 .004
	17	6 .043	5 .015−	4 .004	4 .004
	16	5 .035+	4 .012	3 .003	3 .003
	15	4 .027	3 .008	3 .008	2 .002
	14	3 .018	3 .018	2 .005−	2 .005−
	13	3 .035+	2 .010+	1 .002	1 .002
	12	2 .021	2 .021	1 .005−	1 .005−
	11	2 .040	1 .010+	0 .001	0 .001
	10	1 .020	1 .020	0 .003	0 .003
	9	1 .037	0 .006	0 .006	—
	8	0 .013	0 .013	—	—
	7	0 .025−	0 .025−	—	—
	6	0 .046	—	—	—
10	19	7 .033	6 .009	6 .009	5 .002
	18	6 .036	5 .011	4 .003	4 .003
	17	5 .030	4 .009	4 .009	3 .002
	16	4 .022	4 .022	3 .006	2 .001
	15	4 .047	3 .015−	2 .004	2 .004
	14	3 .030	2 .008	2 .008	1 .002
	13	2 .017	2 .017	1 .004	1 .004
	12	2 .033	1 .008	1 .008	0 .001
	11	1 .016	1 .016	0 .002	0 .002
	10	1 .029	0 .005−	0 .005−	0 .005−
	9	0 .009	0 .009	0 .009	—
	8	0 .018	0 .018	—	—
	7	0 .032	—	—	—

TABLE A-29 (Continued). TABLES FOR TESTING SIGNIFICANCE IN 2 × 2 TABLES WITH UNEQUAL SAMPLES

Left panel:

		a_1	Significance Level 0.05 (0.10)	0.025 (0.05)	0.01 (0.02)	0.005 (0.01)
$n_1=19$	$n_2=9$	19	6 .026	5 .006	5 .006	4 .001
		18	5 .026	4 .007	4 .007	3 .001
		17	4 .020	4 .020	3 .005 −	3 .005 −
		16	4 .044	3 .013	2 .003	2 .003
		15	3 .028	2 .007	2 .007	1 .001
		14	2 .015 −	2 .015 −	1 .003	1 .003
		13	2 .029	1 .006	1 .006	0 .001
		12	1 .013	1 .013	0 .002	0 .002
		11	1 .024	1 .024	0 .004	0 .004
		10	1 .042	0 .007	0 .007	—
		9	0 .013	0 .013	—	—
		8	0 .024	0 .024	—	—
		7	0 .043	—	—	—
	8	19	5 .019	5 .019	4 .004	4 .004
		18	4 .017	4 .017	3 .004	3 .004
		17	4 .044	3 .011	2 .002	2 .002
		16	3 .027	2 .006	2 .006	1 .001
		15	2 .014	2 .014	1 .002	1 .002
		14	2 .027	1 .006	1 .006	0 .001
		13	2 .049	1 .011	0 .001	0 .001
		12	1 .021	1 .021	0 .003	0 .003
		11	1 .038	0 .006	0 .006	—
		10	0 .011	0 .011	—	—
		9	0 .020	0 .020	—	—
		8	0 .034	—	—	—
	7	19	4 .013	4 .013	3 .002	3 .002
		18	4 .047	3 .010 +	2 .002	2 .002
		17	3 .028	2 .006	2 .006	1 .001
		16	2 .014	2 .014	1 .002	1 .002
		15	2 .028	1 .005 +	1 .005 +	0 .001
		14	1 .011	1 .011	0 .001	0 .001
		13	1 .021	1 .021	0 .003	0 .003
		12	1 .037	0 .005 +	0 .005 +	—
		11	0 .010 −	0 .010 −	0 .010 −	—
		10	0 .017	0 .017	—	—
		9	0 .030	—	—	—
		8	0 .048	—	—	—
	6	19	4 .050	3 .009	3 .009	2 .001
		18	3 .031	2 .005 +	2 .005 +	1 .001
		17	2 .015 +	2 .015 +	1 .002	1 .002
		16	2 .032	1 .006	1 .006	0 .000
		15	1 .012	1 .012	0 .001	0 .001
		14	1 .023	1 .023	0 .003	0 .003
		13	1 .039	0 .005 +	0 .005 +	—
		12	0 .010 −	0 .010 −	0 .010 −	—
		11	0 .017	0 .017	—	—
		10	0 .028	—	—	—
		9	0 .045 +	—	—	—
	5	19	3 .036	2 .005 −	2 .005 −	2 .005 −
		18	2 .018	2 .018	1 .002	1 .002
		17	2 .042	1 .006	1 .006	0 .000
		16	1 .014	1 .014	0 .001	0 .001
		15	1 .028	0 .003	0 .003	0 .003
		14	1 .047	0 .006	0 .006	—
		13	0 .011	0 .011	—	—

Right panel:

		a_1	Significance Level 0.05 (0.10)	0.025 (0.05)	0.01 (0.02)	0.005 (0.01)
$n_1=19$	$n_2=5$	12	0 .019	0 .019	—	—
		11	0 .030	—	—	—
		10	0 .047	—	—	—
	4	19	2 .024	2 .024	1 .002	1 .002
		18	1 .009	1 .009	1 .009	0 .001
		17	1 .021	1 .021	0 .002	0 .002
		16	1 .040	0 .004	0 .004	0 .004
		15	0 .008	0 .008	0 .008	—
		14	0 .014	0 .014	—	—
		13	0 .024	0 .024	—	—
		12	0 .037	—	—	—
	3	19	1 .013	1 .013	0 .001	0 .001
		18	1 .038	0 .003	0 .003	0 .003
		17	0 .006	0 .006	0 .006	—
		16	0 .013	0 .013	—	—
		15	0 .023	0 .023	—	—
		14	0 .036	—	—	—
	2	19	0 .005 −	0 .005 −	0 .005 −	0 .005 −
		18	0 .014	0 .014	—	—
		17	0 .029	—	—	—
		16	0 .048	—	—	—
$n_1=20$	$n_2=20$	20	15 .024	15 .024	13 .004	13 .004
		19	14 .046	13 .022	12 .010 −	11 .004
		18	12 .032	11 .015 +	10 .007	9 .003
		17	11 .041	10 .020	9 .009	8 .004
		16	10 .048	9 .024	7 .005 −	7 .005 −
		15	8 .027	7 .012	6 .005 +	5 .002
		14	7 .028	6 .013	5 .005 +	4 .002
		13	6 .028	5 .012	4 .005 −	4 .005 −
		12	5 .027	4 .011	3 .004	3 .004
		11	4 .024	4 .024	3 .009	2 .003
		10	4 .048	3 .020	2 .007	1 .002
		9	3 .041	2 .015 +	1 .004	1 .004
		8	2 .032	1 .010 −	1 .010 −	0 .002
		7	1 .022	1 .022	0 .004	0 .004
		6	1 .046	0 .010 +	—	—
		5	0 .024	0 .024	—	—
	19	20	15 .047	14 .020	13 .008	12 .003
		19	13 .039	12 .018	11 .008	10 .003
		18	11 .026	10 .012	9 .005 −	9 .005 −
		17	10 .032	9 .015 −	8 .006	7 .002
		16	9 .036	8 .017	7 .007	6 .003
		15	8 .038	7 .018	6 .008	5 .003
		14	7 .039	6 .018	5 .007	4 .003
		13	6 .038	5 .017	4 .007	3 .002
		12	5 .035 +	4 .015 +	3 .005 +	2 .002
		11	4 .031	3 .012	2 .004	2 .004
		10	3 .026	2 .009	2 .009	1 .002
		9	2 .019	2 .019	1 .005 +	0 .001
		8	2 .039	1 .012	0 .002	0 .002
		7	1 .026	0 .005 +	0 .005 +	—
		6	0 .012	0 .012	—	—
		5	0 .027	—	—	—

TABLE A-29 (Continued). TABLES FOR TESTING SIGNIFICANCE IN 2 × 2 TABLES WITH UNEQUAL SAMPLES

$n_1 = 20 \quad n_2 = 18$

	a_1	Significance Level 0.05 (0.10)	0.025 (0.05)	0.01 (0.02)	0.005 (0.01)
20	20	14 .041	13 .017	12 .007	11 .003
	19	12 .032	11 .014	10 .006	9 .002
	18	11 .043	10 .020	9 .008	8 .003
	17	10 .050 −	9 .024	7 .004	7 .004
	16	8 .026	7 .011	6 .005 −	6 .005 −
	15	7 .027	6 .012	5 .004	5 .004
	14	6 .026	5 .011	4 .004	4 .004
	13	5 .024	5 .024	4 .009	3 .003
	12	5 .047	4 .020	3 .007	2 .002
	11	4 .011	3 .016	2 .005 +	1 .001
	10	3 .033	2 .012	1 .003	1 .003
	9	2 .024	2 .024	1 .007	0 .001
	8	2 .048	1 .015 −	0 .003	0 .003
	7	1 .031	0 .006	0 .006	—
	6	0 .014	0 .014	—	—
	5	0 .031	—	—	—
17	20	13 .036	12 .014	11 .005 +	10 .002
	19	11 .026	10 .011	9 .004	9 .004
	18	10 .034	9 .015 −	8 .006	7 .002
	17	9 .038	8 .017	7 .007	6 .003
	16	8 .040	7 .018	6 .007	5 .003
	15	7 .039	6 .017	5 .007	4 .002
	14	6 .037	5 .016	4 .006	3 .002
	13	5 .033	4 .013	3 .005 −	3 .005 −
	12	4 .028	3 .010 +	2 .003	2 .003
	11	3 .022	3 .022	2 .007	1 .002
	10	3 .042	2 .015 +	1 .004	1 .004
	9	2 .031	1 .009	1 .009	0 .001
	8	1 .019	1 .019	0 .003	0 .003
	7	1 .037	0 .008	0 .008	—
	6	0 .017	0 .017	—	—
	5	0 .036	—	—	—
16	20	12 .031	11 .012	10 .004	10 .004
	19	11 .049	10 .021	9 .008	8 .003
	18	9 .026	8 .011	7 .004	7 .004
	17	8 .028	7 .012	6 .004	6 .004
	16	7 .028	6 .012	5 .004	5 .004
	15	6 .026	5 .011	4 .004	4 .004
	14	5 .023	5 .023	4 .009	3 .003
	13	5 .046	4 .019	3 .007	2 .002
	12	4 .038	3 .014	2 .004	2 .004
	11	3 .029	2 .010 −	2 .010 −	1 .002
	10	2 .020	2 .020	1 .005 +	0 .001
	9	2 .039	1 .011	0 .002	0 .002
	8	1 .023	1 .023	0 .004	0 .004
	7	1 .045 +	0 .009	0 .009	—
	6	0 .020	0 .020	—	—
	5	0 .041	—	—	—
15	20	11 .026	10 .009	10 .009	9 .003
	19	10 .040	9 .016	8 .006	7 .002
	18	9 .040	8 .019	7 .007	6 .002
	17	8 .047	7 .020	6 .008	5 .003
	16	7 .045 −	6 .019	5 .007	4 .002
	15	6 .040	5 .017	4 .006	3 .002
	14	5 .034	4 .013	3 .004	3 .004

$n_1 = 20 \quad n_2 = 15$

	a_1	Significance Level 0.05 (0.10)	0.025 (0.05)	0.01 (0.02)	0.005 (0.01)
	13	4 .028	3 .010 −	3 .010 −	2 .003
	12	3 .020	3 .020	2 .006	1 .001
	11	3 .039	2 .013	1 .003	1 .003
	10	2 .026	1 .007	1 .007	0 .001
	9	2 .049	1 .015 −	0 .002	0 .002
	8	1 .029	0 .005 +	0 .005 +	—
	7	0 .012	0 .012	—	—
	6	0 .024	0 .024	—	—
	5	0 .048	—	—	—
14	20	10 .022	10 .022	9 .007	8 .002
	19	9 .032	8 .012	7 .004	7 .004
	18	8 .035 +	7 .014	6 .005 −	6 .005 −
	17	7 .035 −	6 .013	5 .005 −	5 .005 −
	16	6 .031	5 .012	4 .004	4 .004
	15	5 .026	4 .009	4 .009	3 .003
	14	4 .020	4 .020	3 .007	2 .002
	13	4 .040	3 .013 −	2 .004	2 .004
	12	3 .029	2 .009	2 .009	1 .002
	11	2 .018	2 .018	1 .005 −	1 .005 −
	10	2 .035 +	1 .010 −	1 .010 −	0 .001
	9	1 .019	1 .019	0 .003	0 .003
	8	1 .037	0 .007	0 .007	—
	7	0 .014	0 .014	—	—
	6	0 .029	—	—	—
13	20	9 .017	9 .017	8 .005 +	7 .002
	19	8 .025 −	8 .025 −	7 .008	6 .003
	18	7 .026	6 .009	6 .009	5 .003
	17	6 .024	6 .024	5 .008	4 .002
	16	5 .020	5 .020	4 .007	3 .002
	15	5 .041	4 .015 +	3 .005 −	3 .005 −
	14	4 .031	3 .011	2 .003	2 .003
	13	3 .022	3 .022	2 .006	1 .001
	12	3 .041	2 .013	1 .003	1 .003
	11	2 .026	1 .007	1 .007	0 .001
	10	2 .047	1 .013	0 .002	0 .002
	9	1 .026	0 .004	0 .004	0 .004
	8	1 .047	0 .009	0 .009	—
	7	0 .018	0 .018	—	—
	6	0 .035 −	—	—	—
12	20	9 .044	8 .014	7 .004	7 .004
	19	7 .018	7 .018	6 .006	5 .002
	18	6 .018	6 .018	5 .006	4 .002
	17	6 .043	5 .016	4 .005 −	4 .005 −
	16	5 .034	4 .012	3 .003	3 .003
	15	4 .025 +	3 .008	3 .008	2 .002
	14	4 .049	3 .017	2 .005 −	2 .005 −
	13	3 .033	2 .010 −	2 .010 −	1 .002
	12	2 .020	2 .020	1 .005 −	1 .005 −
	11	2 .036	1 .009	1 .009	0 .001
	10	1 .018	1 .018	0 .003	0 .003
	9	1 .034	0 .006	0 .006	—
	8	0 .012	0 .012	—	—
	7	0 .023	0 .023	—	—
	6	0 .043	—	—	—

TABLE A-29 (Continued). TABLES FOR TESTING SIGNIFICANCE IN 2 × 2 TABLES WITH UNEQUAL SAMPLES

		a_1	0.05 (0.10)	0.025 (0.05)	0.01 (0.02)	0.005 (0.01)
$n_1=20$	$n_2=11$	20	8 .037	7 .010+	6 .003	6 .003
		19	7 .042	6 .013	5 .004	5 .004
		18	6 .037	5 .012	4 .003	4 .003
		17	5 .029	4 .009	4 .009	3 .002
		16	4 .021	4 .021	3 .006	2 .001
		15	4 .042	3 .014	2 .003	2 .003
		14	3 .028	2 .008	2 .008	1 .001
		13	2 .016	2 .016	1 .003	1 .003
		12	2 .029	1 .007	1 .007	0 .001
		11	1 .014	1 .014	0 .002	0 .002
		10	1 .026	0 .004	0 .004	0 .004
		9	1 .046	0 .008	0 .008	—
		8	0 .016	0 .016	—	—
		7	0 .029	—	—	—
	10	20	7 .030	6 .008	6 .008	5 .002
		19	6 .031	5 .009	5 .009	4 .002
		18	5 .026	4 .007	4 .007	3 .002
		17	4 .018	3 .005+	3 .005-	3 .005-
		16	4 .039	3 .012	2 .003	2 .003
		15	3 .024	3 .024	2 .006	1 .001
		14	3 .045+	2 .013	1 .003	1 .003
		13	2 .025+	1 .006	1 .006	0 .001
		12	2 .045-	1 .011	0 .001	0 .001
		11	1 .021	1 .021	0 .003	0 .003
		10	1 .037	0 .006	0 .006	—
		9	0 .012	0 .012	—	—
		8	0 .022	0 .022	—	—
		7	0 .038	—	—	—
	9	20	6 .023	6 .023	5 .005+	4 .001
		19	5 .022	5 .022	4 .005+	3 .001
		18	4 .016	4 .016	3 .004	3 .004
		17	4 .037	3 .010+	2 .002	2 .002
		16	3 .022	3 .022	2 .005+	1 .001
		15	3 .043	2 .012	1 .002	1 .002
		14	2 .023	2 .023	1 .005-	1 .005-
		13	2 .041	1 .009	1 .009	0 .001
		12	1 .018	1 .018	0 .002	0 .002
		11	1 .032	0 .005-	0 .005-	0 .005-
		10	0 .009	0 .009	0 .009	—
		9	0 .017	0 .017	—	—
		8	0 .029	—	—	—
		7	0 .050-	—	—	—
	8	20	5 .017	5 .017	4 .003	4 .003
		19	4 .015-	4 .015-	3 .003	3 .003
		18	4 .038	3 .009	3 .009	2 .002
		17	3 .022	3 .022	2 .005-	2 .005-
		16	3 .044	2 .011	1 .002	1 .002
		15	2 .022	2 .022	1 .004	1 .004
		14	2 .040	1 .009	1 .009	0 .001
		13	1 .016	1 .016	0 .002	0 .002
		12	1 .029	0 .004	0 .004	0 .004
		11	1 .048	0 .008	0 .008	—
		10	0 .014	0 .014	—	—
		9	0 .024	0 .024	—	—
		8	0 .041	—	—	—

		a_1	0.05 (0.10)	0.025 (0.05)	0.01 (0.02)	0.005 (0.01)
$n_1=20$	$n_2=7$	20	4 .012	4 .012	3 .002	3 .002
		19	4 .042	3 .009	3 .009	2 .001
		18	3 .024	3 .024	2 .005-	2 .005-
		17	3 .050-	2 .011	1 .002	1 .002
		16	2 .023	2 .023	1 .004	1 .004
		15	2 .043	1 .009	1 .009	0 .001
		14	1 .016	1 .016	0 .002	0 .002
		13	1 .029	0 .004	0 .004	0 .004
		12	1 .048	0 .007	0 .007	—
		11	0 .013	0 .013	—	—
		10	0 .022	0 .022	—	—
		9	0 .036	—	—	—
	6	20	4 .046	3 .008	3 .008	2 .001
		19	3 .028	2 .005-	2 .005-	2 .005-
		18	2 .013	2 .013	1 .002	1 .002
		17	2 .028	1 .004	1 .004	1 .004
		16	1 .010-	1 .010-	1 .010-	0 .001
		15	1 .018	1 .018	0 .002	0 .002
		14	1 .032	0 .004	0 .004	0 .004
		13	0 .007	0 .007	0 .007	—
		12	0 .013	0 .013	—	—
		11	0 .022	0 .022	—	—
		10	0 .035	—	—	—
	5	20	3 .033	2 .004	2 .004	2 .004
		19	2 .016	2 .016	1 .002	1 .002
		18	2 .038	1 .005+	1 .005+	0 .000
		17	1 .012	1 .012	0 .001	0 .001
		16	1 .023	1 .023	0 .002	0 .002
		15	1 .040	0 .005-	0 .005-	0 .005-
		14	0 .009	0 .009	0 .009	—
		13	0 .015-	0 .015-	—	—
		12	0 .024	0 .024	—	—
		11	0 .038	—	—	—
	4	20	2 .022	2 .022	1 .002	1 .002
		19	1 .008	1 .008	1 .008	0 .000
		18	1 .018	1 .018	0 .001	0 .001
		17	1 .035+	0 .003	0 .003	0 .003
		16	0 .007	0 .007	0 .007	—
		15	0 .012	0 .012	—	—
		14	0 .020	0 .020	—	—
		13	0 .031	—	—	—
		12	0 .047	—	—	—
	3	20	1 .012	1 .012	0 .001	0 .001
		19	1 .034	0 .002	0 .002	0 .002
		18	0 .006	0 .006	0 .006	—
		17	0 .011	0 .011	—	—
		16	0 .020	0 .020	—	—
		15	0 .032	—	—	—
		14	0 .047	—	—	—
	2	20	0 .004	0 .004	0 .004	0 .004
		19	0 .013	0 .013	—	—
		18	0 .026	—	—	—
		17	0 .043	—	—	—
	1	20	0 .048	—	—	—

TABLE A-30. TABLES FOR DISTRIBUTION-FREE TOLERANCE LIMITS (TWO-SIDED)

Values (r, s) such that we may assert with confidence at least γ that 100P percent of a population lies between the rth smallest and the sth largest of a random sample of n from that population (no assumption of normality required)

	$\gamma = 0.75$				$\gamma = 0.90$			
n \ P	.75	.90	.95	.99	.75	.90	.95	.99
50	5,5	2,1	—	—	5,4	1,1	—	—
55	6,6	2,2	1,1	—	5,5	2,1	—	—
60	7,6	2,2	1,1	—	6,5	2,1	—	—
65	7,7	3,2	1,1	—	6,6	2,2	—	—
70	8,7	3,2	1,1	—	7,6	2,2	—	—
75	8,8	3,3	1,1	—	7,7	2,2	—	—
80	9,8	3,3	2,1	—	8,7	3,2	1,1	—
85	10,9	4,3	2,1	—	8,8	3,2	1,1	—
90	10,10	4,3	2,1	—	9,8	3,2	1,1	—
95	11,10	4,3	2,1	—	9,9	3,3	1,1	—
100	11,11	4,4	2,1	—	10,10	3,3	1,1	—
110	12,12	5,4	2,2	—	11,11	4,3	2,1	—
120	14,13	5,5	2,2	—	12,12	4,4	2,1	—
130	15,14	6,5	3,2	—	13,13	5,4	2,1	—
140	16,15	6,6	3,2	—	14,14	5,5	2,2	—
150	17,17	6,6	3,3	—	16,15	5,5	2,2	—
170	20,19	7,7	4,3	—	18,17	6,6	3,2	—
200	23,23	9,8	4,4	—	21,21	8,7	3,3	—
300	35,35	13,13	6,6	1,1	33,32	12,11	5,5	—
400	47,47	18,18	9,8	2,1	45,44	16,16	8,7	1,1
500	59,59	23,22	11,11	2,1	57,56	21,20	10,9	1,1
600	72,71	28,27	13,13	2,2	68,68	26,25	12,11	2,1
700	84,83	33,32	16,15	3,2	80,80	30,30	14,14	2,2
800	96,96	37,27	18,18	3,3	92,92	35,34	16,16	3,2
900	108,108	42,42	21,20	4,3	104,104	40,39	19,18	3,2
1000	121,120	47,47	23,22	4,4	117,116	44,44	21,20	3,3

	$\gamma = 0.95$				$\gamma = 0.99$			
n \ P	.75	.90	.95	.99	.75	.90	.95	.99
50	4,4	1,1	—	—	3,3	—	—	—
55	5,4	1,1	—	—	4,3	—	—	—
60	5,5	1,1	—	—	4,4	—	—	—
65	6,5	2,1	—	—	5,4	1,1	—	—
70	6,6	2,1	—	—	5,5	1,1	—	—
75	7,6	2,1	—	—	5,5	1,1	—	—
80	7,7	2,2	—	—	6,5	1,1	—	—
85	8,7	2,2	—	—	6,6	2,1	—	—
90	8,8	3,2	—	—	7,6	2,1	—	—
95	9,8	3,2	1,1	—	7,7	2,1	—	—
100	9,9	3,2	1,1	—	8,7	2,2	—	—
110	10,10	3,3	1,1	—	9,8	2,2	—	—
120	11,11	4,3	1,1	—	10,9	3,2	—	—
130	13,12	4,4	2,1	—	11,10	3,3	1,1	—
140	14,13	4,4	2,1	—	12,11	3,3	1,1	—
150	15,14	5,4	2,1	—	13,13	4,3	1,1	—
170	17,16	6,5	2,2	—	15,15	5,4	2,1	—
200	20,20	7,6	3,2	—	18,18	6,5	2,2	—
300	32,31	11,11	5,4	—	29,29	10,9	4,3	—
400	43,43	15,15	7,6	—	40,40	14,13	6,5	—
500	55,54	20,19	9,8	1,1	52,51	18,17	7,7	—
600	67,66	24,24	11,10	1,1	63,63	22,22	9,9	—
700	78,78	29,28	13,13	2,1	75,74	26,26	11,11	1,1
800	90,90	33,33	15,15	2,2	86,86	31,30	13,13	1,1
900	102,102	38,37	18,17	2,2	98,97	35,35	15,15	2,1
1000	114,114	43,42	20,19	3,2	110,109	40,39	18,17	2,1

When the values of r and s given in the table are not equal, they are interchangeable; i.e., for n = 120 with confidence at least 0.75 we may assert that 75% of the population lies between the 14th smallest and the 13th largest values, or between the 13th smallest and the 14th largest values.

Adapted with permission from *Annals of Mathematical Statistics*, Vol. 29, No. 2, June 1958, pp. 599-601, from article entitled "Tables for Obtaining Non-Parametric Tolerance Limits" by Paul N. Somerville.

TABLE A-31. TABLES FOR DISTRIBUTION-FREE TOLERANCE LIMITS (ONE-SIDED)

Largest values of m such that we may assert with confidence at least γ that $100P$ percent of a population lies below the mth largest (or above the mth smallest) of a random sample of n from that population (no assumption of normality required)

n \ P	$\gamma = 0.75$ .75	.90	.95	.99	$\gamma = 0.90$ .75	.90	.95	.99	$\gamma = 0.95$ .75	.90	.95	.99	$\gamma = 0.99$ .75	.90	.95	.99
50	10	3	1	—	9	2	1	—	8	2	—	—	6	1	—	—
55	12	4	2	—	10	3	1	—	9	2	—	—	7	1	—	—
60	13	4	2	—	11	3	1	—	10	2	1	—	8	1	—	—
65	14	5	2	—	12	4	1	—	11	3	1	—	9	2	—	—
70	15	5	2	—	13	4	1	—	12	3	1	—	10	2	—	—
75	16	6	2	—	14	4	1	—	13	3	1	—	10	2	—	—
80	17	6	3	—	15	5	2	—	14	4	1	—	11	2	—	—
85	19	7	3	—	16	5	2	—	15	4	1	—	12	3	—	—
90	20	7	3	—	17	5	2	—	16	5	1	—	13	3	1	—
95	21	7	3	—	18	6	2	—	17	5	2	—	14	3	1	—
100	22	8	3	—	20	6	2	—	18	5	2	—	15	4	1	—
110	24	9	4	—	22	7	3	—	20	6	2	—	17	4	1	—
120	27	10	4	—	24	8	3	—	22	7	2	—	19	5	1	—
130	29	11	5	—	26	9	3	—	25	8	3	—	21	6	2	—
140	31	12	5	1	28	10	4	—	27	8	3	—	23	6	2	—
150	34	12	6	1	31	10	4	—	29	9	3	—	26	7	2	—
170	39	14	7	1	35	12	5	—	33	11	4	—	30	9	3	—
200	46	17	8	1	42	15	6	—	40	13	5	—	36	11	4	—
300	70	26	12	2	65	23	10	1	63	22	9	1	58	19	7	—
400	94	36	17	3	89	32	15	2	86	30	13	1	80	27	11	—
500	118	45	22	3	113	41	19	2	109	39	17	2	103	35	14	1
600	143	55	26	4	136	51	23	3	133	48	21	2	126	44	18	1
700	167	65	31	5	160	60	28	4	156	57	26	3	149	52	22	2
800	192	74	36	6	184	69	32	5	180	66	30	4	172	61	26	2
900	216	84	41	7	208	79	37	5	204	75	35	4	195	70	30	3
1000	241	94	45	8	233	88	41	6	228	85	39	5	219	79	35	3

Adapted with permission from *Annals of Mathematical Statistics*, Vol. 29, No. 2, June 1958, pp. 599-601, from article entitled "Tables for Obtaining Non-Parametric Tolerance Limits" by Paul N. Somerville.

TABLE A-32.   CONFIDENCE ASSOCIATED WITH A TOLERANCE LIMIT STATEMENT

Confidence γ with which we may assert that 100P percent of the population lies between
the largest and smallest of a random sample of n from that population
(continuous distribution assumed)

n	P = .75	P = .90	P = .95	P = .99
3	.16	.03	.01	.00
4	.26	.05	.01	.00
5	.37	.08	.02	.00
6	.47	.11	.03	.00
7	.56	.15	.04	.00
8	.63	.19	.06	.00
9	.70	.23	.07	.00
10	.76	.26	.09	.00
11	.80	.30	.10	.01
12	.84	.34	.12	.01
13	.87	.38	.14	.01
14	.90	.42	.15	.01
15	.92	.45	.17	.01
16	.94	.49	.19	.01
17	.95	.52	.21	.01
18	.96	.55	.23	.01
19	.97	.58	.25	.02
20	.98	.61	.26	.02
25	.99	.73	.36	.03
30	1.00	.82	.45	.04
40	—	.92	.60	.06
50	—	.97	.72	.09
60	—	.99	.81	.12
70	—	.99	.87	.16
80	—	1.00 —	.91	.19
90	—	—	.94	.23
100	—	—	.96	.26

Adapted with permission from *Annals of Mathematical Statistics*, Vol. 29, No. 2, June 1958, pp. 599-601, from article entitled "Tables for Obtaining Non-Parametric Tolerance Limits" by Paul N. Somerville.

TABLE A-33. CRITICAL VALUES OF r FOR THE SIGN TEST

	α for Two-Sided Test					α for Two-Sided Test			
	.01	.05	.10	.25		.01	.05	.10	.25
	α for One-Sided Test					α for One-Sided Test			
n	.005	.025	.05	.125	n	.005	.025	.05	.125
1	—	—	—	—	46	13	15	16	18
2	—	—	—	—	47	14	16	17	19
3	—	—	—	0	48	14	16	17	19
4	—	—	—	0	49	15	17	18	19
5	—	—	0	0	50	15	17	18	20
6	—	0	0	1	51	15	18	19	20
7	—	0	0	1	52	16	18	19	21
8	0	0	1	1	53	16	18	20	21
9	0	1	1	2	54	17	19	20	22
10	0	1	1	2	55	17	19	20	22
11	0	1	2	3	56	17	20	21	23
12	1	2	2	3	57	18	20	21	23
13	1	2	3	3	58	18	21	22	24
14	1	2	3	4	59	19	21	22	24
15	2	3	3	4	60	19	21	23	25
16	2	3	4	5	61	20	22	23	25
17	2	4	4	5	62	20	22	24	25
18	3	4	5	6	63	20	23	24	26
19	3	4	5	6	64	21	23	24	26
20	3	5	5	6	65	21	24	25	27
21	4	5	6	7	66	22	24	25	27
22	4	5	6	7	67	22	25	26	28
23	4	6	7	8	68	22	25	26	28
24	5	6	7	8	69	23	25	27	29
25	5	7	7	9	70	23	26	27	29
26	6	7	8	9	71	24	26	28	30
27	6	7	8	10	72	24	27	28	30
28	6	8	9	10	73	25	27	28	31
29	7	8	9	10	74	25	28	29	31
30	7	9	10	11	75	25	28	29	32
31	7	9	10	11	76	26	28	30	32
32	8	9	10	12	77	26	29	30	32
33	8	10	11	12	78	27	29	31	33
34	9	10	11	13	79	27	30	31	33
35	9	11	12	13	80	28	30	32	34
36	9	11	12	14	81	28	31	32	34
37	10	12	13	14	82	28	31	33	35
38	10	12	13	14	83	29	32	33	35
39	11	12	13	15	84	29	32	33	36
40	11	13	14	15	85	30	32	34	36
41	11	13	14	16	86	30	33	34	37
42	12	14	15	16	87	31	33	35	37
43	12	14	15	17	88	31	34	35	38
44	13	15	16	17	89	31	34	36	38
45	13	15	16	18	90	32	35	36	39

For values of n larger than 90, approximate values of r may be found by taking the nearest integer less than $(n - 1)/2 - k\sqrt{n + 1}$, where k is 1.2879, 0.9800, 0.8224, 0.5752 for the 1, 5, 10, 25% values, respectively.

Adapted with permission from *Introduction to Statistical Analysis* (2d ed.) by W. J. Dixon and F. J. Massey, Jr., Copyright, 1957, McGraw-Hill Book Company, Inc.

TABLE A-34.   CRITICAL VALUES OF $T_\alpha(n)$ FOR THE WILCOXON SIGNED-RANKS TEST

T_α is the integer such that the probability that $T \leq T_\alpha$ is closest to α. For example, for $n = 8$, $\Pr\{T \leq 3\} = .020$ and $\Pr\{T \leq 4\} = .027$; hence we list $T_{.025}(8) = 4$.

n	α for One-Sided Test		
	.025	.01	.005
	α for Two-Sided Test		
	.05	.02	.01
6	0	—	—
7	2	0	—
8	4	2	0
9	6	3	2
10	8	5	3
11	11	7	5
12	14	10	7
13	17	13	10
14	21	16	13
15	25	20	16
16	30	24	20
17	35	28	23
18	40	33	28
19	46	38	32
20	52	43	38
21	59	49	43
22	66	56	49
23	73	62	55
24	81	69	61
25	89	77	68

For large n,

$$T_P(n) = \frac{n(n+1)}{4} - z_{1-P}\sqrt{\frac{n(n+1)(2n+1)}{24}} \text{ approximately}$$

where z is given in Table A 2.

Adapted with permission from *Some Rapid Approximate Statistical Procedures* by F. Wilcoxon, 1949, American Cyanamid Company.

TABLE A-35. CRITICAL VALUES OF SMALLER RANK SUM FOR THE WILCOXON-MANN-WHITNEY TEST

n_1 (Smaller Sample)

n_2	α for 2-Sided Test	α for 1-Sided Test	1	2	3	4	5	6	7	8	9	10	11	12	13	14	15	16	17	18	19	20
3	.20	.10		3	7																	
	.10	.05			6																	
	.05	.025																				
	.01	.005																				
4	.20	.10		3	7	13																
	.10	.05			6	11																
	.05	.025				10																
	.01	.005																				
5	.20	.10		4	8	14	20															
	.10	.05		3	7	12	19															
	.05	.025			6	11	17															
	.01	.005					15															
6	.20	.10		4	9	15	22	30														
	.10	.05		3	8	13	20	28														
	.05	.025			7	12	18	26														
	.01	.005				10	16	23														
7	.20	.10		4	10	16	23	32	41													
	.10	.05		3	8	14	21	29	39													
	.05	.025			7	13	20	27	36													
	.01	.005				10	16	24	32													
8	.20	.10		5	11	17	25	34	44	55												
	.10	.05		4	9	15	23	31	41	51												
	.05	.025		3	8	14	21	29	38	49												
	.01	.005				11	17	25	34	43												
9	.20	.10	1	5	11	19	27	36	46	58	70											
	.10	.05		4	10*	16	24	33	43	54	66											
	.05	.025		3	8	14	22	31	40	51	62											
	.01	.005			6	11	18	26	35	45	56											
10	.20	.10	1	6	12	20	28	38	49	60	73	87										
	.10	.05		4	10	17	26	35	45	56	69	82										
	.05	.025		3	9	15	23	32	42	53	65	78										
	.01	.005			6	12	19	27	37	47	58	71										
11	.20	.10	1	6	13	21	30	40	51	63	76	91	106									
	.10	.05		4	11	18	27	37	47	59	72	86	100									
	.05	.025		3	9	16	24	34	44	55	68	81	96									
	.01	.005			6	12	20	28	38	49	61	73	87									
12	.20	.10	1	7	14	22	32	42	54	66	80	94	110	127								
	.10	.05		5	11	19	28	38	49	62	75	89	104	120								
	.05	.025		4	10	17	26	35	46	58	71	84	99	115								
	.01	.005			7	13	21	30	40	51	63	76	90	105								

n_1	2-sided α	1-sided α	1	2	3	4	5	6	7	8	9	10	11	12	13	14	15	16	17	18	19	20
13	.20	.10	1	7	15	23	33	44	56	69	83	98	114	131	149							
	.10	.05		5	12	20	30	40	52	64	78	92	108	125	142							
	.05	.025		4	10	18	27	37	48	60	73	88	103	119	136							
	.01	.005			7	*13	22	31	41	53	65	79	93	109	125							
14	.20	.10	1	*8	16	25	35	46	59	72	86	102	118	136	154	174						
	.10	.05		*6	13	21	31	42	54	67	81	96	112	129	147	166						
	.05	.025		4	11	19	28	38	50	62	76	91	106	123	141	160						
	.01	.005			7	14	22	32	43	54	67	81	96	112	129	147						
15	.20	.10	1	8	16	26	37	48	61	75	90	106	123	141	159	179	200					
	.10	.05		6	13	22	33	44	56	69	84	99	116	133	152	171	192					
	.05	.025		4	11	20	29	40	52	65	79	94	110	127	145	164	184					
	.01	.005			8	15	23	33	44	56	69	84	99	115	133	151	171					
16	.20	.10	1	8	17	27	38	50	64	78	93	109	127	145	165	185	206	229				
	.10	.05		6	14	24	34	46	58	72	87	103	120	138	156	176	197	219				
	.05	.025		4	12	21	30	42	54	67	82	97	113	131	150	169	190	211				
	.01	.005			8	15	24	34	46	58	72	86	102	119	136	155	175	196				
17	.20	.10	1	9	18	28	40	52	66	81	97	113	131	150	170	190	212	235	259			
	.10	.05		6	15	25	35	47	61	75	90	106	123	142	161	182	203	225	249			
	.05	.025		5	12	21	32	43	56	70	84	100	117	135	154	174	195	217	240			
	.01	.005			8	16	25	36	47	60	74	89	105	122	140	159	180	201	223			
18	.20	.10	1	9	19	30	42	55	69	84	100	117	135	155	175	196	218	242	266	291		
	.10	.05		7	15	26	37	49	63	77	93	110	127	146	166	187	208	231	255	280		
	.05	.025		5	13	22	33	45	58	72	87	103	121	139	158	179	200	222	246	270		
	.01	.005			8	16	26	37	49	62	76	92	108	125	144	163	184	206	228	252		
19	.20	.10	2	9	20	31	43	57	71	87	103	121	139	159	180	202	224	248	273	299	325	
	.10	.05	1	7	16	27	38	51	65	80	96	113	131	150	171	192	214	237	262	287	313	
	.05	.025		5	13	23	34	46	60	74	90	107	124	143	163	*183	205	228	252	277	303	
	.01	.005			9	17	27	38	50	64	78	94	111	129	*148	168	189	210	234	258	283	
20	.20	.10	2	10	21	32	45	59	74	90	107	125	144	164	185	207	230	255	280	306	333	361
	.10	.05	1	7	17	28	40	53	67	83	99	117	135	155	175	197	220	243	268	294	320	348
	.05	.025		5	14	24	35	48	62	77	93	110	128	147	167	188	210	234	258	283	309	337
	.01	.005		3	9	18	28	39	52	66	81	97	114	132	151	172	193	215	239	263	289	315

For larger values of n_1 and n_2, critical values are given to a good approximation by the formula:

$$\frac{n_1}{2}(n_1 + n_2 + 1) - z\left\{\frac{n_1 n_2 (n_1 + n_2 + 1)}{12}\right\}^{\frac{1}{2}}$$

where $z = 1.28$ for $\alpha = .20$ (two-sided test)
$z = 1.64$ for $\alpha = .10$ "
$z = 1.96$ for $\alpha = .05$ "
$z = 2.58$ for $\alpha = .01$ "

Reproduced by permission from Non-Parametric and Shortcut Statistics by M. W. Tate and R. C. Clelland, Copyright, 1957, Interstate Printers and Publishers, Inc.

*Starred values have been corrected to the values given by D. B. Owen, Handbook of Statistical Tables, copyright 1962, Addison-Wesley Publishing Co., Inc.

TABLE A-36. SHORT TABLE OF RANDOM NUMBERS

46	96	85	77	27	92	86	26	45	21	89	91	71	42	64	64	58	22	75	81	74	91	48	46	18
44	19	15	32	63	55	87	77	33	29	45	00	31	34	84	05	72	90	44	27	78	22	07	62	17
34	39	80	62	24	33	81	67	28	11	34	79	26	35	34	23	09	94	00	80	55	31	63	27	91
74	97	80	30	65	07	71	30	01	84	47	45	89	70	74	13	04	90	51	27	61	34	63	87	44
22	14	61	60	86	38	33	71	13	33	72	08	16	13	50	56	48	51	29	48	30	93	45	66	29
40	03	96	40	03	47	24	60	09	21	21	18	00	05	86	52	85	40	73	73	57	68	36	33	91
52	33	76	44	56	15	47	75	78	73	78	19	87	06	98	47	48	02	62	03	42	05	32	55	02
37	59	20	40	93	17	82	24	19	90	80	87	32	74	59	84	24	49	79	17	23	75	83	42	00
11	02	55	57	48	84	74	36	22	67	19	20	15	92	53	37	13	75	54	89	56	73	23	39	07
10	33	79	26	34	54	71	33	89	74	68	48	23	17	49	18	81	05	52	85	70	05	73	11	17
67	59	28	25	47	89	11	65	65	20	42	23	96	41	64	20	30	89	87	64	37	93	36	96	35
93	50	75	20	09	18	54	34	68	02	54	87	23	05	43	36	98	29	97	93	87	08	30	92	98
24	43	23	72	80	64	34	27	23	46	15	36	10	63	21	59	69	76	02	62	31	62	47	60	34
39	91	63	18	38	27	10	78	88	84	42	32	00	97	92	00	04	94	50	05	75	82	70	80	35
74	62	19	67	54	18	28	92	33	69	98	96	74	35	72	11	68	25	08	95	31	79	11	79	54
91	03	35	60	81	16	61	97	25	14	78	21	22	05	25	47	26	37	80	39	19	06	41	02	00
42	57	66	76	72	91	03	63	48	46	44	01	33	53	62	28	80	59	55	05	02	16	13	17	54
06	36	63	06	15	03	72	38	01	58	25	37	66	48	56	19	56	41	29	28	76	49	74	39	50
92	70	96	70	89	80	87	14	25	49	25	94	62	78	26	15	41	39	48	75	64	69	61	06	38
91	08	88	53	52	13	04	82	23	00	26	36	47	44	04	08	84	80	07	44	76	51	52	41	59
68	85	97	74	47	53	90	05	90	84	87	48	25	01	11	05	45	11	43	15	60	40	31	84	59
59	54	13	09	13	80	42	29	63	03	24	64	12	43	28	10	01	65	62	07	79	83	05	59	61
39	18	32	69	33	46	58	19	34	03	59	28	97	31	02	65	47	47	70	39	74	17	30	22	65
67	43	31	09	12	60	19	57	63	78	11	80	10	97	15	70	04	89	81	78	54	84	87	83	42
61	75	37	19	56	90	75	39	03	56	49	92	72	95	27	52	87	47	12	52	54	62	43	23	13
78	10	91	11	00	63	19	63	74	58	69	03	51	38	60	36	53	56	77	06	69	03	89	91	24
93	23	71	58	09	78	08	03	07	71	79	32	25	19	61	04	40	33	12	06	78	91	97	88	95
37	55	48	82	63	89	92	59	14	72	19	17	22	51	90	20	03	64	96	60	48	01	95	44	84
62	13	11	71	17	23	29	25	13	85	33	35	07	69	25	68	57	92	57	11	84	44	01	33	66
29	89	97	47	03	13	20	86	22	45	59	98	64	53	89	64	94	81	55	87	73	81	58	46	42
16	94	85	82	89	07	17	30	29	89	89	80	98	36	25	36	53	02	49	14	34	03	52	09	20
04	93	10	59	75	12	98	84	60	93	68	16	87	60	11	50	46	56	58	45	88	72	50	46	11
95	71	43	68	97	18	85	17	13	08	00	50	77	50	46	92	45	26	97	21	48	22	23	08	32
86	05	39	14	35	48	68	18	36	57	09	62	40	28	87	08	74	79	91	08	27	12	43	32	03
59	30	60	10	41	31	00	69	63	77	01	89	94	60	19	02	70	88	72	33	38	88	20	60	86
05	45	35	40	54	03	98	96	76	27	77	84	80	08	64	60	44	34	54	24	85	20	85	77	32
71	85	17	74	66	27	85	19	55	56	51	36	48	92	32	44	40	47	10	38	22	52	42	29	96
80	20	32	80	98	00	40	92	57	51	52	83	14	55	31	99	73	23	40	07	64	54	44	99	21
13	50	78	02	73	39	66	82	01	28	67	51	75	66	33	97	47	58	42	44	88	09	28	58	06
67	92	65	41	45	36	77	96	46	21	14	39	56	36	70	15	74	43	62	69	82	30	77	28	77
72	56	73	44	26	04	62	81	15	35	79	26	99	57	28	22	25	94	80	62	95	48	98	23	86
28	86	85	64	94	11	58	78	45	36	34	45	91	38	51	10	68	36	87	81	16	77	30	19	36
69	57	40	80	44	94	60	82	94	93	98	01	48	50	57	69	60	77	69	60	74	22	05	77	17
71	20	03	30	79	25	74	17	78	34	54	45	04	77	42	59	75	78	64	99	37	03	18	03	36
89	98	55	98	22	45	12	49	82	71	57	33	28	69	50	59	15	09	25	79	39	42	84	18	70
58	74	82	81	14	02	01	05	77	94	65	57	70	39	42	48	56	84	31	59	18	70	41	74	60
50	54	73	81	91	07	81	26	25	45	49	61	22	88	41	20	00	15	59	93	51	60	65	65	63
49	33	72	90	10	20	65	28	44	63	95	86	75	78	69	24	41	65	86	10	34	10	32	00	93
11	85	01	43	65	02	85	69	56	88	34	29	64	35	48	15	70	11	77	83	01	34	82	91	04
34	22	46	41	84	74	27	02	57	77	47	93	72	02	95	63	75	74	69	69	61	34	31	92	13

Adapted with permission from *A Million Random Digits* by The Rand Corporation, Copyright, 1955, The Free Press.

TABLE A-36 (Continued). SHORT TABLE OF RANDOM NUMBERS

```
05  57  23  06  26  23  08  66  16  11  75  28  81  56  14  62  82  45  65  80  36  02  76  55  63
37  78  16  06  57  12  46  22  90  97  78  67  39  06  63  60  51  02  07  16  75  12  90  41  16
23  71  15  08  82  64  87  29  01  20  46  72  05  80  19  27  47  15  76  51  58  67  06  80  54
42  67  98  41  67  44  28  71  45  08  19  47  76  30  26  72  33  69  92  51  95  23  26  85  76
05  83  03  84  32  62  83  27  48  83  09  19  84  90  20  20  50  87  74  93  51  62  10  23  30

60  46  18  41  23  74  73  51  72  90  40  52  95  41  20  89  48  98  27  38  81  33  83  82  94
32  80  64  75  91  98  09  40  64  89  29  99  46  35  69  91  50  73  75  92  90  56  82  93  24
79  86  53  77  78  06  62  37  48  82  71  00  78  21  65  65  88  45  82  44  78  93  22  78  09
45  13  23  32  01  09  46  36  43  66  37  15  35  04  88  79  83  53  19  13  91  59  81  81  87
20  60  97  48  21  41  84  22  72  77  99  81  83  30  46  15  90  26  51  73  66  34  99  40  60

67  91  44  83  43  25  56  33  28  80  99  53  27  56  19  80  76  32  53  95  07  53  09  61  98
86  50  76  93  86  35  68  45  37  83  47  44  92  57  66  59  64  16  48  39  26  94  54  66  40
66  73  38  38  23  36  10  95  16  01  10  01  59  71  55  99  24  88  31  41  00  73  13  80  62
55  11  50  29  17  73  97  04  20  39  20  22  71  11  43  00  15  10  12  35  09  11  00  89  05
23  54  33  87  92  92  04  49  73  96  57  53  57  08  93  09  69  87  83  07  46  39  50  37  85

41  48  67  79  44  57  40  29  10  34  58  63  51  18  07  41  02  39  79  14  40  68  10  01  61
03  97  71  72  43  27  36  24  59  88  82  87  26  31  11  44  28  58  99  47  83  21  35  22  88
90  24  83  48  07  41  56  68  11  14  77  75  48  68  08  90  89  63  87  00  06  18  63  21  91
98  98  97  42  27  11  80  51  13  13  03  42  91  14  51  23  15  48  07  52  09  40  34  60  85
74  20  94  21  49  96  51  69  99  85  43  76  55  81  36  11  88  68  32  43  08  14  78  05  34

94  67  48  87  11  84  00  85  93  56  43  99  21  74  84  13  56  41  90  96  30  04  19  68  73
58  18  84  82  71  23  66  33  19  25  65  17  90  84  24  91  75  36  14  83  86  22  70  86  89
31  47  28  24  88  49  28  69  78  62  23  45  53  38  78  65  87  44  91  93  91  62  76  09  20
45  62  31  06  70  92  73  27  83  57  15  64  40  57  56  54  42  35  40  93  55  82  08  78  87
31  49  87  12  27  41  07  91  72  64  63  42  06  66  82  71  28  36  45  31  99  01  03  35  76

69  37  22  23  46  10  75  83  62  94  44  65  46  23  65  71  69  20  89  12  16  56  61  70  41
93  67  21  56  98  42  52  53  14  86  24  70  25  18  23  23  56  24  03  86  11  06  46  10  23
77  56  18  37  01  82  20  18  70  79  20  85  77  89  28  17  77  15  52  47  15  30  35  12  75
37  07  47  79  60  75  24  15  31  63  25  93  27  66  19  53  52  49  98  45  12  12  06  00  32
72  08  71  01  73  46  39  60  37  58  22  25  20  84  30  02  03  62  68  58  38  04  06  89  94

55  22  48  46  72  50  14  24  47  67  84  37  32  84  82  64  97  13  69  86  20  09  80  46  75
69  24  98  90  70  29  34  25  33  23  12  69  90  50  38  93  84  32  28  96  03  65  70  90  12
01  86  77  18  21  91  66  11  84  65  48  75  26  94  51  40  51  53  36  39  77  69  06  25  07
51  40  94  06  80  61  34  28  46  28  11  48  48  94  60  65  06  63  71  06  19  35  05  32  56
58  78  02  85  80  29  67  27  44  07  67  23  20  28  22  62  97  59  62  13  41  72  70  71  07

33  75  88  51  00  33  56  15  84  34  28  50  16  65  12  81  56  43  54  14  63  37  74  97  59
58  60  37  45  62  09  95  93  16  59  35  22  91  78  04  97  98  80  20  04  38  93  13  92  30
72  13  12  95  32  87  99  32  83  65  40  17  92  57  22  68  98  79  16  23  53  56  56  07  47
22  21  13  16  10  52  57  71  40  49  95  25  55  36  95  57  25  25  77  05  38  05  62  57  77
97  94  83  67  90  68  74  88  17  22  38  01  04  33  49  38  47  57  61  87  15  39  43  87  00

09  03  68  53  63  29  27  31  66  53  39  34  88  87  04  35  80  69  52  74  99  16  52  01  65
29  95  61  42  65  05  72  27  28  18  09  85  24  59  46  03  91  55  38  62  51  71  47  37  38
81  96  78  90  47  41  38  36  33  95  05  90  26  72  85  23  23  30  70  51  56  93  23  84  80
44  62  20  81  21  57  57  85  00  47  26  10  87  22  45  72  03  51  75  23  38  38  56  77  97
68  91  12  15  08  02  18  74  56  79  21  53  63  41  77  15  07  39  87  11  19  25  62  19  30

29  33  77  60  29  09  25  09  42  28  07  15  40  67  56  29  58  75  84  06  19  54  31  16  53
54  13  39  19  29  64  97  73  71  61  78  03  24  02  93  86  69  76  74  28  08  98  84  08  23
75  16  85  64  64  93  85  68  08  84  15  41  57  84  45  11  70  13  17  60  47  80  10  13  00
36  47  17  08  79  03  92  85  18  42  95  48  27  37  99  98  81  94  44  72  06  95  42  31  17
29  61  08  21  91  23  76  72  84  98  26  23  66  54  86  88  95  14  82  57  17  99  16  28  99
```

TABLE A-36 (Continued). SHORT TABLE OF RANDOM NUMBERS

```
03  46  38  56  84  81  20  89  68  52  45  41  01  71  55  14  18  05  18  01  74  94  50  66  07
74  12  14  57  26  12  48  83  67  04  88  69  05  27  23  68  84  23  52  07  21  67  13  52  01
08  23  73  51  23  92  93  05  54  32  84  46  61  33  92  13  30  91  73  11  30  44  21  71  20
99  21  30  24  79  30  18  06  96  20  62  06  47  96  07  04  82  93  01  56  62  70  43  22  85
96  82  59  39  23  22  20  95  72  00  24  85  63  57  75  88  05  79  13  75  78  64  25  89  85

62  16  18  23  64  50  90  57  50  54  04  96  09  08  17  14  63  17  80  80  56  10  17  11  57
21  40  82  41  45  41  41  89  46  18  55  86  94  32  57  44  12  64  75  12  78  01  13  69  81
13  83  48  82  60  78  96  30  57  13  40  28  10  24  48  73  50  92  70  18  72  86  54  09  76
29  65  33  93  92  99  26  01  86  11  85  42  48  86  59  24  96  35  07  87  67  31  25  89  62
17  49  05  12  13  53  01  98  80  17  83  35  38  14  79  82  83  56  44  51  35  40  70  68  22

14  36  47  29  15  14  22  27  62  93  15  60  43  13  05  25  75  40  08  85  44  70  89  64  13
78  09  76  61  07  48  31  27  48  28  96  11  26  95  03  06  86  81  52  72  66  74  71  60  25
83  17  94  26  39  01  48  68  56  97  05  76  82  89  15  66  81  63  81  96  12  44  71  57  43
87  12  89  46  85  58  09  94  39  92  09  08  76  54  88  82  73  24  94  39  02  79  07  58  27
44  30  30  40  85  96  34  99  87  03  93  03  00  74  18  67  13  97  11  12  59  30  54  51  66

54  56  85  50  81  32  42  53  60  36  98  03  65  10  60  26  52  64  74  35  28  13  24  65  23
65  99  30  88  88  44  91  22  50  72  61  95  90  98  80  65  03  45  04  27  88  70  88  40  49
55  56  01  94  09  94  02  71  85  10  27  20  51  27  86  09  15  11  62  41  03  22  82  10  60
55  78  63  40  57  16  20  17  73  02  76  09  62  95  85  67  75  45  99  63  59  55  88  27  99
83  78  98  57  23  38  95  61  06  58  69  07  35  82  10  35  61  61  66  06  75  45  83  33  70

20  14  56  25  85  78  33  37  34  15  50  63  78  74  56  49  84  72  58  00  93  68  11  47  46
48  04  07  78  13  43  03  62  46  20  06  94  09  27  69  00  71  51  43  84  21  12  86  03  51
61  10  14  39  57  87  76  60  77  02  06  50  15  60  46  22  27  52  87  43  69  58  65  79  02
64  91  36  96  42  22  57  18  13  44  46  81  95  15  37  91  81  63  33  38  39  50  47  45  94
89  53  11  10  33  10  46  41  63  84  20  46  86  41  05  82  95  56  76  23  03  13  94  28  49

96  45  86  42  40  85  95  17  28  74  65  20  70  90  34  33  61  11  01  31  37  28  81  00  31
84  11  25  39  49  31  80  86  53  51  35  48  22  28  25  27  06  38  71  90  50  77  40  41  58
29  75  56  28  39  23  26  12  23  48  89  28  34  08  52  21  05  73  08  04  83  42  91  01  91
68  92  40  32  19  49  20  85  32  69  34  17  99  11  56  39  15  67  55  53  65  29  15  51  32
94  19  67  99  27  70  71  04  43  18  44  18  75  11  70  53  21  60  78  30  92  54  21  02  42

86  84  68  46  85  58  91  23  65  24  71  19  67  18  79  90  83  47  86  32  48  69  97  10  87
63  22  84  35  10  02  05  03  47  93  45  70  25  27  90  32  98  41  45  96  39  86  91  78  79
42  53  20  46  19  11  16  93  21  93  14  91  74  92  31  97  68  24  20  35  19  54  75  37  84
37  90  76  51  58  49  25  58  28  69  55  55  73  10  22  66  79  23  80  03  51  11  00  81  37
20  12  97  40  25  45  94  35  18  65  10  99  31  24  42  14  53  78  41  79  36  57  79  19  76

24  11  65  19  92  46  11  76  64  37  33  23  96  23  73  93  99  53  14  49  40  01  63  17  74
98  21  62  16  29  73  52  06  26  35  30  52  74  61  20  57  45  86  36  54  75  29  64  49  43
02  82  14  07  19  72  77  97  39  77  25  32  60  39  04  04  88  65  47  20  81  72  40  65  48
97  20  87  54  01  93  38  53  07  38  61  00  22  95  65  79  69  26  90  49  24  61  78  19  40
17  86  31  34  32  29  40  23  66  71  14  91  93  75  02  10  13  86  27  32  59  36  40  06  61

75  50  70  16  34  21  99  87  09  37  27  40  66  07  73  13  44  06  10  43  91  11  73  13  97
47  53  77  58  88  52  47  37  21  60  83  58  21  59  82  88  05  35  17  66  33  62  15  09  88
20  93  99  76  58  93  00  39  77  75  59  39  49  61  13  68  11  80  07  72  81  65  95  94  53
91  02  65  18  16  57  93  64  76  45  21  49  51  58  96  12  62  42  10  79  57  44  97  35  66
58  49  25  97  76  12  90  94  85  25  36  40  97  46  71  83  36  55  41  38  49  98  82  70  96

98  51  20  13  77  75  86  22  62  68  36  87  02  47  99  68  80  27  34  10  09  22  84  59  33
05  32  54  17  31  87  20  77  78  80  98  42  48  42  47  41  76  11  41  79  41  48  26  94  59
40  96  49  91  79  57  18  61  50  48  06  07  68  43  07  01  04  06  22  03  11  11  75  95  02
58  43  93  93  53  01  61  75  76  90  25  97  08  76  69  35  65  24  83  85  00  49  37  05  46
76  98  86  43  60  47  85  65  73  62  66  15  98  17  20  43  96  27  87  53  57  37  92  86  46
```

TABLE A-36 (Continued). SHORT TABLE OF RANDOM NUMBERS

```
24  81  06  14  98  24  93  58  63  66  58  26  24  45  65  91  42  68  67  42  61  74  77  93  46
75  55  54  29  67  02  81  01  67  54  08  81  34  00  79  62  38  52  14  88  38  66  59  41  97
49  71  80  54  37  73  34  11  74  14  91  86  82  41  02  76  12  36  71  38  43  72  84  36  27
04  19  48  35  54  98  00  41  47  44  63  13  27  50  18  75  16  72  40  90  02  45  87  82  15
66  15  52  42  22  91  22  96  38  41  03  27  15  67  26  36  81  75  11  82  94  33  62  08  94

10  80  17  67  83  05  31  23  08  07  40  00  60  44  65  70  16  31  73  05  46  41  47  64  68
40  42  27  55  76  82  88  42  76  51  58  49  58  75  38  23  57  06  64  69  46  90  09  55  68
95  57  21  21  25  12  05  41  70  28  03  59  97  37  64  48  69  48  59  60  89  76  35  83  05
57  27  64  94  98  88  93  70  86  59  46  84  08  32  31  75  61  19  49  11  28  46  76  79  28
80  56  69  49  63  83  78  78  76  36  89  51  16  47  35  86  69  96  69  88  91  22  47  24  84

44  51  75  51  08  17  43  53  31  09  60  34  34  61  93  66  01  94  37  13  24  09  75  29  21
55  42  48  76  50  13  89  69  00  05  99  45  82  01  53  86  68  81  36  50  75  20  17  94  47
80  50  67  83  01  97  76  21  64  34  62  43  02  84  38  13  60  26  32  36  81  43  17  56  41
03  64  65  44  02  75  41  33  91  28  82  97  57  38  49  27  26  97  34  44  26  12  00  68  24
14  53  75  37  91  43  95  15  13  26  33  27  45  48  33  00  00  20  69  76  04  87  83  58  32

01  64  43  36  30  71  24  75  92  73  07  81  13  35  46  88  62  80  64  69  86  25  73  92  98
39  38  79  42  17  77  99  55  32  85  13  35  48  49  80  83  59  06  34  94  06  03  61  85  02
74  96  24  94  89  54  66  29  35  88  50  46  65  50  26  62  45  80  61  95  07  99  57  10  54
21  16  54  55  77  46  38  33  88  55  21  56  18  93  32  94  24  80  97  03  78  39  73  87  70
58  51  99  53  96  73  60  77  21  06  76  59  78  55  96  99  07  53  91  95  99  60  56  61  79

46  98  27  95  19  22  29  41  56  76  83  48  49  82  79  79  20  00  26  40  22  50  14  30  73
58  46  36  76  19  18  00  60  50  28  32  44  18  35  99  28  91  50  53  62  21  61  26  46  81
43  05  50  00  20  39  25  46  84  39  27  39  92  42  59  04  64  15  09  35  07  11  25  51  17
84  07  33  83  87  14  33  79  07  66  60  43  66  57  57  57  59  01  78  80  13  77  63  58  10
93  54  23  72  70  09  36  16  24  04  74  05  65  29  64  67  37  28  13  98  01  48  29  75  89

54  46  72  02  34  52  81  38  52  96  14  54  27  32  41  74  84  83  90  01  97  59  87  66  41
43  60  84  28  32  93  91  76  70  31  50  22  09  40  89  64  85  82  76  91  16  71  99  98  70
64  80  80  16  92  46  42  46  47  22  87  16  20  65  82  01  45  21  49  80  17  39  70  74  03
78  70  39  30  06  59  65  14  84  04  82  28  46  64  05  89  81  80  09  89  56  11  27  81  44
14  88  67  03  59  32  15  83  04  01  20  82  92  25  34  88  84  80  76  69  25  10  04  86  02

69  28  06  18  56  78  97  49  14  85  01  58  31  16  20  53  74  03  27  05  80  39  15  67  49
99  68  09  96  36  54  10  77  95  88  90  84  52  16  52  58  87  51  31  71  68  53  11  85  50
01  66  22  15  54  63  83  64  15  30  21  86  48  17  11  68  92  16  17  49  36  05  17  80  24
67  85  26  91  23  14  28  01  76  47  65  12  58  24  27  61  59  43  20  15  93  47  30  56  27
13  91  16  76  91  97  85  48  99  50  40  96  30  66  97  82  66  06  90  97  65  28  44  98  08

95  82  20  95  52  65  95  03  48  75  64  25  04  13  85  80  13  37  08  18  09  28  63  07  69
44  06  82  49  28  27  34  53  42  35  44  12  40  64  35  06  28  14  37  23  97  38  07  60  80
99  22  26  64  15  71  06  96  22  93  77  46  73  57  51  22  54  82  37  99  96  27  25  87  77
08  44  26  12  87  72  42  13  57  77  61  07  94  24  62  17  76  19  45  18  98  11  47  40  31
14  96  76  06  37  32  09  72  81  22  87  70  81  93  78  93  37  22  32  25  38  45  38  03  31

27  86  41  53  58  16  49  99  19  03  62  98  79  81  98  15  03  62  32  93  68  24  14  44  50
99  67  81  61  25  52  97  87  98  15  85  99  01  86  59  00  11  39  32  53  49  18  62  51  65
89  14  37  94  03  22  32  45  42  61  97  83  04  26  30  48  49  40  99  99  69  96  13  94  21
34  13  53  15  32  42  02  58  32  14  83  73  02  82  49  25  62  91  14  94  70  72  64  50  51
72  11  79  75  79  36  07  12  92  61  89  93  77  82  08  23  74  75  67  56  37  45  35  13  44

19  72  57  61  99  08  62  02  26  82  52  90  72  51  94  84  59  79  34  19  95  76  21  49  91
96  99  76  63  90  27  60  94  15  70  17  74  92  31  85  24  47  55  64  51  91  47  13  39  69
44  15  86  76  18  15  57  29  51  62  95  84  20  83  01  11  90  66  80  81  40  43  65  87  35
33  83  94  07  50  18  89  86  16  50  09  97  04  76  51  41  20  56  50  20  33  53  70  10  22
53  07  06  16  30  84  43  40  57  32  18  09  47  16  69  41  03  38  24  02  16  41  58  39  58
```

TABLE A-37.　SHORT TABLE OF RANDOM NORMAL DEVIATES
$m = 0, \sigma = 1$

0.048	1.040	−0.111	−0.120	1.396	−0.393	−0.220	0.422	0.233	0.197
−0.521	−0.563	−0.116	−0.512	−0.518	−2.194	2.261	0.461	−1.533	−1.836
−1.407	−0.213	0.948	−0.073	−1.474	−0.236	−0.649	1.555	1.285	−0.747
1.822	0.898	−0.691	0.972	−0.011	0.517	0.808	2.651	−0.650	0.592
1.346	−0.137	0.952	1.467	−0.352	0.309	0.578	−1.881	−0.488	−0.329
0.420	−1.085	−1.578	−0.125	1.337	0.169	0.551	−0.745	−0.588	1.810
−1.760	−1.868	0.677	0.545	1.465	0.572	−0.770	0.655	−0.574	1.262
−0.959	0.061	−1.260	−0.573	−0.646	−0.697	−0.026	−1.115	3.591	−0.519
0.561	−0.534	−1.730	−1.172	−0.261	−0.049	0.173	0.027	1.138	0.524
−0.717	0.254	0.421	−1.891	2.592	−1.443	−0.061	−2.520	−0.497	0.909
−2.097	−0.180	−1.298	−0.647	0.159	0.769	−0.735	−0.343	0.966	0.595
0.443	−0.191	0.705	0.420	−0.486	−1.038	−0.396	1.406	0.327	1.198
0.481	0.161	−0.044	−0.864	−0.587	−0.037	−1.304	−1.544	0.946	−0.344
−2.219	−0.123	−0.260	0.680	0.224	−1.217	0.052	0.174	0.692	−1.068
1.723	−0.215	−0.158	0.369	1.073	−2.442	−0.472	2.060	−3.246	−1.020
−0.937	1.253	0.321	−0.541	−0.648	0.265	1.487	−0.554	1.890	0.499
−0.568	−0.146	0.285	1.337	−0.840	0.361	−0.468	0.746	0.470	0.171
−1.717	−1.293	−0.556	−0.545	1.344	0.320	−0.087	0.418	1.076	1.669
−0.151	−0.266	0.920	−2.370	0.484	−1.915	−0.268	0.718	2.075	−0.975
2.278	−1.819	0.245	−0.163	0.980	−1.629	−0.094	−0.573	1.548	−0.896
−0.650	0.669	−0.761	0.154	0.872	0.914	−0.563	−1.434	−0.006	−0.975
−1.086	0.810	0.461	−0.528	2.130	−0.218	0.111	−0.412	−0.580	−1.487
−0.143	−1.196	−1.254	−0.133	0.937	−0.475	−2.348	0.618	−0.057	−0.710
−2.072	0.711	1.241	0.066	−0.341	0.356	1.220	0.431	0.263	−1.623
−0.394	−0.368	−2.108	0.605	0.485	2.068	0.687	−1.474	0.071	−1.196
0.174	−1.131	0.870	2.114	0.201	−0.373	−0.284	−0.234	−2.087	−1.304
0.020	0.102	−1.911	−1.132	1.267	0.420	0.791	1.548	−0.147	−0.453
0.297	0.449	−0.604	−0.858	−1.739	1.143	0.131	0.740	−1.596	0.165
1.160	0.253	0.716	−1.032	−0.595	−1.662	0.632	−0.315	−0.374	0.700
−0.351	−0.490	−0.632	−0.409	−0.116	−1.153	−0.266	−0.125	0.489	−0.366
−0.594	−0.214	−0.461	0.030	−0.595	−0.889	0.638	−0.488	0.418	−0.693
−1.882	1.890	−0.236	0.006	0.966	−0.723	0.229	−2.136	−1.017	−0.008
0.041	2.955	−1.526	2.114	−0.540	1.040	0.753	0.025	0.462	1.221
−0.403	1.237	−1.938	−1.704	−0.103	−0.346	1.214	0.826	0.336	−1.140
−0.068	0.599	0.192	1.503	−0.579	−1.485	−1.645	0.302	−1.348	0.553
−0.361	0.958	0.807	0.787	−0.547	−0.074	−1.378	−0.010	−1.096	0.789
−0.251	0.629	0.459	−0.165	0.016	0.489	−1.205	−0.260	−0.256	−0.399
−1.011	0.893	−0.741	−0.514	−0.576	−0.929	0.478	−0.374	1.950	−0.695
0.780	−2.464	−0.522	0.767	−1.657	−0.983	0.217	−0.529	−0.648	1.454
−0.712	−0.355	−0.564	1.052	−0.169	−0.410	1.543	−2.330	−0.008	−0.955
−0.612	−1.068	−0.644	−0.007	−0.835	0.623	0.093	0.105	−0.318	−0.228
−0.064	0.012	−0.676	0.349	0.303	1.539	0.792	−0.101	−0.344	−0.096
−0.379	1.504	2.375	0.498	−0.996	0.174	−1.268	−1.137	−0.618	0.173
1.145	−1.403	0.770	0.799	0.844	−1.361	−1.059	0.128	1.398	0.277
−0.117	0.585	−1.763	−0.632	0.239	−0.854	1.684	1.024	−0.067	−0.045
1.333	1.374	−0.515	−1.655	0.607	−0.885	−0.902	−1.010	−1.297	−0.139
−0.249	−0.747	1.044	−0.930	0.346	0.575	0.335	−1.159	−1.651	−1.642
−1.022	0.085	−1.441	−0.198	0.844	0.697	0.548	−0.080	0.656	0.443
−0.780	−0.534	−0.339	−0.642	−0.902	−0.827	0.071	−0.678	−0.359	−0.479
−0.687	−0.418	0.991	0.331	−1.003	0.061	−1.416	0.876	0.125	−2.246

TABLE A-37 (Continued). SHORT TABLE OF RANDOM NORMAL DEVIATES
$m = 0,\ \sigma = 1$

−0.670	0.518	0.387	0.523	0.641	1.243	0.322	−2.607	−1.097	−0.012
−2.912	1.448	1.343	−0.122	0.726	−0.617	0.609	2.319	−0.450	−1.197
−0.028	−0.790	0.057	1.425	1.940	1.161	−0.878	−0.716	−0.244	−1.151
−1.257	0.774	0.003	0.388	1.060	1.028	−0.236	1.172	0.442	−0.157
2.372	−1.376	−1.318	1.236	0.738	0.337	−0.534	0.090	0.886	0.676
−0.970	0.438	−0.672	−0.180	0.667	1.370	−0.481	0.329	0.842	0.449
−1.228	0.129	−0.426	−0.165	0.028	2.696	1.201	−1.351	0.724	−1.017
−0.369	0.310	0.432	0.237	0.884	−1.224	0.539	0.852	0.497	−0.283
1.161	1.219	1.615	0.336	1.100	−0.528	0.161	0.278	0.675	−1.143
−0.284	2.609	0.792	1.825	−0.249	1.654	0.621	0.979	−1.472	−1.173
−0.578	−0.789	0.106	0.832	−0.597	0.496	−0.561	−1.033	−0.578	−0.378
0.074	0.261	−0.766	−1.046	0.361	−0.043	−1.927	1.527	0.605	1.475
0.230	0.046	0.978	−1.901	1.162	−0.545	0.697	1.151	2.033	0.080
2.162	−0.562	1.190	0.925	−1.057	0.015	−1.371	1.067	−1.080	1.129
−1.020	−1.130	−0.315	0.628	−0.140	2.050	−0.030	−0.629	0.128	−1.221
1.323	−0.836	−0.284	−0.249	−0.768	1.242	−0.879	−0.417	0.013	−0.502
2.329	1.884	0.033	0.598	−0.217	0.260	0.431	−1.914	0.205	1.155
2.761	1.800	−0.562	0.714	−0.407	0.009	−0.724	−1.168	0.247	1.166
−0.232	0.605	−0.023	−0.531	0.542	−0.155	0.697	1.037	−0.316	−0.003
−0.742	0.210	−0.741	−1.099	0.158	2.112	−0.765	−0.319	−0.247	0.345
−1.410	0.413	0.705	1.444	1.057	−0.843	0.043	−0.571	−0.001	0.203
2.272	−0.719	0.679	2.007	−0.180	0.698	−1.137	0.688	−0.571	−0.100
2.832	0.925	−1.350	1.529	−0.260	−1.007	−2.350	−1.501	0.289	1.522
−1.086	−0.558	−0.973	−1.285	−0.021	0.077	0.915	−0.241	0.249	−0.529
0.134	1.815	0.313	1.571	−0.216	2.261	0.696	−0.130	0.393	0.017
0.783	0.600	−0.745	1.127	−0.684	−0.519	0.125	−0.499	1.543	−0.082
0.174	−0.897	0.575	−0.751	0.694	−2.959	0.529	1.587	0.339	−0.813
−1.319	0.556	2.963	1.218	1.199	−1.746	1.611	0.467	−0.490	0.202
1.298	−0.940	−1.143	−1.136	−1.516	0.548	0.629	0.250	−1.087	0.322
−0.676	−1.107	−1.483	0.278	0.493	−0.442	1.078	−0.336	−0.177	−0.057
−1.287	0.775	−1.095	1.161	−1.877	1.874	1.703	−1.619	−0.725	−1.407
0.260	−0.028	−1.982	0.811	0.999	1.662	0.908	1.476	−1.137	−0.945
0.481	1.060	1.441	0.163	0.720	1.490	−0.026	−0.502	0.427	−0.351
0.794	0.725	1.971	0.384	−0.579	−1.079	−1.440	−0.859	−0.346	0.077
0.584	−0.554	1.460	0.791	−0.426	−0.682	0.430	1.922	−2.099	0.221
−0.114	0.379	−0.698	1.570	−0.511	−0.725	0.680	−0.591	−1.091	0.357
−1.128	−1.707	0.921	0.859	−1.506	1.523	−0.900	−0.988	0.264	0.282
0.691	0.153	0.076	1.691	0.553	0.457	−1.107	0.322	0.633	0.007
1.115	0.777	−0.738	0.868	1.484	−1.792	0.950	−0.842	−0.192	0.620
−0.389	0.559	0.670	−0.315	1.234	0.475	1.117	1.286	−0.649	−1.880
0.330	0.750	−0.642	0.148	−0.608	0.866	−1.720	0.653	−0.210	−0.959
−0.333	−0.084	1.239	−0.049	−0.095	−0.197	−0.213	−1.420	−0.491	0.102
1.718	1.111	−0.548	−0.653	1.534	−0.456	−0.395	1.614	−0.531	−0.785
−0.182	0.620	1.178	−1.071	0.444	−0.072	−1.001	1.325	−0.302	−1.119
1.260	−1.192	0.182	−0.397	−0.705	−1.085	−1.492	1.642	0.673	−0.707
−1.204	−1.725	1.695	1.473	0.665	−0.489	0.020	0.267	1.230	0.865
−0.619	0.307	−0.226	−0.096	0.987	−1.195	−1.412	0.433	2.052	0.022
−0.272	−0.096	0.137	−0.361	0.653	−0.156	1.309	−0.480	−0.397	1.302
0.245	−0.690	0.493	−1.123	1.465	0.132	0.582	−0.429	0.225	0.125
0.101	−0.855	0.782	−1.040	2.113	−1.423	−1.010	0.158	0.106	−1.232

TABLE A-37 (Continued). SHORT TABLE OF RANDOM NORMAL DEVIATES
$m = 0,\ \sigma = 1$

0.117	−0.136	0.820	−1.213	0.131	−0.738	0.918	1.002	−0.846	0.288
0.519	−0.787	−1.128	1.100	1.609	0.797	0.382	−1.157	−1.320	−2.056
−0.876	−0.832	−0.788	1.490	−0.923	−0.710	−2.149	−1.967	0.088	1.158
0.311	0.494	0.357	0.025	−0.016	0.448	0.733	−0.199	0.440	0.609
−1.041	0.627	−0.957	0.777	0.304	−0.581	1.495	−1.564	−1.471	−1.097
0.239	0.061	1.091	−0.060	0.521	−0.777	0.461	0.919	−0.091	1.412
−0.151	0.664	0.596	0.370	−0.346	−0.526	−1.557	−0.180	−0.323	0.918
0.962	−0.502	−0.967	0.859	0.916	−1.525	0.064	1.023	0.001	−1.577
1.573	−1.912	−1.010	1.780	−0.771	2.390	−0.188	−0.593	−0.608	−0.561
−0.742	0.137	0.563	0.887	−0.740	−1.410	−0.818	−0.545	1.130	−0.741
−0.143	−1.299	−1.869	0.191	−0.789	−0.296	−2.232	0.268	−1.582	0.389
−1.433	1.169	−0.733	1.176	−0.582	1.060	0.447	0.305	−2.418	−1.209
−1.946	1.045	−1.705	−1.544	1.701	0.972	0.346	−0.341	−1.240	−0.194
−0.885	0.247	−1.230	−1.461	0.175	2.072	1.174	−0.223	−1.106	0.028
−0.046	0.513	−0.201	−0.740	0.727	0.668	−0.433	−0.991	−0.174	1.421
−0.683	−0.161	0.964	−1.182	0.485	0.901	1.321	0.803	−0.727	−0.569
−0.749	−0.029	−1.150	0.122	−0.016	−0.690	1.261	1.884	0.758	−0.035
0.995	0.542	0.448	0.796	0.616	0.261	1.072	−1.153	−1.866	−1.029
0.274	−0.188	−0.846	1.557	0.554	0.514	0.723	−0.322	−0.805	0.178
1.120	−0.396	2.110	−1.469	−0.589	0.779	0.338	−0.093	1.629	0.134
−0.668	−0.678	0.406	0.092	0.944	−0.728	−0.358	−1.206	−0.783	0.510
1.583	−0.730	−0.911	0.126	1.864	−0.296	−0.980	−1.022	0.315	0.274
1.050	1.162	1.236	−2.039	−1.299	−0.722	−0.630	1.359	0.511	0.448
0.477	−0.433	0.110	−0.182	−0.363	0.716	−1.355	1.579	−0.574	0.043
−1.538	0.137	−0.382	0.578	1.053	0.489	1.552	1.520	0.391	−1.026
−0.314	−0.889	−0.913	0.417	0.537	−0.426	−0.100	1.467	0.483	−0.627
0.730	−0.946	−0.231	−0.671	−0.798	1.330	−1.006	−0.123	0.442	1.513
0.276	−0.473	0.477	1.076	0.316	−0.600	−0.146	0.090	−0.608	−1.198
−0.638	−1.270	−0.447	−1.101	−1.107	−1.433	0.349	0.546	−0.283	0.887
0.497	−0.829	0.745	0.469	1.975	0.130	0.367	0.202	−0.433	0.630
−0.769	−0.866	−1.034	−1.615	0.120	0.493	0.103	−0.639	1.732	1.066
−1.384	0.453	0.586	−1.549	−0.421	0.815	−1.319	−0.805	−0.009	−0.100
0.784	1.980	−1.265	0.239	1.189	−0.382	0.047	−0.582	0.806	−1.336
−0.035	−0.514	−0.087	−0.202	0.925	−0.047	−0.926	−1.157	0.498	−1.066
0.678	0.917	0.376	1.282	−1.176	0.622	2.123	0.646	−0.730	0.026
0.179	0.841	−0.298	−2.437	−0.740	−0.039	0.226	0.247	−1.614	0.492
0.111	−0.044	0.209	0.527	0.598	−0.206	−1.042	−0.012	0.757	0.840
1.006	−0.919	0.956	0.808	1.793	−0.079	1.953	−1.494	0.559	1.290
−0.307	−1.174	−0.858	0.039	−1.505	0.037	−0.107	0.120	0.557	1.809
−2.467	0.273	−0.899	−0.691	−1.092	−1.374	1.238	2.046	0.879	0.296
0.275	−1.313	−0.331	0.305	0.404	−0.399	0.591	0.280	−1.802	1.207
−0.514	−0.713	0.501	1.214	0.001	0.360	−0.124	1.373	1.857	−1.135
0.982	−0.139	1.113	−0.433	−0.761	0.182	−0.405	0.714	−0.616	−1.402
−0.071	−0.115	−0.344	0.429	0.316	−0.667	1.676	−0.155	1.085	−1.780
−1.975	−1.416	1.367	−0.592	0.480	0.406	0.701	1.077	−1.475	1.024
0.027	−1.446	−0.464	−1.180	1.223	−1.116	−1.017	1.051	0.051	−0.853
0.016	−1.118	−1.228	1.382	−0.502	0.494	−0.612	2.755	−0.809	−1.216
0.584	−1.410	−0.551	−0.602	−0.381	−0.078	−1.310	1.198	1.359	0.115
0.669	−0.611	−0.452	0.302	−1.026	−0.331	−1.047	0.618	0.931	−0.218
0.070	−1.598	−0.506	−0.812	1.203	−2.110	0.049	0.059	1.890	0.421

TABLE A-37 (Continued). SHORT TABLE OF RANDOM NORMAL DEVIATES
$m = 0, \sigma = 1$

1.801	0.459	1.102	−1.072	−0.336	0.942	−0.290	−0.716	1.396	−0.466
−0.175	−0.754	−0.134	1.231	1.483	−0.149	0.555	1.401	−1.142	0.205
−0.861	−1.460	0.526	0.239	−0.206	2.021	0.313	−0.253	−0.891	1.135
−0.577	0.335	−0.820	0.140	−0.333	0.426	0.209	−0.024	0.323	1.223
0.827	0.802	−0.457	0.560	0.643	−0.729	−0.249	0.338	−0.281	−1.804
−1.344	0.949	−1.459	−1.210	1.016	−0.148	−1.737	0.069	−1.185	0.040
1.476	1.262	−1.428	0.489	−0.523	−0.646	1.721	0.749	0.179	−0.922
0.527	−1.045	0.877	0.646	2.957	−0.972	−1.796	0.309	2.224	−0.070
−0.645	0.117	0.059	−0.080	−1.637	−0.746	1.256	2.520	−0.673	0.994
−0.514	−1.510	−0.714	−1.581	0.905	1.745	1.767	0.682	−0.648	−1.742
−0.656	−0.217	0.287	0.114	1.175	0.791	−0.263	−0.695	−1.348	1.239
−0.778	1.177	0.180	1.156	0.458	1.089	0.339	1.304	0.402	−0.831
0.352	−1.829	−0.645	0.236	0.641	0.920	−1.287	−0.187	−2.339	−0.237
1.352	−0.076	−1.962	0.827	0.252	1.621	0.770	1.324	0.488	−0.037
0.017	0.030	0.211	2.276	0.693	−1.733	0.773	0.652	−0.947	0.148
−0.218	−1.060	−0.553	1.043	2.305	0.380	−0.794	−1.498	1.088	−0.689
1.118	0.816	0.713	0.485	0.185	0.318	−1.050	0.110	0.563	1.177
−1.622	0.436	0.481	0.021	2.070	−0.845	−0.257	−0.680	−0.565	0.024
−1.103	−0.210	−1.088	−0.033	−1.022	0.366	−0.531	2.022	0.210	1.037
−0.677	−0.737	−0.950	−1.517	1.148	0.377	−0.397	−1.902	−0.748	−1.753
1.110	1.120	1.163	1.577	−1.172	−0.133	−0.213	0.154	−0.435	0.218
−0.278	0.569	0.586	1.523	−0.244	−0.170	−1.274	0.874	−1.020	−0.809
0.178	1.314	0.462	−0.253	−0.122	0.108	−1.256	−0.137	1.043	−0.135
0.312	−2.287	−0.655	−1.459	0.075	−0.457	−0.206	−0.326	0.489	−0.149
0.469	−2.066	−0.973	−1.009	−1.410	0.505	0.459	−0.572	−1.186	0.978
−0.730	1.650	0.760	−0.520	−0.671	−0.122	−0.324	−0.202	0.411	−2.103
0.834	0.280	0.744	0.598	0.122	−0.460	−1.310	−1.271	−0.917	0.650
−1.397	−1.053	0.412	1.286	−0.820	−0.371	0.826	−0.666	0.505	0.733
0.238	−0.668	1.861	0.051	0.460	0.079	1.008	−0.487	0.306	−0.061
0.102	−0.907	−0.833	1.103	−0.921	0.145	−0.904	−0.401	0.553	−1.422
−0.160	0.567	−0.638	0.355	0.427	−0.695	−0.846	0.359	1.500	−0.926
0.496	1.179	−0.776	0.511	−1.325	0.275	−0.130	−0.123	1.175	−0.102
0.307	−0.328	−2.474	−0.121	1.371	0.266	1.235	1.827	−0.296	−2.715
−0.559	0.523	1.264	−0.018	−2.791	0.139	1.515	1.976	0.173	−1.728
0.658	−0.261	0.004	−1.296	0.568	−1.215	0.104	0.178	1.126	1.134
−0.856	−2.278	−0.140	−0.164	1.416	−0.043	0.243	−1.399	−0.448	0.120
2.778	0.245	0.282	0.301	−1.506	1.805	1.798	1.078	1.629	−0.648
0.543	0.761	−2.038	−0.533	−0.594	1.742	0.487	1.432	−0.210	−0.358
0.008	−0.445	−2.551	0.935	1.961	−0.270	−1.557	−1.318	−0.744	−0.860
−1.147	−1.151	−0.522	−2.118	−0.667	0.906	0.639	1.005	−0.480	−1.354
−0.851	0.585	0.672	0.481	−0.888	−0.480	0.041	0.345	−0.537	−0.589
0.023	0.609	0.623	0.356	0.279	−0.051	0.158	−0.353	0.776	0.102
−0.257	0.152	−1.413	0.175	0.149	−1.354	0.286	1.794	−0.571	−0.202
−0.421	−0.344	−0.803	0.832	0.256	−1.296	−1.390	0.379	0.955	0.366
−1.681	2.444	−1.025	1.178	−0.827	−0.200	0.727	0.778	0.169	−1.363
0.717	−1.666	1.071	−2.061	−1.367	−0.450	−0.038	−1.004	−1.240	0.901
−1.266	0.256	−1.312	−0.582	−0.351	−1.002	0.648	0.873	0.015	0.641
0.350	0.552	−1.549	−1.680	1.417	−0.769	−0.514	−1.900	1.017	−1.222
−0.186	0.006	0.148	0.560	−1.081	−0.637	−1.968	−0.623	0.009	−0.369
1.359	1.027	0.740	−2.067	0.543	1.099	0.543	0.064	0.589	−0.016

INDEX

The following alphabetical listing includes all topics from the entire Handbook, Sections 1 through 5, inclusive.

Page references have double numerals, identifying both the chapter and page within the chapter. Page numbers for Section 5 (A-Tables) are identified as T-1, T-2, etc., as numbered in that Section to avoid confusion with the pages of Chapter 5. Roman numeral page references indicate pages of the same number in every Section.

A

Acknowledgments, iii
Acton, F. S., 5-46, 20-13
Addison-Wesley Publishing Co., Inc., 20-13
Additivity
   (*See* Transformations)
Aitchison, J., 20-13
Allowances
   table, critical values of L for Link-Wallis test, T-28
α, chosen significance level value, discussion of use and choice of, 3-2
α, error of the first kind, 3-1
Alphabet, Greek, T-1
Alternative Hypothesis
   (*See also*, Hypotheses)
   definition, 1-16
Aluminum alloy, tensile strength of, data sample, 16-6
American Ceramic Society, 14-7
American Cyanamid Company, T-79
American Society for Quality Control, 14-4, -5, -7, -8
American Society for Testing Materials (ASTM), 1-12; 18-3, -4; 21-5
American Soil Sciences Society, 14-7
American Standards Association, 18-3, -4
American Standard Control Chart Method of Controlling Quality During Production
   Z 1.3-1958, 18-3, -4
American Statistical Association, 1-19, 2-12, 5-46, 10-24, 19-4
The American Statistician, 19-1, -2, -3; 21-1
Analysis
   (*See also*: Experiments, Planning and Analysis of; Statistical Analysis)
   Kärber Method, 10-3
   Probit method, 10-8
Analyst, 14-5
Analytical Chemistry, 18-4
Andersen, S. L., 14-5
Anderson, R. L., 6-42, 11-6, 14-5
Anderson, T. W., 10-24
Annals of Mathematical Statistics, 3-6, -11; 4-4, -6, -11, -12, -13; 14-5, -6, -7; 17-6; 20-13; 21-3; T-75, -76, -77
Arc sine Transformation
   (*See* Transformations)
Army Ordnance Corps, ii
ASTM
   (*See* American Society for Testing Materials)
Authorship, i, iii
Averages
   (*See*: Performance, Average; Tests, Distribution-free; Tests, Shortcut)
Average Performance
   (*See*: Performance, Average; Tests, Distribution-free; Tests, Shortcut)

B

Bancroft, T. A., 6-42, 11-6
Bands, Confidence
  (*See* Linear Relationships)
Bartlett, M. S., 5-46, 20-14
Basic Engineering, 14-5
Batteries, capacity of, data sample, 3-32, 4-1, 15-4
Behnken, D. W., 14-5, -6
Berkson, J., 5-46, 10-24
β, error of the second kind, 3-1
$\beta(\delta)$, probability of failure to detect a specified difference, 3-2
Biometrics, 5-46; 10-24; 14-5, -6, -7; 17-6; 20-13
Biometrika, 3-25, -42; 14-5, -6; 20-13; T-18, -26, -34, -46
Biometrika Tables for Statisticians, T-7, -30, -31
Birnbaum, A., 21-6
Blocked Designs
  (*See also:* Block Plans, Chain, Incomplete, and Randomized; Latin Square Plans;
    Randomized Plans; Youden Square Plans)
  discussion, general, 13-1
Blocked Factorials
  (*See* Factorial Experiments)
Block Plans
  (*See also:* Latin Square Plans; Randomized Plans; Youden Square Plans)
  chain block plans
    analysis, 13-21
      data sample, 13-22
      estimating treatment and block effects, 13-24
        example, 13-25
        procedure, 13-24
      symbols, definitions of, 13-21
      table, schematic representation of plan of data sample, 13-22
      table, three blocks with data sample determinations coded, 13-23
      testing and estimating differences in treatment effects, 13-28
        example, 13-29
        procedure, 13-28
    planning, 13-19
      table, schematic presentation of two plans, 13-19
  incomplete block plans
    discussion, general, 13-6
    balanced plans, 13-7
      analysis, 13-14
        data sample, 13-14
        estimating block effects, 13-17
        estimating treatment effects, 13-15
        symbols, definitions of, 13-7
        table, schematic representation of results, 13-13
        testing and estimating differences in block effects, 13-18
          procedure and example. 13-18
        testing and estimating differences in treatment effects, 13-16
          procedure and example, 13-16
      planning, 13-7
        table showing 19 plans, 13-8
  randomized block plans
    analysis, 13-3
      data sample, 13-4
      estimation of block effects, 13-5
        procedure and example, 13-6
      estimation of treatment effects, 13-4
        procedure and example, 13-5
      table, schematic presentation of results, 13-3
      testing and estimating differences in block effects, 13-6
        procedure and example, 13-6
      testing and estimating differences in treatment effects, 13-5
        procedure and example, 13-5
    discussion, general, 13-1
    planning 13-2
Blocks:
  (*See:* Block Plans, Chain, Incomplete, and Randomized; Randomized Plans)
Bose, R. C., 13-46, 14-5
Bowker, A. H., 1-7, -19; 3-7, -12, -13, -14, -18; 4-14
Box, G. E. P., 14-4, -5, -6
Bradley, R. A., 14-4, -5

Brooks, H., 19-4
Brooks, S., 14-6
Brooks, S. H., 14-6
Brown, D. S., 14-7
Brown, J. A. C., 20-13
Brown, W. G., 14-8
Brownlee, K. A., 10-24
Buckland, W. R., 2-15, 6-42
Bureau of Ordnance, U. S. Navy, 10-24
Bush, R. R., 20-13

C

Cambridge University Press, Cambridge, England, 1-19; 3-42; 6-42; 10-24; 20-13; T-6, -30, -31
Cameron, J. M., iii
Carlson, P. G., 19-4
Carr, N. L., 14-7
Carter, R. L., 14-5, -6
Castings, metal, causes of rejection, data sample, 9-6
Cells, chemical, temperature reference, data sample, 13-33
Cement briquettes, breaking-strength of, data sample, 3-41, 15-6
Cestoni, D. J., 14-7
Chand, Uttam, 4-14
Chang, C. D., 14-7
Charts
    (See Control Charts)
Chemical Engineering Progress, 14-7, -8
Chew, V., 11-6; 14-4, -6, -7
χ_P^2, table, values of corresponding to P, T-4
Chi-square tests, 9-1
Clatworthy, W. H., 13-46
Clelland, R. C., T-80
Cochran, W. G., 1-4, -5, -19; 11-6; 12-21; 13-46; 14-4, -5; 20-13
Cochran, W. O., 14-7
Colorimetric methods, relation of two, data sample, 5-27
Columbia University Press, 19-4
Comparing Average Performance
    (See: Performance, average; Performance, several categories; Performance, two-fold classification; Tests, Distribution-free; Tests, Shortcut)
Comparing Materials or Products
    (See: Performance, average; Performance, measured; Performance, several categories; Performance, two-fold classification; Performance, variability of; Tests, Distribution-free; Tests, Shortcut)
Comparing Several Products
    (See: Performance, average; Performance, variability of; Tests, Distribution-free; Tests, Shortcut)
Computations
    (See also, discussions, and the procedures and examples for specific topics of interest)
    formula for s^2, 1-10
    table, factors for computing one-sided confidence limits for σ, T-36
    table, factors for computing two-sided confidence limits for σ, T-34
Computations, Statistical
    notes on, 22-1 through 22-4
    coding, 22-1
        observed and coded results, tabulated example of, 22-1, -2
    rounding, 22-2
        of numbers, 22-2
        of results of a series of arithmetic operations, 22-4
        of results of single arithmetic operations, 22-3
Conclusions
    (See also, Decisions)
    risks involved with exceedingly small samples, 1-19
Concrete, compressive strength of, data sample, 3-26
Confidence Bands
    (See Linear Relationships)

Confidence Belts
  (*See also:* Correlation coefficient; Linear Relationships)
  table of, for the correlation coefficient, T-31
  table of, for proportions, sample sizes greater than 30, T-45
Confidence coefficient
  γ, proportion of samples n for which computed intervals may be expected to bracket
    m or σ, 1-11
Confidence Interval Estimates
  (*See also:* Performance, average; Performance, variability of)
  of average performance, 2-1
  differences in procedure results for variability known and unknown, 2-5
  example of, 1-11
  when variability is known
    general remarks, 2-4
    procedure and example, two-sided interval, 2-5
Confidence Intervals
  advantages of, 21-4
    figure showing confidence intervals, 21-5
  basic concepts, 1-11
  definition of term, as difference from statistical tolerance limits and engineering
    limits, 1-15
  OC curves, deductions from, 21-6
  determining sample size, relation to problem of, 21-6
  figure showing 50%, with less variation as sample size increases, 1-13
  figure showing 50% and 90% intervals, 1-12
  for population mean, knowledge of variability cannot be assumed
    one-sided interval X_r or X_L, 2-3
      procedure and example, 2-4
    two-sided interval X_r and X_L, 2-2
      procedure and example, 2-2
  remarks, concluding, 21-6
  and tests of significance, relation between, 21-1 through 21-6
    comparing averages, a problem in, 21-2
      figure showing OC curves for two-sided t-test ($\alpha = .05$), 21-3
    introduction, discussion of, 21-1
    presenting results, two ways of, 21-2
Confidence Levels
  (*See also,* Confidence Limits)
  choice of t and z values, variability known and unknown, discussion, 2-5
  tables, one-sided distribution-free tolerance limits, T-76
  tables, two-sided distribution-free tolerance limits, T-75
  table, confidence associated with a tolerance limit statement, T-77
Confidence Limits
  (*See also:* Confidence Intervals; Confidence Interval Estimates; Confidence Levels)
  one-sided
    table, factors for computing limits for σ, T-36
    table of, for a proportion, sample sizes less than 30, T-41
  two-sided
    table, factors for computing limits for σ, T-34
    table of, for a proportion, sample sizes less than 30, T-37
Contrasts, table of minimum required for significance in 2×2 tables with equal sample
  sizes, T-55
Cornfield, J., 10-24
Control Charts
  place of, in experimental work, 18-1 through 18-4
    applications of, 18-2
      table of factors for computing 3-sigma control limits, 18-3
      table of formulas for, 18-3
    information provided by, 18-1
      table of tests for locating and identifying specific types of assignable causes, 18-2
    primary objective of, 18-1
Control Limits
  (*See* Control Charts)
Correlation coefficient, table, confidence belts for, T-31
Cowden, D. J., 18-4
Cox, D. R., 11-6
Cox, G. M., 11-6; 12-21; 13-46; 14-4, -5
Crew, E. L., 2-12; T-37, -41
Culling, H. P., 10-24
Curtis, J. M., 10-24
Curtiss, J. H., 20-13

Curves
    (*See also:* Control Charts; Operational Characteristic (OC) Curves)
    figure showing degrees of freedom required to estimate standard deviation with stated precision, 2-12
    figure showing three different normal distributions, 1-8
    figure showing various shapes of, with regard to frequency distributions, 1-8
    normal
        table, values of P corresponding to z_P, T-2
        table, values of z_P corresponding to P, T-3
    use of OC curves to depict discriminatory power of a statistical statement, 3-2

D

d, allowable margin of error in estimates, 2-9
Data
    (*See also:* Conclusions; Data Samples; Decisions; Extreme-Value Data)
    cautions concerning interpretation of, 1-18
    figure showing plot of linear relationships between two variables, 5-2
    plotting, for linear relationships of two variables, 5-1
Data Samples
    aluminum alloy, tensile strength of, 16-6
    batteries, capacity of, 15-4
    breakdowns of electricity meters, 9-4
    burning time of rocket powder, 2-6
    causes of rejection of metal castings, 9-6
    cement briquettes, breaking-strength of, 15-6
    chemical cells, temperature reference, 13-33
    defectives in sample of new product, 8-1
    field trials of two types of mine fuzes, 8-16
    flame tests of fire-retardant treatments
        for factorial experiments, 12-4
        assuming fractional factorial design, 12-19
    inspections and tests of clinical thermometers, 9-2
    nickel, spectographic determination of, 13-22
    peak-voltage test of fuzes, 10-2
    performance of new type of mine fuze, 8-2
    resistors, conversion gain of, 13-4
    resistors, noise measurement of, 13-14
    resistors, reverse-bias collector current of 10, 16-2
    shells, penetration depth of, 15-1
    small-scale comparison test of two types of artillery fuzes, 8-12
    small-scale comparison test of two types of mine fuzes, 8-10
    stopwatches, life tests of three types, 16-13
    thermometers, intercomparison of, 13-14
    thickness of mica washers, 2-1
    transistors, forward current transfer ratio of two types, 16-9
    transistors, output admittance of two types, 16-11
    transistors, reverse-bias collector current of 20, 16-4
    transistors, reverse-bias collector currents of two types, 16-8
    vacuum tube failures, 9-9
    weight of shell powder, 3-3
Davies, O. L., 6-42; 11-6; 12-21; 14-2, -4, -5
Davis, F. A., 2-12; T-37, -41
Day, B. B., 9-9, -10
DeBaun, R. M., 14-6, -7
Decisions
    (*See also:* Conclusions; Data; Statistical Tests; Uncertainties, Expression of)
    approach to a problem, 1-15
    procedure, general remarks on factors involved, 3-2
    using statistics to make, 1-15
Deckman, D. A., 14-7
Defectives, in sample of new product, data sample, 8-1
Degrees of Freedom
    definition of uses in statistics, quote from "A Dictionary of Statistical Terms," 2-3
    figure showing d.f. required to estimate standard deviation with stated precision, 2-12
δ, sign of difference, 3-1
DeLury, D. B., 6-42
Deming, W. E., 1-11, -13, -14; 2-9
U. S. Department of Agriculture, 1-13, -14

Deviates
  (*See also:* Normal Deviates; Random normal deviates)
  table, percentage points of extreme studentized deviate from sample mean, T-30
Deviation
  (*See also:* Deviation, Standard; Performance, Variability of)
  table, factors for computing one-sided confidence limits for σ, T-36
  table, factors for computing two-sided confidence limits for σ, T-34
Deviation Standard
  (*See also:* Deviation; Performance, Variability of)
  figure showing degrees of freedom required to estimate with stated precision, 2-12
  of some simple distributions, figure showing, 2-9
  estimating when no sample data are available, 2-8
  number of measurements (sample size) required to estimate with stated precision, 2-12
    procedure and example, 2-12
  sample range as an estimate of, 2-6
  table, factors for converting range of a sample to an estimate of σ, 2-6
  sample size required to estimate with stated precision, 2-12
Dextrons, molecular weight of, data sample, 3-38
A Dictionary of Statistical Terms, quotes from, 2-3, 6-2
Distribution
  (*See also:* Curves; Distributions; Sampling Distribution)
  bivariate, discussion of, 1-2
  of a characteristic
    not completely defined until methods of measurement or unumeration are fully
      specified, 1-2
    within a population, 1-2
  of one, two, three, or more characteristics in the population, 1-2
  of F, table of percentiles, T-6
  of the t distribution, table of percentiles, T-5
Distribution-free Techniques
  (*See also,* Tests, Distribution-free)
  table, confidence associated with a tolerance limit statement, T-77
  tables for distribution-free tolerance limits
    one-sided, T-76
    two-sided, T-75
  table, critical values of smaller rank sum for Wilcoxon-Mann-Whitney test, T-80
  table, critical values of r for the sign test, T-78
  table, critical values of $T_\alpha(n)$ for Wilcoxon signed-ranks test, T-79
Distribution-free Tests
  (*See* Tests, Distribution-free)
Distribution-free Tolerance Limits
  (*See* Tolerance Limits)
Distribution Mean
  methods for determining measurements and sample size required to establish with
    prescribed accuracy, discussion of, 2-9
Distribution, multivariate, discussion of, 1-2
Distribution, Normal
  cumulative
    values of z_p corresponding to P for normal curve, T-3
    values of P corresponding to z_p for normal curve, T-2
  figure showing three different curves for, 1-8
  determined by m and σ, 1-8
  table, factors for one-sided tolerance limits, T-14
  table, factors for two-sided tolerance limits, T-10
  figure showing percentage of population in various intervals of, 1-9
Distribution, trivariate, discussion of, 1-2
Distribution, univariate, discussion of, 1-2
Distributions
  (*See also,* Extreme-value Data)
  basic concepts, 1-1
  frequency, figure showing various shapes of, 1-8
  properties of
    basic concepts, 1-6
    use of histograms, 1-6
Dive-bombing, methods, data sample, 4-8
Dixon, W. J., 1-19; 10-24; 17-6; T-4, -5, -24, -27, -45, -78
Dover Publications, Inc., 2-12
Draper, N. R., 14-6
Duke University, iii
Duncan, A. J., 18-4
Dwyer, P. S., 6-42
Dykstra, O., 14-6

E

East, D. A., T-34
Eisenhart, C., iii, 1-19, 4-14, 5-46, 14-6, 20-13, 22-4, T-10
Empire Journal of Experimental Agriculture, 20-13
The Engineer, 9-10
Engineering Tolerance Limits
    (*See* Tolerance Limits, Engineering)
Epling, Mary L., iii
Epstein, B., 19-4
Equations and Formulas
    (*See also:* discussions, and the procedures and examples for specific topics of interest)
    analysis of polynomial and multivariable relationships by method of least squares,
      6-1 through 6-42
Errors, definitions of the two types, 1-17
Estimates
    (*See also:* Confidence Interval Estimates; Distribution Mean; Population Mean)
    footnote, tabulation showing situation where s is unbiased estimator of σ, in samples
      of size n, 1-10
Estimation, of mean and deviation, basic concepts, 1-10
Experimental Designs, 13-1 through 13-46
    (*See also:* Blocked Designs; Block Plans, Chain, Incomplete, and Randomized; Ex-
      periments, Planning and Analysis of; Latin Square Plans; Randomized Plans;
      Youden Square Plans)
    in determining optimum conditions and levels, 14-3
Experimental Situation
    (*See* Sensitivity Testing)
Experimentation
    (*See* Experiments, Planning and Analysis of)
Experiments
    (*See also,* Factorial Experiments)
    planning and analysis of 11-1 through 14-8
      experimental design, language of, discussion, 11-5
      experimental pattern, discussion, 11-3
      general considerations in planning, 11-1
      nature of experimentation, discussion, 11-1
      planned grouping, discussion, 11-3
      randomization, need for, discussion, 11-4
      replication, purpose of, discussion, 11-4
      table, requisites and tools for sound experimentation, 11-2
Expressions of Uncertainties
    (*See* Uncertainties, Expression of)
Extreme-value Data
    analyzing statistical techniques, for, 19-1 through 19-4
      distributions of values, discussion of, 19-1
      techniques, use of, 19-1
        largest values, 19-1
          figure showing theoretical distributions of largest values, 19-2
          figure showing an extreme-value plot of maximum atmospheric pressures in
            Bergen, Norway, 1857-1926, 19-3
          missing observations, 19-4
          smallest values, 19-3
Ezekiel, M., 5-40

F

Factors
    table of, for one-sided tolerance limits for normal distributions, T-14
    table of, for two-sided tolerance limits for normal distributions, T-10
Factorials
    (*See* Factorial Experiments)

Factorial Experiments
  (*See also*, Response Function)
  planning and analysis of, 12-1 through 12-21
  terminology, discussions and definitions of, 12-1
  each factor at two levels
    analysis, 12-5
    analysis of main effects and interactions
      estimation by Yates method, discussion, 12-5
        procedure and example, 12-6
        table, analysis of data from data sample, 12-8
      testing for significance of, procedure and example, 12-8
    data sample, 12-4
    estimates of experimental error for factorial-type designs, 12-3
      internal estimates, discussion, 12-3
      estimates from past experience, discussion, 12-3
      figure, examples of response curves showing presence or absence of interactions, 12-2
      fractional factorial experiments
        applications and designs, discussion, 12-14
        data sample, 12-19
        table, fractional factorial plans, 8 factors, 12-16
        analysis of main effects and interactions, 12-19
          Yates' procedure for estimating, discussion, 12-19
          table, Yates' method using data from data sample, 12-20
          testing for significance of, procedure and example, 12-21
        figures showing: a one-half, a one-quarter, and a one-eighth replicate of a 2^7 factorial, 12-15
        tables, reported observations, using data from data sample, 12-4, -19
      when uniform conditions cannot be maintained
        analysis of blocked factorial experiments, 12-13
          main effects and interactions, 12-13
          testing for significance of, procedure, 12-13
        table, blocked factorial plans for 3, 4, 5, 6, and 7 factors, 12-10
        experimental design arrangements, discussion, 12-19
      symbols used, definitions, 12-3
F distribution, table, percentiles of, T-6
Federer, W. T., 11-6
Ferris, C. D., 3-6, -11; 4-4, -6, -11, -12, -13; 21-3
Finney, D. J., 10-24
Fire-retardant treatments, flame tests of, data sample, 12-4, -19
Fisher, R. A., 6-9, -42; 10-24; 11-6; 13-46; 20-13; T-5, -32, -33
Flame tests of fire-retardant treatments, data samples
  for factorial experiments, 12-4
  assuming fractional factorial design, 12-19
Folks, J. L., 14-7
Formulas and Equations
  (*See also*, discussions, and the procedures and examples for specific topics of interest)
  examples, using Σ as shorthand for "the sum of," 1-10
  of s^2, 1-10
Fractional Factorials
  (*See* Factorial Experiments)
Franklin, R. E., Jr., 14-7
Freeman, M. F., 20-13
The Free Press, 1-19; 21-6; T-82, -86
Frequency Distributions
  (*See* Distributions, Frequency)
Freudenthal, A. M., 19-4
Friedman, M., 14-6
Functional Relationships
  (*See also*, Linear Relationships)
  FI and FII as system of linear relationships, 5-3
    FI
      when only one of two variables are affected by errors of measurement, 5-3
      figure showing distribution of pointer readings, 5-4
    FII
      when both variables are subject to errors of measurement, 5-3
      figure showing joint distribution of pointer readings, 5-5
Fuzes
  artillery, small-scale comparison test of two types of, data sample, 8-12
  mine
    field trials of two types of, data sample, 8-16
    performance of new type, data sample, 8-2
    small-scale comparison test of two types of, data sample, 8-10
  peak-voltage test of, data sample, 10-2
  proportion of defective, data sample, 7-1

G

γ, confidence coefficient, 2-12

γ, confidence levels corresponding to values of α, 2-2

γ, proportion of samples n for which computed intervals may be expected to bracket m or σ, 1-11

Gardiner, D. A., 14-6

Geary, R. C., 5-46

Glaser, R. H., 14-7

Glinski, Anna M., T-59

Goldin, J., 14-8

Golub, A., 10-24

Goode, H. P., 1-7

Grandage, A. H. E., 14-6

Grant, E. L., 18-4

Graph papers, probit, normal deviate, and normal ruling, use of to plot probit solution, 10-10

Graybill, F. A., 11-6

Greek alphabet, T-1

Greenwood, J. A., 2-12

Grohskopf, H., 14-7

Grubbs, F. E., 3-6, -11; 4-4, -6, -11, -12, -13; 10-24; 17-6; 18-4; 21-3

Gumbel, E. J., 19-1, -2, -3, -4

H

h, harmonic mean, 4-14

Hackler, W. C., 14-7

Hader, R. J., 14-6, -7; 18-4

Hafner Publishing Company, Inc., 10-24; 11-6; 12-21; 13-46; 14-4, -5; T-32, -33

Hald, A., 17-6

Hamilton, P. A., T-34

Handbook series, ORDP 20-110 through 20-114

  purpose of, ii

  scope of, ii

  topical coverage in individual Sections, iv

Hartley, H. O., 3-42; 6-42; 14-7; T-6, -30, -31

Harvard University Press, T-48, -51

Hastay, M. W., 4-14, 14-6, 20-13, T-10

Heady, E. O., 14-8

Herrera, L., T-55

Hickman, J. B., 14-8

Histograms

  figure showing, 1-7

  steps required in preparing, 1-6

  use of for revealing general nature of population distribution, 1-6

Hodges, J. L., Jr., 10-24

Hoerl, A. E., 14-8

Holt, Rinehart, and Winston, Inc., 5-7

Hotelling, H., 14-7

Houghton Mifflin Company, 5-46

Hooke's law, 5-3

Houseman, E. E., 6-42

Hunt, G. A., 9-6

Hunter, J. S., 14-4, -5, -6, -7

Hypotheses, choice of null and alternative, 1-16

I

Ice, latent heat of fusion of, data sample, 3-23, -30
Imperial Bureau of Soil Science, Harpenden, England, 12-21
Inductive Statistics
   (*See* Statistics, Inductive)
Industrial and Engineering Chemistry, 14-7, -8
Industrial Quality Control, 9-6; 14-4, -5; 17-6; 18-2, -4; T-14
Institute of Radio Engineers, 14-7
Institute of Statistics, Raleigh, N. C., 13-46, 14-6
International Statistical Institute, 9-9, -10; 14-7
Interpretations
   (*See also:* Conclusions; Data; Decisions; Uncertainties, Expression of)
  of data
    cautions to be observed in statistical tests, 1-18
    risks involved in conclusions from small samples, 1-19
Interstate Printers and Publishers, Inc., T-80
Iowa State College, 6-42, 14-8
Richard D. Irwin, Inc., 18-4

J

James, G. S., 3-42
The Johns Hopkins Press, 5-46, 22-4
Johns Hopkins University, Baltimore, Md., 14-6
Johnson, N. L., 15-6, 20-13
Journal of the Aeronautical Sciences, 19-4
Journal, American Ceramic Society, 14-7
Journal, American Statistical Association, 14-5, -6; 21-6
Journal of Applied Physics, 19-4
Journal of Industrial Engineering, 14-8
Journal of Polymer Science, 19-4
Journal of Research, National Bureau of Standards, 19-4
Journal of the Royal Statistical Society, 14-6, 20-13

K

k, number of categories of classification, 9-6
K, factor in approximating limits when m and σ are unknown (form, $\bar{X} - Ks$ and $\bar{X} + Ks$, based on sample statistics $\bar{X}$ and s), 1-14
K, factors, for tolerance limits, normal distributions
  one-sided limits, T-14
  two-sided limits, T-10
K, multiple of s used in setting tolerance limits, 1-14
Kase, S., 19-4
Kärber method of analysis, 10-3
Kempthorne, O., 11-6
Kendall, M. G., 2-15, 6-42, 20-13
Kenworthy, O. O., 14-8
Kern, D. Q., 14-8
Knudsen, L. F., 10-24
Kononenko, O. K., 14-7
Kriegel, W. W., 14-7

L

Latin Square Plans
  analysis, 13-32
  data sample, 13-33
    estimation of row (or column) effects, 13-35
    estimation of treatment effects, 13-33
    symbols, definitions of, 13-32
    testing and estimating differences in row (or column) effects, 13-35
      procedure and example, 13-35
    testing and estimating differences in treatment effects, 13-34
      procedure and example, 13-34
  discussion, general, 13-1
  planning, 13-30
    table of selected Latin squares, 13-31
Least squares theorem, discussion and example equations, 6-3
Lehman, S. Y., iii
Lev, J., 5-7
Levels of Confidence
  (*See* Confidence Levels)
Lieberman, G. J., 1-19; 3-7, -12, -13, -14, -18, -19; 4-14; T-14, -59
Lieblein, J., 19-1, -2, -3, -4
Limits
  (*See:* Confidence Intervals; Tolerance Limits)
Lind, E. E., 4-8
Lindley, D. V., T-04
Lindzey, G., 20-13
Linearity
  (*See:* Linear Relationships; Transformations)
Linear Relationships
  between two variables
    characterizing, discussion, 5-1
    determining form of empirically, procedures for plotting on graph, semilog, and log-log papers, 5-30
    figure showing plotted data, 5-1
    plotting the data, 5-1
    two important systems of, discussion and definitions, 5-3
    table, summary of FI, FII, SI, SII, 5-9
    table, linearizing transformations, changes of variables and formulas to convert resulting constants to original form, 5-31
    transformations, non-linear to linear, discussion and procedures, 5-30
    basic worksheet for all types, 5-10
    functional relationships FI and FII, discussion and definitions, 5-3
      FI relationships
        figure showing, 5-4
        problems and procedures, 5-11
        figure showing Young's modulus of sapphire rods as function of temperature, 5-12
        procedure, best line to be used for estimating y from given values of x, 5-12
        worksheet example of Young's modulus as function of temperature, 5-13
        procedure, confidence interval estimates for: line as a whole; a point on the line; future value of Y corresponding to given value of x, discussion, 5-15
        procedure, predicting $(1-\alpha)$ confidence band for line as a whole, 5-16
          table, computational arrangement for procedure and example calculations, 5-16
        procedure, estimating $(1-\alpha)$ confidence interval for a single point on the line, 5-18
        procedure, estimating $(1-\alpha)$ confidence interval for future value of Y corresponding to given value of x, 5-19
        procedure, estimating confidence interval for slope of true line, 5-19
        procedure, using fitted regression line to obtain interval estimate of x that produced observed new values of Y, 5-20
        procedure, using fitted regression line to choose value of X expected with confidence $(1-\alpha)$ to produce a value Y not less than a specified Q, 5-21
        testing assumption of linear regression, discussion, 5-22
          table, computational arrangement for test of linearity, 5-22
        procedure, testing assumption of linear regression, 5-23
        when intercept is known equal to zero, lines through the origin, discussion, 5-24
          procedure, variance of Y's independent of x, 5-24
          worksheet example, 5-25
          procedure, variance proportional to x, 5-25
          procedure, errors of Y's cumulative (cumulative errors), 5-26

Linear Relationships (cont)
  between two variables (cont)
    FII relationship
      distinguishing features of, discussion, 5-27
      figure showing, 5-5
      procedure, simple method of fitting the line (general case), 5-27
        data sample, 5-27
      figure showing relationship between two methods of determining a chemical constituent, 5-28
      important exceptional case, discussion and examples, 5-29
    statistical relationships SI and SII, discussion and definitions, 5-5
      SI relationship
      discussion with example, 5-6
      figure showing normal bivariate frequency surface, 5-6
      figure showing six contour ellipses for normal bivariate distributions having different values of five parameters, 5-7
      SII relationships
      discussion and example, 5-7
      figure showing effect of restrictions of X or Y on regression of Y on X, 5-8
Link, R. F., T-28
Link-Wallace test, table of critical values of L for, T-28
Linnig, F. J., 18-4
Lipka, J., 5-46
Lord, E., T-26

M

m, arithmetic mean (or "the mean") of the distribution, 1-8
m, average of new material, product, or process, (unknown), 3-3
m, center of gravity of a distribution, 1-8
m, location parameter of a normal distribution, 1-8
m, median of a curve (the center of gravity), 1-8
m, number of materials, etc., to be compared, 9-6
m_0, average performance of a standard material, product, or process (known), 3-3
The Macmillan Company, 11-6
Madhava, K. B., 14-7
Mainland, D., T-55
Mandel, J., 5-46, 18-4
Mantel, N., 10-24
Massey, F. J., Jr., 1-19; 10-24; T-4, -5, -24, -27, -45, -78
Matrix Methods, 6-37
  formulas using triangular factorization of normal equations, 6-37
  triangularization of matrices, 6-38
Maxfield, M. W., 2-12; T-37, -41
McCarthy, P. J., 10-24
McGraw-Hill Book Company, Inc., 1-7, -19; 4-14; 6-42; 10-24; 11-6; 14-6; 17-6; 20-13; 22-4; T-4, -5, -10, -24, -27, -45, -78
Mean, Population
  (*See* Population Mean)
Measured Performance
  (*See* Performance, Measured)
Measurements
  (*See also:* Performance, Measured; Samples)
  number required to establish distribution mean with prescribed accuracy, discussion of methods for determining, 2-9
  number required to establish variability with stated precision, 2-12
Metal castings, causes of rejection, data sample, 9-6
Meters, electricity, breakdowns of, data sample, 9-4
Methods of inductive statistics, 1-2
Metron, 20-13
Mickey, M. R., 14-6
Mooney, R. B., 14-8
Moroney, M. J., 1-19
Mosteller, F., 1-4, -5, -19; 20-13
Multivariable Relationships
  (*See* Polynomial and Multivariable Relationships)

N

n, total number of items, 9-6
n, total number of observations, 1-10
n_1, degrees of freedom for numerator, T-6
n_2, degrees of freedom for denominator, T-6
n_i, size of sample for the ith material, product, or process, 9-6
National Bureau of Standards, 4-14, 6-42, 12-21; 19-1, -4; T-59
Natrella, Mary G., Title pages, iii, 21-1
Nature, 14-6
National Advisory Committee for Aeronautics, Technical Note, 19-4
Naval Ordnance Laboratory, White Oak, Md., 10-24
Naval Ordnance Test Station, China Lake, Calif., 2-13; T-37, -41
New York Academy of Science, 14-7
New York University, 14-6, -7; T-55
Neyman, J., 4-14
New products, defectives in sample of, data sample, 8-1
Nickel, spectographic determination of, data sample, 13-22
Non-linear Relationships
    (See also, Linear Relationships)
    between two variables, transformation to linear, 5-30
Normal Deviates, random, short table of, T-86
Normal Distribution
    (See also, Distribution, Normal)
    determined by m and σ, 1-8
North Carolina Agricultural Experiment Station, 13-46
North Carolina State College, 14-4, -6, -7, -8
ν, degrees of freedom, 2-10
Null Hypothesis
    (See also, Hypotheses)
    definition, 1-16
Numbers
    (See Random Numbers)

O

Observations, table of, criteria for rejection of outlying, T-27
OC Curves
    (See: Curves; Operating Characteristic (OC) Curves; Performance Average; Performance, Variability of; Statistical Analysis; Statistical Tests)
Oliver and Boyd, London, 2-15; 6-29, -42; T-5, -32, -33
Oliver and Boyd, Ltd., Edinburgh, 11-6; 13-46; 14-2, -4, -5
Olmstead, P. S., 18-2, -4
Olson, L. R., 14-7
Operating Characteristics
    (See: Operating Characteristic (OC) Curves; Performance Average; Performance, Variability of; Statistical Analysis; Statistical Tests)
Operating Characteristic (OC) Curves
    (See also: Curves; Performance, Average; Performance Variability of; Statistical Analysis; Statistical Tests)
    of a statistical test, 1-17
    figures showing curves for
        one-sided χ^2 test, to determine whether σ_1 exceeds σ_0 ($\alpha = .05$), 4-4
        one-sided χ^2 test, to determine whether σ_1 is less than σ_0 ($\alpha = .05$), 4-6
        one-sided F-test, to determine whether σ_A exceeds σ_B ($\alpha = .05$; $n_A = n_B$), 4-11
        one-sided F-test, to determine whether σ_A exceeds σ_B ($\alpha = .05$: $n_A = n_B$, $3n_A = 2n_B$, $2n_A = n_B$), 4-12
        one-sided F-test, to determine whether σ_A exceeds σ_B ($\alpha = .05$; $n_A = n_B$, $2n_A = 3n_B$; $n_A = 2n_B$), 4-13
        one-sided normal test ($\alpha = .01$), 3-19
        one-sided normal test ($\alpha = .05$), 3-18
        two-sided normal test ($\alpha = .01$), 3-2
        two-sided normal test ($\alpha = .05$), 3-11
        one-sided t-test ($\alpha = .01$), 3-15
        one-sided t-test ($\alpha = .05$), 3-14
        two-sided t-test ($\alpha = .01$), 3-7
        two-sided t-test ($\alpha = .05$), 3-6, 21-3

Optimum Conditions or Levels
  (*See also*, Response Function)
  discussion, general, 14-1
  experimental designs to determine, 14-3
  experiments to determine, 14-1 through 14-8
  finding the optimum, 14-3
  recommended sources for further study, 14-4
Orthogonal Polynomials
  (*See* Polynomial and Multivariable Relationships)
Outliers, Treatment of, 17-1 through 17-6
  rejecting observations
    discussion of problem, 17-1
    in routine experimental work, 17-2
    in a single experiment
      extreme observations in only one direction considered rejectable, 17-4
        mean and standard deviation unknown, sample is only source of information, 17-4
          Dixon criterion, procedure, 17-4
        mean unknown, value of standard deviation assumed, 17-5
          extreme standardized deviate from sample mean, procedure, 17-5
        mean and standard deviation unknown, independent external estimate of deviation available, 17-5
          extreme studentized deviate from sample mean; the Nair criterion, procedure, 17-5
        mean and standard deviation known, 17-6
          procedure and example, 17-6
      extreme observations in either direction considered rejectable, 17-3
        mean unknown, value for standard deviation assumed, 17-3
          procedure, 17-3
        mean and standard deviation unknown, sample is only source of information, 17-3
          Dixon criterion, procedure and example, 17-3
        mean and standard deviation unknown, independent external estimate of deviation available, 17-3
          studentized range, procedure, 17-3
        mean and standard deviation known, 17-4
          procedure and example, 17-4
  table, criteria for rejection of outlying observations, T-27
Owen, D. B., 2-15, T-59

P

P, proportion of elements in a population, 1-8, -9
Pachares, J., T-18
Pearson, E. S., 3-42; 4-14; 6-42; T-6, -30, -31
Penguin Books, Inc., 1-19
Percentages
  (*See also:* Performance, Average; Performance, Variability of)
  figure showing percentage of population in various intervals of normal distribution, 1-9
  table, percentage points of extreme studentized deviate from sample mean, T-30
  table, percentiles of the χ^2 distribution, T-4
  table, F distribution, T-6
  table, $F' = \dfrac{w_A}{w_B}$, T-24
  table, for $\varnothing$, T-26
  table, for $\varnothing'$, T-26
  table, for the studentized range, q, T-18
  table, for the t-distribution, T-5
Performance Average
  (*See also:* Tests, Distribution-free; Tests, Shortcut)
  best single estimate of, 2-1
    procedure and example, 2-2
  comparing materials or products
    discussion, 3-1
    statistical tests, discussion of uses in testing for differences, 3-1
  confidence interval estimates of, 2-1
    general remarks, 2-2

Performance, Average (cont)
  estimating from a sample, discussion, 2-1
  comparing new product with a standard
    discussion, 3-3
    table, summary of Chapter 3 techniques for comparing, 3-4
    does new product differ from a standard
      (σ known) two-sided normal test
        operating characteristics of test, 3-9
        figure showing OC curves ($\alpha = .01$) , 3-12
        figure showing OC curves ($\alpha = .05$) , 3-11
        procedure and example, 3-8
        selection of sample size n , 3-9
      (σ unknown) two-side t-test
        operating characteristics of test, 3-5
        figure showing OC curves ($\alpha = .01$) , 3-7
        figure showing OC curves ($\alpha = .05$) , 3-6
        procedure and example, 3-4
        selection of sample size n , 3-5
    does new product exceed a standard
      (σ known) one-sided normal test
        operating characteristics of test, 3-17
        figure showing OC curves ($\alpha = .01$) , 3-19
        figure showing OC curve ($\alpha = .05$) , 3-18
        procedure and example, 3-16
        selection of sample size n , 3-17
    does new product exceed a standard (cont)
      (σ unknown) one-sided t-test
        operating characteristics of test, 3-13
        figure showing OC curves ($\alpha = .01$) , 3-15
        figure showing OC curves ($\alpha = .05$) , 3-14
        procedure and example, 3-13
        selection of sample size n , 3-16
    is new product less than a standard
      (σ known) one-sided normal test
        operating characteristics of test, 3-21
        figure showing OC curves ($\alpha = .01$) , 3-19
        figure showing OC curves ($\alpha = .05$) , 3-18
        procedure and example, 3-21
        selection of sample size n , 3-22
      (σ unknown) one-sided t-test
        operating characteristics of test, 3-20
        figure showing OC curves ($\alpha = .01$) , 3-15
        figure showing OC curves ($\alpha = .05$) , 3-14
        procedure and example, 3-20
        selection of sample size n , 3-21
  comparing two materials, products, or processes
    discussion, 3-22
    table, summary of Chapter 3 techniques for comparing, 3-22
    do products A and B differ
      σ_A and σ_B known, two-sided normal test
        operating characteristics of test, 3-31
        figure showing OC curves ($\alpha = .05$) , 3-11
        procedure and example, 3-30
        selection of sample size n , 3-31
      σ_A and σ_B unknown, but assumed equal, two-sided t-test
        operating characteristics of test, 3-24
        figure showing probability of rejection of hypothesis $m_A = m_B$, 3-25
        procedure and example, 3-24
        selection of sample size n , 3-26
      σ_A and σ_B unknown, cannot be assumed equal, two-sided t-test
        discussion of test procedure, 3-28
        figure showing OC curves ($\alpha = .05$) , 3-6
        procedure and example, 3-27
      paired observations
        discussion, 3-31
        operating characteristics of test, 3-32
        procedure and example, 3-32
        selection of number of pairs n , 3-33

Performance, Average (cont)
 comparing two materials, products, or processes (cont)
  does product A exceed B
   σ_A and σ_B known, one-sided normal test
    operating characteristics of test, 3-38
    figure showing OC curves ($\alpha = .01$) , 3-19
    figure showing OC curves ($\alpha = .05$) , 3-18
    procedure and example, 3-37
    selection of sample size n , 3-38
   paired observations
    discussion, 3-38
    operating characteristics of test, 3-39
    procedure and example, 3-39
    selection of number of pairs n , 3-40
   σ_A and σ_B unknown, but assumed equal, one-sided t-test
    operating characteristics of test, 3-35
    figure showing OC curves ($\alpha = .01$) , 3-15
    figure showing OC curves ($\alpha = .05$) , 3-14
    procedure and example, 3-34
    selection of sample size n , 3-35
   σ_A and σ_B unknown, cannot be assumed equal
    procedure and example, 3-36
 comparing several products
  do t products differ, equal sample sizes
   discussion, 3-40
   procedure and example, 3-41
Performance, Measured
 characterizing of a material, product, or process, 2-1
Performance, Qualitative
 characterizing of
  data sample, 7-1
  discussion, 7-1
  one-sided confidence intervals, 7-3
  approximate limits for $n > 30$ (one-sided), procedure and example, 7-3
  exact limits for $n \leq 30$ (one-sided), 7-3
  exact limits for $n > 30$ (one-sided), 7-3
  best single estimate of true proportion, procedure and example, 7-1
  confidence interval estimates of true proportion, 7-2
   two-sided intervals, 7-2
   approximate limits for $n > 30$ (two-sided), procedure and example, 7-2
   exact limits for $n \leq 30$ (two-sided), 7-2
   exact limits for $n > 30$ (two-sided), 7-2
  sample size required to estimate true proportion;
   discussion, 7-4
   with a specified limit of error in both directions ($\pm \delta$) , 7-4
    graphical method
     discussion, 7-4
     procedure and example, 7-4
    numerical method
     discussion, 7-5
     procedure and example, 7-5
   with a specified limit in only one direction ($+ \delta$ or $- \delta$)
    discussion, 7-5
    procedure and example, 7-6
Performance, Several Categories
 comparing materials or products with respect to (chi-square test)
  discussion of classification scheme, 9-1
  test of association between two methods of classification
   data sample, 9-9
   discussion, 9-8
   procedure and example, 9-9
   table, computational arrangement for data sample on vacuum tube failures, 9-10
  comparing with a standard
   data sample, 9-2
   procedure and example, 9-3
   table, computational arrangement for data sample on clinical thermometers, 9-3
  comparing with a theoretical standard
   data sample, 9-4
   procedure and example, 9-5
   table, computational arrangement for data sample on electricity meters, 9-5
  comparing two or more products
   data sample, 9-6
   definitions of symbols used, 9-6
   procedure and example, 9-6
   simplified computation for $m = 2$, 9-8
   simplified computation for $m = 2$ when $n_1 = n_2$, 9-8
   table, computational arrangement for data sample on metal castings, 9-7

Performance, Two-fold Classification
  comparing materials or product with respect to, discussion, 8-1
  comparing observed proportion with a standard
    does new product differ from a standard
      procedure for $n \leq 30$, 8-1
        data sample, 8-1
        procedure and example, 8-2
      procedure for $n > 30$, 8-2
        data sample, 8-2
        procedure and example, 8-3
    does new product exceed a standard
      procedure for $n \leq 30$, 8-3
        procedure and example, 8-3
      procedure for $n > 30$, 8-4
        procedure and example, 8-4
    is new product less than a standard
      procedure for $n \leq 30$, 8-5
        procedure and example, 8-5
      procedure for $n > 30$, 8-5
        procedure and example, 8-5
    sample size required to detect a difference of prescribed magnitude
      when sign of difference *is* important, 8-7
        procedure and example, 8-8
      when sign of difference *is not* important, 8-6
        procedure and example, 8-6
  comparing two observed proportions
    discussion, 8-9
    table, observed frequencies from two samples from two mutually-exclusive categories, 8-9
    table, rearranged for use with Table A-29, 8-12
    when sample sizes are equal
      data sample, 8-10
      discussion, 8-9
      does product A differ from B, 8-10
        procedure and example, 8-10
      does product A exceed B, 8-11
        procedure and example, 8-11
    when sample sizes are large
      does product A differ from B, 8-16
        data sample, 8-16
        procedure and example, 8-16
      does product A exceed B, 8-18
        procedure and example, 8-18
    when sample sizes are unequal and small
      does product A differ from B, 8-12
        data sample, 8-12
        data, rearranged for use with Table A-29, 8-13
        procedure and example, 8-12
      does product A exceed B, 8-14
        data sample, 8-14
        data, rearranged for use with Table A-29, 8-15
        procedure and example, 8-14
    sample size required to detect a difference of prescribed magnitude
      when the sign of difference *is* important, 8-20
        procedure and example, 8-20
      when sign of difference *is not* important, 8-18
        procedure and example, 8-19

Performance, Variability of
  estimating, general discussion, 2-6
  estimating when no sample data are available, discussion, 2-8
  single estimates of s^2 and s, procedure and example, 2-6
  one-sided confidence interval estimates for (s_L or s_U), discussion, 2-7
    procedure and example, 2-8
  two-sided confidence interval estimates for (s_L and s_U), procedure and example, 2-7

Performance, Variability of (cont)
  comparing new material or product with a standard
    discussion, 4-1
    does new product differ from a standard, 4-1
      operating characteristics of test, 4-2
      procedure and example, 4-2
    does new product exceed a standard, 4-3
      operating characteristics of test, 4-3
      figure showing OC curves of one-sided χ^2-test ($\alpha = .05$) and various n values, 4-4
      procedure and example, 4-3
      selection of sample size, 4-4
    is new product less than a standard, 4-5
      operating characteristics of test, 4-6
      figure showing OC curves of one-sided χ^2-test ($\alpha = .05$) and various n values, 4-6
      procedure and example, 4-5
      selection of sample size, 4-7
  comparing two materials or products
    discussion, 4-8
    does product A differ from B, 4-8
      operating characteristics of test, 4-9
      procedure and example, 4-9
    does product A exceed B, 4-9
      operating characteristics of test, 4-10
      figure showing OC curves of one-sided F-test ($\alpha = .05$; $n_A = n_B$) , 4-11
      figure showing OC curves of one-sided F-test ($\alpha = .05$; $n_A = n_B$, $3n_A = 2n_B$, $2n_A = n_B$) , 4-12
      figure showing OC curves of one-sided F-test ($\alpha = .05$; $n_A = n_B$, $2n_A = 3n_B$, $n_A = 2n_B$) , 4-13
      procedure and example, 4-10
      selection of sample size, 4-11
Pesek, J. T., 14-8
Planning
  (*See* Experiments, Planning and Analysis of)
Pike, F. P., 14-8
Plates, surface hardness of, data sample, 3-34
Plotting
  (*See:* Data: Histograms; Linear Relationships; Plotting paper)
Plotting paper, procedures for use of to determine form of a relationship empirically, 5-30
Polynomial and Multivariable Relationships
  analysis by method of least squares, 6-1
  discussion of many-variable relationships and analysis techniques, 6-1
  correlated measurement errors, 6-22
    discussion of procedures and examples, 6-22
    examples, 6-23
    procedures, 6-22
  inequality of variance, 6-19
    discussion of procedures and examples, 6-19
    examples, 6-21
    procedures, 6-20
  least squares theorem, discussion and example equations, 6-3
  matrix methods, 6-37
    formulas using triangular factorization of normal equations, 6-37
    remarks on values needed for computations, 6-41
    triangularization of matrices, 6-38
  multiple measurements at one or more points, discussion and example equations, 6-17
  multivariable functional relationships, 6-4
    discussion of procedures and examples, with data sample and equations, 6-5
    use and assumptions, discussion and sample of tabulated data and equations, 6-4
    formation of normal equations, Step (1)
      example, 6-7
      procedure, 6-6
    solution of normal equations, Step (2)
      example, 6-9
      procedure, 6-8
    calculation of deviation between predicted and observed values of Y's, Step (3)
      example, 6-11
      procedure, 6-10
    estimation of σ^2 , Step (4)
      example, 6-11
      procedure, 6-10
    estimation standard deviations of the coefficients, Step (5)
    example, 6-13
    procedure, 6-12

Polynomial and Multivariable Relationships (cont)
  multivariable functional relationships (cont)
    standard deviation of a linear function of the β's, Step (6)
      example, 6-13
      procedure, 6-12
    standard deviation of a predicted point, Step (7)
      example, 6-13
      procedure, 6-12
    analysis of variance test of significance of group of $p < k$ of coefficients, Step (8),
      procedure, 6-14
    analysis of variance test of significance of last coefficient, Step (8), example, 6-15
    confidence interval estimates, Step (9)
      example, 6-17
      procedure, 6-16
  polynomial fitting, 6-18
    discussion and example equations, 6-18
  use of orthogonal polynomials with equally spaced x values, 6-26
    discussion of procedures and examples, 6-26
    equations showing β's as a function of α's for polynomials up to 5th degree, 6-36
    sample table of orthogonal polynomials, 6-28
    Step (1), example, 6-31
      procedure, 6-31
    Step (2), example, 6-31
      procedure, 6-30
    Step (3), example, 6-33
      procedure, 6-32
    Step (4), example, 6-33
      procedure, 6-32
    Step (5), example, 6-33
      procedure, 6-32
    Step (6), example, 6-35
      procedure, 6-34
  polynomials, up to 5th degree, equation showing β's as a function of α's, 6-36
Population Mean, Estimation of
  using a single sample
    procedure and example for determining sample size required, 2-10
  using sample taken in two stages
    discussion of method, 2-10
    procedure and example for determining sample size required, 2-11
Populations
  concepts, 1-1
  examples of, 1-1
  importance of knowing "parent" population from which sample is taken, 1-5
  types of "parent" populations, 1-5
Powder
  (*See also*, Rocket powder)
  weight of for shells, data sample, 3-3
Prentice-Hall, Inc., 1-19; 3-7, -12, -13, -14, -18, -19; 4-14; 18-4
Princeton University, T-28
Probability Level
  one-sided and two-sided tests
    tables for testing significance in 2×2 tables with unequal sample sizes, T-59
Probit Method of Analysis, 10-8
  (*See also*, Sensitivity Testing)
  table, maximum and minimum working probits and range, T-33
  table, weighting coefficients for, T-32
Probit paper, use of to plot probit solution, 10-10
Probits
  (*See* Probit Method of Analysis)
Proportion
  table, arc sine transformation for, T-54
  table, confidence belts for (sample sizes greater than 30), T-45
  table, one-sided confidence limits for (sample sizes less than 30), T-41
  table, two-sided confidence limits for (sample sizes less than 30), T-37
  table, cumulative normal distribution, values of P corresponding to z_p for normal
    curve, T-2
  table, sample sizes required for comparing with a standard, sign of difference *is* im-
    portant, T-51
  table, sample sizes required for comparing with a standard, sign of difference *is not*
    important, T-48
Proschan, F., 17-6
Publications, referenced for adapted, reproduced, quoted, or recommended statistical
  works
  American Standard Control Chart Method of Controlling Quality During Production,
    Z 1.3 − 1958, 18-3, -4

Publications (Cont)
  The American Statistician, 19-1, -2, -3; 21-1
  Analyst, 14-5
  Analytical Chemistry, 18-4
  Annals of Mathematical Statistics, 3-6, -11; 4-4, -6, -11, -12, -13; 14-5, -6, 7; 17-6;
    20-13; 21-3; T-75, -76, -77
  ASTM Manual of Quality Control of Materials, 18-3, -4; 21-5
  Basic Engineering, 14-5
  Biometrics, 5-46; 14-5, -6, -7; 17-6; 20-13
  Biometrika, 3-25, -42; 14-5, -6; 20-13; T-18, -26, -34, -46
  Biometrika Tables for Statisticians, T-7, -30, -31
  Chemical Engineering Progress, 14-7, -8
  A Dictionary of Statistical Terms, 2-3, 6-2
  Empire Journal of Experimental Agriculture, 20-13
  The Engineer, 9-10
  Industrial and Engineering Chemistry, 14-7, -8
  Industrial Quality Control, 9-6; 14-4, -5; 17-6; 18-2, -4; T-14
  Journal of the Aeronautical Sciences, 19-4
  Journal, American Ceramic Society, 14-7
  Journal of American Statistical Association, 1-19; 2-12; 5-46; 10-24; 14-5, -6; 19-4;
    21-6
  Journal of Applied Physics, 19-4
  Journal of Industrial Engineering, 14-8
  Journal of Polymer Science, 19-4
  Journal of Research, National Bureau of Standards, 19-4
  Journal of the Royal Statistical Society, 14-6, 20-13
  Metron, 20-13
  National Bureau of Standards Applied Mathematics Series, 19-4
  National Bureau of Standards News Bulletin 38, 19-1
  Nature, 14-6
  Proceedings of The Royal Society A, 19-4
  Review, International Statistical Institute, 14-7
  Rubber Age, 5-46
  Tappi, 14-7
  Technometrics, 14-5, -6, -7
  Washington University Studies, New Series, Science and Technology, 17-6
Publishers, of adapted, reproduced, or recommended statistical works
  Addison-Wesley Publishing Co., Inc., 20-13
  American Cyanamid Company, T-79
  American Society for Quality Control, 14-4, -5, -7, -8
  American Society for Testing Materials (ASTM), 1-12; 18-3, -4; 21-5
  American Soil Sciences Society, 14-7
  American Standards Association, 18-3, -4
  American Statistical Association, 1-19, 2-12, 5-46, 10-24, 19-4
  Cambridge University Press, 1-19; 3-42; 6-42; 10-24; 20-13; T-6, -30, -31
  Columbia University Press, 19-4
  Dover Publications, Inc., 2-12
  The Free Press, 1-19; 21-6; T-82, -86
  Hafner Publishing Company, Inc., 10-24; 11-6; 12-21; 13-46; 14-4, -5; T-32, -33
  Harvard University Press, T-48, -51
  Holt, Rinehart, and Winston, Inc., 5-7
  Houghton Mifflin Company, 5-46
  International Statistical Institute, 9-9, -10; 14-7
  Interstate Printers and Publishers, Inc., T-80
  Institute of Radio Engineers, 14-7
  Institute of Statistics, Raleigh, N. C., 13-46, 14-6
  Iowa State College, 6-42, 14-8
  Richard D. Irwin, Inc., 18-4
  The Johns Hopkins Press, 5-46, 22-4
  Johns Hopkins University, Baltimore, Md., 14-6
  McGraw-Hill Book Company, Inc., 1-7, -19; 4-14; 6-42; 10-24; 11-6; 14-6; 17-6; 18-4;
    20-13; 22-4; T-4, -5, -10, -24, -27, -45, -78
  National Advisory Committee for Aeronautics, 19-4
  New York Academy of Science, 14-7
  New York University, 14-6, -7; T-55
  North Carolina Agricultural Experiment Station, 13-46
  North Carolina State College, 14-4, -6, -7, -8
  Oliver and Boyd, Ltd., Edinburgh, 11-6; 13-46; 14-2, -4, -5
  Oliver and Boyd, Ltd., London, 2-15; 6-29; T-5, -32, -33
  Penguin Books, Inc., 1-19
  Prentice-Hall, Inc., 1-19; 3-7, -12, -13, -14, -18, -19; 4-14; 18-4
  Princeton University, T-28
  The Rand Corporation, 1-6, -19; T-82, -86
  Sandia Corporation, 2-15
  Stanford University, T-59

Publishers (Cont)
  University College, London, 3-41
  University of London, 4-14
  University of Toronto Press, 6-42
  U. S. Government Printing Office, 6-42, 12-21
  Van Nostrand, Inc., 18-4
  John Wiley & Sons, Inc., 1-8, -11, -19; 2-9; 5-46; 6-42; 11-6; 12-21; 13-40; 14-4, -5,
    -6, -7; 17-6

Q

Qualitative Performance
  (*See* Performance, Qualitative)
Quenouille, M. H., 11-6

R

r, table, critical values of, for sign test (one-sided and two-sided tests), T-78
R, range (difference between largest and smallest), 1-2
R_i, $(i = 1, 2, \ldots)$ as sample distribution of muzzle velocities in samples of size 10, 1-2
R_i, where $i = 1, 2, \ldots$, collectively determine sampling distribution of range, 1-2
The Rand Corporation, 1-6, -19; T-82, -86
Randomization
  (*See:* Block Plans, Randomized; Experiments, Planning and Analysis of; Randomized
    Plans; Random Sampling)
Randomized Plans
  analysis, 13-2
  completely-randomized plans, 13-1
  discussion, general, 13-1
  table, schematic presentation of results, 13-2
Random normal deviates, short table of, T-86
Random numbers, short table of, T-82
Random Sampling
  basic concepts, 1-4
  simple (or unrestricted), 1-4
  selection of sample
    basic concepts, 1-6
    discussion of methods, 1-6
    use of tables of random numbers, 1-6
Range
  table, factors for converting to estimate of σ ($= Range/d_n$) , 2-6
  table, maximum and minimum working probits and range, T-33
  of n observations, defined as difference between highest and lowest of the n values, 2-6
  table, percentiles of the studentized range q , T-18
  sample range as an estimate of standard deviation, 2-6
Rank sum, table of critical values of smaller, for the Wilcoxon-Mann-Whitney test
  (one-sided and two-sided), T-80
Read, D. R., 14-7
Rejecting Observations
  (*See* Outliers, Treatment of)
Rejection
  (*See also:* Outliers, Treatment of)
  of outlying observations, table of criteria for, T-27
  figure showing probability of rejection of hypothesis $m_A = m_B$ when true, plotted
    against θ , 3-25
Relationships
  (*See:* Functional Relationships; Linear Relationships; Polynomial and Multivariable
    Relationships; Statistical Relationships)
Replication
  (*See* Experiments, Planning and Analysis of)
Resistors
  conversion gain of, data sample, 13-4
  noise measurement of, data sample, 13-14
  reverse-bias collector current of 10, data sample, 16-2

Response Function, 14-1
  in a factorial experiment, 14-1
  figure showing a response surface, 14-2
  figure showing contours for a response surface with 2^2 factorial design, 14-2
Results, Final
  (*See* Uncertainties, Expression of)
Review, International Statistical Institute, 14-7
Richey, G. G., 5-46
Rider, P. R., 17-6
Rietz, H. L., 5-46
Ringelman, R. E., 14-7
Roberts, H. V., 1-19, 21-6
Rocket powder, burning time of, data sample, 2-6
Rockwell hardness table, for use in preparing histograms, 1-7
Rosenblatt, M., 10-24
Roth, P. B., 14-8
The Royal Society A, Proceedings of, 19-4
Rubber Age, 5-46

S

s, standard deviation estimate computed from n measurements on new product (used where σ is unknown), 3-3
s, unbiased estimator of σ, 1-10
s^2, best unbiased sample estimate of variance, in estimate of σ, 1-10
s^2, formula of, for computational purposes, 1-10
SI, statistical relationship, when errors of measurement are negligible compared to variation of each item, 5-6
SII, statistical relationship, when range of one or two variables is preselected or restricted, 5-6
Samples, concepts, 1-1
Sample mean, table, percentage points of extreme deviate, T-30
Sample Range
  (*See* Range)
Sample Size
  (*See also:* Measurements; Population mean; and selection of sample size, under specific topics of interest)
  number required to establish distribution mean with prescribed accuracy, discussion of methods for determining, 2-9
  table, sizes required to detect prescribed differences in averages, when sign of difference IS important, T-17
  table, sizes required to detect prescribed differences in averages, when sign of difference IS NOT important, T-16
  table, sizes required for comparing a proportion with a standard, when sign of difference IS important, T-48
  table, sizes required for comparing a proportion with a standard, when sign of difference IS NOT important, T-48
Sampling
  (*See also*, Random Sampling)
  importance of knowing the "parent" population from which sample is taken, 1-5
  principles of, 1-4
  quote on randomization, 1-5
  techniques, 1-4
Sampling Distribution
  of X for samples of size 10, 1-2
  figure showing distribution of sample mean $\bar{X}$ for samples of various sizes from same normal distribution, 1-11
  figure showing distribution of sample variance s^2 for samples of various sizes from same normal distribution, 1-11
Sampling, Random
  (*See* Random Sampling)
Sampling scheme, conditions to be insured by, 1-4
Sanderson, B. S., 14-8
Sandia Corporation, 2-15
Sandomire, M. M., 2-12
Sapphire rods, Young's modulus vs., temperature for, data sample, 5-11
Savage, L. J., 14-6
Scarborough, J. B., 5-30, -46; 22-4
Scheffé, H., 11-6

Schneider, A. M., 14-7
Sensitivity Testing
  applications of term, 10-1
  data, collecting and analyzing, discussion of methods, 10-2
  data sample, 10-2
  experimental situation, discussion and examples, 10-1
  Kärber method of analysis
    discussion, 10-3
    selection of stimulus levels, 10-3
    general solution for, 10-4
      example, 10-5
      procedure, 10-4
      table, example analysis data, 10-5
    simplified solution for special case, test levels equally spaced, equal numbers of
      items tested at each level, 10-6
      example, 10-7
      procedure, 10-6
      table, example analysis data, 10-7
  probit method of analysis
    discussion, 10-8
    method, basis of, discussion and formulas, 10-9
    selection of stimulus level, 10-8
    solutions, discussion, 10-9
    exact probit solution, discussion, 10-16
      example, 10-17
      procedure, 10-16
      table, example analysis data, 10-17
      example for additional iteration, 10-19
      procedure for additional iteration, 10-18
      table, example analysis data for second iteration, 10-19
    graphical solutions, discussion, 10-10
      example, 10-11
      procedure, 10-10
      table, example analysis data, 10-11
      figure showing probit regression line, fitted by eye, 10-13
    using probit regression line for prediction, 10-21
      estimate of proportion expected to respond at specified levels, 10-21
      estimates of stimulus levels, 10-21
    testing whether line is adequate representation of data, 10-20
      example, 10-20
      procedure, 10-20
      table, test of linearity, example final probit equation, 10-20
  when stimulus levels cannot be controlled, discussion, 10-24
  up-and-down design, 10-22
    discussion of method, 10-22
    procedure, 10-23
Severo, N. C., iii
Shells, penetration depth of, data sample, 15-1
Shewell, C. T., 14-8
Shewhart, W. A., 1-13; -14; 18-4
Shrikhande, S. S., 13-46
Shortcut Tests
  (*See* Tests, Shortcut)
σ, distance from m to either of two inflection points on normal distribution curve
  ("radius of gyration" of distribution about m) , 1-8
σ, measure of the spread, scatter, or dispersion of a normal distribution, 1-8
σ, standard deviation (or population mean; population standard deviation), 1-8
σ, known standard deviation of new product, 3-3
σ_0, known variability of a standard, measured by its standard deviation, 4-1
σ^2, second moment about m , 1-8
σ^2, variance of the distribution, 1-8
Σ, example formulas, using as shorthand for "the sum of," 1-10
Signed-ranks Test
  table, critical values of smaller rank sum for Wilcoxon-Mann-Whitney test (one-
    sided and two-sided), T-80
  table, critical values of $T_\alpha (n)$ for, (one-sided and two-sided), T-79
Significance
  (*See*, Tests of Significance)
Significance Level
  of a statistical test, 1-17
  choice of, for statistical tests, 1-17
  table, minimum contrasts required for, in 2×2 tables with equal sample sizes, T-55
    T-55
  tables, for testing significance in 2×2 tables with unequal sample sizes (one-sided
    and two-sided tests), T-59

Significant Contrasts
  (*See,* Contrasts)
Sign Test
  (*See also,* Tests, Distribution-free)
  table, critical values of r for (one-sided and two-sided tests), T-78
Skewness
  figure showing frequency distributions of various shapes, 1-8
Smith, A. C., 14-7
Smith, W. N., 14-7
Square Plans
  (*See:* Latin Square Plans; Youden Square Plans)
Somerville, P. N., iii; T-75, -76, -77
Staircase Methods
  (*See,* Sensitivity Testing, Up-and-Down Designs)
Standard Deviation
  (*See* Deviation, Standard)
Stanford University, T-59
Statement of Tolerance Limits
  (*See* Tolerance Limits)
Statistical Analysis
  (*See also:* Distribution-free Technique; Sensitivity Testing; Tests of Significance)
  Kärber method, 10-3
  probit method, 10-8
  table, percentiles of the χ^2 distribution, T-4
  of samples from binomial distributions
    table, arc sine transformations for proportions, T-54
    table, confidence belts for proportions for $n > 30$ (confidence coefficients .90, .95, .99), T-45
    table, confidence limits for a proportion (one-sided), T-41
    table, confidence limits for a proportion (two-sided), T-37
    table, minimum contrasts required for significance in 2×2 tables with equal samples, T-55
    table, sample size required for comparing proportion with a standard, sign of difference NOT important, T-48
      , sign of difference IS important, T-51
    table for testing significance in 2×2 tables with unequal samples, T-59
  of samples from normal distributions
    table, confidence belts for correlation coefficient (confidence coefficient .95), T-31
    table, criteria for rejection of outlying observations, T-27
    table, critical values of L for Link-Wallace test, T-28
    table, factors for one-sided tolerance limits, T-14
    table, factors for two-sided tolerance limits, T-10
    table, factors for computing one-sided confidence limits for σ, T-36
    table, factors for computing two-sided confidence limits for σ, T-34
    table, maximum and minimum working probits and range, T-33
    table, percentiles of F', T-24
    table, percentiles for $\emptyset$, T-26
    table, percentiles for $\emptyset'$, T-26
    table, percentage points of extreme studentized deviate from sample mean, T-30
    table, percentiles of the studentized range q, T-18
    table, sample sizes required to detect prescribed differences in averages, sign of difference NOT important, T-16
      , sign of difference IS important, T-17
    table, weighting coefficients for probit analysis, T-32
Statistical Computations
  (*See* Computations, Statistical)
Statistical concepts, basic, 1-1, -19
Statistical Inferences
  discussion, definition, and examples of, 1-3
  as estimates of magnitude of population characteristics, 1-3
  as tests of hypotheses regarding population characteristics, 1-3
Statistical methods, inductive, 1-1
Statistical Relationships
  (*See also,* Linear Relationships)
  between two variables
    problems and procedures for, 5-31
    SI relationships
      data sample, 5-33
      discussion and examples, 5-31
      estimating confidence band for line as a whole,
        procedure and example, 5-36
        table, computational arrangement for, 5-37
      confidence interval estimate for slope of true regression line, procedure and example, 5-38

Statistical Relationships (cont)
  between two variables (cont)
    SI relationships (cont)
      confidence interval estimate for single (future) value of Y corresponding to chosen value of X, procedure and example, 5-38
      estimating confidence interval for single point on line, procedure and example, 5-37
      confidence interval estimates for line as a whole, a point on the line, single Y corresponding to new value of X, 5-36
      figure showing the line and confidence limit for the line, using relationship between two methods of estimating tread life, 5-35
      degree of relationship of X and Y as measured by correlation coefficient; procedure and example, 5-40
      procedure, best line for estimating $\bar{Y}_x$ from given values of X, 5-33
        worksheet example, 5-34
      best line for predicting $\bar{X}_Y$ from given values of Y, procedure and example, 5-39
      figure showing relationship between two methods of estimating tire tread life, 5-32
      figure showing two regression lines, using relationship between two methods of estimating tread life, 5-39
      using regression line for prediction; using fitted line equation; and example of predicted values, 5-35
    SII relationships
      data sample, 5-40
      discussion, 5-40
      example worksheet, 5-41
      confidence band for line as a whole, procedure and example, 5-43
        table, computational arrangement and example calculations for, 5-44
      confidence interval estimates for: line as a whole; a point on the line; a single Y corresponding to new value of X, 5-42
      confidence interval for slope of true line, procedure and example, 5-45
      confidence interval for a single point on the line, procedure and example, 5-44
      confidence interval for a single (future) value of Y corresponding to chosen value of X, procedure and example, 5-45
      best line for estimating $\bar{Y}_x$ from given value of X, procedure, 5-41
      figure showing relationship between two methods, range of one method restricted, 5-42
Statistical Techniques
  (See Extreme-value Data)
Statistical Tests
  application to experimental results in making decisions, 3-1
  cautions concerning interpretations of data, 1-18
  use of OC curve to depict discriminatory power of, 3-2
  uses in testing for differences in average performance, discussion, 3-1
Statistical Tolerance Limits
  (See Tolerance limits, Statistical)
Statistics
  preliminary considerations, 1-1
  using to make decisions, 1-15
Statistics, Inductive
  methods of, discussion, 1-2
  use of inductive methods to learn about population characteristics from study of samples, 1-2
Stiehler, R. D., 5-46
Stopwatches, life tests of three types, data sample, 16-13
Studentized Range
  (See Range)
Sutcliffe, M., T-55
Swan, A. W., 9-10
Sweeney, R. F., 14-8
Switlyk, G., 14-8
Symbols
  (See also: discussions, and the procedures and examples for specific topics of interest)
  definitions for m, m_0, $\bar{X}$, s, and σ, 3-3
Systems
  (See Linear Relationships)

T

Tables
   (*See also*, specific topic of interest)
   arrangement of A-Tables, discussion, T-1
   referenced A-Tables, T-1 through T-89
   of random numbers, T-82
      example of use of, 1-6
Rockwell hardness reading as first step in preparing a histogram, 1-7
Tappi, 14-7
Tate, M. W., T-80
Taussky, O., 6-42
t-distribution, table of percentiles, T-5
Techniques
   (*See:* Discussions of, in front of Sections 1 through 4; Distribution-free Techniques)
Technometrics, 14-5, -6, -7
Testing, Sensitivity
   (*See*, Sensitivity Testing)
Tests
   (*See also:* Significance Level; Statistical Tests)
   of significance
      table, cumulative normal distribution, values of P, T-2
      table, cumulative normal distribution, values of z_p, T-3
      table, minimum contrast required for significance in 2×2 tables with equal samples, T-55
      table, percentiles of F distribution, T-6
      table, percentiles of t distribution, T-5
      table, percentiles of χ^2 distribution, T-4
Tests, Distribution-free, 16-1 through 16-14
   discussion, general, 16-1
   comparing average of new product with a standard, 16-2
      data sample, 16-2
      does new differ from standard
         the sign test, 16-2
            procedure and example, 16-2
         the Wilcoxon signed-ranks test, 16-3
            procedure and example, 16-3
      does new exceed standard, 16-4
         data sample, 16-4
         the sign test, 16-4
            procedure and example, 16-4
         the Wilcoxon signed-ranks test, 16-5
            procedure and example, 16-5
      is new less than standard, 16-6
         data sample, 16-6
         the sign test, 16-6
            procedure and example, 16-6
         the Wilcoxon signed-ranks test, 16-7
            procedure and example, 16-7
   comparing averages of several products, 16-13
      do t products differ, 16-13
         data sample, 16-13
         procedure and example, 16-14
         work table for data sample, 16-13
   comparing averages of two products, 16-8
      discussion, general, 16-8
      does A differ from B, 16-8
         the sign test for paired observations, 16-8
            data sample, 16-8
         the Wilcoxon-Mann-Whitney test for two independent samples, 16-9
            data sample, 16-9
            procedure and example, 16-10
      does A exceed B, 16-10
         the sign test for paired observations, 16-11
            procedure and example, 16-11
         the Wilcoxon-Mann-Whitney test for two independent samples, 16-11
            data Sample, 16-11
            procedure and example, 16-12

Tests, Shortcut
  shortcut for small samples from normal populations, 15-1 through 15-8
  discussion, general, 15-1
  comparing average of new product with a standard, 15-1
    does new differ from standard, 15-1
      data sample, 15-1
      procedure and example, 15-2
    does new exceed standard, 15-2
      procedure and example, 15-2
    is new less than standard, 15-3
      procedure and example, 15-3
  comparing averages of several products, 15-6
    do t products differ, 15-6
      data Sample, 16-6
      procedure and example, 15-6
  comparing averages of two products, 15-4
    does A differ from B, 15-4
      data sample, 15-4
      procedure and example, 15-4
    does A exceed B, 15-5
      procedure and example, 15-5
  comparing variability of performance, 15-7
    does A differ from B, 15-7
      procedure and example, 15-7
    does A exceed B, 15-8
      procedure and example, 15-8
Tests of Significance
  (See also: Confidence Intervals)
  and confidence intervals, relation between, 21-1
    introduction, discussion of, 21-1
    comparing averages, a problem in, 21-2
      figure showing OC curves for two-sided t-test ($\alpha = .05$), 21-3
    presenting results, two ways of, 21-2
Thermometers, clinical, inspections and tests of, data sample, 9-2
Thermometers, intercomparison of, data sample, 13-40
θ, ratio of variances, 3-28
Thompson, John I. and Co., iii
Tidwell, P. W., 14-8
Tippett, L. H. C., 1-6, -11, -19; 20-13
Tires
  estimated tread wear of, two methods, data sample, 5-33
  estimated tread wear of, 5-40
Tolerance Limits
  (See also, Distribution-free Techniques)
  table, confidence associated with a statement of, T-77
  tables, one-sided distribution-free limits, T-76
  tables, two-sided distribution-free limits, T-75
  table, factors for normal distributions, T-14
  table, factors for normal distributions (two-sided), T-10
  engineering, definition of term, as different from confidence intervals and statistical
    tolerance limits, 1-15
  statistical
    basic concepts and examples, 1-14
    definition of term, as different from confidence intervals and engineering tolerance
      limits, 1-15
    two-sided and one-sided values, discussion of, 2-13
    figure showing computed limits for 99.7% of population, with intervals tending
      to a fixed size as sample size increases, 1-14
    determining one-sided limits with stated precision (X_U or X_L), procedure and
      example, 2-14
    determining two-sided limits with stated precision (X_U and X_L), procedure and
      example, 2-14
    determining limits independent of form of distribution (distribution-free), dis-
      cussion of methods, 2-15
    one-sided limits (distribution-free), procedure, 2-15
    two-sided limits (distribution-free), procedure, 2-15
    one-sided limits for normal distribution, discussion, 2-14
    two-sided limits for normal distribution, discussion, 2-13

Transformations
    table, arc sine for proportions, T-54
    of non-linear to linear relationships between two variables, 5-30
    use of, 20-1 through 20-13
      need for, discussion of, 20-1
    normality and normalizing
      normality, importance of, 20-1
      normalization by averaging, 20-2
      normalizing transformations, 20-2
        figure showing examples of normalizing effect of frequently used transformations, 20-3
    inequality of variances, variance-stabilizing transformations, 20-4
      equality of variances, importance of, 20-4
      linearity, additivity, and associated transformations, 20-9
        definition and importance of, 20-9
        remarks, concluding, 20-11
        transformation of data to achieve, 20-11
      variance inhomogeneity, types of, 20-5
        table showing some frequently used transformations, 20-5
      variance-stabilizing transformations, 20-6
        figure showing six examples of variance-stabilizing effect of frequently used transformations, 20-7
Transistors, forward current transfer ratio of two types, data sample, 16-9
Transistors, output admittance of two types, data sample, 16-11
Transistors, reverse-bias collector current of 20, data sample, 16-4
Transistors, reverse-bias collector currents of two types, data sample, 16-8
Treatment of Outliers
    (*See* Outliers, Treatment of)
Treloar, A. E., 1-8
Trickett, W. H., 3-42
Tubes
    cutoff bias of, data sample, 4-5
    vacuum, failures of, data sample, 9-9
Tukey, J. W., 1-4, -5, -19; 10-24; 20-13
Turner, W. R., 14-7
Two-fold Classification
    (*See*, Performance, Two-fold Classification)

U

u, computed test criterion, 3-4
Umland, A. W., 14-7
Uncertainties, Expression of
    of final results, 23-1 through 23-6
      definitions of four distinct cases, 23-2
        examples:
          of case 1, 23-2
          of case 2, 23-3
          of case 3, 23-4
          of case 4, 23-5
      discussion of problem, 23-1
Universities
    Cambridge, 1-19; 3-42; 6-42; 10-24; T-6, -30, -31
    Columbia, N. Y., 19-4
    Duke, iii
    Johns Hopkins, 5-46, 14-6
    Iowa State, 6-42, 14-8
    of London, 4-14
    New York, 14-6, -7; T-55
    Princeton, T-28
    Stanford, T-59
    of Toronto, 6-42
    Washington, 17-6
University College, London, 3-41, 15-6
University of Toronto Press, 6-42
Up-and-Down Design, 10-22
    (*See also*, Sensitivity Testing, Up-and-Down design)

U. S. Government
  Army Ordnance Corp, ii
  Department of Agriculture, 1-13, -14
  National Bureau of Standards, 4-14; 6-42; 12-21; 19-1, -4; T-59
  Naval Ordnance Laboratory, White Oak, Md., 10-24
  Naval Ordnance Test Station, China Lake, Calif., 2-12; T-37, -41
  Navy Bureau of Ordnance, 10-24
  Printing Office, 6-42, 12-21, 19-4

V

Vacuum tubes, failures, data sample, 9-9
VanDyke, J., T-59
Van Nostrand, Inc., 18-4
Van Winkle, M., 14-7
Variability
  (*See also:* Deviation, Standard; Performance, Variability of; Tests, Shortcut)
  number of measurements required to establish with stated precision, 2-12
Variables
  (*See* Linear Relationships)
Variances, Inequality of
  (*See* Transformations)
Variance-stabilizing Transformations
  (*See* Transformations)
Vaswani, R., 14-8

W

Washers, mica, thickness of, data sample, 2-1
Washington University, 17-6
Walker, H. M., 5-7
Wallace, D. L., T-28
Wallis, W. A., 1-19, 4-14, 14-6, 20-13, 21-6, T-10
Weaver, C. L., 3-6, -11; 4-4, -6, -11, -12, -13; 21-3
Weighting, table of coefficients for probit analysis, T-32
Welch, B. L., 3-25, -42
Werimont, G., 18-4
Whidden, P., 3-25, -42
Wilcoxon, F., 2-79
Wilcoxon-Mann-Whitney Test
  (*See* Tests, Distribution-free)
Wilcoxon-Signed ranks Test
  (*See* Tests, Distribution-free)
John Wiley & Sons, Inc., 1-8, -11, -19; 2-9; 5-46; 6-42; 11-6; 12-21; 13-40; 14-4, -5, -6, -7; 17-6; 20-13
Wilson, K. B., 14-6
Wilson, E. B., Jr., 11-6, 17-6
Worksheets
  basic, for all types of linear relationships, 5-10
  example of FI relationship, Young's modulus as function of temperature, 5-13
  for FI relationships, intercept known to be zero, variance of Y's independent of x, 5-25
  example of SI relationship, 5-34
  example of SII relationship, 5-41

X

X, representing any value in a population, 1-8
$X_1 : X_2, \ldots, X_n$
    different sets of observations of any element in a population sample, 1-10
    observations taken at random from normal population, 1-10
$\bar{X}$: average muzzle velocity of 10 rounds, 1-2
    best unbiased sample estimate of m, 1-10
    average of sample of n measurements on new product, 3-3
    sample mean, 1-10
$\bar{X}_i$: average of measurements of n, 1-2
    average muzzle velocity of each of many sets of 10 rounds, 1-2

Y

Yates, F., 6-29, -42; 10-24; 12-21; 13-46; T-5, -32, -33
Yates' method for obtaining estimates of main effects and interactions for two-level
    factorials, 12-5 through 12-21
Youden, W. J., 11-6, 13-40, 18-4
Youden Square Plans
    analysis, 13-40
        data sample, 13-40
        estimation of column effects, 13-44
        estimation of row effects, 13-45
        estimation of treatment effects, 13-41
        symbols, definitions of, 13-36
        testing and estimating differences in column effects, 13-44
            procedure and example, 13-44
        testing and estimating differences in row effects, 13-45
            procedure and example, 13-45
        testing and estimating differences in treatment effects, 13-43
            procedure and example, 13-43
    planning, 13-36
        table showing arrangement of eight plans, 13-37
Youle, P. V., 14-6
Young's modulus, as example data, 5-20, -21
Young's modulus vs. temperature for sapphire rods
    data sample, 5-11
    figure showing (FI), 5-12
    example worksheet (FI), 5-13
    figure showing computed regression line and confidence interval for the line, 5-14
    table, computational arrangement for test of linearity, 5-22
Youtz, C., 20-13

Z

z, distance from population mean in units of the standard deviation, 1-8
z, the standard normal variable, T-2, -3
Zelen, M., 19-4

☆ U. S. GOVERNMENT PRINTING OFFICE : 1974 O - 554-184